wais®-III
WECHSLER ADULT INTELLIGENCE SCALE – THIRD EDITION

wms®-III
WECHSLER MEMORY SCALE – THIRD EDITION

TECHNICAL
MANUAL

P9-CQQ-310

THE
PSYCHOLOGICAL
CORPORATION®

A Harcourt Assessment Company

2 3 4 5 6 7 8 9 10 11 12 A B C D E

SPECIAL ACKNOWLEDGMENT

After the decision was made to revise the WAIS–R and the WMS–R instruments, The Psychological Corporation asked Dr. Nelson Butters to form an advisory panel of individuals recognized as scientists–practitioners. The purpose of the panel was to provide consultation regarding content revision and research design as well as direction related to the integration of these two instruments. The core members of this panel were Drs. Robert Bornstein, Gordon Chelune, Robert Heaton, and Robert Ivnik. The advisory panel reviewed our progress on the development of the tests at key points and formally met approximately twice yearly to provide consultation regarding possible revisions. Unfortunately, Dr. Butters became ill early on in the project and his untimely death prevented his seeing these tests published. Nevertheless, his contributions can be clearly seen in the final versions of the WAIS–III and the WMS–III. Although it was not feasible to incorporate all of the panel's suggestions into the final scales, their contributions have greatly enhanced the WAIS–III and the WMS–III. We are exceedingly indebted to our advisory panel and want to formally acknowledge their invaluable contributions.

David Tulsky and Jianjun Zhu, WAIS–III Project Directors
Mark F. Ledbetter, WMS–III Project Director

CONTENTS

Tables

Figures

CHAPTER 1

Introduction

In clinical practice, measures of intellectual functioning and memory are often administered concurrently so that a broad spectrum of cognitive abilities can be examined. In view of this purpose, the *Wechsler Adult Intelligence Scale—Third Edition* (WAIS–III; Wechsler, 1997a) and the *Wechsler Memory Scale—Third Edition* (WMS–III; Wechsler, 1997b) were codeveloped and share similar research methodologies, normative samples, and similar clinical validation procedures. As a result, these two instruments provide a means of assessing a broad range of cognitive abilities and now allow for more meaningful comparisons between intellectual ability and memory functioning.

This update of the *WAIS–III—WMS–III Technical Manual* contains the psychometric, technical, and basic interpretive information for the WAIS–III and WMS–III. This manual includes the following updated material:

- Predicted achievement scores and discrepancy tables for the *Wechsler Individual Achievement Test–Second Edition* (WIAT–II; The Psychological Corporation, 2002a, 2002b, 2002c)
- Norms for Digit Span Backward
- Bidirectional cumulative frequency distributions for WAIS–III and WMS–III Index scores
- New factor analytic studies of the WMS–III
- Review of recent research studies and clinical methods related to the WAIS–III/WMS–III and
  - demographically adjusted norms
  - the *Wechsler Test of Adult Reading* (The Psychological Corporation, 2001)
  - short forms of the WAIS–III
  - the *Wechsler Abbreviated Scale of Intelligence* (WASI; The Psychological Corporation, 1999)
  - serial/sequential assessment
  - malingering studies
  - clinical studies
  - factor analytic studies of the combined WAIS–III and WMS–III

Chapter 1 of this Manual reviews the basic theories underlying intelligence and memory. Chapter 2 describes the sampling and data-handling procedures, and Chapter 3 presents data relevant to the reliability of the two instruments. Chapter 4 presents evidence of the validity and clinical utility of the WAIS–III and WMS–III, including results from studies conducted since their original publication. Chapter 5 presents guidelines for interpreting the various scores obtained from the two scales. The appendixes provide additional information, such as intercorrelation tables and normative data for intellectual ability–memory discrepancies and intellectual ability–academic achievement discrepancies.

Concept of Intelligence

The concept of intelligence has been a hotly debated topic since the turn of the century. Wechsler took a more ecological approach and conceived of intelligence as a multidimensional construct, one that manifests itself in many forms. He originally defined intelligence as the "capacity of the individual to act purposefully, to think rationally, and to deal effectively with his environment" (1944, p. 3). He considered intelligence not only as a global entity but also as an aggregate of specific abilities. Wechsler explained that intelligence is global because it characterizes the individual's behavior as a whole. It is also specific because it is composed of elements or abilities that are qualitatively different.

Wechsler maintained this definition of intelligence throughout his career. He believed that intelligence should be measured by both verbal and performance tasks, each of which measured ability in a different way and which could be aggregated to form a general, global construct. However, particularly later in his career, Wechsler began exploring "nonintellective" factors of intelligence, including the abilities to perceive and respond to social, moral, and aesthetic values (Wechsler, 1975). Wechsler was keenly aware that the results of factor analytic studies accounted for only a percentage of the overall variance of intelligence, and he believed that another group of attributes contributed to this unexplained variance. According to Wechsler, these attributes are made up of basic human motivations, attitudes, and personality traits, such as persistence, goal awareness, enthusiasm, and other conative dispositions not tapped directly by existing measures of intellectual ability. Wechsler also hypothesized that these attributes influence an individual's performance on such measures, as well as the individual's effectiveness in daily living and in meeting the world and its challenges.

The subtests Wechsler selected and developed tap many different mental abilities, which together reflect an individual's overall ability. Some require abstract reasoning, whereas others require perceptual skills, verbal skills, and processing speed. All of these abilities are valued to varying degrees by our society, and all relate to behavior that is generally considered intelligent in one way or another. None of the subtests by itself, however, was designed to assess the entire range of cognitive abilities. For example, a subtest may require the examinee to use primarily perceptual skills but not abstract reasoning; another subtest may require the individual to recall specific information but not to perceive spatial relationships.

Wechsler viewed his intelligence scales as clinical instruments that sample an individual's abilities. He also believed that the abilities represented by these tests are not always developed equally in most "normal" individuals. Experience has shown that peaks and valleys are typical of the scores obtained by most individuals, a pattern indicating that intellectual abilities are developed in different ways and result in different profiles of cognitive strengths and weaknesses.

Although tests of intellectual ability, such as the WAIS–III, provide a considerable amount of information about an individual's relative intellectual strengths and weaknesses in a relatively short amount of time, the clinician should view each examinee as unique and take into account nonintellective factors and other life-history information when interpreting the test results. Emphasizing the importance of this approach, Matarazzo (1972, 1990) reminded the clinician of the necessity of considering an individual's life history (e.g., social and medical history and linguistic and cultural background) as part of a comprehensive assessment. Test scores, behavioral observations, and life histories are critical sources of information in all diagnostic assessments, but clinicians should keep in mind that they themselves are the cornerstone of any assessment. Those who are responsible for interpreting the results of intelligence testing must be careful to distinguish between cognitive abilities, conative factors (i.e., personality traits, such as anxiety, persistence, and goal awareness), and other nonintellective variables that contribute to test performance (Wechsler, 1950).

Concept of Memory and Learning

The term *memory* has been conceptualized and used in many different ways. The concept of memory is closely linked to learning because memory is the natural outcome of learning. Squire (1987) provided an excellent definition of learning and memory: "Learning is the process of acquiring new information, while memory refers to the persistence of learning in a state that can be revealed at a later time" (p. 3).

A widely recognized view is that memory consists of a short-term system and a long-term system (R. C. Atkinson & Shiffrin, 1968). In its most basic form, short-term memory refers to a temporary storage (usually from only seconds to 1–2 minutes), whereas long-term memory refers to the permanent or more stable storage of memories. The process by which information is transformed into mental representations is referred to as *encoding*. The process of bringing stored information into conscious awareness, or remembering, is referred to as *retrieval*.

In current psychological theories of learning and memory, long-term memory is often categorized as either *procedural* or *declarative* memory. Procedural memory effects a change in a person's behavior on the basis of experiences without the person's necessarily having conscious access to the events that produced the change in behavior (Squire & Butters, 1992). These behaviors, such as driving a car when one already knows how to drive or knowing how to get back and forth to work or school, are considered to be performed automatically. In contrast, declarative memory is the ability to store and retrieve specific pieces or bits of information or knowledge (Squire & Butters, 1992).

Declarative memory can be further divided into *semantic* and *episodic* memory. Semantic memory involves memories for general facts and concepts. Episodic memory involves information that is situation- and context-specific. In view of this conceptual framework, the WMS–III is primarily a measure of declarative episodic memory. That is, the information that is presented is novel and contextually bound by the testing situation and requires the examinee to learn and retrieve information.

Considerable research into the neurological basis for memory functioning and impairment has accumulated. A thorough critique of the research investigating the neural circuitry of memory is beyond the scope of this Manual (for such reviews see Squire, 1992, and Squire & Butters, 1992); however, a brief synopsis is provided. The neural circuitry involving the cortical and subcortical limbic structures of the medial temporal lobes, especially the hippocampus, amygdala, and related diencephalic structures, have been implicated as important structures for memory functioning (Squire, 1992; Squire & Butters, 1992). Historically, hemispheric differences in memory processing have been suggested, specifically that verbal memory may be predominantly processed in the left temporal lobe structures, whereas visual and perceptual memory may be processed predominantly in the corresponding structures of the right hemisphere (Milner, 1968). However, evidence for hemispheric specificity for auditory and visual stimuli is far from consistent in the literature. Other brain regions may also affect memory functioning. Lesions of diencephalon structures (e.g., the medial–dorsal nuclei of the thalamus) may result in reduced memory functioning at a different stage of the encoding–retrieval process (Squire & Butters, 1992).

Lesions of the frontal lobe may also result in memory dysfunction. This memory dysfunction differs from anterograde amnesia, both quantitatively and qualitatively, and is associated with decreased learning efficiency due to a failure to employ effective encoding and retrieval strategies, greater susceptibility to interference effects, problems monitoring recall for redundant or incorrect information, and breakdown of recall for event order, time, and source of information (Malloy & Richardson, 1994; Stuss, Alexander, et al., 1994; Stuss & Benson, 1984, 1986; Stuss, Eskes, & Foster, 1994). Differences in patterns of memory performance have been found useful in discriminating among clinical groups with cerebral dysfunction or functional disorders resulting from various neuropathological or psychological processes (Butters et al., 1988; Delis et al., 1991; Massman, Delis, Butters, Dupont, & Gillin, 1992).

Concept of Working Memory

Working memory denotes a person's information-processing capacity. Daneman and Carpenter (1980) credited Newell and his colleagues with the term "working memory" (Newell, 1973; Newell & Simon, 1972) when they developed their model of an information-processing system. The concept of working memory has replaced (or updated) the concept of short-term memory. This conceptual workspace is currently viewed as an active part of the information-processing system as opposed to the traditional short-term memory, which was viewed as the passive storage buffer. Therefore, the concepts of working memory and short-term memory are similar because both refer to the temporary storage of incoming information and because both are limited in capacity. However, the two concepts differ in one key aspect: Short-term memory is viewed as a *passive* form of memory, whereas working memory is viewed as an *active* form. Traditional short-term memory refers to the passive storage of information while that information either becomes encoded into long-term memory or is forgotten. Working memory, on the other hand, serves as more than a temporary storage space for incoming information. Rather, it is where calculations and manipulations of information occur. Furthermore, as Baddeley and Hitch (1974) pointed out, this component stores the products or output of these calculations and transformations in addition to the original information.

The measurement of working memory dates back to the early experiments conducted by Baddeley and Hitch (1974). Traditionally, this construct has been measured by presenting a large amount of information to the examinee. The examinee must first process or transform this information and then retain the end product. The task of recalling the information may occur immediately after the presentation of material, as in the Digit Span subtest.

However, when tasks increase in complexity (e.g., more information is presented), the working memory system becomes increasingly taxed. Baddeley (1986) stated,

> if learning and/or retrieval were limited by the amount of available attentional capacity, then requiring a subject to perform a second attention-demanding task during learning or retrieval should cause performance impairment. Furthermore . . . the greater the extent to which a process was limited by available attention, the more susceptible it should be to disruption by an attention-demanding task. (p. 39)

Tasks that have been developed to test the maximum attention span either increase the amount of information that must be stored during a single task or require the examinee to perform two tasks simultaneously. De Jonge and de Jong (1996), building on the distinctions made by Turner and Engle (1989), categorized these two types of tasks as *simple span* and *complex span* tasks. The simple span tasks measure the storage component of working memory because they deemphasize the manipulation of the material. The Digits Forward part of the WAIS–III and WMS–III Digit Span subtest is an example of a simple span task. In complex span tasks, both the storage and processing of information are involved simultaneously. For example, the examinee must perform two different types of mental processes at the same time, such as reading sentences aloud while remembering the last word of the previous sentence (see Daneman & Carpenter, 1980). A working memory span task also becomes complex by increasing the amount of material that must be manipulated. For example, the task requires the examinee to perform more extensive calculations on the material that has been stored in memory, such as mentally solving arithmetic problems. Both the WAIS–III Arithmetic subtest, which requires the examinee to perform somewhat complex arithmetic calculations mentally, and Digits Backward of the Digit Span subtest, which requires the examinee to reorder number sequences mentally, are complex tasks because they require calculation or reordering of the information. Despite the distinctions between simple and complex tasks proposed by de Jonge and de Jong, their research has shown that these types of working memory tasks are related and that both form a single dimension.

Working memory tasks have been distinguished according to visual and verbal material (Baddeley, 1986; J. T. E. Richardson, 1996). Baddeley and Hitch (1974) originally proposed a multiple-component system of working memory. Building on this theory, some researchers believe that working memory has three distinct components, which serve as "workspace buffers" for information that is to be processed (Logie, 1996). The system comprises a central executive processor and two "slave" systems. The two slave systems are the phonological loop, where verbal material is stored and processed, and the visuospatial sketch pad, where spatial material is stored and processed (Baddeley, 1986, 1992; Logie, 1995, 1996).

Although this three-component theory is popular, other researchers have deemphasized the distinction between the verbal (phonological loop) and the visual (visuospatial sketch pad) components (see J. T. E. Richardson, 1996). The WAIS–III and the WMS–III also deemphasize the distinction between verbal and visual material. The WAIS–III measures working memory with tasks in which the material is presented auditorily, whereas the WMS–III Working Memory Index is equally weighted with one visual task and one auditory task.

Though the specifics of a working memory model are disputed, most cognitive psychologists agree that the core of any definition of working memory involves the temporary storage of material that is in an active state. Carlson, Khoo, Yaure, and Schneider (1990) have pointed out that there is a single workspace, which is limited, and that this single-workspace model holds whether or not the working memory is divided into subsystems (p. 195).

Recent literature has suggested that working memory is a key component of learning (Kyllonen, 1987; Kyllonen & Christal, 1987, 1990; Woltz, 1988). An individual-differences model of working memory predicts that the greater the working memory is, the greater the attention and learning capabilities will be. According to this theory, working memory is responsible for learner differences in a wide variety of learning tasks. Building on E. H. Cooper and Pantle's (1967) "total time hypothesis," which states that the amount of information learned is a direct function of the amount of time spent learning, Baddeley (1986) proposed that the crucial factor is not necessarily time, but rather the amount of processing that can occur. Cognitive psychologists have posited that working memory is one of the important predictors of the individual differences in learning, intellectual ability, and fluid reasoning (Kyllonen, 1987; Kyllonen & Christal, 1990; Sternberg, 1980). According to Kyllonen (1987), working memory capacity, along with information-processing speed, a declarative/factual knowledge base, and a procedural knowledge base, underlies the individual's ability to learn new information. Research has provided initial support for this premise of the relationship between working memory and reasoning tasks (de Jong & Das–Smaal, 1995; Fry & Hale, 1996; Jurden, 1995; Kyllonen & Christal, 1990). Although working memory and reasoning appear related, there is also ample evidence suggesting that the two constructs are not identical but are quite distinct (Carlson et al., 1990; de Jonge & de Jong, 1996; Kyllonen & Christal, 1990). In sum, the research indicates that working memory capacity is an important moderating variable of learning.

Antecedents of the WAIS–III and the WMS–III

Wechsler's original intelligence test, the *Wechsler–Bellevue Intelligence Scale* (1939), was a milestone in the history of intelligence testing because it incorporated both verbal and performance scales and yielded scores for those scales in addition to an overall composite score. Further, the Wechsler–Bellevue was innovative because it provided deviation IQ scores that were based on standard scores computed with the same distributional characteristics at all ages. Wechsler (1944) constructed the test by collecting a sample that matched the population of the United States on several key variables (e.g., age, sex, education level, occupation level) and then by normalizing the scores. The Wechsler–Bellevue and its descendants, including the WAIS–III, have each included a group of different subtests that contribute to global IQ scores. These features and the structure of the test have remained intact through the years since the Wechsler–Bellevue. With each revision, the norms were updated, outdated items replaced, and scoring rules changed.

The WMS–III is the most recent revision of the original *Wechsler Memory Scale* (Wechsler, 1945) and the *Wechsler Memory Scale—Revised* (WMS–R; Wechsler, 1987). Like its predecessors, the WMS–III is an individually administered, clinical instrument designed to assess important domains of memory and learning in older adolescent and adult populations. Although the WMS–III has maintained many aspects of its predecessors, significant improvements have been made to the test in response to both current research and theory and the needs of clinicians. With each successive version, clinicians have been provided flexibility in the content and scope of memory assessment, from a general screening to a more intensive, detailed analysis of memory functioning.

Development of the Scales

The developmental phases of the WAIS–III and the WMS–III are very similar, and both included the following five broad stages:

- a review of the existing items and development of new items and subtests;

- pilot testing of the revised items and subtests to investigate psychometric characteristics;

- a national tryout study to examine item difficulties, item bias, subtest functioning, and factor structure (concurrent with the tryout, the scales were administered to various clinical groups in order to investigate clinical utility);

- a large national standardization study to collect normative information, to investigate bias, and to make final item and subtest decisions; and

- multiple studies conducted concurrently with standardization to determine the reliability, concurrent validity, construct validity, and clinical utility of the test.

The following sections provide overviews of the developmental phases of the WAIS–III and the WMS–III and provide the rationale for the revisions of the *Wechsler Adult Intelligence Scale—Revised* (WAIS–R; Wechsler, 1981) and the WMS–R (Wechsler, 1987).

WAIS–III

The decision to revise the WAIS–R involved the following issues:

- **Updating of Norms.** Because there is a real phenomenon of IQ-score inflation over time, norms for a test of intellectual functioning should be updated regularly (Flynn, 1984, 1987; Matarazzo, 1972). Data suggest that an examinee's IQ score will generally be higher when outdated rather than current norms are used. The inflation rate of IQ scores is about 0.3 points each year. Therefore, if the mean IQ score of the U.S. population on the WAIS–R was 100 in 1981, the inflation might cause it to be about 105 in 1997. Some of Matarazzo's and Flynn's suggested causes of this IQ-score inflation in the general population are improvement in the education system, improved nutrition, better health conditions, and increased dissemination of information. Regardless of the reasons for these changes in test performance, periodic updating of the norms is essential; otherwise, average IQ scores will gradually drift upward and give a progressively deceptive picture of an individual's performance relative to the expected scores in his or her own age group.

  The normative data have been updated by the restandardization of the instrument. The WAIS–III sampling plan included 2,450 individuals aged 16–89 years. The sample was divided into 13 age groups and stratified on key demographic variables, including age, sex, education level, and geographic region according to the U.S. census data (U.S. Bureau of the Census, 1995). A complete description of the obtained sampling matrix is provided in Chapter 2 of this Manual.

- **Extension of the Age Range.** Individuals in the United States are living longer. Current estimates place the average life expectancy at birth to be over 78 years for women and over 72 years for men (Rosenberg, Ventura, Maurer, Heuser, & Freedman, 1996). The WAIS–R provides normative information for individuals only up to 74 years of age; therefore, it does not address the significant population of adults over 74 years of age. In the United States, the current population of adults aged 75 years and older is approximately 15 million, or 6%, of the total population across all age groups (U.S. Bureau of the Census, 1997). Furthermore, the proportion of older adults is expected to increase.

  Because of the growing population of older adults, the age range of the WAIS–III extends through 89 years of age. Additionally, the stimuli were modified to reflect this change: Artwork was redrawn, stimuli were enlarged, and the use of bonus points for quick performance was deemphasized. A new subtest, Matrix Reasoning, which does not require manual manipulation or quick performance, was added to the Performance scale. All of these features make the scale more appropriate for an older adult population.

- **Modification of Items.** In most assessment instruments, some items become outdated over time. The WAIS–R items are no exception. In the Information subtest, for instance, the content of some items is too chronologically remote for younger examinees. Moreover, contemporary methodologies for testing item bias were used for the WAIS–III item selection.

  Problematic items were identified and deleted on the basis of formal reviews of the items and empirical data from statistical and bias analyses. The formal reviews were conducted by experts in crosscultural research, intelligence testing, or both. Reviews were collected at three key points during the development of the test, with approximately 20–25 reviews obtained at each stage. During the very initial stages of the project, all WAIS–R subtests and items were reviewed by internal and external reviewers for potential bias, datedness, content relevance, and clinical utility. Bias experts evaluated items in terms of content and potential bias. During the tryout phase and again during the standardization phase of the project, content and bias experts reviewed the items and identified those that were potentially problematic.

  Along with these reviews, empirical data were used to test hypotheses and to assist in the decision process. First, on the basis of item statistics and item bias analyses of the WAIS–R standardization sample data, biased or dated items were deleted or rewritten. The retained items were then tested in three pilot studies (with sample sizes ranging from 113 to

168 examinees). Once again, the empirical data (item difficulty and item correlations with the relevant subtest total score) were used to select those items to be tested in the nationwide tryout study. For the tryout, 446 participants composed the sample, which was stratified according to age, sex, education level, race/ethnicity, and geographic region. Item analyses based on the tryout data were performed for each subtest to determine the item sets for standardization. Data from an oversampling of 162 African American and Hispanic examinees helped the project team detect and remove items that were potentially biased against either of these groups. Results from traditional Mantel–Haenszel bias analysis (Holland & Thayer, 1988) and item response theory (IRT) bias analyses (Hambleton, 1993) provided further data on potentially problematic items. During the standardization phase, the procedures were repeated. Item analyses based on the standardization data were performed for each subtest to determine the item sets for the final version.

Item bias analyses based on an IRT method require data from a large number of examinees. Certain item parameters must be estimated through an iterative process. This process requires responses to each item on each subtest by a minimum of 200 individuals in both the focal and comparison groups. Although the sampling data (see Tables 2.2–2.13) indicate that an ample number of examinees were tested, not every examinee necessarily completed every item because of discontinue rules. Furthermore, estimations based on the data collected during the tryout phase suggested that a sufficient number of examinees might not complete the most difficult items. Therefore, an oversampling of 200 African American and Hispanic participants were tested without discontinue rules so that the item bias analyses could be repeated with sufficient observed item scores for both of these groups. On the basis of these empirical analyses and the content reviews, items that did not meet acceptable criteria were removed.

- **Updating Artwork.** Because much of the WAIS–R artwork has become outdated and is not likely to be attractive to examinees, the WAIS–III artwork has been made more contemporary. Moreover, some of the visual stimuli have been enlarged so that individuals with visual acuity problems will not be at a disadvantage.

Several steps were taken to make the WAIS–III stimuli more attractive. The Picture Completion items were redrawn, enlarged, and colorized. Despite concerns that colorizing the artwork might change the nature of the task, colored pictures were deemed more relevant and ecologically valid (i.e., easily transferred to real-life situations). The Picture Arrangement cards also were redrawn and modernized. Several WAIS–R items had been derived from comic strips popular at the time the previous editions were developed, and these items were removed. Improvements were also made to the Object Assembly subtest. The WAIS–III Object Assembly Layout Shield is constructed of sturdy card stock so that it can stand alone and includes the item instructions. The puzzle pieces feature numbers printed on the back to assist the examiner in laying out the pieces in the specified arrangement. Finally, the Digit Symbol—Coding subtest features more space between the key and the items to prevent left-handed examinees from blocking the key from view as they work.

- **Extension of Floor and Enhancement of Clinical Utility.** The IQ scores of the WAIS–R do not extend downward far enough to discriminate adequately among examinees with mild to moderate mental retardation. For the oldest age group (70–74 years), the WAIS–R Verbal IQ (VIQ) scores extend only 2.67 SDs below the mean. On the Performance scale, a 70-year-old individual who cannot respond correctly to even one Performance item on any of the Performance subtests can still obtain a WAIS–R Performance IQ (PIQ) score of 61 points. The restricted floor is not limited to the IQ scores; the WAIS–R subtest scores are scaled to about 3 SDs below the mean, but often there are not enough easy items to permit accurate scaling to this level.

  On the WAIS–III, the range of possible scores has been extended downward. Easier items, which are administered if a basal criterion is not met, were added to several subtests. In the WAIS–III, the Full Scale IQ (FSIQ) scores extend downward to 45, the VIQ scores to 48, and the PIQ scores to 47. Data were collected on individuals diagnosed with mild or moderate mental retardation according to the *Diagnostic and Statistical Manual of Mental Disorders—Fourth Edition* (*DSM–IV*; American Psychiatric Association, 1994) and the American Association of Mental Retardation criteria (1992). Partially on the basis of these data, IQ scores in this range were extrapolated downward to make assessment more feasible at this lower end of functioning.

  Additionally, new diagnostic features were included to help the examiner test the limits of performance or to examine more closely the types of errors that examinees make. These features make the WAIS–III more useful in the field of neuropsychology. For instance, an optional procedure for testing incidental learning following Digit Symbol—Coding administration (Hart, Kwentus, Wade, & Hamer, 1987; E. Kaplan, Fein, Morris, & Delis, 1991) was added to the WAIS–III.

- **Decreased Reliance on Timed Performance.** Six of the WAIS–R subtests have time limits, and many of their items include bonus points for quick performance. Such time constraints are especially problematic for older adults, whose processing speed is expected to decrease. Although processing speed is important and should be tested, measures of other intellective processes should not be confounded by this factor. Therefore, for the WAIS–III, a new nonverbal subtest (Matrix Reasoning) that does not have time limits was created. Additionally, the number of items with time-bonus points was decreased in the existing subtests.

To decrease the reliance of the PIQ score on quick performance and subsequent bonus points, Matrix Reasoning, a nonverbal, unspeeded subtest of abstract reasoning, was added to the Performance scale. It replaces Object Assembly as a standard subtest. Object Assembly, which relies heavily on bonus points for quick performance, is now an optional subtest and is not required for computing WAIS–III IQ or Index scores.

- **Enhancement of Fluid Reasoning Measurement.** Several theories of cognitive functioning emphasize the assessment of fluid reasoning (e.g., Carroll, 1997; Cattell, 1943, 1963; Cattell & Horn, 1978; Sternberg, 1995). Fluid reasoning is the "ability to perform mental operations, such as manipulation of abstract symbols" (Sternberg, 1995, p. 437). Matrix-reasoning types of tasks, for example, are considered typical measures of this type of ability. The WAIS–R has been criticized for not having subtests that sufficiently measure abstract, fluid reasoning. The new WAIS–III subtest, Matrix Reasoning, has been added to enhance measurement of this domain.

- **Strengthening the Theoretical Basis.** Current research suggests that cognitive functioning encompasses more than what is measured by VIQ and PIQ scores. For instance, in their review of the literature of the various factor analytic studies of the WAIS–R, Leckliter, Matarazzo, and Silverstein (1986) showed that most researchers have found a model with three factors (verbal comprehension, perceptual organization, and memory/freedom from distractibility). In addition to the traditional IQ scores, the WAIS–III includes Index scores, which are measures of more discrete factors and domains.

From the beginning of the WAIS–III project, attempts were made to include new subtests that would be related to a hypothesized third factor (Working Memory) and to a hypothesized fourth factor (Processing Speed). These factors have been labeled "mediators" in cognitive functioning because the component skills have been found to be important to learning (Kyllonen & Stephens, 1990; Woltz, 1988). Kyllonen and Christal (1990) have demonstrated the relationship between working memory and *g*, or global intellectual ability. Kyllonen (1987) has also advanced a formal theory of cognitive functioning in which working memory and processing speed are core components in the acquisition of new information. Therefore, two new subtests were developed for the WAIS–III. Letter–Number Sequencing was designed as a measure of working memory, and Symbol Search was designed as a measure of processing speed.

Factor analyses of the WAIS–III standardization data support a model of four indexes: verbal comprehension, perceptual organization, working memory, and processing speed. This organization of the WAIS–III subtests into more discrete cognitive domains, or indexes, is especially important because working memory and processing speed, which are related to learning acquisition, can be distinguished from the verbal comprehension tasks and perceptual organization tasks. This breakdown can be especially useful for diagnosing learning disabilities, attention-deficit/hyperactivity disorder (ADHD), and other cognitive deficiencies.

- **Statistical Linkage to Other Measures of Cognitive Functioning and Achievement.** The *Wechsler Intelligence Scale for Children—Third Edition* (WISC–III; Wechsler, 1991) was co-normed with the *Wechsler Individual Achievement Test* (WIAT; The Psychological Corporation, 1992). This linkage provides examiners more information about the interrelationship of a broader spectrum of cognitive abilities. This co-norming has also enabled examiners to "predict" an examinee's achievement scores on the basis of his or her intellectual ability score. To allow for such predictions with the WAIS–III, the WAIS–III and the WIAT were linked for 16- to 19-year-olds.

  Additionally, because memory and intellectual ability in adults are commonly tested concurrently, the WAIS–III and the WMS–III were co-normed. A sample of 1,250 individuals took both the WAIS–III and the WMS–III in a counterbalanced order. These data allow direct comparison of intelligence and memory through normative information.

- **Extensive Testing of Reliability and Validity.** Finally, the developmental phase of the WAIS–III included additional studies of psychometric properties of the scale. In a study of the stability of the instrument, 394 examinees were retested from 2 to 12 weeks after the first testing. Evidence of the concurrent validity of the WAIS–III was provided by correlation studies between the WAIS–III and the following instruments: the WAIS–R, the WISC–III, the WIAT, the *Stanford–Binet Intelligence Scale—Fourth Edition* (R. L. Thorndike, Hagen, & Sattler, 1986), and the *Standard Progressive Matrices* (Raven, 1976). Finally, for evidence of the construct validity and the clinical utility of the scale, the WAIS–III was administered to individuals with neuropsychological deficits (e.g., Alzheimer's dementia, traumatic brain injury), mental retardation, psychiatric disorders, learning disabilities, and hearing impairments.

WMS–III

In 1987, the WMS was revised for the first time (see Prigatano, 1977, 1978, for critical reviews of the WMS). The WMS–R provided improved norms, extensive scoring rules, additional subtests for measuring delayed recall of information, and other new subtests with visually presented stimuli. These additional subtests were developed by Wechsler, although, the final revision was not published until after his death. The WMS–R has been the subject of numerous research studies since its publication. Although the WMS–R provided clear advantages over its predecessor, several comprehensive reviews have identified areas in which the scale could be improved (Chelune, Bornstein, & Prifitera, 1990; Elwood, 1991; Loring, 1989).

During the initial phases of the WMS–III development, all WMS–R subtests and items were reviewed for potential cultural and sex bias, appropriateness of content, theoretical basis, and clinical utility. Expert bias reviewers evaluated the WMS–R items, and approximately 20 clinical psychologists and neuropsychologists evaluated the scale in terms of content, psychometrics, and clinical utility. Additionally, a standing advisory panel met about twice yearly to review the developmental research, to consult on technical and content issues, and to provide direction regarding the standardization sampling and the validation studies with clinical groups.

During the early stages of development, numerous small pilot studies were conducted, and the results of these studies provided data on the various psychometric characteristics of new subtests and for the revised subtests. Additional pilot studies involving various clinical groups provided information on clinical utility and on both examiner and examinee friendliness. These studies resulted in additional refinements to content, administration procedures, and scoring.

The next major phase of development consisted of a national tryout with approximately 450 individuals who were administered both the WMS–III and the WAIS–III. All items and subtests were evaluated for cultural and sex bias, psychometric characteristics, administration procedures, clinical utility, and underlying factorial structure. Scoring studies were performed for the Logical Memory, Visual Reproduction, and Family Pictures subtests to investigate their reliability and clinical sensitivity. On the basis of these results, the subtests for the standardization of the WMS–III were selected. In addition to the battery of memory subtests, the standardization version included a number of other measures for the purpose of evaluating concurrent validity.

In summary, the solicited reviews of the WMS–R, an extensive review of the published literature, and the recommendations from the advisory panel identified a number of ways in which the WMS–R could be improved. These improvements fell into two broad categories: normative/psychometric issues and content/score configuration issues. A summary of the identified issues and how these issues were addressed and incorporated in the WMS–III follows.

Normative/Psychometric Issues

- **Standardization Sample Size, Age Range, and Representativeness.** The WMS–R standardization sample consisted of six age groups, each of which included approximately 50 individuals. The total sample size was approximately 300 individuals who ranged in age from 16 to 74 years. Although the standardization sample of the WMS–R was relatively small compared to those of other contemporary Wechsler scales, it was comparable to the samples for the original WAIS and other contemporary neuropsychological instruments. The concerns underlying a small sample size are an increased likelihood of greater measurement error and a less accurate estimate of population parameters. Also, the normative age range of the WMS–R, like that of the WAIS–R, is limited to individuals younger than 75 years of age. Finally, because memory is a subset of overall intellectual functioning, it is important for the individuals in the standardization sample to be representative of the general population in terms of overall ability level.

  The WMS–III standardization sample included 1,250 individuals ranging in age from 16 to 89 years. The sample was divided into 13 age groups. The first 11 age groups, spanning ages 16–79, included 100 participants each. The last two age groups, 80–84 and 85–89, each included 75 participants. Within each standardization stratification variable, the WMS–III was randomly administered to one half of the WAIS–III standardization sample. In this way, the ability levels of the WMS–III standardization participants would be representative of the general population.

- **Interpolated Norms.** Normative scores for three of the WMS–R age groups (18–19 years, 25–34 years, and 45–54 years) were interpolated on the basis of the scores of the adjacent sampled age groups. To the degree that age-based memory performance is nonlinear, interpolation of norms may not fully capture the relationship. Although no definitive evidence shows a nonlinear relationship for the nonsampled age groups, it was recommended that each age group be sampled.

  For the WMS–III, each age group in the standardization sample was sampled. None of the normative scores for the WMS–III age groups were interpolated. Normative evidence from the WMS–III has demonstrated that for comparable constructs between the two instruments, there is indeed a linear relationship for the nonsampled age groups in the WMS–R for which norms were interpolated.

- **Scale Reliability.** The reliability coefficients of some of the WMS–R indexes and subtests are lower than desirable. In general, reduced reliability decreases the scale's clinical sensitivity and results in larger confidence intervals. The restriction of scale range is one reason for these low reliabilities in the WMS–R. For example, the Figural Memory subtest has only four items, and the Mental Control subtest has only three items.

Reliability coefficients for the WMS–III Primary subtests and Primary Indexes are generally higher than those of the WMS–R. Average subtest internal consistency reliability coefficients range from the .70s to the .90s. With one exception, average composite reliability coefficients of the Primary Indexes range in the .80s and .90s. The Auditory Recognition Delayed Index has a reliability coefficient of .74.

Content/Scoring Configuration Issues

- **Visual Memory Stimuli.** There is little empirical evidence that the WMS–R visual memory subtests are adequate measures of a hypothetical "pure" visual memory system or that they are differentially sensitive for individuals with unilateral hemispheric lesions (Chelune & Bornstein, 1988; Heilbronner, 1992; Loring, 1989; Naugle, Chelune, Cheek, Lüders, & Awad, 1993). Research has also indicated that performance on the Visual Reproduction subtest can be confounded by the effects of constructional dyspraxia (Haut, Weber, Demarest, Keefover, & Rankin, 1996; Haut, Weber, Wilhelm, Keefover, & Rankin, 1994), and that a direct-copy condition would help in interpreting performance on this subtest (E. Kaplan, 1988).

On the basis of the reviews, two of the three WMS–R visual memory subtests were deleted from the scale: Figural Memory and Visual Paired Associates. Five experimental subtests of visually presented memory stimuli were developed as possible replacements for these two. For these possible replacement subtests, an effort was made to include visual stimuli that would make verbal encoding difficult. Rather than purporting to tap exclusively a hypothetical verbal or visual memory system, the WMS–III distinguishes between auditory and visual memory by the modality of presentation of the subtests. Preliminary studies of the WMS–III (presented in Chapter 4 of this Manual) support the discriminant validity of the auditory and visual memory measures.

- **Internal Validity.** Factor analytic studies of the WMS–R have not yielded a factor solution consistent with the index structure of the WMS–R. Support for a two-factor solution—General Memory and Attention/Concentration—when only immediate memory subtests are entered into the analysis has been reported in several studies (e.g., Bornstein & Chelune, 1988; Roid, Prifitera, & Ledbetter, 1988). The index configuration of the WMS–III was not constructed on the basis of factor analysis. Rather, the indexes were constructed on the basis of clinically meaningful aspects of clinical memory assessment. Chapter 4 of this Manual presents the results of confirmatory factor analyses for various conceptualizations of dimensions of memory. These results provide support for the index structure of the WMS–III.

- **Recognition Versus Recall Memory.** Because the WMS–R does not provide standardized recognition trials, it is limited as a means of identifying specific retrieval problems. It has been suggested that such specificity may help to distinguish between clinical groups (Butters et al., 1988).

  Whenever possible, recognition measures were added to the WMS–III and are administered immediately after measures of delayed recall. The Auditory Recognition Delayed Index was added to the memory indexes. This index can be contrasted to the Auditory Delayed Index, which is composed of parallel recall measures.

CHAPTER 2

Standardization and Norms Development

Standardization

Description of the Samples

The WAIS–III and WMS–III normative information presented in this Manual is based on national standardization samples representative of the U.S. population of adults aged 16–89 years. A stratified sampling plan ensured that the standardization samples included representative proportions of adults according to each selected demographic variable. An analysis of data gathered in 1995 by the U.S. Bureau of the Census provided the basis for stratification along the following variables: age, sex, race/ethnicity, education level, and geographic region. The following sections present the characteristics of the WAIS–III and WMS–III standardization samples.

- **Age.** The standardization sample for the WAIS–III included 2,450 adults. For the WMS–III standardization sample, 1,032 adults were tested. This standardization sample was weighted to match the 1995 census data and each age group was required to have an average full scale IQ score of 100. This weighting method yielded a sample of 1,250, which was used for both the norming of the WMS–III and the working memory factor on the WAIS–III, as well as for any related analyses reported in this manual. Each sample was divided into 13 age bands: 16–17, 18–19, 20–24, 25–29, 30–34, 35–44, 45–54, 55–64, 65–69, 70–74, 75–79, 80–84, 85–89. These samples improve on the WAIS–R and WMS–R samples, which included 1,880 and approximately 300 adults aged 16–74, respectively. Except for the two oldest age groups, each WAIS–III group included 200 partici- pants; the 80–84 age group included 150 participants, and the 85–89 age group included 100 participants. For the WMS–III, 100 participants were included in each age group except the two oldest groups, which consisted of 75 participants each.

  In addition to the basic standardization samples, 437 individuals were tested so that at least 30 participants for the WAIS–III and 20 participants for the WMS–III would be included in each educational level within each age group. The data from these additional cases were treated as oversampling data and were excluded from the basic standardization samples. These additional data were collected for later research investigating the relationships between cognitive abilities and education level.

- **Sex.** The standardization sample consisted of an equal number of male and female participants in each age group from 16 through 64. The older age groups included more women than men, in proportions consistent with census data.

- **Race/Ethnicity.** For each age group in the standardization samples, the proportions of Whites, African Americans, Hispanics, and other racial/ethnic groups were based on the racial/ethnic proportions of individuals within each age band within the U.S. population according to the 1995 Census data.

  An additional 200 African American and Hispanic individuals were administered the WAIS–III without discontinue rules. This oversampling provided a sufficient number of item scores across all items for item bias analyses.

- **Educational Level.** The samples were stratified according to the following five education levels based on the number of years of school completed: ≤ 8 years, 9–11 years, 12 years, 13–15 years, and ≥ 16 years. For examinees aged 16–19, parent education was used.

- **Geographic Region.** The United States was divided into the four major regions specified by the Census reports (see Figure 2.1): Northeast (NE), North Central (NC), South (S), and West (W). The number of participants from each region was proportionate to the population in each region.

Figure 2.1. Standardization Sampling Sites

Locating and Testing the Samples

The collection of standardization data was achieved primarily through the use of marketing research firms in 28 U.S. cities in the Northeast, North Central, South, and West regions. These firms used various methods to recruit participants to fit the sampling plan matrix; these included random telephone calls, newspaper advertisements, and flyers placed in senior centers and with various community organizations. Additionally, independent examiners from most states recruited and tested examinees. All participants were paid an incentive fee to participate.

All potential standardization participants were medically and psychiatrically screened with a self-report questionnaire. Table 2.1 lists the criteria by which individuals were disqualified from the standardization sample.

Table 2.1. Exclusionary Criteria for the Standardization Samples

- Color-blindness
- Uncorrected hearing loss
- Uncorrected visual impairment
- Current treatment for alcohol or drug dependence
- Consumption of more than three alcoholic beverages on more than two nights a week
- Seeing a doctor or other professional for memory problems or problems with thinking
- Upper extremity disability that would affect motor performance (e.g. ability to put puzzles together)
- Any period of unconsciousness for 5 minutes or more
- Head injury resulting in hospitalization for more than 24 hours
- Medical or psychiatric condition that could potentially affect cognitive functioning, such as
  - Stroke
  - Electroconvulsive treatment
  - Epilepsy
  - Brain surgery
  - Encephalitis
  - Meningitis
  - Multiple sclerosis
  - Parkinson's disease
  - Huntington's chorea
  - Alzheimer's dementia
  - Schizophrenia
  - Bipolar disorder
- Currently taking antidepressant, antianxiety, or antipsychotic medication

Representativeness of the Samples

The percentages of the U.S. population and the WAIS–III and WMS–III standardization samples according to race/ethnicity are presented in Figure 2.2. Percentages according to geographic region are presented in Figure 2.3. Tables 2.2–2.13 present detailed demographic information for the U.S. population and for the WAIS–III and the WMS–III standardization samples. Tables 2.2–2.4 provide the proportions of the U.S. population, the WAIS–III sample, and the WMS–III sample, respectively, according to age, race/ethnicity, and education. Tables 2.5–2.7 provide the proportions according to age, sex, and education. Tables 2.8–2.10 provide the proportions by age, sex, and race/ethnicity, and Tables 2.11–2.13 provide the proportions by age, race/ethnicity, and geographic region. These data indicate a close correspondence between the two samples and U.S. Census proportions.

WMS–III Weighted Sampling

Tulsky and Ledbetter (2000) described the weighted sampling methodology used for the development of the WMS–III normative sample. An analysis of the WAIS–III and WMS–III standardization data revealed that some of the age groups did not have an average intellectual ability of 100 and that some of the age groups did not fully represent the U.S. population according to some of the stratification variables. The WMS–III normative sample was therefore weighted so that each age group more closely represented the census data and more closely approximated an average intellectual ability of 100. The actual WMS–III standardization sample consisted of 1,032 participants. From these, protocols were randomly selected within the stratification parameters for duplication to derive the final WMS–III weighted normative sample of 1,250.

Case weighting improves the overall representativeness of the sample. Moreover, the weighting does not bias the results if the initial sample is representative of the subpopulations in general. Compared to the samples for previous versions of the scale, the WMS–III sample represents a marked improvement. Furthermore, the WMS–III is the only commercially available memory test to have been extensively normed on a stratified, random, representative sample of the general population with concurrent collection of intellectual ability.

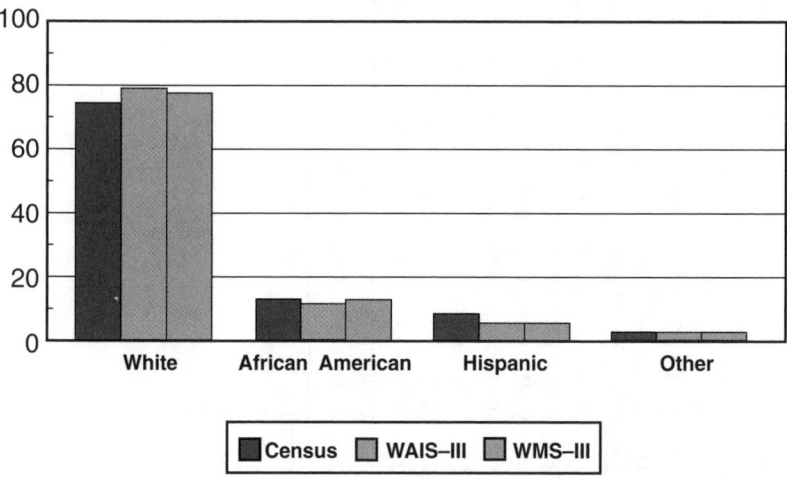

Figure 2.2. Race/Ethnicity Characteristics of the U.S. Population and WAIS–III and WMS–III Standardization Samples

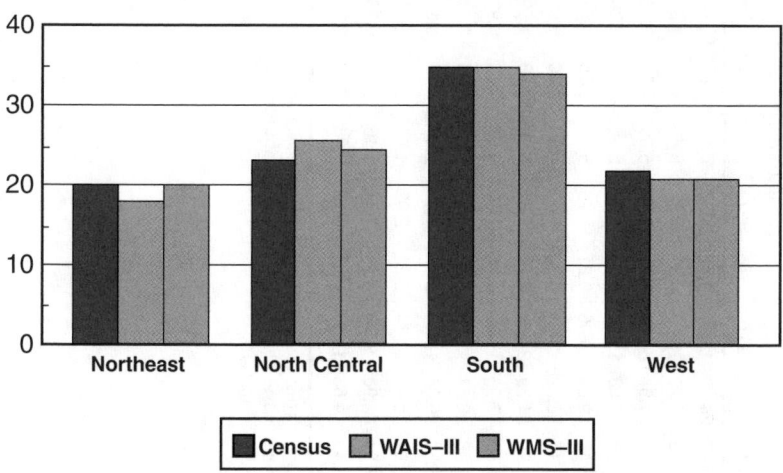

Figure 2.3. Geographic Region Characteristics of the U.S. Population and WAIS–III and WMS–III Standardization Samples

Table 2.2. Percentages of the U.S. Population by Age, Race/Ethnicity, and Education

Age	White					African American					Hispanic					Other				
	≤8	9–11	12	13–15	≥16	≤8	9–11	12	13–15	≥16	≤8	9–11	12	13–15	≥16	≤8	9–11	12	13–15	≥16
16–17	1.13	4.41	20.42	24.77	18.11	0.82	3.37	5.43	4.87	1.27	3.47	2.66	2.70	2.09	0.84	0.39	0.50	0.50	1.10	1.15
18–19	1.28	4.06	18.60	25.70	18.23	0.94	3.23	5.89	4.23	1.80	3.76	2.96	3.06	1.94	0.90	0.36	0.33	0.84	0.96	0.94
20–24	0.85	5.21	21.80	31.37	9.09	0.21	2.25	5.08	5.73	0.76	2.46	3.00	4.00	3.82	0.41	0.07	0.38	0.79	2.19	0.52
25–29	0.82	4.37	22.53	21.38	19.95	0.06	1.73	5.60	4.00	2.08	3.01	2.76	3.82	2.67	1.20	0.20	0.23	0.77	1.33	1.50
30–34	0.80	4.72	25.42	19.93	20.96	0.21	1.76	5.17	3.75	1.78	2.82	2.05	3.40	2.44	1.22	0.12	0.17	1.03	0.97	1.30
35–44	1.26	4.42	25.15	22.02	22.29	0.33	1.61	4.65	3.60	1.90	2.31	1.23	2.66	1.97	0.98	0.24	0.26	0.84	0.84	1.45
45–54	2.12	4.97	25.94	21.39	24.34	0.67	1.85	3.68	2.46	1.59	2.55	1.04	1.87	1.24	0.71	0.29	0.25	0.98	0.64	1.41
55–64	5.56	8.73	31.56	17.95	17.03	1.75	2.10	3.47	1.60	0.93	3.12	0.88	1.42	0.84	0.50	0.34	0.30	0.85	0.46	0.59
65–69	8.68	12.10	31.98	16.64	13.68	2.56	2.19	2.49	0.95	0.74	3.19	0.71	1.19	0.34	0.43	0.51	0.32	0.50	0.42	0.39
70–74	11.17	11.57	33.32	16.94	12.14	2.77	1.97	1.97	0.79	0.34	2.74	0.68	0.73	0.27	0.26	0.88	0.24	0.59	0.36	0.28
75–79	16.03	13.02	30.97	15.49	11.74	3.21	2.09	1.40	0.42	0.21	2.07	0.32	0.66	0.35	0.16	0.78	0.24	0.60	0.12	0.11
80–84	22.67	14.73	27.94	12.96	8.56	4.15	1.71	1.16	0.57	0.35	2.31	0.43	0.59	0.06	0.13	0.41	0.27	0.55	0.25	0.20
85–89	26.00	13.11	22.40	14.63	11.30	4.55	0.76	0.98	0.32	0.58	2.69	0.41	0.64	0.05	0.10	0.75	0.20	0.35	0.05	0.13

Note. U.S. population data are from *Current Population Survey, March 1995* [Machine-readable data file] by U.S. Bureau of the Census, 1995, Washington, DC: U.S. Bureau of the Census (Producer/Distributor). Education is number of years completed; for examinees aged 16–19 years, education is based on parent education.

Table 2.3. **Demographic Characteristics of the WAIS–III Standardization Sample: Percentages by Age, Race/Ethnicity, and Education**

Age	n	White					African American					Hispanic					Other				
		≤8	9–11	12	13–15	≥16	≤8	9–11	12	13–15	≥16	≤8	9–11	12	13–15	≥16	≤8	9–11	12	13–15	≥16
16–17	200	1.5	4.5	23.0	24.0	16.5	0.5	2.5	6.0	4.5	1.5	2.5	3.0	4.5	1.0	—	—	—	2.0	1.5	1.0
18–19	200	1.5	4.5	22.5	23.0	15.5	1.0	3.0	5.5	6.0	1.5	3.0	2.5	3.0	3.5	0.5	—	0.5	1.0	1.5	0.5
20–24	200	1.0	5.5	23.5	30.5	9.5	1.0	2.0	6.5	4.5	0.5	2.0	3.0	4.0	3.5	0.5	—	0.5	—	1.5	0.5
25–29	200	1.5	4.5	26.0	20.0	19.5	0.5	2.0	5.5	3.0	2.0	2.5	2.0	3.0	2.5	1.5	—	1.0	2.0	0.5	0.5
30–34	200	3.0	5.5	27.0	20.5	19.5	—	2.0	4.5	4.5	2.0	1.0	1.0	1.5	2.5	1.0	0.5	1.0	0.5	2.0	0.5
35–44	200	1.5	3.0	26.5	22.5	24.0	1.0	1.0	4.0	3.0	2.5	2.0	0.5	2.5	2.0	1.0	—	0.5	1.0	—	1.5
45–54	200	3.5	5.0	28.5	20.0	21.5	1.0	2.5	4.0	2.0	1.5	3.5	1.5	1.0	1.0	0.5	—	0.5	—	1.0	1.5
55–64	200	8.5	9.5	32.5	15.0	16.0	1.5	2.5	3.5	1.5	1.5	3.0	1.0	1.0	0.5	—	0.5	—	1.0	0.5	0.5
65–69	200	12.5	12.0	35.0	13.5	12.5	3.0	2.0	2.0	1.5	1.0	1.5	0.5	1.0	0.5	0.5	0.5	—	—	0.5	—
70–74	200	12.0	12.5	34.5	13.5	12.5	2.5	1.5	3.0	0.5	1.0	1.0	1.5	1.5	0.5	0.5	0.5	—	0.5	0.5	—
75–79	200	14.5	14.0	34.5	14.5	12.0	2.5	1.0	2.5	0.5	0.5	2.0	—	—	—	—	—	—	—	0.5	1.0
80–84	150	26.0	15.3	27.3	9.3	10.0	3.3	2.0	1.3	0.7	1.3	2.7	—	—	—	—	—	—	—	0.7	—
85–89	100	28.0	15.0	27.0	10.0	11.0	3.0	1.0	—	1.0	—	2.0	—	—	—	1.0	—	1.0	—	—	—

Note. N = 2,450. Education is number of years completed; for examinees aged 16–19 years, education is based on parent education. Cells in which data are not reported indicate that standardization protocols for persons meeting the relevant criteria were not collected.

Table 2.4. Demographic Characteristics of the WMS–III Standardization Sample: Percentages by Age, Race/Ethnicity, and Education

Age	n	White					African American					Hispanic					Other				
		≤8	9–11	12	13–15	≥16	≤8	9–11	12	13–15	≥16	≤8	9–11	12	13–15	≥16	≤8	9–11	12	13–15	≥16
16–17	100	—	8.0	22.0	23.0	16.0	2.0	3.0	5.0	3.0	3.0	2.0	4.0	3.0	1.0	—	—	—	2.0	—	3.0
18–19	100	1.0	4.0	21.0	23.0	19.0	2.0	2.0	5.0	6.0	3.0	2.0	3.0	5.0	1.0	1.0	—	—	1.0	—	1.0
20–24	100	—	6.0	23.0	33.0	9.0	1.0	3.0	5.0	5.0	—	2.0	—	4.0	4.0	1.0	1.0	1.0	—	2.0	—
25–29	100	2.0	6.0	25.0	20.0	17.0	—	2.0	7.0	3.0	2.0	2.0	2.0	3.0	3.0	3.0	—	—	1.0	—	2.0
30–34	100	3.0	8.0	28.0	18.0	18.0	—	3.0	4.0	3.0	3.0	1.0	2.0	—	3.0	—	1.0	1.0	1.0	2.0	1.0
35–44	100	2.0	3.0	28.0	22.0	21.0	—	1.0	5.0	3.0	2.0	2.0	1.0	2.0	3.0	1.0	—	1.0	2.0	—	1.0
45–54	100	2.0	6.0	27.0	21.0	23.0	—	4.0	3.0	2.0	1.0	3.0	—	1.0	1.0	2.0	—	1.0	—	1.0	2.0
55–64	100	7.0	10.0	29.0	17.0	16.0	1.0	2.0	6.0	1.0	1.0	3.0	1.0	1.0	1.0	—	2.0	—	1.0	1.0	—
65–69	100	11.0	13.0	34.0	14.0	12.0	4.0	2.0	3.0	1.0	1.0	2.0	2.0	—	—	1.0	—	—	—	—	—
70–74	100	14.0	13.0	35.0	15.0	10.0	3.0	2.0	4.0	—	—	—	1.0	2.0	—	1.0	—	—	—	—	1.0
75–79	100	20.0	13.0	32.0	13.0	9.0	—	2.0	3.0	—	2.0	3.0	—	—	—	—	—	—	—	2.0	—
80–84	75	28.0	16.0	26.7	8.0	9.3	2.7	—	1.3	1.3	1.3	4.0	—	—	—	—	—	—	—	1.3	—
85–89	75	29.3	13.3	20.0	10.7	14.7	5.3	1.3	—	1.3	—	1.3	—	1.3	—	1.3	—	—	—	—	—

Note. *Weighted N* = 1,250. Education is number of years completed; for examinees aged 16–19 years, education is based on parent education. Cells in which data are not reported indicate that standardization protocols for persons meeting the relevant criteria were not collected.

Table 2.5. Percentages of the U.S. Population by Age, Sex, and Education

Age	Male ≤8	9–11	12	13–15	≥16	Female ≤8	9–11	12	13–15	≥16	Total ≤8	9–11	12	13–15	≥16
16–17	2.67	5.19	14.92	16.21	12.29	3.14	5.75	14.14	16.62	9.07	5.81	10.94	29.06	32.84	21.36
18–19	3.05	5.98	14.35	16.90	12.01	3.29	4.59	14.04	15.92	9.86	6.33	10.57	28.39	32.83	21.87
20–24	2.05	5.69	16.98	20.57	4.43	1.55	5.15	14.69	22.55	6.35	3.60	10.84	31.67	43.12	10.78
25–29	2.25	4.59	16.95	13.88	12.24	1.84	4.50	15.78	15.51	12.48	4.08	9.09	32.72	29.38	24.72
30–34	2.27	4.75	17.64	12.18	12.74	1.67	3.94	17.37	14.91	12.51	3.94	8.69	35.02	27.09	25.26
35–44	2.30	3.84	16.23	13.31	13.86	1.85	3.68	17.06	15.12	12.75	4.15	7.52	33.29	28.43	26.62
45–54	3.02	3.77	14.18	11.97	16.00	2.62	4.34	18.29	13.77	12.04	5.64	8.11	32.47	25.74	28.04
55–64	5.51	5.27	15.31	9.75	11.77	5.26	6.75	21.99	11.11	7.28	10.76	12.02	37.30	20.86	19.05
65–69	7.74	6.36	14.27	8.07	9.05	7.20	8.96	21.89	10.28	6.19	14.94	15.31	36.16	18.35	15.24
70–74	8.03	6.40	13.26	7.65	7.92	9.54	8.05	23.35	10.70	5.10	17.56	14.45	36.62	18.35	13.02
75–79	9.99	5.89	12.27	7.39	6.50	12.11	9.79	21.36	8.99	5.72	22.10	15.68	33.63	16.38	12.22
80–84	12.15	5.88	8.91	5.78	4.15	17.39	11.25	21.33	8.07	5.09	29.54	17.13	30.24	13.84	9.24
85–89	10.28	4.86	6.59	3.66	4.15	23.71	9.62	17.77	11.40	7.96	33.99	14.49	24.36	15.05	12.11

Note. U.S. population data are from *Current Population Survey, March 1995* [Machine-readable data file] by U.S. Bureau of the Census, 1995, Washington, DC: U.S. Bureau of the Census (Producer/Distributor). Education is number of years completed; for examinees aged 16–19 years, education is based on parent education.

Table 2.6. Demographic Characteristics of the WAIS-III Standardization Sample: Percentages by Age, Sex, and Education

Age	n	Male					Female					Total				
		≤8	9–11	12	13–15	≥16	≤8	9–11	12	13–15	≥16	≤8	9–11	12	13–15	≥16
16–17	200	2.5	6.0	15.5	15.5	10.5	2.0	4.0	20.0	15.5	8.5	4.5	10.0	35.5	31.0	19.0
18–19	200	2.5	5.5	15.0	17.5	9.5	3.0	5.0	17.0	16.5	8.5	5.5	10.5	32.0	34.0	18.0
20–24	200	1.5	5.5	17.0	20.0	6.0	2.5	5.5	17.0	20.0	5.0	4.0	11.0	34.0	40.0	11.0
25–29	200	2.0	5.0	17.5	14.5	11.0	2.5	4.5	19.0	11.5	12.5	4.5	9.5	36.5	26.0	23.5
30–34	200	3.0	4.5	17.5	13.5	11.5	1.5	5.0	16.0	16.0	11.5	4.5	9.5	33.5	29.5	23.0
35–44	200	2.0	2.0	19.0	13.0	14.0	2.5	3.0	15.0	14.5	15.0	4.5	5.0	34.0	27.5	29.0
45–54	200	4.5	6.0	16.0	11.0	12.5	3.5	3.5	17.5	13.0	12.5	8.0	9.5	33.5	24.0	25.0
55–64	200	6.5	7.0	19.5	7.0	10.0	7.0	6.0	18.5	10.5	8.0	13.5	13.0	38.0	17.5	18.0
65–69	200	7.0	7.0	17.0	6.5	7.5	10.5	7.5	21.0	9.5	6.5	17.5	14.5	38.0	16.0	14.0
70–74	200	7.0	6.5	16.5	7.5	6.5	9.0	9.0	23.0	7.5	7.5	16.0	15.5	39.5	15.0	14.0
75–79	200	8.0	6.0	17.5	5.5	4.5	11.0	9.0	19.5	10.0	9.0	19.0	15.0	37.0	15.5	13.5
80–84	150	10.0	5.3	12.0	4.0	4.7	22.0	12.0	16.7	6.7	6.7	32.0	17.3	28.7	10.7	11.3
85–89	100	13.0	4.0	9.0	3.0	3.0	20.0	13.0	18.0	8.0	9.0	33.0	17.0	27.0	11.0	12.0

*Note. N = 2,450. Education is number of years completed; for examinees aged 16–19 years, education is based on parent education.

Table 2.7. Demographic Characteristics of the WMS–III Standardization Sample: Percentages by Age, Sex, and Education

Age	n	Male					Female					Total				
		≤8	9–11	12	13–15	≥16	≤8	9–11	12	13–15	≥16	≤8	9–11	12	13–15	≥16
16–17	100	4.0	6.0	15.0	15.0	10.0	—	9.0	17.0	12.0	12.0	4.0	15.0	32.0	27.0	22.0
18–19	100	2.0	3.0	15.0	16.0	14.0	3.0	6.0	17.0	14.0	10.0	5.0	9.0	32.0	30.0	24.0
20–24	100	2.0	5.0	21.0	17.0	5.0	2.0	5.0	11.0	27.0	5.0	4.0	10.0	32.0	44.0	10.0
25–29	100	1.0	5.0	18.0	14.0	12.0	3.0	5.0	18.0	12.0	12.0	4.0	10.0	36.0	26.0	24.0
30–34	100	4.0	6.0	17.0	12.0	11.0	1.0	8.0	16.0	14.0	11.0	5.0	14.0	33.0	26.0	22.0
35–44	100	2.0	2.0	20.0	13.0	13.0	2.0	4.0	17.0	15.0	12.0	4.0	6.0	37.0	28.0	25.0
45–54	100	2.0	5.0	16.0	12.0	15.0	3.0	6.0	15.0	13.0	13.0	5.0	11.0	31.0	25.0	28.0
55–64	100	7.0	6.0	18.0	9.0	10.0	6.0	7.0	19.0	11.0	7.0	13.0	13.0	37.0	20.0	17.0
65–69	100	5.0	7.0	16.0	7.0	10.0	12.0	10.0	21.0	8.0	4.0	17.0	17.0	37.0	15.0	14.0
70–74	100	7.0	7.0	18.0	6.0	6.0	10.0	9.0	23.0	9.0	5.0	17.0	16.0	41.0	15.0	11.0
75–79	100	9.0	6.0	14.0	6.0	7.0	14.0	9.0	21.0	9.0	5.0	23.0	15.0	35.0	15.0	12.0
80–84	75	12.0	6.7	9.3	4.0	4.0	22.7	9.3	18.7	6.7	6.7	34.7	16.0	28.0	10.7	10.7
85–89	75	10.7	2.7	5.3	4.0	8.0	25.3	12.0	16.0	8.0	8.0	36.0	14.7	21.3	12.0	16.0

Note. Weighted N = 1,250. Education is number of years completed; for examinees aged 16–19 years, education is based on parent education.

Table 2.8. Percentages of the U.S. Population by Age, Sex, and Race/Ethnicity

| Age | Male | | | | Female | | | | Total | | | |
---	White	African American	Hispanic	Other	White	African American	Hispanic	Other	White	African American	Hispanic	Other
16–17	35.39	7.99	6.11	1.79	33.45	7.77	5.64	1.86	68.84	15.76	11.75	3.65
18–19	36.34	8.09	6.16	1.71	31.52	8.00	6.46	1.72	67.86	16.09	12.62	3.43
20–24	33.91	6.43	7.43	1.95	34.40	7.61	6.27	2.00	68.32	14.04	13.70	3.95
25–29	34.57	6.16	7.02	2.15	34.48	7.31	6.43	1.88	69.05	13.47	13.45	4.03
30–34	35.64	5.75	6.45	1.76	36.18	6.92	5.48	1.83	71.82	12.67	11.93	3.59
35–44	37.71	5.55	4.50	1.78	37.42	6.54	4.64	1.85	75.13	12.09	9.15	3.63
45–54	38.93	4.61	3.57	1.83	39.82	5.64	3.85	1.75	78.75	10.26	7.42	3.57
55–64	39.42	4.27	2.92	1.01	41.42	5.58	3.83	1.55	80.84	9.85	6.75	2.56
65–69	37.82	3.83	2.77	1.06	45.27	5.10	3.08	1.07	83.08	8.93	5.86	2.13
70–74	37.13	3.17	2.12	0.84	48.02	4.66	2.56	1.50	85.15	7.84	4.68	2.34
75–79	36.73	2.92	1.53	0.86	50.52	4.41	2.04	0.99	87.25	7.33	3.56	1.85
80–84	31.86	2.89	1.28	0.84	55.00	5.05	2.24	0.84	86.86	7.94	3.52	1.68
85–89	26.21	1.65	1.20	0.48	61.22	5.55	2.69	1.00	87.43	7.20	3.89	1.48

Note. U.S. population data are from *Current Population Survey, March 1995* [Machine-readable data file] by U.S. Bureau of the Census, 1995, Washington, DC: U.S. Bureau of the Census (Producer/Distributor).

Table 2.9. Demographic Characteristics of the WAIS–III Standardization Sample: Percentages by Age, Sex, and Race/Ethnicity

Age	n	Male				Female				Total			
		White	African American	Hispanic	Other	White	African American	Hispanic	Other	White	African American	Hispanic	Other
16–17	200	35.0	7.5	6.0	1.5	34.5	7.5	5.0	3.0	69.5	15.0	11.0	4.5
18–19	200	33.5	7.5	7.0	2.0	33.5	9.5	5.5	1.5	67.0	17.0	12.5	3.5
20–24	200	34.5	7.0	6.5	2.0	35.5	7.5	6.5	0.5	70.0	14.5	13.0	2.5
25–29	200	35.0	8.5	5.5	1.0	36.5	4.5	6.0	3.0	71.5	13.0	11.5	4.0
30–34	200	37.5	5.5	4.5	2.5	38.0	7.5	2.5	2.0	75.5	13.0	7.0	4.5
35–44	200	38.0	6.5	4.0	1.5	39.5	5.0	4.0	1.5	77.5	11.5	8.0	3.0
45–54	200	39.5	4.5	5.0	1.0	39.0	6.5	2.5	2.0	78.5	11.0	7.5	3.0
55–64	200	39.0	5.5	3.5	2.0	42.5	5.0	2.0	0.5	81.5	10.5	5.5	2.5
65–69	200	40.0	3.0	2.0	—	45.5	6.5	2.0	1.0	85.5	9.5	4.0	1.0
70–74	200	40.0	2.5	1.5	—	45.0	6.0	3.5	1.5	85.0	8.5	5.0	1.5
75–79	200	36.0	3.5	1.5	0.5	53.5	3.5	0.5	1.0	89.5	7.0	2.0	1.5
80–84	150	33.3	2.0	0.7	—	54.7	6.7	2.0	0.7	88.0	8.7	2.7	0.7
85–89	100	30.0	1.0	1.0	—	61.0	4.0	2.0	1.0	91.0	5.0	3.0	1.0

Note. $N = 2{,}450$. Cells in which data are not reported indicate that standardization protocols for persons meeting the relevant criteria were not collected.

Table 2.10. Demographic Characteristics of the WMS–III Standardization Sample: Percentages by Age, Sex, and Race/Ethnicity

Age	n	Male				Female				Total			
		White	African American	Hispanic	Other	White	African American	Hispanic	Other	White	African American	Hispanic	Other
16–17	100	34.0	8.0	6.0	2.0	35.0	8.0	4.0	3.0	69.0	16.0	10.0	5.0
18–19	100	36.0	9.0	5.0	—	32.0	9.0	7.0	2.0	68.0	18.0	12.0	2.0
20–24	100	36.0	7.0	5.0	2.0	35.0	7.0	6.0	2.0	71.0	14.0	11.0	4.0
25–29	100	35.0	7.0	8.0	—	35.0	7.0	5.0	3.0	70.0	14.0	13.0	3.0
30–34	100	36.0	6.0	4.0	4.0	39.0	7.0	2.0	2.0	75.0	13.0	6.0	6.0
35–44	100	37.0	6.0	4.0	3.0	39.0	5.0	5.0	1.0	76.0	11.0	9.0	4.0
45–54	100	40.0	4.0	4.0	2.0	39.0	6.0	3.0	2.0	79.0	10.0	7.0	4.0
55–64	100	39.0	5.0	4.0	2.0	40.0	6.0	2.0	2.0	79.0	11.0	6.0	4.0
65–69	100	41.0	3.0	1.0	—	43.0	8.0	4.0	—	84.0	11.0	5.0	—
70–74	100	37.0	3.0	4.0	—	50.0	6.0	—	—	87.0	9.0	4.0	—
75–79	100	36.0	3.0	3.0	—	51.0	4.0	—	3.0	87.0	7.0	3.0	3.0
80–84	75	34.7	—	1.3	—	53.3	6.7	2.7	1.3	88.0	6.7	4.0	1.3
85–89	75	28.0	1.3	1.3	—	60.0	6.7	2.7	—	88.0	8.0	4.0	—

Note. Weighted N = 1,250. Cells in which data are not reported indicate that standardization protocols for persons meeting the relevant criteria were not collected.

Table 2.11. Percentages of the U.S. Population by Age, Race/Ethnicity, and Geographic Region

Age	White				African American				Hispanic				Other			
	NE	NC	S	W	NE	NC	S	W	NE	NC	S	W	NE	NC	S	W
16–17	13.68	20.45	20.28	14.43	2.40	3.41	8.79	1.16	1.94	0.79	3.41	5.61	0.62	0.33	0.64	2.06
18–19	15.22	19.46	21.76	11.43	2.60	3.04	9.49	0.96	1.97	0.66	4.19	5.80	0.49	0.38	0.67	1.88
20–24	14.27	19.65	22.08	12.31	2.31	2.75	8.12	0.86	1.74	1.22	4.13	6.61	0.62	0.54	0.82	1.97
25–29	14.96	19.02	22.12	12.94	2.24	2.53	7.71	0.99	1.76	0.84	4.15	6.70	0.57	0.66	0.90	1.89
30–34	14.69	19.15	23.41	14.56	2.09	2.18	7.05	1.34	1.64	0.82	3.87	5.60	0.67	0.38	0.68	1.86
35–44	15.71	20.27	24.01	15.13	1.88	2.12	6.91	1.17	1.40	0.62	2.98	4.15	0.55	0.35	0.71	2.02
45–54	17.27	20.08	26.12	15.29	1.88	1.90	5.68	0.79	1.08	0.43	2.70	3.21	0.57	0.33	0.81	1.87
55–64	16.44	21.00	28.42	14.97	1.97	1.86	5.17	0.86	1.24	0.38	2.36	2.77	0.37	0.24	0.46	1.50
65–69	18.42	20.55	28.66	15.46	1.42	1.76	5.08	0.67	0.77	0.29	2.36	2.44	0.25	0.27	0.26	1.36
70–74	19.68	20.86	28.12	16.49	1.39	1.68	4.17	0.59	0.73	0.26	1.66	2.03	0.24	0.19	0.25	1.65
75–79	20.15	22.21	28.56	16.33	1.21	1.34	4.23	0.56	0.54	0.11	1.29	1.63	0.21	0.13	0.29	1.22
80–84	21.79	22.36	25.83	16.88	1.15	1.28	5.07	0.44	0.47	0.16	1.62	1.27	0.10	0.17	0.44	0.97
85–89	19.68	23.99	27.12	16.65	0.73	1.33	4.94	0.19	0.46	0.23	2.00	1.21	0.15	0.10	0.10	1.14

Note. U.S. population data are from *Current Population Survey, March 1995* [Machine-readable data file] by U.S. Bureau of the Census, 1995, Washington, DC: U.S. Bureau of the Census (Producer/Distributor).

Table 2.12. Demographic Characteristics of the WAIS–III Standardization Sample: Percentages by Age, Race/Ethnicity, and Geographic Region

Age	n	White				African American				Hispanic				Other			
		NE	NC	S	W	NE	NC	S	W	NE	NC	S	W	NE	NC	S	W
16–17	200	17.5	20.0	16.0	16.0	2.5	5.5	6.0	1.0	1.5	2.0	3.5	4.0	0.5	1.5	1.5	1.0
18–19	200	19.5	13.5	19.0	15.0	3.0	4.5	8.5	1.0	2.5	1.5	7.0	1.5	—	1.0	2.0	0.5
20–24	200	12.0	19.0	27.0	12.0	3.0	3.0	4.5	4.0	1.0	2.0	6.0	4.0	1.0	0.5	—	1.0
25–29	200	12.5	17.5	26.5	15.0	2.5	1.5	5.5	3.5	1.5	1.5	8.0	0.5	1.0	1.5	0.5	1.0
30–34	200	13.0	19.0	27.5	16.0	2.5	5.5	4.0	1.0	—	—	6.5	0.5	—	1.5	1.5	1.5
35–44	200	12.5	23.5	21.5	20.0	2.5	3.0	3.5	2.5	—	—	6.5	1.5	2.0	—	1.0	—
45–54	200	12.5	28.5	24.0	13.5	1.5	2.5	5.0	2.0	—	—	6.0	1.5	—	1.0	1.5	0.5
55–64	200	16.0	20.5	29.0	16.0	1.0	5.0	2.0	2.5	—	—	5.0	0.5	0.5	—	1.0	1.0
65–69	200	17.0	17.5	31.0	20.0	1.5	3.0	4.0	1.0	—	—	4.0	—	0.5	—	—	0.5
70–74	200	16.0	20.0	30.5	18.5	1.5	3.0	2.5	1.5	0.5	—	3.5	1.0	—	0.5	1.0	—
75–79	200	17.0	24.5	27.5	20.5	1.0	3.5	1.0	1.5	—	—	2.0	—	—	0.5	1.0	—
80–84	150	18.0	20.7	28.7	20.7	0.7	2.7	5.3	—	—	—	2.0	0.7	—	—	0.7	—
85–89	100	12.0	31.0	22.0	26.0	—	2.0	3.0	—	—	—	2.0	1.0	—	—	—	1.0

Note. $N = 2,450$. Cells in which data are not reported indicate that standardization protocols for persons meeting the relevant criteria were not collected.

Table 2.13. Demographic Characteristics of the WMS–III Standardization Sample: Percentages by Age, Race/Ethnicity, and Geographic Region

Age	n	White				African American				Hispanic				Other			
		NE	NC	S	W	NE	NC	S	W	NE	NC	S	W	NE	NC	S	W
16–17	100	14.0	21.0	23.0	11.0	5.0	4.0	7.0	—	3.0	—	4.0	3.0	—	3.0	2.0	—
18–19	100	17.0	18.0	21.0	12.0	2.0	7.0	8.0	1.0	3.0	2.0	5.0	2.0	—	—	2.0	—
20–24	100	15.0	16.0	25.0	15.0	3.0	3.0	4.0	4.0	—	2.0	4.0	5.0	2.0	1.0	—	1.0
25–29	100	16.0	13.0	23.0	18.0	1.0	5.0	3.0	5.0	2.0	3.0	7.0	1.0	1.0	1.0	—	1.0
30–34	100	15.0	19.0	26.0	15.0	4.0	4.0	4.0	1.0	—	—	5.0	1.0	—	2.0	1.0	3.0
35–44	100	18.0	19.0	21.0	18.0	3.0	3.0	3.0	2.0	—	—	7.0	2.0	3.0	—	1.0	—
45–54	100	18.0	20.0	25.0	16.0	2.0	2.0	6.0	—	—	—	4.0	3.0	—	1.0	2.0	1.0
55–64	100	19.0	18.0	26.0	16.0	1.0	7.0	—	3.0	—	—	5.0	1.0	—	—	2.0	2.0
65–69	100	23.0	18.0	26.0	17.0	1.0	3.0	6.0	1.0	—	—	5.0	—	—	—	—	—
70–74	100	19.0	22.0	28.0	18.0	3.0	4.0	1.0	1.0	1.0	—	2.0	1.0	—	—	—	—
75–79	100	18.0	22.0	28.0	19.0	—	5.0	1.0	1.0	—	—	3.0	—	—	2.0	1.0	—
80–84	75	18.7	21.3	28.0	20.0	1.3	2.7	2.7	—	—	—	2.7	1.3	—	—	1.3	—
85–89	75	9.3	25.3	26.7	26.7	—	1.3	6.7	—	—	—	2.7	1.3	—	—	—	—

Note. Weighted N = 1,250. Cells in which data are not reported indicate that standardization protocols for persons meeting the relevant criteria were not collected.

Quality-Control Procedures

The quality-control procedures used in collecting the WAIS–III and WMS–III standardization data were designed to facilitate proper test administration and to ensure that the test responses were accurately scored.

Examiner Qualification Procedures

One of the first steps taken to ensure the quality of the administration was to recruit examiners who had extensive testing experience. Before being selected to participate in the standardization, examiners completed a detailed background questionnaire that asked for information about their education and professional experience, WAIS–R or WISC–III administration experience, WMS–R administration experience, certification, and licensing status. Those selected were very familiar with individual assessment practices and with WAIS–R, WISC–III, or WMS–R administration. The majority were certified or licensed professionals working in private or public facilities.

Although the overall test format of the WAIS–III does not differ significantly from that of the previous edition, a number of content and procedural changes could have affected correct test administration. Moreover, several of the examiners were unfamiliar with the WMS–R. Therefore, all potential examiners were required to study a training manual and to receive training, either in person or by videotape, on the correct administration of both the WAIS–III and the WMS–III. The majority of the examiners also attended a training workshop conducted by a member of the development team.

After training, each examiner submitted WAIS–III and WMS–III practice protocols. All practice protocols were evaluated within 48 hours according to detailed guidelines that focused on the completeness of administration and accuracy of scoring. Examiners received detailed written and oral critiques of their practice protocols, the majority of which were correctly administered and scored. To address the few frequently occurring administration and scoring errors, the development team sent a newsletter to all examiners, alerting them to potentially problematic areas.

During the data collection, the development team carefully checked all protocols within 72 hours of receipt, according to protocol check-in forms (one for the WAIS–III and one for the WMS–III). Protocols were evaluated for completeness of administration and recording and accuracy of scoring. If necessary, feedback was provided to the examiners.

Scoring Studies

To refine the scoring criteria of those subtests for which many acceptable responses are possible (Vocabulary, Similarities, Information, and Comprehension on the WAIS–III and Logical Memory, Family Pictures, and Visual Reproduction on the WMS–III), the development team conducted several scoring studies.

For the WAIS–III, two scoring studies were conducted. For the first study, the development team used all 446 WAIS–III tryout protocols and the first 527 standardization protocols. Using the tryout protocols, the team designed a preliminary coding system for the responses to the four target Verbal subtests. For this coding system, the team expanded and refined the criteria of the 0-, 1-, and 2-point scoring categories. The team then assigned a unique code to each unique response or group of similar responses (i.e., responses with the same salient elements). As standardization protocols were received, responses were coded and categorized. If a response did not fit an existing category, a new code was added. Two team members independently coded each response, identified discrepancies between the code assignments, and resolved the differences so that each response had only one code. At this point, the team members had to agree on the grouping of responses and the assignment of codes but not on what score value to assign to a code. As appropriate, new codes were added and "redundant" codes removed.

After the codes were assigned, the team evaluated the quality of responses and assigned a score value (0, 1, or 2) to each code on the basis of the accuracy of the response. The overall subtest performance and item–total correlations were then calculated. For this purpose, items that had low item–total correlations, poor IRT fit statistics, or other indicators of poor psychometric suitability (e.g., bias) were not included in the total subtest score.

The remainder of the scoring study was an iterative process. The scoring criteria for all items were continuously reviewed, with particular focus on those items that had lower item–total correlations. Several iterations were performed and resulted in changes either in the coding rule or in the items making up the total score. After each iteration (i.e., changing a score value or adding or dropping an item), item statistics were recomputed. Only one change was made at each iteration. If the change in the scoring or in the inclusion or exclusion of an item improved the item–total correlations and the reliability of the subtest, the change was retained. When the final iteration was completed, three individuals with extensive knowledge of Verbal subtest scoring rules reviewed the final scoring rules, made minor modifications to eliminate any remaining areas of confusion, and deleted or modified inappropriate and redundant sample responses. Additionally, the development team reviewed the final item sets to ensure that content validity had been maintained.

The second scoring study was designed to replicate the results of the first study, with a larger number of scorers. Using the final codes from the first study, a group of trained scorers coded Vocabulary, Similarities, Information, and Comprehension responses from an additional 1,038 standardization protocols. Two scorers scored each protocol. When their codes did not agree, a third scorer resolved discrepancies so that, in the end, each item response was assigned only one code. (Interscorer agreement data are presented in Chapter 3.)

The codes were then translated into score values according to the same scoring criteria developed in the first scoring study. Analyses focused on overall subtest reliability coefficients, item–total correlations, and item bias. Results between the first and second scoring studies were very consistent. Only a few minor changes were made in the scoring rules on the basis of scorer comments, and, in a few instances, new codes were developed for some of the more "novel" responses. The final step was to drop the codes and to return to the traditional score points. The remaining standardization protocols were scored according to the traditional score points rather than the codes.

For the WMS–III, multiple scoring studies were conducted during both the tryout and standardization phases for the Logical Memory, Family Pictures, and Visual Reproduction subtests. The scoring studies involved both expert content reviews and empirical analyses. The empirical scoring studies included evaluation of internal consistency, test–retest stability, intrascorer agreement, and clinical sensitivity and specificity. A variety of alternate scoring schemes were evaluated on the basis of expert content reviews and the empirical findings.

Quality Assurance of Scoring and Data Entry

For all of the subtests on the WAIS–III and the WMS–III, the following procedure was used to ensure the quality of scoring and data entry for the standardization protocols. Each protocol was scored and the scores entered by two well-trained scorers working independently. A daily discrepancy analysis between the two sets of scores was run and discrepancies resolved by a third scorer. Scorers received feedback on scoring errors and additional training if needed. Over the course of the data entry, the average agreement between scorers on the nonverbal subtests exceeded 97%, and the average agreement on the four Verbal subtests (Vocabulary, Similarities, Information, and Comprehension) exceeded 90%.

To prevent scoring drift, scorers did not discuss scoring rules with other scorers and discussed responses about which they were unsure only with the members of the development team. Most important, *anchor protocols* were used. An anchor protocol was an actual standardization protocol that had been scored by the development team or by a well-trained scorer. Selected protocols were compared to the scores of the anchor protocols. If the two scorers made the same scoring errors on a protocol, then the comparison to the anchor protocol revealed the scoring drift. Scorers received feedback immediately to prevent the repetition of the errors and to correct for the scoring drift. (An interrater agreement study was conducted to evaluate the scoring performed in clinical practice. This study is described in Chapter 3.)

Other Quality-Assurance Procedures

In addition to the quality-assurance procedures just described, several other procedures were employed to ensure the consistency of data handling. For example, the computer program accepted values only within specified ranges. After all protocols were double-scored, the scores double-entered, and discrepancies resolved, the development team computed the frequencies of all variables. A special "data clean-up" team further checked for any out-of-range values accidentally entered into the data bank. Additionally, subtest score outliers were statistically evaluated and carefully scrutinized. The development team also randomly scored multiple protocols and compared the results to the final data file. All of these quality assurance procedures guaranteed the integrity of the WAIS–III and WMS–III standardization data.

Norms Development

This section summarizes the procedures for deriving the subtest, IQ, and Index scores for the WAIS–III and the WMS–III and provides the rationale for the procedures.

Derivation of Subtest Scaled Scores

For most subtest scores, each age group's raw scores were converted to percentiles and then to a scale with a mean of 10 and a standard deviation of 3. This conversion was accomplished by preparing a cumulative frequency distribution of raw scores for each age group, normalizing these distributions, and calculating the appropriate scaled score for each raw score. For each subtest, the progression of means, skewness, and variance values across the age groups were examined, and minor sampling fluctuations smoothed. The progression of scaled scores within an age group and from age group to age group was then examined, and minor irregularities were eliminated by further smoothing. The WAIS–III and WMS–III administration and scoring manuals present scaled-score equivalents of subtest raw scores. For some of the supplementary subtests, the raw-score distributions were clearly nonnormal; for these raw scores, the normative information is presented as cumulative percentages.

Conversion of Scaled Scores to IQ and Index Scores

In the WAIS–R, the scaled score for each subtest is based on the scores of a nonimpaired reference group composed of examinees aged 20–34 years. Wechsler corrected the scores at the IQ level but thought that the subtest scaled scores for adults should be based on the performance of such a reference group. Wechsler chose examinees 20–34 years old because he believed that optimal performance tended to occur at these ages. In the WAIS–III, however, the scaled score is based on the scores obtained by the examinee's same-age normative group. The WAIS–III, therefore, represents a shift in how the subtest scaled scores and IQ scores are determined. There were two reasons for this shift.

First, optimal performance does not occur consistently at ages 20–34 or across subtests. For instance, Kaufman, Reynolds, and McLean (1989) demonstrated that for some subtests, the age effect is not as important as other variables. For the Performance subtests, especially for speeded tasks, performance rapidly and steadily declines with age. For the Verbal subtests, however, after the age of 30, the age effect decreases when education level is controlled. In general, the Verbal subtest scores are less related to age than are the Performance subtest scores.

Second, and perhaps more important, the method used in the WAIS–R often leads to interpretive errors. Such misinterpretations are due, in part, to the low subtest scaled scores that older individuals typically receive when their scores are compared to the scores of a younger reference group. Compared to the scores of their same-age peers, the performance of these same older individuals might be average. This point is emphasized by recent research. Recent data clearly show that the decline in cognitive functioning after age 50 and especially after age 75 can be quite severe (Powell, 1994). Powell demonstrated that on a test of neurocognitive functioning, the performance of highly educated adults (medical doctors) older than 75 years was 26% lower than that of younger doctors. Storandt (1994) and Nettelbeck and Rabbitt (1992) described the sensory and psychomotor changes that accompany the aging process and concluded that many functions, including hearing, visual acuity, response speed, and visual processing speed, all greatly decline in the older adult. Most telling, however, is the work by Ivnik et al. (1992) and by J. J. Ryan, Paolo, and Brungardt (1990). Their work involved the collection of normative data for the WAIS–R and WMS–R for individuals older than 74 years. J. J. Ryan et al. (1990) found that the mean Performance subtest score was approximately 1.5 SDs lower than the mean of the reference group for individuals 75–79 years old and even lower for individuals aged 80 and older. Even for the Verbal subtests, the mean ranged from 0.5 SD to 1 SD lower than the reference-group mean. According to these data, older adults may appear significantly impaired or "abnormal" in subtest scores when their performance is compared to that of a young reference group. Their subtest scores, however, may actually be average when compared to that of their same-age peers. Though Wechsler was aware of this difference, he viewed the age-corrected subtest scores as optional (Wechsler, 1955, 1981) and corrected scores at the IQ level.

Ivnik et al. (1992) deviated away from the traditional method of reference-group comparisons in calculating the performance of these older adults. Instead of using the reference-group scores, they compared each individual's performance to the performance of others of similar age. If compared to the reference group's scores, an examinee's scaled scores would have appeared extremely impaired even though the examinee's performance was average for the examinee's age. By using a method similar to that used for the Wechsler children's scales (e.g., the WISC–III), Ivnik et al. adjusted the scaled scores for normal aging differences.

Similar problems have been avoided in the WAIS–III because the norms were calculated in the same way as they were for the Wechsler children's scales. The correction for age occurs at the subtest scaled-score level, and these subtest scaled scores are summed to calculate the IQ and Index scores. (Comparisons to the reference group [20- to 34-year-olds] can be made, but these scores should not be summed to calculate IQ or Index scores.)

The WMS–III also represents a shift in the way Index scores are constructed. In the WMS–R, subtest scaled scores were not derived. Instead, raw scores of the contributing subtests were summed, and that sum was converted to an age-adjusted Index score. In some cases, raw scores were weighted before the sums of raw scores were obtained. For the WMS–III, age-corrected subtest scaled scores were first derived and then summed to construct the Index scores. The WMS–III therefore parallels the WAIS–III in the manner in which Index scores are derived. This method of deriving Index scores ensures that an Index score is equally weighted by its component scaled scores. As with the WAIS–III, the score correction for age takes place at the scaled-score level.

The addition of reference-group scaled scores at the subtest level in the WMS–III is also new. Reference-group subtest scores are intended to be supplementary and should never be summed to obtain Index scores.

Derivation of IQ and Index Scores

The sums of subtest scaled scores for the WAIS–III IQ and Index scores and the WMS–III Index scores were formed by summing each individual's actual age-corrected scaled scores on the relevant subtests. For each age group, the means and standard deviations of the sums of scaled-score distributions were calculated and are reported in Appendix A of this Manual.

The data on these sums of scaled scores demonstrated a high degree of similarity within each of the scales and indexes. An analysis of variance revealed no statistically significant variation by age group in the mean scores for the scales and indexes. Moreover, the results of Bartlett's test for homogeneity of variance applied across the age groups indicated that the variance did not differ significantly by age. Consequently, the age groups were combined to construct the tables of IQ and Index score equivalents of sums of scaled scores.

For each scale, the distribution of the sums of scaled scores was converted to a scale with a mean of 100 and a standard deviation of 15. This conversion was accomplished by preparing a cumulative frequency distribution of actual sums of scaled scores for each scale and index, smoothing and normalizing these distributions, and then calculating the appropriate IQ or Index score equivalent for each sum of scaled scores. Successive adjustments were based on computerized smoothing and visual inspection of the distributions. Tables 2.14 and 2.15 list the subtest scores that contribute to each of the WAIS–III IQ scales and indexes and the WMS–III indexes, respectively.

Age-Adjusted and Reference-Group Norms

As discussed previously, two sets of normative scores were derived for the WAIS–III and the WMS–III. The first set of normative scores is based on age-corrected subtest scores. In general, when clinical questions dictate comparisons of an individual's performance to that of his or her age peers, the age-corrected norms should be used. Moreover, the age-corrected scaled scores are summed to obtain the IQ and Index scores for both the WAIS–III and the WMS–III.

The second set of norms is based on the performance of a reference group that consisted of the participants in the standardization sample between the ages of 20 and 34. In terms of key demographic variables (sex, race/ethnicity, education level, and geographic region), the reference group is representative of the U.S. Census proportions for this age range. In general, when clinical questions dictate comparisons of an individual's performance to that of a reference group, these norms should be used. The reference-group subtest scaled scores should not be summed to derive IQ or Index scores.

Table 2.14. WAIS–III Subtest Composition of IQ and Index Scores

Subtest	VIQ	PIQ	FSIQ	VCI	POI	WMI	PSI	Optional Subtest
Picture Completion		✓	✓		✓			
Vocabulary	✓		✓	✓				
Digit Symbol—Coding		✓	✓				✓	
Similarities	✓		✓	✓				
Block Design		✓	✓		✓			
Arithmetic	✓		✓			✓		
Matrix Reasoning		✓	✓		✓			
Digit Span	✓		✓			✓		
Information	✓		✓	✓				
Picture Arrangement		✓	✓					
Comprehension	✓		✓					
Symbol Search [a]							✓	
Letter–Number Sequencing [a]						✓		
Object Assembly [a]								✓

[a] The Symbol Search, Letter–Number Sequencing, and Object Assembly subtests can substitute for other subtests under certain circumstances. Refer to the *WAIS–III Administration and Scoring Manual* for a discussion.

Table 2.15. WMS–III Subtest Composition of Index and Composite Scores

Subtest	Aud Imm	Vis Imm	Imm Mem	Aud Del	Vis Del	Aud Rec Del	Gen Mem	Wkg Mem	Single-Trial Learning	Learning Slope	Retrieval	Retention	Supplemental Scores
Info & Orientation													
Total Score													✓
Logical Memory I													
Recall Total Score	✓		✓										
1st Recall Total Score									✓				
Learning Slope										✓			
Thematic Total Score													✓
Faces I													
Recognition Total Score		✓											
Verbal Paired Assoc I													
Recall Total Score	✓		✓										
1st Recall Total Score									✓				
Learning Slope										✓			
Family Pictures I													
Recall Total Score		✓	✓										
Word Lists I													
1st Recall Total Score													✓
Recall Total Score													✓
Contrast 1													✓
Learning Slope													✓
Contrast 2													✓
Vis Rep I													
Recall Total Score													✓

Table 2.15. WMS–III Subtest Composition of Index and Composite Scores *(continued)*

Subtest	Primary Indexes								Auditory Process Composites				
	Aud Imm	Vis Imm	Imm Mem	Aud Del	Vis Del	Aud Rec Del	Gen Mem	Wkg Mem	Single-Trial Learning	Learning Slope	Retrieval	Retention	Supplemental Scores
L–N Sequencing													
Total Score								✓					
Spatial Span													
Forward Total Score													✓
Backward Total Score													✓
Total Score								✓					
Mental Control													
Total Score													✓
Digit Span													
Total Score													✓
Logical Memory II													
Recall Total Score				✓			✓						
Percent Retention													
Thematic Total Score												✓	
Log Mem/Verb Pair Assoc													
Aud Rec Del Total Score						✓	✓						
Retrieval Total Score											✓		
Faces II													
Recognition Total Score					✓		✓						
Percent Retention													
Verbal Paired Assoc II													
Recall Total Score				✓			✓					✓	
Percent Retention													

Table 2.15. WMS–III Subtest Composition of Index and Composite Scores (continued)

Subtest	Primary Indexes								Auditory Process Composites				Supplemental Scores
	Aud Imm	Vis Imm	Imm Mem	Aud Del	Vis Del	Aud Rec Del	Gen Mem	Wkg Mem	Single-Trial Learning	Learning Slope	Retrieval	Retention	
Family Pictures II													
Recall Total Score					✓		✓						
Percent Retention													✓
Word Lists II													
Delayed Recall													✓
Delayed Recognition													✓
Percent Retention													✓
Vis Rep II													
Recall Total Score													✓
Recognition Total Score													✓
Copy													✓
Discrimination													✓
Percent Retention													✓

CHAPTER 3

Reliability and Score Differences

The statistical properties of the WAIS–III and the WMS–III presented in this chapter determine the confidence examiners can have in the accuracy of obtained scores. The psychometric properties that are critical for the interpretation of scores are reliability and stability coefficients, standard errors of measurement, confidence intervals, statistical significance of the differences between scores, and frequency of score differences (i.e., base rates). This chapter reports and discusses these statistics as they relate to the quantitative interpretation of scores on the WAIS–III and the WMS–III.

Reliability

The reliability of a test refers to the accuracy, consistency, and stability of test scores across situations (Anastasi & Urbina, 1997). Classical test theory posits that a test score is an approximation of an individual's hypothetical *true score*, that is, the score he or she would receive if the test were perfectly reliable. The difference between the hypothetical true score and the individual's obtained test score is *measurement error*. A reliable test will have relatively small measurement error and consistent measurement results within one administration and on different occasions. The reliability of a test should always be considered in the interpretation of obtained test scores and differences between an individual's test scores on multiple occasions.

Reliability Coefficients

The reliability of each WAIS–III subtest (except Digit Symbol—Coding and Symbol Search) was estimated from the item scores from a single administration. The items of each subtest were first rank-ordered on the basis of item response theory (IRT) difficulty estimates. The subtest items were divided (by an odd–even split) to form two half-tests. The variances of the two half-tests were also compared to ensure that there was no significant statistical difference. The reliability coefficient of the subtest is the correlation between the total scores of the two half-tests corrected by the Spearman–Brown formula for the full subtest (Crocker & Algina, 1986).

Because Digit Symbol—Coding and Symbol Search are speeded subtests, the split-half coefficient is not a proper estimate of reliability. Therefore, test–retest stability coefficients were used as the reliability estimates for these subtests. These stability coefficients were based on the scores of four age groups (16–29, 30–54, 55–74, and 75–89) participating in the test–retest study described later in this chapter. The stability coefficient is the correlation between the scores on the first and second testings corrected for the variability of the standardization sample (Allen & Yen, 1979; Magnusson, 1967). For each subtest, the overall mean coefficients across the 13 age groups were calculated with Fisher's z transformation. For each of the normative age groups, the reliability coefficient is the one for the broader age band that includes that normative age group.

For the WMS–III Primary subtest scores, the split-half internal consistency methodology just described was used to estimate reliability coefficients. For a number of WMS–III supplemental subtest scores, however, internal consistency is not an appropriate measure because of a variety of factors, such as item-presentation format and dependency between items. For supplemental subtest scores, therefore, reliability estimates were computed according to generalizability theory. Generalizability coefficients, first introduced by Cronbach, Rajaratnam, and Gleser (1963), can be considered analogues to traditional reliability estimates (e.g., Brennen, 1983; Cronbach, Gleser, Nanda, & Rajaratnam, 1972; Franzen, 1989). With this methodology, sources of variance were partitioned according to the familiar analysis of variance (ANOVA) method. A repeated-measures ANOVA method and the scores obtained by participants in the standardization sample who completed the WMS–III on two separate occasions were used to calculate the coefficients. For these analyses, this subsample was divided into two age bands, 16–54 years (n = 141) and 55–89 years (n = 156).

The reliability coefficients of the WAIS–III IQ scales and indexes and the WMS–III indexes were calculated with the formula recommended by Guilford (1954) and Nunnally (1978). Table 3.1 presents the internal consistency reliability coefficients for the WAIS–III subtests, IQ scales, and indexes, and Table 3.2 presents the reliability coefficients for the WMS–III Primary subtest scores and Primary Indexes. Table 3.3 presents the generalizability coefficients and standard errors of measurement for selected WMS–III supplemental subtest scores. For the WAIS–III and the WMS–III, the overall reliability coefficient for each subtest, scale, and index is the average coefficient across the 13 age groups calculated with Fisher's z transformation.

As the data in Table 3.1 indicate, the average reliability coefficients of most of the WAIS–III subtests (except Picture Arrangement, Symbol Search, and Object Assembly) range from .82 to .93. For the Vocabulary, Digit Span, Information, and Matrix Reasoning subtests, the coefficients are extremely high (≥.90). The coefficients for Arithmetic, Comprehension, Letter–Number Sequencing, Picture Completion, Digit Symbol—Coding, Similarities, and Block Design range from .82 to .88. Symbol Search has an average test–retest coefficient of .77, which is relatively high for test–retest reliability. The co-efficients for Picture Arrangement and Object Assembly are lower, .74 and .70, respectively, but are equal to or greater than the reliability coefficients obtained for the WAIS–R subtests. The low reliability of Object Assembly for older adults contributed to the decision to exclude this subtest from the computation of IQ and Index scores.

The average reliability coefficients for WAIS–III IQ scales and indexes range from .88 to .97 and are generally higher than those of the individual subtests that compose the IQ scale or index. This difference occurs because each subtest represents only a small portion of an individual's entire intellectual functioning, whereas the IQ and Index scores summarize the individual's performance on a broader sample of abilities. Therefore, the extremely high reliability coefficients (in the .90s) for the WAIS–III IQ scales and indexes are expected. The somewhat lower reliability coefficient for the WAIS–III Processing Speed Index score ($r = .88$) is expected because of the relatively small number of subtests composing this index. Overall, the WAIS–III has higher reliability coefficients than does the WAIS–R.

The WMS–III reliability coefficients for subtest scores that contribute to the Primary Indexes are presented in Table 3.2. The average reliability coefficients across age groups for these subtest scores range from .74 to .93, with a median reliability of .81. The average reliability coefficients for the Primary Indexes range from .74 to .93, with a median reliability of .87. As expected, the reliability coefficients for the Primary Indexes are generally higher than those for the individual subtest components that compose them. All of these coefficients represent a substantial improvement in reliability compared to the reliability of the WMS–R scores. The reliability coefficients for the supplemental subtest scores that were calculated from the generalizability study are shown in Table 3.3. These average coefficients range from .72 to .87, with a median reliability coefficient of .77. The average supplemental subtest scores generally have lower reliability compared to that of the subtest scores that contribute to the Primary Index scores.

Table 3.1. Reliability Coefficients of the WAIS–III Subtests, IQ Scales, and Indexes by Age Group

Subtest/Scale/Index	Age Group													Average r_{xx}[a]	Reference Group
	16–17	18–19	20–24	25–29	30–34	35–44	45–54	55–64	65–69	70–74	75–79	80–84	85–89		
V	.90	.93	.94	.92	.94	.93	.92	.94	.95	.93	.93	.94	.93	.93	.93
S	.81	.85	.82	.86	.85	.88	.89	.88	.87	.85	.86	.89	.89	.86	.84
A	.88	.88	.87	.89	.88	.90	.90	.91	.91	.89	.86	.87	.77	.88	.88
DS	.90	.91	.90	.92	.90	.92	.91	.93	.93	.90	.90	.87	.84	.90	.91
I	.89	.90	.91	.91	.93	.89	.89	.92	.93	.90	.92	.91	.91	.91	.92
C	.84	.86	.86	.82	.86	.84	.83	.80	.87	.86	.81	.86	.79	.84	.85
LN	.77	.88	.77	.77	.82	.75	.86	.79	.78	.88	.75	.86	.87	.82	.79
PC	.82	.76	.81	.86	.79	.81	.81	.87	.88	.87	.82	.82	.82	.83	.82
CD[b]	.81	.81	.81	.81	.84	.84	.84	.86	.86	.86	.87	.87	.87	.84	.82
BD	.88	.88	.90	.90	.88	.88	.85	.88	.87	.83	.79	.81	.76	.86	.89
MR	.87	.89	.88	.91	.88	.91	.89	.93	.94	.91	.90	.89	.84	.90	.89
PA	.70	.71	.70	.79	.66	.77	.75	.75	.80	.77	.66	.74	.81	.74	.72
SS[b]	.74	.74	.74	.74	.82	.82	.82	.79	.79	.79	.75	.75	.75	.77	.77
OA	.73	.70	.73	.71	.75	.71	.78	.72	.77	.68	.59	.64	.50	.70	.73
VIQ	.96	.97	.97	.97	.97	.97	.97	.98	.98	.97	.97	.97	.96	.97	.97
PIQ	.93	.93	.93	.95	.93	.94	.94	.95	.96	.95	.93	.94	.94	.94	.94
FSIQ	.97	.97	.98	.98	.98	.98	.98	.98	.98	.98	.97	.98	.97	.98	.98
VCI	.94	.96	.96	.96	.96	.96	.96	.97	.97	.96	.96	.97	.96	.96	.96
POI	.93	.92	.94	.95	.93	.94	.93	.95	.95	.94	.91	.92	.90	.93	.94
WMI	.93	.95	.93	.93	.94	.93	.95	.94	.94	.94	.91	.94	.91	.94	.93
PSI	.86	.87	.86	.87	.89	.89	.90	.90	.90	.89	.88	.89	.89	.88	.87

[a] Average reliability coefficients were calculated with Fisher's z transformation.
[b] For Digit Symbol—Coding and Symbol Search, test–retest reliability coefficients are reported.

Table 3.2. Reliability Coefficients of the WMS–III Primary Subtest Scores and Primary Indexes by Age Group

Subtest/Index	Age Group													Average r_{xx}[a]	Reference Group
	16–17	18–19	20–24	25–29	30–34	35–44	45–54	55–64	65–69	70–74	75–79	80–84	85–89		
Logical Memory I															
Recall Total Score	.86	.86	.86	.88	.90	.88	.89	.85	.87	.81	.91	.88	.90	.88	.88
Faces I															
Recognition Total Score	.79	.79	.75	.76	.78	.77	.80	.71	.69	.69	.68	.65	.70	.74	.76
Verbal Paired Associates I															
Recall Total Score	.91	.91	.91	.93	.93	.95	.94	.95	.94	.94	.93	.96	.93	.93	.92
Family Pictures I															
Recall Total Score	.76	.73	.77	.88	.85	.86	.83	.77	.78	.77	.73	.86	.83	.81	.84
Letter–Number Sequencing															
Total Score	.77	.88	.77	.77	.82	.75	.86	.79	.78	.88	.75	.86	.87	.82	.79
Spatial Span															
Total Score	.76	.83	.84	.85	.85	.82	.73	.81	.71	.75	.71	.79	.77	.79	.85
Logical Memory II															
Recall Total Score	.71	.73	.75	.76	.75	.84	.82	.74	.78	.77	.80	.87	.83	.79	.75
Faces II															
Recognition Total Score	.71	.82	.76	.77	.74	.83	.81	.72	.71	.69	.66	.68	.69	.74	.76
Verbal Paired Associates II															
Recall Total Score	.73	.82	.83	.86	.88	.88	.79	.84	.82	.87	.87	.80	.76	.83	.86
Family Pictures II															
Recall Total Score	.78	.72	.82	.82	.87	.85	.86	.79	.82	.84	.79	.90	.91	.84	.84
Auditory Recognition Delayed															
Total Score	.69	.64	.78	.79	.70	.74	.70	.70	.73	.71	.78	.79	.82	.74	.76
Auditory Immediate	.90	.93	.92	.94	.95	.93	.94	.93	.94	.92	.95	.95	.93	.93	.94
Visual Immediate	.82	.80	.83	.84	.85	.85	.86	.81	.78	.79	.79	.84	.84	.82	.84
Immediate Memory	.86	.91	.91	.92	.93	.92	.94	.91	.92	.89	.91	.93	.91	.91	.92
Auditory Delayed	.76	.85	.85	.88	.88	.90	.87	.85	.86	.87	.89	.90	.85	.87	.87
Visual Delayed	.79	.82	.85	.82	.83	.87	.87	.81	.81	.80	.80	.85	.86	.83	.83
Auditory Recognition Delayed	.69	.64	.78	.79	.70	.74	.70	.70	.73	.71	.78	.79	.82	.74	.76
General Memory	.84	.87	.92	.92	.91	.93	.92	.90	.91	.90	.92	.93	.93	.91	.92
Working Memory	.83	.91	.87	.87	.89	.85	.84	.87	.82	.88	.79	.88	.87	.86	.88

[a] Average reliability coefficients were calculated with Fisher's z transformation.

Table 3.3. Generalizability Coefficients and Standard Errors of Measurement of Selected WMS–III Supplemental Subtest Scores

Subtest	Generalizability Coefficient			Standard Error of Measurement		
	Ages 16–54	Ages 55–89	Average[a]	Ages 16–54	Ages 55–89	Average SE_M
Logical Memory I						
Thematic Total Score	.75	.78	.77	1.50	1.41	1.45
Word Lists I						
Recall Total Score	.76	.82	.79	1.47	1.27	1.37
Visual Reproduction I						
Recall Total Score	.72	.84	.79	1.59	1.20	1.41
Spatial Span						
Forward Total Score	.72	.75	.74	1.59	1.50	1.54
Backward Total Score	.72	.71	.72	1.59	1.62	1.60
Mental Control						
Total Score	.85	.89	.87	1.16	0.99	1.08
Digit Span						
Total Score	.87	.84	.86	1.08	1.20	1.14
Logical Memory II						
Thematic Total Score	.78	.79	.79	1.41	1.37	1.39
Word Lists II						
Recall Total Score	.79	.80	.80	1.37	1.34	1.36
Recognition Total Score	.71	.81	.76	1.62	1.31	1.47
Visual Reproduction II						
Recall Total Score	.70	.82	.77	1.64	1.27	1.47
Recognition Total Score	.65	.82	.75	1.77	1.27	1.54
Copy Total Score	.72	.74	.73	1.59	1.53	1.56

[a] The average was computed with Fisher's z transformation.

Standard Errors of Measurement and Confidence Intervals

The standard error of measurement (SE_M) provides an estimate of the amount of error in an individual's observed test score. Because the standard error of measurement is inversely related to the reliability of a subtest, the greater the reliability is, the smaller the standard error of measurement is, and the more confidence the examiner can have in the precision of the observed test score. Measurement error is commonly expressed in terms of standard deviation units; that is, the standard error of measurement is the standard deviation of the measurement error distribution. The standard error of measurement is calculated with the formula,

$$SE_M = SD\sqrt{1 - r_{xx}},$$

where SE_M represents the standard error of measurement, SD is the standard deviation unit of the scale, and r_{xx} is the reliability coefficient of the scale. Comparisons between the standard errors of measurement of the subtest scaled scores and the IQ and Index scores should not be made because they are based on different standard deviation units. Because the standard deviation is 3 for the subtest scaled scores and 15 for the IQ and Index scores, for both the WAIS–III and WMS–III, the standard errors of measurement of the subtest scaled scores usually appear smaller than those of the IQ and Index scores. In fact, the IQ and Index scores are actually more accurate measures than any of the individual subtest scaled scores.

The standard errors of measurement for the WAIS–III subtests, IQ scales, and indexes are shown in Table 3.4, and for the WMS–III, in Table 3.5. The standard errors of measurement for those subtest scores that were used in the generalizability study are provided in Table 3.3.

The standard error of measurement is used to calculate the confidence interval, or the band of scores, around the observed score in which the individual's true score is likely to fall. Confidence intervals provide another means of expressing the precision of test scores. The examiner can use confidence intervals to report an individual's score as an interval that is likely to contain the individual's true score. Confidence intervals also serve as a reminder that measurement error is inherent in all test scores and that the observed test score is only an estimate of true ability. For example, if a 64-year-old examinee obtained a WAIS–III FSIQ score of 102, the examiner can be 95% confident that the individual's true IQ score falls in the range of 98–106 (because the 95% confidence interval is $102 \pm 1.96\ SE_M$, where the SE_M is 2.07), and 90% confident that the individual's true IQ score is in the range of 99–105 ($102 \pm 1.65\ SE_M$). Confidence intervals based on the standard error of measurement are calculated by the following formula:

Table 3.4. Standard Errors of Measurement of the WAIS–III Subtest, IQ, and Index Scores by Age Group

Subtest/Scale/Index	Age Group													Average SE_M[a]	Reference Group
	16–17	18–19	20–24	25–29	30–34	35–44	45–54	55–64	65–69	70–74	75–79	80–84	85–89		
V	0.95	0.79	0.73	0.85	0.73	0.79	0.85	0.73	0.67	0.79	0.79	0.73	0.79	0.79	0.77
S	1.31	1.16	1.27	1.12	1.16	1.04	0.99	1.04	1.08	1.16	1.12	0.99	0.99	1.12	1.19
A	1.04	1.04	1.08	0.99	1.04	0.95	0.95	0.90	0.90	0.99	1.12	1.08	1.44	1.05	1.04
DS	0.95	0.90	0.95	0.85	0.95	0.85	0.90	0.79	0.79	0.95	0.95	1.08	1.20	0.94	0.92
I	0.99	0.95	0.90	0.90	0.79	0.99	0.99	0.85	0.79	0.95	0.85	0.90	0.90	0.91	0.87
C	1.20	1.12	1.12	1.27	1.12	1.20	1.24	1.34	1.08	1.12	1.31	1.12	1.37	1.21	1.17
LN	1.44	1.04	1.44	1.44	1.27	1.50	1.12	1.37	1.41	1.04	1.50	1.12	1.08	1.30	1.39
PC	1.27	1.47	1.31	1.12	1.37	1.31	1.31	1.08	1.04	1.08	1.27	1.27	1.27	1.25	1.27
CD	1.31	1.31	1.31	1.31	1.20	1.20	1.20	1.12	1.12	1.12	1.08	1.08	1.08	1.19	1.27
BD	1.04	1.04	0.95	0.95	1.04	1.04	1.16	1.04	1.08	1.24	1.37	1.31	1.47	1.14	0.98
MR	1.08	0.99	1.04	0.90	1.04	0.90	0.99	0.79	0.73	0.90	0.95	0.99	1.20	0.97	0.99
PA	1.64	1.62	1.64	1.37	1.75	1.44	1.50	1.50	1.34	1.44	1.75	1.53	1.31	1.53	1.60
SS	1.53	1.53	1.53	1.53	1.27	1.27	1.27	1.37	1.37	1.37	1.50	1.50	1.50	1.43	1.45
OA	1.56	1.64	1.56	1.62	1.50	1.62	1.41	1.59	1.44	1.70	1.92	1.80	2.12	1.66	1.56
VIQ	2.87	2.49	2.59	2.45	2.46	2.47	2.51	2.35	2.16	2.54	2.59	2.52	3.04	2.55	2.50
PIQ	4.03	4.09	3.83	3.43	3.96	3.54	3.52	3.27	3.01	3.40	4.04	3.62	3.77	3.67	3.75
FSIQ	2.58	2.38	2.37	2.18	2.32	2.23	2.23	2.07	1.90	2.19	2.47	2.31	2.56	2.30	2.29
VCI	3.61	3.13	3.16	3.05	2.88	3.02	3.02	2.77	2.69	3.12	2.93	2.78	2.93	3.01	3.03
POI	4.03	4.33	3.82	3.44	4.08	3.75	3.97	3.36	3.24	3.70	4.41	4.17	4.78	3.95	3.79
WMI	3.98	3.31	3.94	3.88	3.70	3.87	3.51	3.71	3.69	3.54	4.44	3.77	4.43	3.84	3.84
PSI	5.56	5.52	5.60	5.46	5.00	4.91	4.75	4.83	4.77	4.98	5.10	5.08	5.01	5.13	5.36

Note. The standard errors of measurement are reported in scaled-score units for the subtests and in IQ/index units for the IQ and Index scores. The reliability coefficients shown in Table 3.1 and the population standard deviation (i.e., 3 for the subtests and 15 for the IQ and Index scores) were used to compute the standard errors of measurement.

[a] The average SE_Ms were calculated by averaging the sum of the squared SE_Ms for each age group and obtaining the square root of the result.

Table 3.5. Standard Errors of Measurement of the WMS–III Primary Subtest Scores and Primary Indexes by Age Group

Subtest/Index	Age Group													Average SE_M[a]	Reference Group
	16–17	18–19	20–24	25–29	30–34	35–44	45–54	55–64	65–69	70–74	75–79	80–84	85–89		
Logical Memory I															
Recall Total Score	1.12	1.12	1.12	1.04	0.95	1.04	0.99	1.16	1.08	1.31	0.90	1.04	0.95	1.07	1.04
Faces I															
Recognition Total Score	1.37	1.37	1.50	1.47	1.41	1.44	1.34	1.62	1.67	1.67	1.70	1.77	1.64	1.54	1.46
Verbal Paired Associates I															
Recall Total Score	0.90	0.90	0.90	0.79	0.79	0.67	0.73	0.67	0.73	0.73	0.79	0.60	0.79	0.78	0.83
Family Pictures I															
Recall Total Score	1.47	1.56	1.44	1.04	1.16	1.12	1.24	1.44	1.41	1.44	1.56	1.12	1.24	1.34	1.22
Letter–Number Sequencing															
Total Score	1.44	1.04	1.44	1.44	1.27	1.50	1.12	1.37	1.41	1.04	1.50	1.12	1.08	1.30	1.39
Spatial Span															
Total Score	1.47	1.24	1.20	1.16	1.16	1.27	1.56	1.31	1.62	1.50	1.62	1.37	1.44	1.39	1.17
Logical Memory II															
Recall Total Score	1.62	1.56	1.50	1.47	1.50	1.20	1.27	1.53	1.41	1.44	1.34	1.08	1.24	1.40	1.49
Faces II															
Recognition Total Score	1.62	1.27	1.47	1.44	1.53	1.24	1.31	1.59	1.62	1.67	1.75	1.70	1.67	1.54	1.48
Verbal Paired Associates II															
Recall Total Score	1.56	1.27	1.24	1.12	1.04	1.04	1.37	1.20	1.27	1.08	1.08	1.34	1.47	1.25	1.14
Family Pictures II															
Recall Total Score	1.41	1.59	1.27	1.27	1.08	1.16	1.12	1.37	1.27	1.20	1.37	0.95	0.90	1.24	1.21
Auditory Recognition Delayed															
Total Score	1.67	1.80	1.41	1.37	1.64	1.53	1.64	1.64	1.56	1.62	1.41	1.37	1.27	1.54	1.48
Auditory Immediate	4.74	3.97	4.24	3.67	3.35	3.97	3.67	3.97	3.67	4.24	3.35	3.35	3.97	3.88	3.77
Visual Immediate	6.36	6.71	6.18	6.00	5.81	5.81	5.61	6.54	7.04	6.87	6.87	6.00	6.00	6.31	6.00
Immediate Memory	5.61	4.50	4.50	4.24	3.97	4.24	3.67	4.50	4.24	4.97	4.50	3.97	4.50	4.44	4.24
Auditory Delayed	7.35	5.81	5.81	5.20	5.20	4.74	5.41	5.81	5.61	5.41	4.97	4.74	5.81	5.57	5.41
Visual Delayed	6.87	6.36	5.81	6.36	6.18	5.41	5.41	6.54	6.54	6.71	6.71	5.81	5.61	6.20	6.12
Auditory Recognition Delayed	8.35	9.00	7.04	6.87	8.22	7.65	8.22	8.22	7.79	8.08	7.04	6.87	6.36	7.71	7.40
General Memory	6.00	5.41	4.24	4.24	4.50	3.97	4.24	4.74	4.50	4.74	4.24	3.97	3.97	4.56	4.33
Working Memory	6.18	4.50	5.41	5.41	4.97	6.00	6.00	5.41	6.36	5.20	6.87	5.20	5.41	5.63	5.27

Note. The standard errors of measurement are reported in scaled-score units for the subtests and in index units for the indexes. The reliability coefficients shown in Table 3.2 and the population standard deviation (i.e., 3 for the subtests and 15 for the Index scores) were used to compute the standard errors of measurement.

[a] The average SE_Ms were calculated by averaging the sum of the squared SE_Ms for each age group and obtaining the square root of the result.

Confidence Interval of p = Observed Score $\pm zp(SE_M)$,

where p is the confidence level, such as 90% or 95%; and zp is the z value associated with the confidence level, which can be located in the normal probability tables.

The confidence intervals provided in Tables A.3–A.8 in the *WAIS–III Administration and Scoring Manual* and in Table E.1 in the *WMS–III Administration and Scoring Manual* were derived by a slightly different method. The 90% and 95% confidence intervals for the WAIS–III IQ and Index scores and the WMS–III Index scores are based on the *estimated true score* and the *standard error of estimation* (SE_E) according to the method proposed by Dudek (1979) and Glutting, McDermott, and Stanley (1987). The estimated true score is obtained by the formula,

Estimated True Score = $100 + r_{xx} (X - 100)$,

where X is the observed composite score, and r_{xx} is the reliability coefficient of the related composite scale. The standard error of estimation is derived by the formula proposed by Stanley (1971):

$$SE_E = 15 \sqrt{1 - r_{xx}} \, (r_{xx}),$$

where SE_E is the standard error of estimation, 15 is the standard deviation of the composite score, and r_{xx} is the reliability coefficient of the related composite scale. This method centers the confidence interval on the estimated true score rather than on the observed score, and in turn, results in an asymmetrical interval around the observed score. This asymmetry occurs because the estimated true score will always be closer to the mean of the scale than will be the observed score. Therefore, a confidence interval based on the estimated true score and the standard error of estimation is a correction for true-score regression toward the mean. Because the reliability of the WAIS–III and WMS–III composite scores are relatively high, the confidence intervals calculated with the standard error of measurement centered on the obtained score and those calculated with the standard error of estimation centered on the estimated true score will be very close. Also, confidence intervals calculated by either method are interpreted in the same way.

Test–Retest Stability

The stability of scores of the WAIS–III and the WMS–III was assessed in separate studies. For each instrument, participants were tested twice, with a test–retest interval ranging from 2 to 12 weeks. For the WAIS–III, the mean retest interval was 34.6 days, and for the WMS–III, 35.6 days. The WAIS–III sample included 394 participants, with roughly 30 participants from each of the 13 age groups. The sample had the following composition: 50.3% female and 49.7% male; 77.4% White, 13.5% African American, 6.1% Hispanic, and 3% of other racial/ethnic origin. The education-level composition of the WAIS–III sample was 11.9%, ≤8 years; 13.2%, 9–11 years; 37.2%, 12 years; 22.2%, 13–15 years; and 15.5%, ≥16 years. The WMS–III test–retest sample of 297 participants consisted of approximately 10–30 individuals in each of the 13 age groups. The WMS–III test–retest sample had the following demographic composition: 48.1% female and 51.9% male; 78.8% White, 13.5% African American, 6.1% Hispanic, and 1.6% of other racial/ethnic origin. The education-level composition of the WMS–III sample was 12.1%, ≤8 years; 13.8%, 9–11 years; 37.7%, 12 years; 20.2%, 13–15 years; and 16.2%, ≥16 years.

For the WAIS–III, the test–retest stability coefficients were calculated for four pooled age groups: 16–29, 30–54, 55–74, and 75–89 years. The WMS–III stability coefficients were calculated for two pooled age groups: 16–54 and 55–89 years. The WAIS–III mean scores, standard deviations, and uncorrected and corrected coefficients for each of the four age groups for both testing occasions are presented in Tables 3.6–3.9. The average test–retest stability coefficients across all age groups are included in Table 3.9. The corresponding WMS–III reliabilities and descriptive statistics for the Primary subtest scores and Primary Indexes are presented in Tables 3.10 and 3.11, respectively. The average stability coefficients across all age groups are included in Table 3.11. The retest stability coefficients were corrected for the variability of the standardization sample (Allen & Yen, 1979; Magnusson, 1967).

As the data in Tables 3.6–3.9 indicate, the WAIS–III scores possess adequate stability across time and for all age groups. The average stability coefficients for Vocabulary and Information are excellent (in the .90s); the stability coefficients of Similarities, Arithmetic, Digit Span, Comprehension, Digit Symbol—Coding, and Block Design are very good (in the .80s); those of the other subtests are fairly good (in the .70s). As the data also indicate, the mean retest scores are higher than the scores from the first testing. These differences, mainly due to practice effects, are about 2.0–3.2 points for the VIQ score, 3.7–8.3 points for the PIQ score, and 3.2–5.7 points for the FSIQ score.

As the data in Table 3.11 show, the average WMS–III test–retest stability coefficients range from .62 to .82 (median = .71) for the Primary subtest scores and from .70 to .88 (median = .82) for the Primary Indexes. Although three of the Primary Indexes have adequate reliabilities in the .70s, the majority of

Table 3.6. Stability Coefficients of the WAIS–III Subtests, IQ Scales, and Indexes: Age Group 16–29

Subtest/Scale/Index	First Testing Mean	SD	Second Testing Mean	SD	r_{12}	Corrected r^a
V	10.6	2.5	10.8	2.5	.85	.89
S	10.3	3.0	10.9	3.0	.73	.74
A	10.2	2.6	10.8	2.5	.80	.86
DS	10.2	2.5	10.7	2.9	.75	.83
I	10.1	2.7	10.7	2.9	.92	.94
C	10.5	2.4	10.9	2.3	.67	.78
LN	10.6	2.3	10.7	2.9	.48	.70
PC	10.6	2.9	12.9	2.7	.66	.67
CD	10.2	3.0	11.4	2.9	.80	.81
BD	10.3	2.6	11.3	2.7	.77	.83
MR	10.2	2.7	10.3	2.6	.70	.75
PA	10.3	2.7	11.5	3.0	.60	.67
SS	10.1	2.7	11.1	2.8	.69	.74
OA	10.2	2.6	12.5	3.6	.64	.74
VIQ	101.4	11.9	104.6	12.6	.91	.94
PIQ	101.6	12.2	109.8	12.7	.83	.88
FSIQ	101.7	11.7	107.4	12.4	.91	.95
VCI	101.7	12.7	104.2	13.3	.89	.92
POI	101.6	13.3	108.9	13.3	.79	.83
WMI	101.9	12.5	104.8	14.5	.82	.87
PSI	100.7	14.6	106.7	14.6	.83	.84

Note. N = 100. For the Letter–Number Sequencing subtest and the Working Memory Index, N = 70.

[a] Correlations were corrected for the variability of the standardization sample (Allen & Yen, 1979; Magnusson, 1967).

Table 3.7. Stability Coefficients of the WAIS–III Subtests, IQ Scales, and Indexes: Age Group 30–54

Subtest/Scale/Index	First Testing		Second Testing			Corrected
	Mean	SD	Mean	SD	r_{12}	r^a
V	9.9	3.0	10.0	3.0	.93	.94
S	10.1	2.7	10.4	3.0	.85	.88
A	10.0	3.2	10.3	3.2	.87	.87
DS	9.6	2.7	10.0	2.9	.79	.83
I	10.0	2.8	10.6	2.8	.93	.94
C	10.1	3.0	10.2	2.9	.80	.81
LN	9.9	2.9	10.6	3.0	.74	.78
PC	10.3	3.0	12.7	3.2	.79	.79
CD	9.6	2.9	10.7	3.2	.84	.84
BD	10.2	2.7	10.9	3.0	.86	.88
MR	10.1	2.6	10.4	3.0	.69	.75
PA	10.0	2.8	11.2	3.2	.70	.73
SS	10.2	2.9	10.7	2.7	.80	.82
OA	10.0	3.0	11.6	3.6	.78	.78
VIQ	99.3	14.4	101.3	14.9	.95	.96
PIQ	99.9	13.8	108.2	16.6	.88	.90
FSIQ	99.6	14.3	104.7	15.7	.96	.96
VCI	99.8	14.1	101.9	15.1	.95	.95
POI	100.7	14.3	108.1	16.2	.86	.88
WMI	99.4	15.2	102.5	15.6	.90	.90
PSI	99.2	14.1	103.8	14.6	.87	.88

Note. N = 102. For the Letter–Number Sequencing subtest and Working Memory Index, N = 64.

[a] Correlations were corrected for the variability of the standardization sample (Allen & Yen, 1979; Magnusson, 1967).

Table 3.8. Stability Coefficients of the WAIS–III Subtests, IQ Scales, and Indexes: Age Group 55–74

Subtest/Scale/Index	First Testing		Second Testing			Corrected
	Mean	SD	Mean	SD	r_{12}	r[a]
V	9.8	2.7	10.0	2.8	.92	.93
S	10.1	2.9	10.5	2.6	.84	.85
A	9.6	3.0	9.9	3.1	.86	.88
DS	9.7	2.6	10.1	2.8	.85	.89
I	10.2	3.0	10.7	2.9	.93	.93
C	10.1	2.9	10.2	2.6	.83	.85
LN	10.1	2.9	10.4	2.9	.77	.80
PC	10.0	2.8	11.6	2.9	.82	.85
CD	10.2	3.1	11.0	3.0	.85	.86
BD	9.9	2.8	10.1	2.8	.77	.80
MR	9.5	2.8	9.7	2.9	.78	.81
PA	10.0	2.9	11.2	3.4	.62	.67
SS	10.2	2.9	10.7	3.0	.77	.79
OA	10.0	2.6	11.0	3.0	.76	.82
VIQ	99.0	14.1	101.1	14.2	.97	.97
PIQ	99.1	14.2	104.8	15.7	.91	.92
FSIQ	99.0	14.3	102.9	15.0	.96	.97
VCI	99.9	14.6	101.8	14.0	.96	.96
POI	98.3	13.5	102.3	14.8	.89	.92
WMI	99.1	12.8	101.3	13.7	.90	.93
PSI	100.9	14.8	104.7	15.3	.89	.90

Note. N = 104. For the Letter–Number Sequencing subtest and the Working Memory Index, N = 81.

[a] Correlations were corrected for the variability of the standardization sample (Allen & Yen, 1979; Magnusson, 1967).

Table 3.9. Stability Coefficients of the WAIS–III Subtests, IQ Scales, and Indexes: Age Group 75–89

Subtest/Scale/Index	First Testing		Second Testing		r_{12}	Corrected r^a	Average All Age Groups
	Mean	SD	Mean	SD			
V	9.8	2.7	10.2	2.8	.85	.88	.91
S	9.6	2.9	10.3	3.0	.82	.83	.83
A	10.1	3.0	10.6	3.1	.83	.84	.86
DS	9.7	2.6	9.6	2.7	.69	.73	.83
I	10.1	2.7	10.7	3.1	.94	.94	.94
C	9.9	2.6	10.2	3.0	.75	.79	.81
LN	10.0	3.1	10.5	3.4	.71	.71	.75
PC	10.1	3.1	11.0	3.4	.82	.82	.79
CD	9.6	2.8	10.2	3.3	.91	.91	.86
BD	9.7	2.9	10.0	3.2	.76	.77	.82
MR	10.2	2.6	10.1	3.1	.72	.76	.77
PA	10.1	3.2	10.8	3.4	.71	.68	.69
SS	10.1	3.1	9.9	3.5	.80	.80	.79
OA	9.9	2.9	10.8	3.2	.65	.68	.76
VIQ	98.9	13.0	101.3	14.7	.94	.95	.96
PIQ	99.4	15.2	103.1	18.7	.93	.93	.91
FSIQ	99.0	14.1	102.2	16.3	.96	.96	.96
VCI	98.9	13.4	102.1	14.8	.93	.95	.95
POI	99.6	14.1	102.3	17.6	.89	.90	.88
WMI	100.2	14.2	101.5	15.9	.85	.85	.89
PSI	99.0	14.9	100.3	17.4	.92	.92	.89

Note. N = 88. For the Letter–Number Sequencing subtest and Working Memory Index, N = 67.

[a] Correlations were corrected for the variability of the standardization sample (Allen & Yen, 1979; Magnusson, 1967).

Table 3.10. Stability Coefficients of the WMS–III Primary Subtest Scores and Primary Indexes: Age Group 16–54

Primary Subtest Scores/ Primary Indexes	First Testing		Second Testing			Corrected
	Mean	SD	Mean	SD	r_{12}	r^a
Logical Memory I						
Recall Total Score	10.2	3.2	12.1	3.1	.77	.74
Faces I						
Recognition Total Score	10.5	2.8	13.2	3.3	.64	.70
Verbal Paired Associates I						
Recall Total Score	10.4	2.7	11.8	3.0	.77	.81
Family Pictures I						
Recall Total Score	10.5	2.9	12.4	2.9	.61	.63
Letter–Number Sequencing						
Total Score	10.3	2.6	10.7	2.9	.61	.71
Spatial Span						
Total Score	10.2	2.7	10.4	2.6	.65	.72
Logical Memory II						
Recall Total Score	10.2	3.1	12.5	3.0	.77	.76
Faces II						
Recognition Total Score	10.6	2.8	12.8	2.7	.58	.63
Verbal Paired Associates II						
Recall Total Score	10.5	2.8	11.1	2.3	.73	.77
Family Pictures II						
Recall Total Score	10.4	3.0	12.6	2.9	.67	.68
Auditory Recog Delayed						
Total Score	10.1	2.9	11.4	3.0	.60	.62
Auditory Immediate	101.7	14.4	111.5	16.3	.84	.85
Visual Immediate	102.8	13.7	117.1	16.2	.74	.77
Immediate Memory	102.8	14.5	117.6	17.9	.84	.85
Auditory Delayed	101.9	14.1	110.6	13.9	.82	.83
Visual Delayed	103.0	14.7	117.4	15.7	.74	.75
Auditory Recog Delayed	100.6	14.4	106.9	15.0	.60	.62
General Memory	102.5	14.6	115.4	15.9	.87	.87
Working Memory	100.8	12.4	103.1	14.3	.70	.79

Note. N = 141.

[a] Correlations were corrected for the variability of the standardization sample (Allen & Yen, 1979; Magnusson, 1967).

Table 3.11. Stability Coefficients of the WMS–III Primary Subtest Scores and Primary Indexes: Age Group 55–89

Primary Subtest Scores/ Primary Indexes	First Testing		Second Testing			Corrected r^a	Average All Ages Corrected r
	Mean	SD	Mean	SD	r_{12}		
Logical Memory I							
Recall Total Score	9.6	2.8	11.3	3.1	.77	.80	.77
Faces I							
Recognition Total Score	10.1	3.1	12.1	3.8	.64	.63	.67
Verbal Paired Associates I							
Recall Total Score	9.6	3.1	11.1	3.6	.84	.83	.82
Family Pictures I							
Recall Total Score	9.7	3.1	11.1	3.1	.70	.68	.66
Letter–Number Sequencing							
Total Score	10.0	3.0	10.3	3.2	.75	.77	.74
Spatial Span							
Total Score	10.0	3.0	10.0	3.1	.69	.70	.71
Logical Memory II							
Recall Total Score	9.9	2.9	12.1	3.0	.74	.76	.76
Faces II							
Recognition Total Score	10.4	3.0	12.2	3.8	.63	.61	.62
Verbal Paired Associates II							
Recall Total Score	9.6	3.0	10.8	3.3	.79	.79	.78
Family Pictures II							
Recall Total Score	10.0	3.1	11.3	3.1	.73	.73	.71
Auditory Recog Delayed							
Total Score	9.6	2.7	10.8	3.2	.71	.76	.70
Auditory Immediate	97.3	14.8	107.2	17.9	.85	.85	.85
Visual Immediate	99.3	16.3	109.6	18.8	.76	.73	.75
Immediate Memory	98.0	16.9	110.2	19.8	.84	.82	.84
Auditory Delayed	98.5	14.6	108.7	17.1	.84	.85	.84
Visual Delayed	101.1	15.4	111.3	18.9	.76	.76	.76
Auditory Recog Delayed	98.2	13.7	104.0	16.2	.71	.76	.70
General Memory	99.1	15.7	110.6	18.7	.88	.88	.88
Working Memory	100.0	14.8	101.0	15.7	.80	.80	.80

Note. N = 156.

[a] Correlations were corrected for the variability of the standardization sample (Allen & Yen, 1979; Magnusson, 1967).

the indexes have stability coefficients in the .80s. With the exception of the working memory subtests and the Working Memory Index, the WMS–III mean subtest scaled scores and mean Index scores increased by roughly 0.33 *SD* to 1 *SD* from the first to second testings. Smaller gains in retest performance would be expected with test–retest intervals of relatively longer duration. In general, the older pooled age group (i.e., 55–89 years) show smaller retest gains than do the 16–54 age group.

Stability coefficients for the WMS–III supplemental subtest scores were evaluated by two methods. First, many of the supplemental scores were evaluated in a manner similar to that used for the Primary subtest scores, that is, by test–retest correlation coefficients. A second method of evaluating score stability was used because many of the WMS–III supplemental subtest scores have relatively small raw-score ranges, and, therefore, some of the score distributions are highly skewed (e.g., Information and Orientation Total Score). Because the test–retest correlation coefficients for many of these scores may be artificially low due to restriction of range, a decision-consistency methodology was used. With this approach, the subtest scaled scores are divided into ranges, and the consistency of the decision range, or classification, from test to retest is assessed. The decision-consistency reliability indicates the concordance of the decisions in terms of percent correct classification.

Cutpoints were established for WMS–III subtest scaled scores based on standard deviation units from their respective means. The scaled scores were divided into four groups: ≤3, 4–5, 6–13, and ≥14. Decision-consistency reliability was then assessed by comparing the classifications of the first testing to the classifications of the second testing.

Table 3.12 presents the stability coefficients and descriptive statistics for the WMS–III supplemental subtest scores for two age groups: 16–54 ($n = 141$) and 55–89 ($n = 156$). Those stability coefficients reported as percentages represent decision-consistency coefficients, and the stability coefficients reported as decimal fractions are test–retest correlation coefficients. The decision-consistency coefficients range from 50% to 100%, and the average test–retest stability coefficients range from .56 to .80. In general, those subtest scores that are derived from differences between two scores (e.g., Word Lists I Contrast 1 and 2) or the ratio of two scores (i.e., percent retention scores) demonstrate the lowest reliabilities.

Interscorer Agreement

Because the scoring criteria for most of the WAIS–III and WMS–III subtests are simple and objective, interscorer agreement is very high, averaging in the high .90s. However, some of the subtests of both scales require more judgment in scoring. Therefore, for both the WAIS–III and the WMS–III, special studies were conducted to evaluate subtest score agreement between scorers.

The subtests targeted for the WAIS–III study were three of the Verbal subtests—Vocabulary, Similarities, and Comprehension. A subsample divided into two groups of 60 was randomly selected from the standardization sample. This subsample had the following composition: 53% female and 47% male; 81.5% White, 12.6% African American, 4.2% Hispanic, and 1.7% of other racial/ethnic origin. For each group of this subsample, three raters independently scored each of the 60 protocols. The interrater reliability coefficients for the three Verbal subtests were very high: .95 (Vocabulary), .93 (Similarities), and .91 (Comprehension).

For the WMS–III study, 10 protocols from each of the age groups were randomly selected from the standardization sample and were independently scored twice. The interscorer reliability coefficients for Logical Memory I and II, Family Pictures I and II, and Visual Reproduction I and II (i.e., the WMS–III subtests requiring the most scoring judgment) were all greater than .90.

For both studies, the interrater reliability coefficients were calculated according to the appropriate intraclass correlation procedures (Shrout & Fleiss, 1979) to account for scorer leniency. These results show that although these subtests require more scoring judgment, they can be scored very reliably.

Table 3.12. Stability Coefficients of the WMS–III Supplemental Subtest Scores

Subtest	Age Group 16–54					Age Group 55–89				
	First Testing		Second Testing		Stability Coefficient[a]	First Testing		Second Testing		Stability Coefficient[a]
	Mean	SD	Mean	SD		Mean	SD	Mean	SD	
Information & Orientation										
Total Score[b]	13.7	0.7	13.8	0.5	100%	13.7	0.6	13.7	0.7	100%
Logical Memory I										
1st Recall Total Score	10.1	3.1	12.4	3.1	66%	9.5	2.9	11.5	3.2	73%
Learning Slope	10.1	3.0	9.3	2.6	72%	10.3	3.0	9.6	3.0	71%
Thematic Total Score	10.0	3.1	12.0	2.9	.61	9.8	3.0	11.2	3.1	.64
Verbal Paired Associates I										
1st Recall Total Score	10.2	3.0	12.5	3.3	70%	9.7	2.8	11.8	3.7	74%
Learning Slope	10.2	2.9	8.4	2.5	70%	9.9	3.0	9.1	2.7	78%
Word Lists I										
1st Recall Total Score	10.3	2.8	11.8	3.3	60%	9.9	2.9	11.4	3.2	76%
Recall Total Score	10.3	3.0	11.6	3.3	.61	9.9	3.0	11.0	3.3	.72
Learning Slope	9.7	2.9	8.7	2.6	77%	10.1	3.0	9.6	2.8	81%
Contrast 1	9.7	3.2	8.0	3.5	54%	11.1	3.0	8.6	3.4	56%
Contrast 2	10.1	3.0	10.8	2.9	68%	9.9	3.1	10.9	2.9	70%
Visual Reproduction I										
Recall Total Score	10.4	2.8	11.3	2.6	.60	10.1	3.1	11.5	3.2	.71
Spatial Span										
Forward Total Score	10.1	2.9	10.3	2.9	.60	10.3	2.9	9.9	3.0	.62
Backward Total Score	10.2	3.0	10.6	2.6	.59	9.9	2.9	10.2	3.3	.62
Mental Control										
Total Score	9.8	2.6	10.0	2.5	.77	9.7	2.8	10.0	2.5	.80
Logical Memory II										
Thematic Total Score	10.0	2.9	11.9	2.4	.69	9.9	2.9	11.7	3.0	.68
Percent Retention	10.3	2.7	11.8	2.6	64%	10.1	3.1	12.0	2.9	62%

Table 3.12. Stability Coefficients of the WMS–III Supplemental Subtest Scores
(continued)

Subtest	Age Group 16–54					Age Group 55–89				
	First Testing		Second Testing		Stability	First Testing		Second Testing		Stability
	Mean	SD	Mean	SD	Coefficient[a]	Mean	SD	Mean	SD	Coefficient[a]
Faces II										
Percent Retention	10.2	3.0	10.2	2.5	81%	10.4	2.7	10.4	2.7	89%
Family Pictures II										
Percent Retention	10.0	2.9	10.5	2.5	85%	10.2	3.0	10.5	3.0	86%
Verbal Paired Associates II										
Percent Retention	10.3	2.8	10.9	2.2	90%	9.9	3.0	11.0	3.0	74%
Word Lists II										
Recall Total Score	9.9	3.1	11.2	3.1	.62	9.9	3.0	10.9	3.2	.67
Recognition Total Score	10.3	2.7	10.7	2.4	.63	10.0	3.1	10.0	3.0	.66
Percent Retention	9.7	3.2	11.2	3.3	58%	10.0	2.9	11.0	3.1	84%
Visual Reproduction II										
Recall Total Score	10.4	2.8	11.3	2.6	.60	10.1	3.1	11.5	3.2	.71
Recognition Total Score	10.1	2.8	12.1	2.2	.56	10.2	2.8	12.0	2.8	.73
Copy Total Score	10.1	2.8	9.9	2.9	.60	10.2	3.0	10.1	2.9	.59
Discrimination Total Score[b]	6.7	0.6	6.8	0.5	100%	6.5	0.8	6.5	0.8	100%
Percent Retention	10.2	2.8	12.8	2.4	50%	10.5	3.0	4.7	3.1	64%

Note. N = 141 for Age Group 16–54; N = 156 for Age Group 55–89.

[a] Coefficients reported as percentages are decision-consistency reliabilities; those reported as decimal fractions are test–retest correlations.
[b] Statistics are based on raw scores.

Score Differences

Differences Between IQ Scores and Index Scores

An important consideration in interpreting the performance of individual examinees is the amount of difference between the IQ scores and between the Index scores on the WAIS–III and between the Index scores on the WMS–III. The issue of score differences has two quite different aspects—the statistical significance of the difference and the *base rate*, or frequency, of the difference in the population. These aspects can best be described as two questions: Is the difference real and not due to measurement error? Is the difference clinically meaningful?

Statistical Significance of IQ and Index Score Differences

A statistically significant difference between scores, for example, between the VIQ and the PIQ scores, refers to the likelihood that obtaining such a difference by chance is very low (e.g., $p < .05$) if the "true" difference between the scores is zero (Matarazzo & Herman, 1985). The level of significance reflects the level of confidence the examiner can have that the difference between the scores, called the *difference score*, is a true difference.

The difference between scores required for significance is computed from the *standard error of measurement of the difference* ($SE_{M Diff}$). This statistic provides an estimate of the standard deviation of the sampling distribution of the difference between the two obtained IQ or Index scores. Multiplying the standard error of measurement of the difference by an appropriate z value yields the amount of difference required for statistical significance at any given level of confidence.

The differences between WAIS–III VIQ and PIQ scores and between any pair of Index scores required for statistical significance are presented in Appendix B of the *WAIS–III Administration and Scoring Manual*. The critical values are provided for the .15 and .05 levels of significance for the 13 age groups. Appendix F of the *WMS–III Administration and Scoring Manual* presents the analogous tables for differences between WMS–III Primary Index scores and between Primary and supplemental subtest scores. Although these differences vary slightly from age group to age group, average values for all of the age groups, which are given in the last row of each table, are generally sufficient for the purpose of assessing differences in an examinee's abilities.

Frequency of IQ and Index Score Differences

The base rate of the difference between two scores refers to the prevalence or frequency of such an observed difference in the general population. Often the difference between an individual's VIQ and PIQ scores is significant in the statistical sense but is not at all rare among individuals in the general population. The statistical significance between scores and the rarity of the difference are two different issues and consequently have different implications for test interpretation. (For a detailed discussion of the distinction between statistically and clinically meaningful differences between scores, see Payne & Jones, 1957, and Silverstein, 1981.)

The frequencies of various differences between the WAIS–III VIQ and PIQ scores and between Index scores that occurred in the WAIS–III standardization sample are presented in Table B.2 of the *WAIS–III Administration and Scoring Manual.*[1] The table provides the percentage of examinees whose scores differed by the given amount or more, regardless of the direction of the difference. For example, about 17.6% of the examinees obtained VIQ and PIQ scores that differed by 15 or more points; 23.1% of the examinees obtained VCI and POI scores that differed by 15 or more points, whereas only about 8.8% of the standardization sample obtained VCI and POI scores that differed by 22 or more points. Table F.2 in Appendix F of the *WMS–III Administration and Scoring Manual* provides analogous information (i.e., frequencies of score differences of various magnitudes in the standardization sample) for the Primary Index scores.

Differences Between a Single Subtest Score and an Average of Subtest Scores

Very often the performance of an individual on the subtests of a Wechsler intelligence scale varies across different subtests. An evaluation of the variability helps the examiner identify the strengths and weaknesses of the examinee's cognitive functioning. As with differences between the IQ and Index scores, the interpretation of a particular subtest score as especially high or low should take into account the statistical significance of the observed difference and estimates of population base rates.

---

[1] Analysis of variance indicated no significant difference in the average VIQ–PIQ score discrepancies or in the average discrepancies between various pairs of Index scores across age groups. Matarazzo and Herman (1985) have demonstrated that VIQ–PIQ discrepancies vary as a function of ability level. Similar findings were obtained for the WAIS–III; therefore, supplemental tables have been included in Appendix D of this Manual. The user is cautioned that when an examinee has sustained neuropsychological damage and current ability functioning may be compromised, such differences may be misleading (Heaton, Baade, & Johnson, 1978; Parsons & Prigatano, 1978).

A common procedure for evaluating an individual's cognitive strengths or weaknesses involves the comparison of an individual's single subtest scaled score to his or her average scaled score on a group of subtests or all subtests. For instance, an examinee's scaled score on the Information subtest may be compared to his or her average scaled score on the 6 or 7 subtests of the Verbal scale or to an overall average of 11, 12, or 13 subtests. A single score that is significantly greater than the individual's own mean score may reflect a relative strength, whereas one that is significantly less than the mean may indicate a relative weakness. The procedure for testing such differences for statistical significance was originally suggested by Davis (1959). Silverstein (1982) refined the procedure to account for the fact that several comparisons are being made simultaneously.

The interpretation of the difference between a single subtest score and the individual's own mean score is an intraindividual comparison. Strengths and weaknesses identified in this way are strengths and weaknesses relative to the individual's own general ability level. Therefore, a subtest scaled score that is high in absolute value, that is, well above 10, may still represent a relative weakness for an individual of extremely high general ability; on the other hand, a fairly low scaled score may indicate a relative strength for an individual of generally limited ability.

Significance of Differences Between a Single Subtest Score and an Average of Subtest Scores

For the WAIS–III, the minimum differences between an individual's subtest scaled score and the average scores of various groups of subtests are provided in Appendix B of the *WAIS–III Administration and Scoring Manual*. Table B.3 provides this information for comparing a single subtest scaled score to the average of various sums of scaled scores. These minimum differences are the differences required for statistical significance at the .15 and .05 levels of significance. For example, as indicated in the table, a Vocabulary scaled score that is at least 1.70 points greater or less than an individual's average of scaled scores on the 6 Verbal subtests is significantly different from that mean score at the .15 level, whereas a difference greater than 1.99 points is significant at the .05 level.

Frequency of Differences Between a Single Subtest Score and an Average of Subtest Scores

As with the differences between the composite scores (e.g., between IQ scores or between Index scores), a difference between a single subtest scaled score and the average of a group of subtest scores may be statistically significant but not especially unusual in the population. Thus, the fact that an individual's scaled score on a single subtest, for example, Information, is significantly less than the individual's average scaled score of the Verbal subtests does not necessarily indicate that the difference is clinically meaningful. For this purpose, the estimated base rate of the difference, which is the frequency of such a difference occurring in the standardization sample, can be very useful, because it indicates whether the difference is rare or common in the general population.

Table B.3 in Appendix B of the *WAIS–III Administration and Scoring Manual* provides data on the frequencies of differences for the entire WAIS–III standardization sample, which are the estimated base rates of the general population. According to this table, for example, a difference of 3 or more points between the Information subtest scaled score and the average of the 6 Verbal subtests occurred in only 5% of the entire standardization sample.

Differences Between Subtest Scores

Statistical Significance of Differences Between Subtest Scaled Scores

Very often the difference between scaled scores on a particular pair of subtests may be of interest for a variety of reasons. For example, an individual's score on Similarities may be 4 scaled-score points greater than the score on Vocabulary, and the examiner should know whether such a difference is statistically significant before interpreting it. Also, because most of the WMS–III indexes are made up of two subtest scores, the examiner may want to evaluate the significance of the difference between the scaled scores on the two subtests that compose an index.

As mentioned previously, an individual may not perform at similar levels across different subtests. Differences of any given amount between two subtest scaled scores may occur either because of chance fluctuation or because of a true difference in abilities. As with the difference between IQ or Index scores, the standard error of measurement of the difference between two subtest scores is used to determine the minimum difference required for statistical significance. Table B.4 in the *WAIS–III Administration and Scoring Manual* presents the average of these minimum differences across all age groups at the .15 and .05 levels of significance for every possible pair of WAIS–III subtests. For example, a scaled-score difference of 2.68 points or more between Vocabulary and Similarities is significant at the .05 level. In other words, the examiner can be 95% confident that this difference is significant. Similar information is provided in the *WMS–III Administration and Scoring Manual*. Tables F.3 and F.4 show the minimum differences between subtest scaled scores at the .15 and .05 levels of significance across all age groups for the Primary subtests and the supplemental subtests, respectively.

Intersubtest Scatter

Intersubtest scatter is the variability of an individual's scaled scores across the subtests (Matarazzo, Daniel, Prifitera, & Herman, 1988). Such variability has frequently been considered diagnostically significant. Although various measures of scatter are possible, the scatter index used in this Manual is the easiest to obtain: the simple difference between the individual's highest and lowest subtest scaled scores.

Before interpreting the scatter exhibited in a particular test record, however, the examiner should consider how common such a scatter is in the population. The cumulative percentages of intersubtest scatter within various WAIS–III scales (e.g., Verbal, Performance, Full Scale, and indexes) are reported in Table B.5 of the *WAIS–III Administration and Scoring Manual*. The percentages are based on the data from the entire WAIS–III standardization sample so that examiners can estimate whether a particular scatter is common or rare in the general population. For example, only 3.7% of the entire standardization sample obtained a scatter of 9 scaled-score points or more within the 6 Verbal subtests. On the other hand, 71.2% obtained a scatter of 6 or more scaled-score points on the 11 subtests contributing to the FSIQ score.

Discrepancies Between Digit Span Forward and Backward

The WAIS–III and WMS–III Digit Span scaled score is based on the combined raw scores for Digits Forward and Digits Backward. Digits Forward and Digits Back-ward, however, may involve different cognitive processes, which may be differentially impaired in certain clinical groups (E. Kaplan et al., 1991; Lezak, 1995). For example, a study by Rudel and Denckla (1974) found that children with developmental disorders involving putative right hemisphere deficits had impaired performance on Digits Backward relative to their Digits Forward performance.

In order to facilitate comparisons of Digits Forward and Digits Backward scores, Table B.6 in the *WAIS–III Administration and Scoring Manual* provides the cumulative percentages for the longest forward and backward digit spans for each age group and the entire WAIS–III standardization sample. The means, standard deviations, and medians are also provided. Table B.7 provides the cumulative percentages of the differences between the longest Digits Forward and Digits Backward spans for each age group and the entire standardization sample, along with the means, standard deviations, and medians of these differences. Tables F.5 and F.6 in the *WMS–III Administration and Scoring Manual* provide identical information.

Summary

This chapter has presented information not only on the reliability of scores but also on differences between a variety of derived scores, including statistical significance and frequency. The accompanying tables provide data necessary for the interpretation of relative strengths and weaknesses. Seemingly large discrepancies between two scores, for example, may not necessarily be statistically significant, and some statistically significant differences may not be rare in the related population. The examiner, however, should keep in mind that measurement error contributes to part of observed-score differences and that the errors in the differences between composite scores (e.g., between VIQ and PIQ scores) will be smaller than the measurement errors in the differences between subtest scaled scores. This pattern occurs because the IQ scales and indexes are more reliable than the subtests. As always, when interpreting scores, the examiner should integrate relevant information from a variety of sources, including the individual's life history, educational background, and other test scores, in addition to the information on the statistical properties of the WAIS–III and WMS–III test scores presented in this chapter.

CHAPTER 4

Evidence Base for Validity of the WAIS–III and WMS–III

Multiple research studies were conducted as part of the WAIS–III and WMS–III standardization. These studies provide evidence for the validity and applicability of the WAIS–III and WMS–III and yield important information for clinicians regarding their use. In the 5 years since the original publication of the two instruments, subsequent research studies have yielded data on the WAIS–III and WMS–III in the context of the diagnosis, treatment, and exploration of the pathological processes of specific neurological, psychiatric, and developmental disorders. This chapter integrates the findings from these studies with those of the previous studies published as part of the original Manual. The discussions are organized around specific research hypotheses and clinical applications. The data are provided as ongoing evidence of validity for the WAIS–III and WMS–III and with the expectation that continuing research will expand and refine our knowledge of these assessment instruments.

Evidence Based on Internal Structure

In their classic article, Campbell and Fiske (1959) presented a theoretical methodology for interpreting the patterns of correlations in a multitrait–multimethod matrix to provide evidence of *convergent validity* and *discriminant validity*. Their original methodology was based on the relationships between similar constructs measured by different methods as well as apparently dissimilar constructs and the examination of correlational patterns in a matrix where some variables are predicted to be correlated (convergent validity) and other variables are predicted to have less relationship (discriminant validity). The relationships between correlation coefficients were also interpreted relative to the reliability of the various scales. Data supporting a priori hypotheses about the pattern of the relationships provide evidence of construct validity. Evidence of convergent validity is provided when two variables that were expected to be correlated are, indeed, related. Low correlations between two variables that were not expected to be related provide evidence of discriminant validity.

Because evidence of the validity of a test can be found in the correlations of its subtests with each other and with groups of subtests, the relationships among the various subtests, scales, and indexes of the WAIS–III and of the WMS–III were examined.

WAIS–III Intercorrelations

For the WAIS–III intercorrelation studies, several assumptions were made. First, it was assumed that there is a general trait of intelligence, or a *g* factor, and that because of the *g* factor, all of the WAIS–III subtests, even those measuring apparently different abilities, would have some degree of relation to one another. The importance of the *g* factor has been a much-debated topic. However, from Spearman's (1904, 1932/1970) original work to Carroll's (1993) more recent work, results of study after study have indicated a relation between all ability measures (Brody, 1992; Gustafsson, 1984; Neisser et al., 1996; Sternberg, 1980). For example, in an extensive review study, Carroll (1993) investigated the factor structure in over 450 data sets and found that a general intelligence factor was present throughout those data sets. For the WAIS–III, it was assumed that all subtests would have at least low to moderate correlations with each other.

Second, the subtests contributing to the VIQ scale were expected to have higher correlations with each other than with subtests composing the PIQ scale. For example, the correlations between Vocabulary and Similarities would be much higher than correlations between either of these two subtests and any of the Performance subtests (e.g., Picture Completion, Digit Symbol—Coding, and Block Design). Similarly, correlations between two Performance subtests were expected to be higher than correlations between a Performance subtest and a subtest of another scale.

Third, according to previous research (e.g., J. Cohen, 1952a, 1952b, 1957a, 1957b; Wechsler, 1991), intellectual functioning is broken down into more discrete domains of ability: verbal comprehension, perceptual organization, working memory (freedom from distractibility), and processing speed. The subtests contributing to a domain were predicted to have higher correlations with other subtests within the same domain than with subtests measuring other abilities.

Fourth, evidence from previous studies has indicated that some subtests are more related than others to the general intelligence factor. For instance, Picture Completion, Vocabulary, Similarities, Block Design, and Information tend to be more related to the *g* factor than are the other WAIS–III subtests (see Kaufman, 1975, 1990, 1994; Sattler, 1992). The following predictions were made on the basis of this evidence. Those subtests that have been shown to have high "*g* loadings," even those subtests contributing to different IQ scales (i.e., Verbal and Performance) or different indexes, would have relatively high correlations with each other. However, two subtests with high g loadings and on the same IQ scale or index (e.g., Vocabulary and Information) would have higher intercorrelations than two subtests with high g loadings but on different scales or indexes (e.g., Vocabulary and Block Design).

Finally, studies of previous Wechsler scales have indicated that two subtests—Picture Arrangement and Arithmetic—have split loadings across different factors. Picture Arrangement has significant loadings on both the Verbal and Performance scales. Arithmetic has been shown to split between the Verbal scale and the Working Memory (Freedom From Distractibility) Index (Wechsler, 1991). Therefore, the WAIS–III correlation matrix was predicted to show these splits, with these two subtests having apparently similar correlations with other subtests from both of the respective factors.

The results of the WAIS–III intercorrelations averaged across all 13 age groups are presented in Table 4.1. More detailed results of the WAIS–III intercorrelation analyses are presented in Appendix A of this Manual, which includes 13 intercorrelation matrices, one for each of the 13 age groups. Each table includes the correlations of each subtest with each of the other subtests and with the sums of scaled scores for each of the IQ scales and indexes. The correlation of a scale with one of its contributing subtests (e.g., Performance scale with Picture Completion) was corrected by the removal of that subtest score from the sum of the scaled scores in order to control for inflated correlations. These corrected coefficients appear in the main body of each table, and the uncorrected coefficients appear in the shaded area on the right. The intercorrelations of the IQ scales and indexes appear in the lower right portion of each table. Some of these correlations are inflated because the two correlated scales have subtests in common (e.g., Verbal with Full Scale). The correlation matrix for the overall sample is the average correlation across all 13 age groups computed with Fisher's z transformation (see Table 4.1).

The high magnitude of the intercorrelations among the majority of the subtests supports the premise that a general intelligence, or g, factor is present. As the data in Table 4.1 show, most of the subtests tend to correlate with each other at least at a moderate level. Statistically, all intersubtest correlations are significant. This tendency of high intersubtest correlations supports the notion of a g factor, which pervades several different types of abilities. The pattern of WAIS–III intercorrelations is very similar to that found for the WAIS–R and other Wechsler intelligence tests, in which most of the subtests have significant correlations with the other subtests.

Table 4.1. Intercorrelations of WAIS–III Subtest Scaled Scores and Sums of Scaled Scores for IQ Scales and Indexes: All Ages

Subtest/Scale/Index	V	S	A	DS	I	C	LN	PC	CD	BD	MR	PA	SS	OA	Verbal	Perf.	Full	VC	PO	WM	PS
V															.89		.84	.93			
S	.76														.85		.81	.90			
A	.60	.57													.80		.78			.83	
DS	.45	.40	.52												.65		.61			.83	
I	.77	.70	.63	.40											.86		.81	.90			
C	.75	.70	.57	.39	.70										.84		.80				
LN	.50	.46	.55	.57	.47	.44														.85	
PC	.47	.48	.40	.30	.46	.46	.41									.76	.67		.81		
CD	.44	.40	.43	.36	.38	.37	.44	.39								.68	.61				.91
BD	.50	.52	.54	.36	.48	.49	.43	.52	.41							.79	.73		.85		
MR	.54	.54	.58	.42	.53	.52	.47	.48	.40	.60						.79	.75		.83		
PA	.53	.52	.44	.33	.54	.50	.39	.49	.37	.49	.50					.76	.71				
SS	.48	.48	.52	.41	.46	.44	.49	.49	.65	.53	.48	.45									.91
OA	.44	.47	.39	.26	.40	.45	.29	.52	.33	.61	.49	.46	.47								
Verbal	.83	.77	.70	.51	.79	.76	.62	.53	.49	.59	.64	.59	.57	.50		.75	.95	.95	.71	.82	.58
Perf.	.65	.65	.63	.47	.63	.62	.57	.60	.50	.66	.65	.60	.69	.64			.92	.71	.94	.65	.75
Full	.80	.76	.72	.52	.76	.75	.64	.60	.53	.66	.69	.63	.66	.59				.90	.87	.80	.70
VC	.83	.78	.66	.46	.78	.79	.52	.52	.45	.55	.59	.58	.52	.48					.67	.65	.53
PO	.61	.62	.61	.43	.59	.59	.53	.55	.49	.65	.62	.59	.60	.65						.63	.60
WM	.61	.56	.60	.62	.59	.56	.64	.45	.46	.51	.59	.43	.53	.34							.55
PS	.50	.49	.52	.42	.46	.45	.51	.48	.65	.52	.48	.45	.65	.44							
Mean	10.0	10.0	10.0	10.0	10.0	10.1	10.0	10.0	10.0	10.1	10.0	10.0	10.1	10.0	60.2	50.1	110.3	30.1	30.1	30.2	20.0
SD	3.0	3.0	3.1	3.0	3.0	3.0	3.1	3.0	3.0	3.0	3.0	3.0	3.0	3.0	14.7	11.3	24.4	8.2	7.4	7.5	5.5

Second, the Verbal subtests do have higher correlations with other Verbal subtests than with Performance subtests. A similar, but less distinct, pattern is observed between the Performance subtests; that is, most of the Performance subtests correlate more highly with each other than with the Verbal subtests. The pattern is not as distinct, however, because some of the Performance subtests (generally those with higher g loadings, such as Block Design and Matrix Reasoning) tend to have reasonably high correlations with the Verbal subtests that also have high g loadings.

The magnitudes of the correlations within the Verbal scale and within the Performance scale show some variability. The patterns indicate that the subtests within a specific ability or domain (e.g., Working Memory or Processing Speed) intercorrelate more highly with each other than with other measures with higher g loadings. For instance, the subtests of the PSI tend to have higher intercorrelations with each other than with subtests on other indexes: Digit Symbol–Coding has a relatively high correlation with Symbol Search but smaller correlations with other Performance and Verbal subtests. Similarly, the intercorrelations between Arithmetic, Digit Span, and Letter–Number Sequencing of the Working Memory Index range from .52 to .57, which, except for the Arithmetic subtest, are much higher than the intercorrelations with other Verbal and Performance subtests.

The exceptions to the patterns of high within-factor correlations detected in previous Wechsler scales are also found in the WAIS–III. For instance, the Performance subtest that tends to be related most to verbal skills is Picture Arrangement, for which examinees can "talk out" the solutions to the problems.

In general, the patterns of correlations hold true throughout the age groups. More important, they provide evidence of convergent and discriminant validity (Campbell & Fiske, 1959), and they parallel the typical relations found in the WAIS–R. These data support the expectation that subtests of similar functioning correlate more highly with each other than with tests measuring different types of functioning. Furthermore, the intercorrelations between the subtests on the WMI and between the subtests on the PSI support the inclusion of the Letter–Number Sequencing and Symbol Search subtests in their respective indexes. In all, these correlations are evidence of convergent validity of both the IQ and Index scores.

Lower correlations between variables that are not expected to be correlated are evidence of discriminant validity. For example, this pattern occurs between Letter–Number Sequencing and the subtests not related to the third factor. Additional evidence of discriminant validity is found in the relatively lower correlations across domains than within domains. For example, the intercorrelations between Verbal subtests (ranging in the .70s) are higher than those between VCI and POI subtests (ranging from the .40s to the .50s).

WMS–III Intercorrelations

Similar to the intercorrelation studies for the WAIS–III subtests, scales, and indexes, there were a number of a priori expectations for the WMS–III intercorrelation studies. First, because the WMS–III is designed to measure memory functioning, it was assumed that all of the memory subtest and index scores would show at least low to moderate intercorrelations. Second, it was expected that the immediate and corresponding delayed measures would generally be most highly correlated. Third, the visually presented subtests and auditorily presented subtests were generally expected to correlate more highly with their modality-specific counterparts. Subtests within a particular index were also expected to correlate more highly with each other than with subtests of other indexes. Finally, because some WMS–III subtests yield multiple scores and because these scores may contribute to different Primary indexes, relatively high correlation coefficients between scores that contain the same subtest components would be expected. For example, a relatively high correlation coefficient between Logical Memory I Recall scaled score and the Auditory Recognition Delayed scaled score would be expected because the recognition component of Logical Memory II partially contributes to this latter score.

The intercorrelations of the WMS–III Primary subtest scaled scores and of the Primary Indexes and Auditory Process Composites based on the entire standardization sample are shown in Tables 4.2 and 4.3, respectively. The means and standard deviations for each subtest and index are also provided. The correlations for the overall sample are the average correlations across all 13 age groups computed with Fisher's z transformation. The intercorrelations, means, and standard deviations for the WMS–III Primary subtests, Primary Indexes, and Auditory Process Composites for each of the 13 age groups are presented in Appendix A of this Manual. Additionally, Appendix A presents similar information for the Primary subtest scaled scores and selected supplemental subtest scaled scores for three age bands.

As expected and as shown in Tables 4.2 and 4.3, the intercorrelation coefficients of the Primary subtest scores and the Primary Indexes range from low to very high. Intercorrelations of the immediate and delayed conditions of the Primary subtests are also in the expected range, generally showing the highest degree of association. The Letter–Number Sequencing and Spatial Span subtests generally show the lowest correlations with the other memory subtests. This same pattern also occurs between the Working Memory Index and the other memory indexes. Overall, the auditorily presented subtests intercorrelate highly with other auditorily presented subtests. The visually presented subtests, Faces and Family Pictures, are not as highly correlated as

Table 4.2. Intercorrelations of WMS–III Primary Subtest Scaled Scores: All Ages

Subtest	LM I Recall	Faces I Recog	VPA I Recall	Fam Pic I Recall	L–N Sequencing	Spatial Span	LM II Recall	Faces II Recog	VPA II Recall	Fam Pic II Recall	Aud Rec Del
LM I Recall											
Faces I Recognition	.14										
VPA I Recall	.48	.18									
Fam Pic I Recall	.40	.30	.34								
L–N Sequencing	.41	.13	.35	.27							
Spatial Span	.27	.13	.20	.23	.45						
LM II Recall	.85	.20	.50	.44	.39	.27					
Faces II Recognition	.16	.67	.21	.30	.20	.15	.22				
VPA II Recall	.43	.19	.81	.32	.35	.20	.46	.22			
Fam Pic II Recall	.43	.30	.36	.91	.28	.27	.46	.28	.36		
Aud Rec Del	.70	.18	.46	.35	.37	.25	.68	.22	.44	.38	
Mean	10.0	10.0	10.0	10.0	10.0	10.0	10.0	10.0	10.0	10.0	10.0
SD	3.0	3.0	3.0	3.0	3.1	3.0	3.0	3.0	3.0	3.0	3.0

Table 4.3. Intercorrelations of WMS–III Indexes and Composites: All Ages

	Primary Indexes								Auditory Process Composites			
	Aud Imm	Vis Imm	Imm Mem	Aud Del	Vis Del	Aud Rec Del	Gen Mem	Wkg Mem	Single-Trial Learning	Learning Slope	Retention	Retrieval
Primary Indexes												
Auditory Immediate												
Visual Immediate	.38											
Immediate Memory	.84	.82										
Auditory Delayed	.88	.42	.79									
Visual Delayed	.42	.84	.75	.46								
Aud Rec Del	.58	.30	.53	.57	.33							
General Memory	.81	.68	.90	.88	.78	.66						
Working Memory	.42	.28	.43	.42	.33	.32	.46					
Auditory Process Composites												
Single-Trial Learning	.90	.34	.75	.75	.36	.52	.70	.37				
Learning Slope	.23	.15	.23	.34	.19	.19	.29	.17	-.10			
Retention	.52	.34	.52	.78	.36	.36	.66	.29	.43	.12		
Retrieval	-.09	-.04	-.08	-.25	-.03	.45	.03	.02	-.02	-.16	-.31	
Mean	20.0	20.0	40.0	20.1	20.1	10.0	50.1	20.0	20.0	20.1	20.0	0.0
SD	5.2	4.9	8.4	5.1	4.8	3.0	10.6	5.2	4.9	4.4	4.7	2.6

expected. The slightly higher correlations between Family Pictures and the auditorily presented subtests may suggest the role of verbal mediation for this visually presented subtest.

Table 4.3 also includes the intercorrelations of the Primary Indexes with the Auditory Process Composites. The Single-Trial Learning Composite is highly correlated with the auditory indexes, whereas the Learning Slope Composite has relatively lower correlations with all of the indexes. The Retention Composite is most highly correlated with measures of delayed memory, whereas the Retrieval Composite generally has low correlations with the indexes. The Retrieval Composite has an inverse relationship with the Auditory Delayed Index (which is based on recall) and a correspondingly positive relationship with the Auditory Recognition Delayed Index. The direction of this relationship is expected because the Retrieval Composite represents the difference between auditory recognition and auditory recall, with positive scores indicating that recognition is higher relative to recall and with negative scores indicating the opposite pattern.

WAIS–III Factor Analytic Studies

The application of factor analytic techniques to the Wechsler intelligence and memory scales has yielded important information regarding the underlying constructs assessed by these measures. The results of factor analytic studies on previous versions of the these instruments influenced the development of subtests and the composition of indexes for the most recent revision.

According to Wechsler's theory (see Chapter 1), the subtests of a multifaceted scale, such as the WAIS–III, can be aggregated into two domains—Verbal and Performance—which can be further aggregated into one score, the FSIQ score. Not until the 1950s was solid evidence of additional factors demonstrated (see J. Cohen, 1952a, 1952b, 1957a, 1957b). Examiners began using factor-based scores and began finding clinical utility in breaking out the domains into more discrete units of functioning (Kaufman, 1990, 1994). Researchers and clinicians have made various suggestions about how to use these additional scores clinically (see Kaufman, 1994; Sattler, 1992; G. E. Smith et al., 1992). Furthermore, some of the initial clinical research has shown that examinees with different clinical conditions or diagnoses are more likely to exhibit certain patterns of scores (Prifitera & Dersh, 1992; Wechsler, 1991). On the basis of data supporting a four-factor model in the WISC–III, the WAIS–III project included plans for new subtests that would tap more discrete functioning, specifically working memory and processing speed. The Letter–Number Sequencing and Symbol Search subtests were added to enhance these additional indexes. Table 4.4 illustrates the a priori hypothesis about the predicted factor structure for the WAIS–III.

Table 4.4. Predicted Factor Structure of the WAIS–III

Verbal Comprehension Factor	Perceptual Organization Factor	Working Memory Factor	Processing Speed Factor
Vocabulary	Block Design	Digit Span	Digit Symbol—Coding
Similarities	Matrix Reasoning	Arithmetic	Symbol Search
Information	Picture Completion	Letter–Number	
Comprehension	Object Assembly	Sequencing	
	Picture Arrangement		

Numerous factor analytic methods were applied to the WAIS–III standardization data to test the factor structure. Both exploratory and confirmatory factor analyses were performed, and the results of numerous extraction and rotation methods were compared and contrasted. The factor analyses fell into five broad steps. Initially, comparability with the WISC–III was tested with factor analysis. The second step was to test whether the addition of the new subtests strengthened the four-factor structure. Third, the stability of the factor structure was tested across different age groups. Fourth, the four-factor model was tested against alternative models in a confirmatory analysis. Fifth, the final composition of the indexes was developed.

Exploratory Factor Analysis

Exploratory analyses were run in different ways. When possible, data from the entire standardization sample (N = 2,450) were used. For other analyses, data from those in the WAIS–III standardization sample who also completed the WMS–III (*weighted N* = 1,250) were used. Sometimes the standardization sample was split into five age groups as a way of checking the consistency across age: 16–19 years, 20–34 years, 35–54 years, 55–74 years, and 75–89 years. For other analyses, different sets of variables were added and subtracted from the analyses to test the effects of the inclusion or exclusion of certain subtests. Throughout most of these analyses, a four-factor solution was supported.

The initial step in the examination of the factor structure of the WAIS–III was an exploratory analysis to determine if a pattern of results similar to that obtained for the WISC–III could be replicated in the WAIS–III. For this comparison analysis, two sets of subtests were used. The first set included the 12 subtests in common between the WISC–III and the WAIS–III, that is, the 11 traditional WAIS–R subtests and Symbol Search. The second set included the 13 primary subtests of the WAIS–III (excluding Object Assembly). A principal axis method (principal axis methodology is also called common factor analyses) was used, and the factors were not restricted to an orthogonal rotation. When factors are correlated, as they were in this case, the model may be "overfitted" and produce "Haywood" cases if multiple iterations are allowed for estimating communalities. Therefore, each analysis was restricted to two iterations (see Gorsuch, 1983, for a review).

Gorsuch (1983, 1996) and others have suggested that factor solutions be evaluated not only according to empirical criteria but also according to the criterion of "psychological meaningfulness." Therefore, the results presented here have been interpreted in light of the research literature discussed earlier, the statistical criteria, and the model of intelligence presented in the WISC–III (see Wechsler, 1991). For these analyses, four factors were specified to be retained.

The factor pattern loadings based on the first set of subtests are presented in Table 4.5. In general, these results replicate the four-factor solution that was found in the WISC–III. Not surprisingly, the Vocabulary, Similarities, Information, and Comprehension subtests all load most strongly on the first factor, the Verbal Comprehension factor. The results also indicate a strong second factor, Perceptual Organization, and two additional factors, Processing Speed (third) and Working Memory (fourth). These results are very similar to those found for the WISC–III.

Table 4.5. WISC–III Subtest Set: Exploratory Factor Pattern Loadings for Four-Factor Solutions

	Verbal Comprehension	Perceptual Organization	Working Memory	Processing Speed
Vocabulary	**.89**	-.07	.01	.06
Similarities	**.76**	.12	-.02	.01
Information	**.82**	-.03	.09	-.03
Comprehension	**.79**	.09	.01	-.06
Picture Completion	.13	**.56**	-.11	.13
Block Design	-.04	**.70**	.19	-.03
Picture Arrangement	.32	**.39**	-.05	.07
Object Assembly	-.01	**.80**	-.04	-.05
Arithmetic	.26	.04	**.52**	.04
Digit Span	.11	-.07	**.45**	.15
Digit Symbol—Coding	.02	-.05	.02	**.73**
Symbol Search	-.04	.17	.07	**.65**

Note. The interfactor correlations range from .63 to .73, magnitudes indicating that the amount of shared variance between any two factors is equal to or less than 53%.

The second step was to determine if the new subtests strengthened the four-factor structure, as anticipated. For this analysis, the 13 primary subtests from the WAIS–III were used, with Object Assembly, the optional subtest, excluded. As with the previous analyses, the correlations for the overall sample and a principal axis method with an oblique rotation were used. Also as before, the analysis was restricted to two iterations.

The results of this analysis, shown in Table 4.6, also support a four-factor solution for the WAIS–III. The first factor is again the Verbal Comprehension factor, with the highest loadings by the Vocabulary, Information, Similarities, and Comprehension subtests. The second factor appears to be Perceptual Organization, with the highest loadings by the Block Design, Matrix Reasoning, Picture Completion, and Picture Arrangement subtests. The third factor is defined by the highest loadings by the Digit Span, Letter–Number Sequencing, and Arithmetic subtests. In fact, the inclusion of the new Letter–Number Sequencing subtest made this factor more salient because the pattern of the factor loadings appears stronger, and more variance is explained by this third factor. The fourth factor, Processing Speed, is made up of the Digit Symbol—Coding and Symbol Search subtests.

Table 4.6. WAIS–III Subtest Set: Exploratory Factor Pattern Loadings for Four-Factor Solutions

	Verbal Comprehension	Perceptual Organization	Working Memory	Processing Speed
Vocabulary	**.89**	-.10	.05	.06
Similarities	**.76**	.10	-.03	.03
Information	**.81**	.03	.06	-.04
Comprehension	**.80**	.07	-.01	-.03
Picture Completion	.10	**.56**	-.13	.17
Block Design	-.02	**.71**	.04	.03
Matrix Reasoning	.05	**.61**	.21	-.09
Picture Arrangement	.27	**.47**	-.09	.06
Arithmetic	.22	.15	**.51**	-.04
Digit Span	.00	-.06	**.71**	.03
Letter–Number Sequencing	.01	.02	**.62**	.13
Digit Symbol—Coding	.02	-.03	.08	**.68**
Symbol Search	-.01	.16	.07	**.63**

Note. The interfactor correlations range from .60 to .77, magnitudes indicating that the amount of shared variance between any two factors is equal to or less than 60%.

The purpose of the next analysis was to test the stability of the factor structure across age. For this analysis, the standardization sample was divided into five age bands: 16–19, 20–34, 35–54, 55–74, and 75–89. Because there were from two to three age groups in each band, the subtest correlations of the age groups were averaged according to Fisher's z transformation. As before, a principal axis method with an oblique rotation was used, iterations were limited to two, and four factors were specified to be retained. Tables 4.7–4.10 provide the results of this analysis.

Table 4.7. WAIS–III Factor Pattern Loadings for Verbal Comprehension Factor by Five Age Bands

Subtest	Age Bands				
	16–19	20–34	35–54	55–74	75–89
Vocabulary	.90	.89	.92	.88	.86
Similarities	.69	.83	.74	.74	.68
Information	.79	.83	.71	.75	.83
Comprehension	.82	.81	.84	.76	.77
Picture Completion	-.01	.00	.13	.23	.22
Block Design	.08	.00	-.01	-.05	-.01
Matrix Reasoning	.11	.10	.13	.02	.06
Picture Arrangement	.26	.31	.22	.26	.30
Arithmetic	.32	.30	.16	.16	.27
Digit Span	-.06	-.02	.02	.02	.16
Letter–Number Sequencing	-.04	-.03	-.01	.07	.06
Digit Symbol—Coding	.05	.02	-.02	-.01	-.06
Symbol Search	-.06	-.02	.05	.02	-.15

Note. For the youngest four age bands, the interfactor correlations are between .57 and .80. Lower interfactor correlations were obtained for the oldest age band, ranging from .48 to .67.

Table 4.8. WAIS–III Factor Pattern Loadings for Perceptual Organization Factor by Five Age Bands

Subtest	Age Bands				
	16–19	20–34	35–54	55–74	75–89
Vocabulary	-.09	-.07	-.07	-.13	-.06
Similarities	.16	.04	.07	.18	.04
Information	.07	-.01	.16	.02	-.05
Comprehension	.02	.06	.00	.13	.07
Picture Completion	**.52**	**.67**	**.49**	**.53**	.02
Block Design	**.67**	**.59**	**.68**	**.73**	.39
Matrix Reasoning	**.49**	**.46**	**.67**	**.63**	**.42**
Picture Arrangement	**.41**	**.56**	**.56**	**.50**	.05
Arithmetic	-.02	.09	.30	.19	.21
Digit Span	.01	-.11	-.11	-.04	.01
Letter–Number Sequencing	.01	.11	.02	-.05	-.03
Digit Symbol—Coding	-.09	-.09	.01	.03	-.06
Symbol Search	.19	.17	.09	.22	.04

Note. For the youngest four age bands, the interfactor correlations are between .57 and .80. Lower interfactor correlations were obtained for the oldest age band, ranging from .48 to .67.

Table 4.9. WAIS–III Factor Pattern Loadings for Working Memory Factor by Five Age Bands

Subtest	Age Bands				
	16–19	20–34	35–54	55–74	75–89
Vocabulary	-.01	.10	-.04	.10	.08
Similarities	-.03	-.04	.07	-.06	.02
Information	-.07	.04	.12	.18	.01
Comprehension	.01	-.06	-.05	.00	.03
Picture Completion	-.07	.00	-.12	-.16	-.12
Block Design	.02	.21	-.01	.03	-.06
Matrix Reasoning	.24	.31	.02	.26	.02
Picture Arrangement	.04	-.18	-.04	-.06	-.05
Arithmetic	**.45**	**.47**	**.41**	**.56**	**.44**
Digit Span	**.76**	**.79**	**.72**	**.68**	**.58**
Letter–Number Sequencing	**.79**	**.70**	**.71**	**.60**	**.62**
Digit Symbol—Coding	.04	.03	.07	.07	.39
Symbol Search	-.02	.04	.04	.07	.37

Note. For the youngest four age bands, the interfactor correlations are between .57 and .80. Lower interfactor correlations were obtained for the oldest age band, ranging from .48 to .67.

Table 4.10. WAIS–III Factor Pattern Loadings for Processing Speed Factor by Five Age Bands

Subtest	Age Bands				
	16–19	20–34	35–54	55–74	75–89
Vocabulary	.09	-.01	.10	.08	.00
Similarities	-.03	.01	-.02	.02	.18
Information	.03	-.01	-.15	-.08	.07
Comprehension	-.06	.02	.07	-.02	-.03
Picture Completion	.19	-.01	.21	.16	**.62**
Block Design	.00	.01	.13	.07	**.51**
Matrix Reasoning	-.05	-.05	.01	-.07	.30
Picture Arrangement	-.08	.04	-.02	.04	**.47**
Arithmetic	.14	.05	-.01	-.03	-.09
Digit Span	.01	.06	.02	.00	-.09
Letter–Number Sequencing	-.01	-.01	.08	.18	.11
Digit Symbol—Coding	**.74**	**.72**	**.70**	**.68**	**.52**
Symbol Search	**.72**	**.65**	**.66**	**.59**	**.59**

Note. For the youngest four age bands, the interfactor correlations are between .57 and .80. Lower interfactor correlations were obtained for the oldest age band, ranging from .48 to .67.

In general, the factor structure resulting from this analysis confirmed the previous results. For the four youngest age bands, the pattern found for the overall sample is nearly identical. For the oldest age band, the subtest loadings on the Verbal Comprehension and Working Memory factors are consistent with the results for the four other age bands. The subtest loadings on the Perceptual Organization and Processing Speed factors, however, are less clear. For this age band, the Picture Completion, Block Design, Picture Arrangement, Digit Symbol—Coding, and Symbol Search subtests all have high loadings on the Processing Speed factor (see Table 4.10). Matrix Reasoning and Block Design have relatively high loadings ($\geq .39$) on the Perceptual Organization factor as well (see Table 4.8). Therefore, the subtests that loaded on the Perceptual Organization factor in the previous analysis (i.e., Picture Completion and Picture Arrangement) no longer load on the expected factor. Instead, these two subtests load on the Processing Speed factor. Matrix Reasoning, an untimed measure of abstract reasoning, loads on the Perceptual Organization factor. Block Design, which requires some abstract problem-solving skills, has a secondary yet significant loading on this Perceptual Organization factor.

It is unclear whether this pattern is caused by chance fluctuations or age effects on the subtests composing the POI and PSI. The pattern may also occur because most of the Performance subtests have time limits, and, therefore, the processing speed on these subtests was heavily weighted for this oldest age band. In spite of these results, the factor structure is quite consistent with the global results. Moreover, results of the confirmatory analyses and clinical validity studies support the use of the four Index scores for an older adult population.

Confirmatory Factor Analysis

Based on theory, research, and exploratory analyses, a factor model can be derived for a cognitive battery such as the WAIS–III and confirmed with structural-equation modeling (Bentler, 1980; Bentler & Wu, 1993; Bollen, 1989; Jöreskog, 1993). Confirmatory factor analysis is similar to exploratory factor analysis. Both are methods of data reduction by which variables are grouped into a smaller number of underlying related factors. A subtest that is a measure of a factor is said to have a high loading on (or correlation with) that factor. Confirmatory factor analysis differs from an exploratory approach, however, because the grouping of subtests is made a priori rather than being generated by a computer algorithm. Instead, the examiner predicts, on the basis of theory and previous research, how the data may be grouped into factors. The specific relations between the variables (in this case, subtests) and a latent underlying factor (in this case, the WAIS–III indexes) are specified in a model, and that model is tested to determine if the correlations between the variables support this a priori structure. In the following analyses, different models were tested and compared with one another so that the WAIS–III structure could be determined. Confirmatory factor analyses were performed on the data for the entire standardization sample and for the five age bands described earlier: 16–19, 20–34, 35–54, 55–74, and 75–89. For each of these confirmatory sets (the overall sample and the five age groups), the following four structural models were tested. Each of these structural models was compared to a general, one-factor model. As with the exploratory analyses, the Object Assembly subtest was not included in these analyses.

- Model 1 (One Factor): All 13 subtests on a general factor

- Model 2 (Two Factors): 7 Verbal subtests and 6 Performance subtests

- Model 3 (Three Factors): 5 Verbal Comprehension subtests, 4 Perceptual Organization subtests, and 4 Attentional subtests (i.e., Digit Symbol—Coding, Digit Span, Letter–Number Sequencing, and Symbol Search) on Factor 3

- Model 4 (Four Factors): 4 Verbal Comprehension subtests, 4 Perceptual Organization subtests, 3 Working Memory subtests, and 2 Processing Speed subtests

- Model 5 (Five Factors): Similar to a model suggested by Woodcock (1990, 1997) and Flanagan and McGrew (1997), with the Verbal Comprehension/Knowledge factor (4 subtests), Perceptual Organization/Visual Processing factor (4 subtests), Processing Speed factor (2 subtests), Memory factor (2 subtests), and Quantitative Ability/Numerical Ability factor (1 subtest—Arithmetic)

Successive factor models were evaluated according to a variety of goodness-of-fit indexes, with emphasis given to those that are less sensitive to sample size (N) or to the number of degrees of freedom (df) (see Bollen & Long, 1993; Marsh, Balla, & McDonald, 1988; Tanaka, 1993). Thus, the chi-square index (χ^2) divided by degrees of freedom (χ^2/df) was used to calculate the Tucker–Lewis Index (TLI; Tucker & Lewis, 1973), which has been shown to be particularly robust to differences in sample size and degrees of freedom. The goodness-of-fit index adjusted for degrees of freedom (AGFI), from Jöreskog and Sörbom (1993), was also used. The fit of the data to each of the five models was also evaluated according to the root mean squared residual (RMSR) index, a measure of the degree of reproduction of the covariance matrix from the model estimates. Finally, the successive improvement in model fit, moving from one to five factors is shown by the χ^2 difference. The TLI shows the comparative fit of each model to the one-factor model. The results of each of these goodness-of-fit analyses are presented in Table 4.11.

The results shown in Table 4.11 confirm that the four-factor model best fits the data for the total sample and for most of the age bands. The results show that the fit improves as the number of factors increases. Significant improvements in "model fit" were found on each fit statistic from a two-factor to a three-factor solution and again from a three-factor to a four-factor solution. Also, both the four-factor and five-factor solutions are roughly equivalent overall, with slightly better fit statistics for the four-factor solution for most of the age bands. When the data for the total sample were analyzed, a slight yet significant improvement in the χ^2 statistic and slight improvements in the RMSR were found in the five-factor solution. However, there was no improvement on the AGFI, χ^2/df, and TLI statistics. Overall, these confirmatory analyses support a four-factor solution.

Table 4.11. WAIS–III Goodness-of-Fit Statistics for Confirmatory Factor Analysis

Model	Goodness-of-Fit Index					Improvement		
	χ^2	df	χ^2/df	AGFI	RMSR	χ^2	df	TLI
Total Sample (N = 1,250)								
One-Factor	1159.8	64	18.1	.782	.537			
Two-Factor	741.6	63	11.8	.867	.483	418.1	1	0.37
Three-Factor	473.4	61	7.8	.913	.327	268.2	2	0.60
Four-Factor	238.2	58	4.1	.954	.221	235.3	3	0.82
Five-Factor	222.1	54	4.1	.954	.202	16.1	4	0.82
Ages 16–19 (n = 200)								
One-Factor	220.1	64	3.4	.782	.575			
Two-Factor	184.6	63	2.9	.817	.571	35.6	1	0.21
Three-Factor	123.7	61	2.0	.877	.394	60.9	2	0.58
Four-Factor	82.2	58	1.4	.910	.307	41.5	3	0.83
Five-Factor	77.1	54	1.4	.908	.280	5.1	4	0.83
Ages 20–34 (n = 300)								
One-Factor	342.4	64	5.3	.730	.614			
Two-Factor	253.9	63	4.0	.813	.612	88.5	1	0.30
Three-Factor	144.5	61	2.4	.900	.379	109.4	2	0.67
Four-Factor	81.4	58	1.4	.936	.280	63.0	3	0.91
Five-Factor	76.5	54	1.4	.935	.257	4.9	4	0.91
Ages 35–64 (n = 300)								
One-Factor	203.5	64	3.2	.776	.529			
Two-Factor	138.9	63	2.2	.854	.463	64.7	1	0.45
Three-Factor	101.8	61	1.7	.887	.361	37.1	2	0.68
Four-Factor	59.5	58	1.0	.935	.236	42.3	3	1.00
Five-Factor	57.8	54	1.1	.931	.227	1.7	4	0.95
Ages 65–74 (n = 200)								
One-Factor	289.5	64	4.5	.790	.463			
Two-Factor	184.1	63	2.9	.873	.377	105.4	1	0.46
Three-Factor	158.1	61	2.6	.882	.334	25.9	2	0.54
Four-Factor	98.9	58	1.7	.924	.245	59.2	3	0.80
Five-Factor	97.5	54	1.8	.920	.240	1.5	4	0.77
Ages 75–89 (n = 250)								
One-Factor	306.7	64	4.8	.724	.651			
Two-Factor	187.4	63	3.0	.836	.557	119.2	1	0.47
Three-Factor	142.7	61	2.3	.870	.476	44.7	2	0.66
Four-Factor	96.7	58	1.7	.913	.324	46.0	3	0.82
Five-Factor	85.4	54	1.6	.916	.286	11.4	4	0.84

For the oldest age band, the five-factor solution is slightly, yet insignificantly, better than the four-factor solution. Both of these models are better than the three-factor solution that had been in question for this oldest age band in the exploratory factor analysis. Nevertheless, the four-factor solution was determined to be a more parsimonious and clinically useful solution than the five-factor model. The four-factor solution comprises Verbal Comprehension, Perceptual Organization, Working Memory, and Processing Speed. This solution has empirical support across the age ranges. It is also an improvement over the five-factor model in which the fifth factor is defined by only one subtest (Arithmetic). This model is clearly a superior solution to a one-, two-, or three-factor solution and more parsimonious than a five-factor one.

Composition of the Index Scores

The final step of the WAIS–III factor analyses was to determine the composition of the Index scores. The 13 subtests were not automatically included in the four indexes. Instead, analyses were conducted to determine if all 13 subtests were needed, specifically, if the Vocabulary, Information, Comprehension, and Similarities subtests were needed for the VCI and if the Block Design, Matrix Reasoning, Picture Completion, and, perhaps, Picture Arrangement subtests were needed for the POI. A procedure similar to that employed by G. E. Smith et al. (1992, 1994), that is, hierarchical regression analysis, was used to determine if three subtests would suffice for each of these indexes. The results of regression analyses indicated that three subtests are sufficient to adequately measure the ability tapped by each of these indexes. Therefore, for the VCI, Comprehension, which requires a longer administration time and more judgment in scoring than do the Vocabulary, Similarities, and Information subtests, was omitted from the VCI. Likewise, Picture Arrangement, which tends to have a significant secondary loading on the Verbal Comprehension factor, was omitted from the POI. The POI is therefore composed of Picture Completion, Block Design, and Matrix Reasoning.

Because at least two or three variables are needed to define a stable factor, the WMI and PSI were left intact. The third factor (Working Memory) is defined by Digit Span, Letter–Number Sequencing, and Arithmetic, and the fourth factor (Processing Speed) is made up of Digit Symbol—Coding and Symbol Search. All four of the Index scores have a mean of 100 and a standard deviation of 15 (see the *WAIS–III Administration and Scoring Manual* for further discussion).

Saklofske, Hildebrand, and Gorsuch (2000) reported results of the factor analytic structure of the WAIS–III in the Canadian standardization sample ($N = 1,105$). The authors replicated the four-factor structure reported for the U.S. standardization sample. The confirmatory models resulted in factor loadings that were very similar between the two samples for all of the subtests and their respective factors.

Arnau and Thompson (2000) evaluated the WAIS–III standardization data utilizing a second-order confirmatory factor analytic model. Their analysis yielded support for the four-factor structure reported for the standardization sample with a second-order general ability factor that correlated with the first-order factors. The authors noted that a modified model that allowed for Picture Arrangement and Arithmetic to load on Verbal Comprehension and allowed for covariance of error terms between Block Design and Object Assembly and Digit Span and Letter–Number Sequencing resulted in a slightly better model. Arnau and Thompson (2000) noted that complex loadings of these subtests are supported in previous research. Ward, Ryan, and Axelrod (2000) reported similar findings to those reported here and in the original *WAIS-III–WMS–III Technical Manual* but suggested that although fit statistics are better for more complex models, the models with fewer factors have good fit statistics and are more parsimonious.

Factor analytic studies support the configuration and structure of the WAIS–III Index and IQ scores. In general, these factors have similar subtest loadings across studies and across age-bands. For the oldest age group (75–89 years), the factor analytic results of the standardization sample data indicated a greater overlap among measures of processing speed and perceptual organization. Further research is needed to replicate this finding in older adults; however, clinicians and researchers should note this shift in the relationship among subtests when interpreting patterns of test results for older populations.

Development of a Short Version of the WAIS–III

J.J. Ryan, Lopez, and Werth (1998) administered the WAIS–III to 62 patients and reported administration times considerably longer than those for healthy individuals composing the normative sample. The extended testing time for administering the full WAIS–III has resulted in the development of several short forms for estimating IQ scores (Blyler, Gold, Iannone, & Buchanan, 2000; Pilgrim, Meyers, Bayless, & Whetstone, 1999; J.J. Ryan, 1999; J.J. Ryan & Ward, 1999). These studies use Ward's (1990) seven-subtest model, or a variation of that model, for estimating intellectual functioning. Ward's model is composed of Picture Completion, Digit Symbol–Coding, Similarities, Block Design, Arithmetic, Digit Span, and Information; the variation includes the same subtests except Block Design, for which Matrix Reasoning is substituted (J.J. Ryan, 1999; J.J. Ryan & Ward, 1999). The examiner is cautioned that the development of short forms based on selected, specific subtests reduces the reliability of a composite score. Axelrod (2002) reported short-form reliability coefficients of .92–.96 compared to those for the IQ and Index scores based on all contributing subtests, .94–.98. Therefore, the published confidence intervals for the IQ and Index scores do not apply to short forms. Published tables for the determination of significant differences and base rates of difference scores between IQ and Index scores and between IQ and memory index scores do not apply to short forms. These require the reliability coefficient of the composite scores, and base-rate tables are affected by the relative score distributions of the composites and the correlation between the composites. Studies of the effects of administering the selected short-form subtests separately from the full WAIS–III are needed to determine whether performance on the subtests is equivalent in the context of the short forms and full battery.

Finally, a composite score should not be reported if there are significant differences in performance among the subtests that make up the composite. The use of a short form may occlude an examinee's profile variability that would have been evident in his or her performance on the full battery of subtests.

Development of a General Ability Index

Tulsky, Saklofske, Wilkins, and Weiss (2001) developed an alternative index of general intellectual ability based on the eight subtests that compose the VCI and POI (i.e. those with the highest loadings on the general ability factor g). Tulsky et al. used the WAIS–III standardization sample data to derive the norms for a general ability index (GAI) and proposed that the GAI is a better measure of general cognitive ability than the FSIQ because it is composed of subtests that are more interrelated and have the highest loadings on g, and the GAI subtests are those most likely to be spared the effects of brain insult and thus to provide a more stable estimate of general ability.

However, the interpretation of the GAI as opposed to the FSIQ should be informed by the knowledge that GAI intentionally excludes measures of working memory and processing speed, which may be differentially sensitive to brain injury and pathology (see the later discussion).

Wechsler Abbreviated Scale of Intelligence

The WASI (1999) was developed by The Psychological Corporation to provide a fast, reliable method of estimating intellectual functioning in examinees aged 6–89 years. The WASI is composed of four subtests and yields estimated

FSIQ scores based on either two or four subtests. The VIQ and PIQ can also be estimated if all four subtests are administered. The subtests measure similar constructs as those measured by the WAIS–III, WISC–III, and WISC–IV (in development) but do not contain the same content. The WASI subtests are alternate forms of the corresponding subtests of the WAIS–III, WISC–III, and WISC–IV. The WASI was normed on a large, nationally representative standardization sample and is directly linked to the WAIS–III and WISC–III. Predicted intellectual functioning and prediction intervals are provided. The WASI may be completed in 15–30 minutes based on the number of subtests administered.

Axelrod (2002) compared estimated VIQ, PIQ and FSIQ scores based on the WASI and prorated WAIS–III short forms. The WASI scores exhibited higher reliability and similar level of association with WAIS–III measures (controlling for part–whole associations) as the prorated short-form scores. Axelrod reported better prediction of IQ scores with the short forms based on actual versus predicted discrepancies. This conclusion does not account for the presence of part–whole associations, which cannot be statistically controlled in a difference-score methodology. The strength of the association between two variables affects the distribution of difference scores; specifically, when the inflated association due to part–whole relationships is not controlled, the difference scores will overestimate the predictive accuracy of the short forms.

WMS–III Factor Analytic Studies

The construction of WMS–III composites and Indexes was based on theoretical principles and on the results of research on the test's predecessors. An initial confirmatory factor analysis of the data from the WMS–R standardization sample and a mixed clinical sample indicated that a two-factor solution was the best fit. These two factors consisted of an immediate memory dimension and an attention/concentration dimension (Roid et al., 1988). Measures of delayed recall were not included in these analyses. Roth, Conboy, Reeder, and Boll (1990) reported that when delayed recall measures were added to the analyses and the method variance shared by the immediate and delayed measures was controlled for, a three-factor solution produced the best fit of the data from a sample of individuals with closed head injury. This three-factor solution consisted of attention/concentration, immediate memory, and delayed memory. Using a similar methodology that controlled for method variance, Burton, Mittenberg, and Burton (1993) found that the three-factor solution found by Roth et al. (1990) also best fit the observed relationships in the WMS–R standardization data. With findings consistent with this three-factor solution, Woodard (1993) reported that the attention/concentration, immediate memory, and delayed memory dimensions were the best fit of several competing models of the data from a mixed clinical sample of individuals who had sustained mild, diffuse brain injury.

The results from these WMS–R studies suggest at least three general conclusions. First, in all of these studies, those measures that compose the construct of attention/concentration and the memory measures were identified as separate dimensions. Second, when both the immediate and delayed memory measures were used in the model, a three-factor solution appeared to best fit the data based on both normally functioning and clinical samples. These studies of two- and three-factor dimensions of the WMS–R provide evidence of construct validity for two useful dimensions of clinical memory assessment (i.e., attention/concentration versus memory, and immediate memory versus delayed memory). Third, the separation of the memory measures (whether immediate or delayed) into modality-specific dimensions does not provide a more parsimonious explanation than does conceptualizing memory as a unidimensional construct.

In the original publication of the technical manual, the results of confirmatory factor analytic studies were reported as best supporting a five-factor model. The five factor-model specified working memory, auditory immediate memory, auditory delayed memory, visual immediate memory, and visual delayed memory factors. Millis, Malina, Bowers, and Ricker (1999) used the correlation matrices provided in the technical manual but failed to replicate the results reported there. The authors noted the presence of inadmissible parameter estimates (e.g., correlations exceeding 1.0) that were attributable to the very high correlations between immediate and delayed memory factors. The authors concluded that model specification errors (immediate versus delayed) produced results that indicated higher correlations between subtests across factors compared to the correlations among measures within the factor. The authors also concluded that the low correlation between Faces and Family Pictures and the overall low communality estimates for the Faces subtests contributed to the model-specification problems. Despite not having empirical support for the differentiation between immediate and delayed memory in the factor analytic study, the authors advised the continued use of immediate and delayed index scores on clinical and theoretical grounds and also suggested that further research is needed.

Subsequent to the publication of Millis et al.'s (1999) findings, The Psychological Corporation, in conjunction with Millis, completed further study of the WMS–III factor structure. Price, Tulsky, Millis, and Weiss (in press), analyzed the original WMS–III standardization data using confirmatory factor analytic procedures and confirmed the results in a cross-validation study. Five models were tested:

- Model 1 (One Factor): General Memory
- Model 2 (Two Factors): Working Memory and Memory

- Model 3 (Three Factors): Working Memory, Immediate Memory, and Delayed Memory

- Model 4 (Three Factors): Working Memory, Visual Memory, and Auditory Memory

- Model 5 (Five Factors): Working Memory, Auditory Immediate Memory, Auditory Delayed Memory, Visual Immediate Memory, and Visual Delayed Memory.

In the models specifying more than one factor, the factor scores were allowed to co-vary. The reassessment of the factor structure originally reported in the *WAIS–III—WMS–III Technical Manual* was conducted to provide clinicians with the most up-to-date modeling of the WMS–III latent structure. This study included an assessment of the data for nonnormality, an analysis of the model for all three age groups combined and for each of the three age groups separately, and a cross-validation of the results with data from an independent sample.

Parameter estimates were derived with maximum likelihood procedures. Models were compared through the computation and analysis of multiple fit indices including the likelihood ratio chi-square (χ^2) statistics; the rescaled (robust) chi-square statistics (corrects for multivariate nonnormality), the adjusted goodness-of-fit index (AGFI), the root mean error square of approximation (RMSEA), the nonnormed fit index (NNFI), the comparative fit index (CFI), the relative chi-square, the Akaike information criterion (AIC; Akaike, 1987), and the expected cross-validation index (ECVI). The models were screened for model-specification errors, that is, inappropriately estimated parameter values and positive definiteness of the covariance matrices. Table 4.12 presents the results of these analyses for the calibration sample (i.e., the WMS–III standardization sample), and Table 4.13 presents the results for the cross-validation sample. Results are presented for each of the three age groups and for the total group.

The results confirm the work of Millis et al. (1999); that is, Models 3 and 5 were identified as having nonpositive covariance matrices and boundary solution violations due to an estimated correlation of greater than .99 for immediate and delayed memory. These errors indicate the high degree of multicolinearity between immediate and delayed memory measures, which results in inaccurate model estimations and precludes the use of factor analysis for validating this structure.

Table 4.12. WMS–III Calibration (Standardization) Sample Goodness–of–Fit Statistics for Confirmatory Factor Analyses

Age Group/Model	χ^2	χ^2 (Robust)	df	χ^2/df	p	AGFI	RMSEA	NNFI	CFI	AIC	ECVI	90% ECVI
Ages 16–29 (n = 400)												
1	150.78	142.73	31	4.60	.00	.88	.09	.93	.95	190.73	.48	.39–58
2	90.61	86.72	30	2.89	.00	.92	.07	.96	.97	136.72	.34	.28–42
3[a]	90.51	85.55	28	3.05	.00	.92	.07	.96	.97	139.55	.35	.29–43
4	73.50	72.55	28	2.59	.00	.93	.06	.97	.98	126.55	.32	.26–39
5[a]	65.63	63.74	21	3.03	.00	.92	.07	.96	.98	131.74	.33	.28–40
Ages 30–64 (n = 400)												
1	58.01	58.44	31	1.88	.00	.95	.04	.98	.99	106.44	.27	.22–33
2	40.32	40.31	30	1.34	.02	.96	.03	.99	1.00	90.31	.23	.20–28
3[a]	38.96	38.49	28	1.37	.09	.96	.03	.99	1.00	110.00	.23	.21–28
4	36.05	35.91	28	1.28	.14	.97	.03	.99	1.00	89.91	.23	.21–27
5[a]	22.25	21.71	21	1.03	.42	.97	.00	1.00	1.00	89.71	.22	.22–26
Ages 65–89 (n = 450)												
1	119.81	116.40	31	3.75	.00	.91	.08	.95	.97	164.40	.37	.30–45
2	76.75	72.50	30	2.41	.00	.94	.06	.97	.98	122.50	.27	.23–34
3[a]	69.12	65.73	28	2.34	.00	.94	.05	.97	.98	119.73	.27	.22–33
4	61.73	55.72	28	1.99	.00	.95	.04	.98	.99	109.72	.24	.21–30
5[a]	37.38	33.82	21	1.61	.04	.95	.04	.98	.99	101.82	.26	.22–31
Ages 16–89 (n = 1,250)												
1	243.74	238.98	31	7.70	.00	.93	.07	.96	.97	286.98	.23	.19–27
2	126.63	124.68	30	4.15	.00	.96	.05	.98	.99	174.68	.14	.12–17
3[a]	123.54	121.18	28	4.32	.00	.96	.05	.98	.99	175.18	.14	.12–17
4	93.80	90.16	28	3.22	.00	.97	.04	.99	.99	144.16	.12	.09–14
5[a]	64.54	61.53	21	2.93	.00	.97	.03	.99	.99	129.53	.10	.08–13

Note. From "Redefining the factor structure of the Wechsler Memory Scale–III: Confirmatory factor analysis with cross-validation," by L. R. Price, D. Tulsky, S. Millis, and L. Weiss, in press, *Journal of Clinical and Experimental Neuropsychology.* Adapted with permission. The weighted WMS–III sample (*N* = 1,250) was used for this analysis. Model 1 = one factor; Model 2 = two-factor oblique (auditory memory and working memory); Model 3 = three-factor oblique (immediate memory, delayed memory, and working memory with separate immediate and delayed conditions); Model 4 = three-factor oblique (auditory memory, visual memory, and working memory, with combined immediate and delayed subtests); Model 5 = five-factor oblique (auditory immediate, visual immediate, auditory delayed, visual delayed, and working memory).

[a] Inadmissible model estimates and violation of boundary solutions.

Table 4.13. WMS–III Cross-Validation Sample Goodness–of–Fit Statistics for Confirmatory Factor Analyses

Age Group/Model	χ^2	χ^2 (Robust)	df	χ^2/df	p	AGFI	RMSEA	NNFI	CFI	AIC	ECVI	90% ECVI
Ages 16–29 (n = 448)												
1	84.64	80.93	31	2.61	.00	.94	.06	.98	.98	128.93	.27	.22–33
2	49.02	47.00	30	1.57	.03	.96	.03	.99	.99	97.00	.20	.17–25
3[a]	44.32	42.37	28	1.51	.04	.96	.03	.99	.99	96.37	.20	.17–24
4	44.72	43.10	28	1.54	.03	.96	.03	.99	.99	97.10	.20	.17–25
5[a]	24.79	23.36	21	1.11	.33	.97	.01	1.00	1.00	91.36	.19	.18–22
Ages 30–64 (n = 259)												
1	39.95	38.71	31	1.25	.16	.94	.03	.99	.99	86.71	.34	.31–41
2	25.57	23.91	30	0.79	.78	.96	.00	1.00	1.00	73.91	.31	.31–34
3[a]	21.92	19.91	28	0.71	.87	.97	.00	1.01	1.00	73.91	.33	.33–35
4	22.67	21.03	28	0.75	.82	.97	.00	1.01	1.00	75.03	.32	.32–34
5[a]	18.85	16.70	21	0.80	.73	.96	.00	1.00	1.00	84.70	.34	.34–38
Ages 65–89 (n = 151)												
1	74.95	70.88	31	2.28	.00	.84	.09	.93	.95	118.88	.79	.65–98
2	54.28	47.10	30	1.57	.02	.88	.06	.96	.97	97.10	.65	.55–80
3[a]	50.78	43.50	28	1.55	.03	.88	.06	.96	.98	97.50	.65	.56–80
4	39.28	35.99	28	1.28	.14	.90	.04	.98	.99	89.99	.60	.55–73
5[a]	30.22	27.39	21	1.30	.16	.90	.04	.98	.99	95.39	.64	.59–75
Ages 16–89 (n = 858)												
1	122.02	120.13	31	3.87	.00	.95	.06	.98	.98	168.13	.20	.16–24
2	126.63	124.68	30	4.15	.00	.96	.05	.98	.99	174.68	.14	.12–17
3[a]	44.63	41.44	28	1.48	.05	.98	.02	1.00	1.00	95.44	.11	.09–14
4	38.23	36.69	28	1.31	.13	.98	.02	1.00	1.00	90.69	.11	.09–13
5[a]	19.70	18.45	21	0.89	.62	.99	.00	1.00	1.00	86.45	.10	.10–12

Note. From "Redefining the factor structure of the Wechsler Memory Scale–III: Confirmatory factor analysis with cross-validation," by L. R. Price, D. Tulsky, S. Millis, and L. Weiss, in press, *Journal of Clinical and Experimental Neuropsychology.* Adapted with permission. Model 1 = one factor; Model 2 = two-factor oblique (auditory memory and working memory); Model 3 = three-factor oblique (immediate memory, delayed memory, and working memory with separate immediate and delayed conditions); Model 4 = three-factor oblique (auditory memory, visual memory, and working memory, with combined immediate and delayed subtests); Model 5 = five-factor oblique (auditory immediate, visual immediate, auditory delayed, visual delayed, and working memory).

[a] Inadmissible model estimates and violation of boundary solutions.

On the basis of the fit measures in the calibration sample and ECVI values from the cross-validation study, Price et al. (in press) concluded that Model 4 has the best fit to the data. In this model, the subtests load onto three factors: Auditory Memory, Visual Memory, and Working Memory. Table 4.14 provides the factor loadings of Model 4 for the calibration and cross-validation samples. Table 4.15 provides the interfactor correlations for Model 4, and Table 4.16 presents the invariance statistics for Model 4 for the calibration and cross-validation samples.

Table 4.14. Standardized Parameter Estimates for Model 4

WMS–III Subtest	WMS–III Calibration Sample (N = 1,250)				Cross-Validation Sample (N = 858)			
	Auditory Memory	Visual Memory	Working Memory	R^2	Auditory Memory	Visual Memory	Working Memory	R^2
Letter–Number Sequencing			.84	.64			.83	.68
Logical Memory Delayed	.78			.60	.76			.58
Logical Memory Immediate	.77			.54	.77			.59
Spatial Span			.55	.32			.57	.32
Verbal Paired Associates Delayed	.63			.37	.64			.42
Verbal Paired Associates Immediate	.66			.42	.69			.48
Family Pictures Delayed		.79		.60		.69		.48
Faces Immediate		.37		.14		.38		.15
Faces Delayed		.39		.14		.43		.18
Family Pictures Immediate		.75		.56		.66		.43

Note. From "Redefining the factor structure of the Wechsler Memory Scale–III: Confirmatory factor analysis with cross-validation," by L. R. Price, D. Tulsky, S. Millis, and L. Weiss, in press, *Journal of Clinical and Experimental Neuropsychology.* Adapted with permission.

Table 4.15. Interfactor Correlations for the Calibration and Cross-Validation Samples for Model 4

Factor	Calibration Sample (N = 1,250)			Cross-Validation Sample (N = 858)		
	1	2	3	1	2	3
Auditory Memory						
Visual Memory	.74			.82		
Working Memory	.65	.49		.72	.57	

Note. From "Redefining the factor structure of the Wechsler Memory Scale–III: Confirmatory factor analysis with cross-validation," by L. R. Price, D. Tulsky, S. Millis, and L. Weiss, in press, *Journal of Clinical and Experimental Neuropsychology.* Adapted with permission.

Table 4.16. WMS–III Invariance Statistics for Model 4 for the Calibration and Cross-Validation Samples

Method	χ^2	df	F^a	AGFI	AIC	CFI	NNFI	RMSEA	ECVI	90% CI
M_1	90.16	28	.07	.97	144.16	.99	.99	.04	.12	.09–.14
M_2	113.86	35	.33	.96	153.86	.98	.98	.05	.18	.14–.22
M_3	141.35	38	.34	.96	175.35	.98	.99	.06	.20	.16–.25
M_4	171.52	48	.33	.96	185.52	.97	.98	.05	.21	.17–.27

Note. From "Redefining the factor structure of the Wechsler Memory Scale–III: Confirmatory factor analysis with cross-validation," by L. R. Price, D. Tulsky, S. Millis, and L. Weiss, in press, *Journal of Clinical and Experimental Neuropsychology.* Adapted with permission. Cross-validation $N = 1,250$; calibration $N = 858$. M_1 = Free estimated model; M_2 = Equality of factor loadings; M_3 = Equity of factor loadings, factor variance/covariance; M_4 = Equity of factor loadings, factor variance/covariance, and error variances.

[a] Maximum likelihood fitting function.

Tulsky and Price (in press) developed norms based on the collapsing of the immediate and delayed recall indexes into new visual and auditory memory indexes. The clinical utility of these new factors will need to be investigated in future studies. Despite their findings, Price et al. (in press) did not recommend that clinicians discontinue the use of the immediate versus delayed memory composites solely on the basis of the inability of factor analysis to provide statistical support for that original model. The theoretical rationale for the development of the configuration and procedures for the WMS–III are detailed in Chapter 1 of this Manual. A review of clinical research investigations into the nature and severity of memory impairments associated with specific neurological disorders is presented later in this chapter. The performance of these clinical groups on the WMS–III indexes is also reported there. The Psychological Corporation recommends the continued use of the immediate and delayed indexes on the basis of both clinical and theoretical considerations.

Correlation Between the WAIS–III and the WMS–III

Although the WAIS–III and WMS–III index scores were derived independently of one another, the co-norming of the tests creates the opportunity for evaluating the relationship between measures of intelligence and memory. Understanding this relationship enables the clinician to better evaluate the patterns of strengths and weaknesses. Moreover, the studies described here establish the degree of relationship between intelligence and memory and provide support for the use of significant discrepancy models as a means of determining relative impairment in memory compared to general intellectual ability. If intelligence and memory are unrelated, then performance discrepancies may be common and potentially lack clinical meaningfulness. These studies also provide evidence of divergent validity and establish that the tests, although related, measure different constructs.

The WAIS–III IQ and Index scores and the WMS–III Index scores were intercorrelated for the purpose of evaluating the relationships between the two scales. The sample for this analysis was the WMS–III standardization sample because each WMS–III standardization participant was also administered the WAIS–III. The WAIS–III and the WMS–III were administered in counterbalanced order during the same testing session. The demographic characteristics for this sample are described in Chapter 2 of this Manual. It was anticipated that the WAIS–III IQ and Index scores would be moderately correlated with the WMS–III Index scores, that is, that most correlations would range from the .30s to the .60s. Furthermore, the WMS–III visual indexes were expected to correlate more highly with the WAIS–III PIQ scale and POI than with the VIQ scale and VCI. The opposite pattern for the WMS–III auditory indexes was also anticipated; that is, these indexes would correlate more highly with the WAIS–III verbal measures than with the WAIS–III performance measures. Finally, the Working Memory indexes of the two scales were expected to correlate highly.

Table 4.17 presents the correlation coefficients, means, and standard deviations of the sample's performance on the two tests. The correlation coefficients between the WMS–III auditory and visual indexes and the WAIS–III VIQ and PIQ scales are in the expected direction. This pattern of correlations between the WMS–III auditory indexes and the WAIS–III VCI and between the WMS–III visual indexes and the WAIS–III POI is relatively higher in magnitude than the other correlations, with one exception. The WMS–III Visual Delayed Index correlates equally with the WAIS–III VCI and POI. All WMS–III indexes are moderately correlated with the WAIS–III PSI, with correlations ranging from .35 (Visual Immediate Index) to .55 (Working Memory Index). The high correlation between the WMS–III Working Memory Index and the WAIS–III Working Memory Index (.82) is expected because they measure a similar construct in addition to sharing one subtest. The correlations between this WMS–III index and the other WAIS–III measures are in the moderate range, from .51 (VCI) to .68 (FSIQ).

The pattern of correlations provides evidence of divergent validity, that is, that the two scales measure different constructs. Some modality-specific effects can be observed: WAIS–III Performance measures display a higher correlation with visual memory than do the WAIS–III Verbal measures; WAIS–III Verbal measures correlate higher with auditory memory measures

Table 4.17. Correlations Between the WAIS–III and the WMS–III

| | WAIS-III | | | | | | | WMS-III | |
	VIQ	PIQ	FSIQ	VCI	POI	WMI	PSI	Mean	SD
WMS-III									
Auditory Immediate	.58	.52	.59	.57	.46	.47	.42	99.9	14.9
Visual Immediate	.30	.39	.36	.29	.32	.26	.35	99.8	15.0
Immediate Memory	.53	.54	.57	.52	.47	.44	.46	99.9	15.2
Auditory Delayed	.54	.50	.57	.54	.44	.45	.42	100.0	14.9
Visual Delayed	.35	.44	.42	.36	.36	.30	.39	100.1	15.1
Auditory Recognition Delayed	.47	.44	.49	.47	.38	.42	.38	100.1	15.0
General Memory	.56	.56	.60	.56	.48	.47	.48	100.0	15.1
Working Memory	.62	.65	.68	.51	.62	.82	.55	100.0	14.8
WAIS-III									
Mean	100.5	100.0	100.3	100.5	99.8	100.0	100.2		
SD	14.5	14.5	14.5	14.7	14.4	15.0	14.6		

Note. N = 1,250.

than with visual memory measures. Overall, the WAIS–III measures correlate highest with auditory memory than with visual memory. Interestingly, processing speed did not display a more significant correlation with visual memory measures than with auditory measures. All of the WMS–III visual memory measures have a brief stimulus exposure time, and impairments in visual processing speed might have a more adverse effect on these tasks than on auditory memory tasks. The results indicate similar levels of association between the WAIS–III PSI and visual and auditory memory performance, with the correlations with auditory measures slightly higher than those with visual measures. Clinically, impairment in general intellectual functioning would be expected to have an effect on memory measures, particularly working memory, general memory, immediate memory, and auditory immediate memory measures. If intellectual impairment affects performance on memory, the effects on visual memory tasks may be less observable.

The results of this study support the association between intelligence and memory and the potential utility of discrepancy models for determining weaknesses and impairment in memory relative to general ability level. In subsequent research, Hawkins and Tulsky (2001) reported base rates for FSIQ versus GMI stratified by FSIQ level. The results of this study indicated that at higher IQ levels, general memory is more frequently lower than IQ. The opposite trend was observed for individuals with lower IQs; that is, general memory scores were often greater than IQ scores. These findings will enable the clinician to determine the base rates of discrepancies, which can aid in the interpretation of an individual's performance.

Joint WAIS–III/WMS–III Factor Analysis

The co-norming of the WAIS–III and WMS–III has enabled researchers to perform more sophisticated studies of the relationship between intelligence and memory, specifically, studies to define and differentiate the factors that underlie intellectual and memory assessment. In one such study, Tulsky and Price (in press) examined the combined WAIS–III/WMS–III factor structure, applying confirmatory factor analytic procedures. The authors used all the WAIS–III subtests except Object Assembly and included all of the WMS–III subtests (including Visual Reproduction and Word Lists). The authors developed several measurement models, which they assessed using multiple fit indicators. Their results were similar to those reported in the Price et al. (in press) study.

Tulsky, Ivnik, Price, and Wilkins (in press) concluded that a six-factor model demonstrated the best fit to the data. This model specified the following factors: Verbal Comprehension, Visual–Perceptual Organization, Working Memory, Processing Speed, Auditory Memory, and Visual memory. As in the

WMS–III factor analysis reported previously, the results of the joint WAIS–III/WMS–III factor analysis suggest that memory functions cluster by the modality of sensory input. The authors prorated norms to parallel the observed factor structure. Further, the authors developed an alternate visual memory index, substituting Visual Reproduction for Faces, citing the relatively lower loading of Faces on the Visual Memory factor (Tulsky et al., in press).

The work by Tulsky and Price (in press) and Tulsky et al. (in press) provides further evidence of the structure of the WAIS–III and the WMS–III. However, it is still not clear whether these findings reflect the neurological structure of memory or an artifact related to the statistical interdependence of the immediate and delayed tasks within each modality. More clinical research and brain-imaging studies of the underlying structure of memory are needed before firm conclusions regarding the composition of the memory composites can be made. The alternate memory indexes developed by Tulsky et al. will provide researchers with flexibility in determining the most diagnostic composites for their specific populations.

As with any composite, if the scores on the subtests that make up the composite differ significantly, the composite score should not be reported as representative of the individual's functioning in that domain. Ryan, Ament, and Arb (2000) calculated values for determining significant differences between WMS–III subtest scores.

Convergent Evidence for the WAIS–III as a Measure of Intellectual Functioning

The WAIS–III is the most recent revision of the WAIS (Wechsler, 1955). The constellation of tasks and composition of index scores has been changed in the current version; however, the primary function of the WAIS–III, as with its predecessors, is the assessment of intellectual functioning. The preliminary evidence that the WAIS–III measures intellectual ability was gathered from a series of comparative and concurrent validity studies. In these studies, the WAIS–III was correlated with established tests of intelligence, with the expectation that WAIS–III IQ and Index scores would correlate highly with these other measures of intelligence.

Correlations With the WAIS–R

A sample of 192 adults aged 16–74 ($M = 43.5$ years, $SD = 20.2$) were administered the WAIS–R and the WAIS–III in counterbalanced order. The interval between testings ranged from 2 to 12 weeks, with a median of 4.7 weeks.

Participants were recruited according to the same methods used to select the standardization sample. The sample had the following composition: 51.6% female and 48.4% male; 79.2% White, 11.5% African American, 6.8% Hispanic, and 2.5% of other racial/ethnic origin.

Table 4.18 presents the correlation coefficients, means, and standard deviations of the sample's performance on the two tests. The correlation coefficients were calculated in a two-step process to account for differential practice effects. In the first step, the coefficients were calculated separately

Table 4.18. Correlations Between the WAIS–R and the WAIS–III

Subtest/Scale/Index	WAIS–R Mean[a]	SD	WAIS–III Mean[a]	SD	r_{12}[b]
Vocabulary	10.8	2.8	10.2	2.8	.90
Similarities	11.3	2.7	10.4	3.0	.79
Arithmetic	10.1	2.7	10.4	3.0	.80
Digit Span	10.4	3.1	10.3	3.3	.82
Information	10.5	2.8	10.5	3.0	.83
Comprehension	11.0	2.9	10.5	2.9	.76
Letter–Number Sequencing	—	—	—	—	—
Picture Completion	11.1	2.6	10.7	3.0	.50
Digit Symbol—Coding	11.8	3.0	10.6	3.1	.77
Block Design	11.4	2.9	10.7	3.0	.77
Matrix Reasoning	—	—	10.3	2.8	—
Picture Arrangement	11.1	2.8	10.5	3.2	.63
Symbol Search	—	—	10.1	3.0	—
Object Assembly	11.3	3.1	10.4	3.0	.69
VIQ	103.4	14.5	102.2	15.1	.94
PIQ	108.3	14.4	103.5	15.4	.86
FSIQ	105.8	14.3	102.9	15.2	.93
VCI	—	—	101.9	14.4	—
POI	—	—	102.9	14.8	—
WMI	—	—	—	—	—
PSI	—	—	101.7	15.0	—

Note. N = 192. Correlations were computed separately for each order of administration in a counterbalanced design and corrected for the variability of the WAIS–III standardization sample (Guilford & Fruchter, 1978).

[a] The values in the Mean columns are the average of the means of the two administration orders.

[b] The weighted average was obtained with Fisher's z transformation.

for each order of administration in the counterbalanced design and corrected for the variability of the WAIS–III standardization sample (Guilford & Fruchter, 1978). In the second step, the average coefficients of the correlations (of the two administration orders) were calculated with Fisher's z transformation procedure.

The correlation coefficients for the sample are .94, .86, and .93 for the VIQ, PIQ, and FSIQ scores, respectively. The magnitude of these correlations suggests that the WAIS–III measures essentially the same constructs as does the WAIS–R.

A comparison of the mean IQ scores shows that the WAIS–III FSIQ score is 2.9 points less than the WAIS–R FSIQ score and that the WAIS–III VIQ and PIQ scores are 1.2 points and 4.8 points less than the corresponding WAIS–R scores. These differences between the WAIS–III and WAIS–R scores are expected and similar to those found between previous revisions of the Wechsler scales. Such differences are expected to occur according to the work by Matarazzo (1972) and Flynn (1984, 1987), which suggests that when an examinee's performance is referenced to outdated norms rather than to current ones, the IQ score will be inflated.

Table 4.19 provides the ranges of expected WAIS–III IQ scores for selected WAIS–R IQ scores. The ranges of the expected WAIS–III IQ scores associated with particular WAIS–R scores are relatively narrow near the middle of the IQ score distribution (i.e., 100) and wider at the upper and lower score levels. In addition, WAIS–III and WAIS–R PIQ scores can be expected to differ more than VIQ scores do. The expected score ranges reported in Table 4.19 reflect 95% confidence intervals. (Note that some of the WAIS–III IQ scores did not cover the selected WAIS–R score, because the WAIS–III is relatively harder than its predecessor.)

Table 4.19. Expected WAIS–III IQ Scores for Selected WAIS–R IQ Scores

	WAIS–III IQ Score Range		
WAIS–R IQ Score	VIQ	PIQ	FSIQ
55	50–55	47–54	49–54
70	66–70	62–68	65–69
85	82–85	78–82	81–83
100	98–99	94–96	96–98
115	113–115	109–112	111–113
130	128–131	123–127	126–129
145	142–147	137–143	140–145

Note. Ranges are 95% confidence intervals based on linear equating (Angoff, 1984, Design II.B) of data for 192 adults administered both tests in counterbalanced order.

Correlations With the WISC–III

The WISC–III and WAIS–III were administered in counterbalanced order to a sample of 184 16-year-olds, recruited according to the same methods used to select the standardization sample. The interval between testings ranged from 2 to 12 weeks, with a median of 4.6 weeks. The sample had the following composition: 47.8% female and 52.2% male; 77.7% White, 12.5% African American, 6.0% Hispanic, and 3.8% of other racial/ethnic origin.

Table 4.20. Correlations Between the WISC–III and the WAIS–III

Subtest/Scale/Index	WISC–III		WAIS–III		r_{12}[b]
	Mean[a]	SD	Mean[a]	SD	
Vocabulary	10.0	2.6	10.3	3.0	.83
Similarities	11.1	3.4	10.9	3.3	.68
Arithmetic	10.4	3.3	11.0	3.3	.76
Digit Span	10.4	3.4	10.3	2.8	.73
Information	10.3	2.9	10.6	3.2	.80
Comprehension	10.5	3.5	10.3	3.0	.60
Letter–Number Sequencing	—	—	10.0	3.4	—
Picture Completion	11.3	2.9	10.6	3.0	.45
Digit Symbol—Coding	10.9	3.6	10.8	2.9	.77
Block Design	10.4	3.4	11.0	3.1	.80
Matrix Reasoning	—	—	10.7	2.6	—
Picture Arrangement	10.2	2.9	10.7	3.0	.31
Symbol Search	11.3	3.2	10.6	2.8	.67
Object Assembly	10.4	3.3	10.7	2.7	.61
Mazes	10.5	3.3	—	—	—
VIQ	103.0	15.2	103.5	15.6	.88
PIQ	104.5	15.1	104.9	14.2	.78
FSIQ	103.9	15.2	104.6	15.1	.88
VCI	103.0	14.8	103.6	16.2	.87
POI	104.0	14.7	104.4	14.7	.74
WMI[c]	102.8	16.2	101.1	16.2	.80
PSI	106.4	15.4	103.7	14.4	.79

Note. N = 184. Correlations were computed separately for each order of administration in a counterbalanced design and corrected for the variability of the WAIS–III standardization sample (Guilford & Fruchter, 1978).

[a] The values in the Mean columns are the average of the means of the two administration orders.

[b] The weighted average was obtained with Fisher's *z* transformation.

[c] For this variable, *N* = 44

Table 4.20 presents the correlation coefficients, means, and standard deviations of the subtest scaled scores, IQ scores, and Index scores on the two tests. The correlation coefficients were calculated in a two-step process to account for differential practice effects. In the first step, the coefficients were calculated separately for each order of administration in the counterbalanced design and corrected for the variability of the WAIS–III standardization sample (Guilford & Fruchter, 1978). In the second step, the average coefficients of the correlations (of the two administration orders) were calculated with Fisher's z transformation procedure.

The correlation coefficients between the WAIS–III and WISC–III IQ scores are very high and statistically significant: .88, .78, and .88 for the VIQ, PIQ, and FSIQ scores, respectively. Moreover, the magnitude of these correlations is high enough to indicate that the two instruments are measuring the same, or very similar, constructs. These results are relatively higher than those found between the WISC–R and the WAIS–R (Wechsler, 1981). Correlations between the WISC–III and WAIS–III Index scores are similar, with coefficients of .87, .74, .80, and .79 for the VCI, POI, WMI, and PSI scores, respectively. As shown in Table 4.20, the mean IQ and Index scores of the WAIS–III are nearly equivalent to the corresponding mean WISC–III IQ and Index scores.

Table 4.21 presents the ranges of expected WAIS–III IQ scores for selected WISC–III IQ scores. The ranges of expected WAIS–III scores associated with particular WISC–III scores are relatively narrow near the middle of the IQ distribution (i.e., 100) and wider at the upper and lower score levels. This pattern occurs because the error variance of equating increases as the scores deviate from the mean. The expected score ranges reported in Table 4.21 reflect 95% confidence intervals.

Table 4.21. Expected WAIS–III IQ Scores for Selected WISC–III IQ Scores

| | WAIS–III IQ Score Range | | |
WISC–III IQ Score	VIQ	PIQ	FSIQ
55	50–58	56–64	53–60
70	67–72	71–77	69–74
85	83–87	85–89	85–88
100	99–102	100–102	100–102
115	115–117	113–116	114–117
130	129–134	126–131	128–132
145	144–150	138–145	142–148

Note. Ranges are 95% confidence intervals based on linear equating (Angoff, 1984, Design II.B) of data for 184 16-year-olds administered both tests in counterbalanced order.

Correlations With the
Standard Progressive Matrices

The *Standard Progressive Matrices* (SPM; Raven, 1976) and the WAIS–III were administered to a sample of 26 adults aged 16–45 ($M = 28.6$, $SD = 10.8$). The sample had the following composition: 53.8% female and 46.2% male; 96.2% White and 3.8% of other racial/ethnic origin.

Table 4.22 reports the correlation coefficients, means, and standard deviations between the WAIS–III IQ and Index scores and the total score on the SPM. The correlation coefficients were corrected for the variability of the standardization sample. Because the Letter–Number Sequencing subtest was not administered, the WMI score could not be calculated; therefore, data are reported for the Arithmetic and Digit Span subtests. Also, because the WAIS–III Matrix Reasoning subtest and the SPM are similar tasks, the correlation between the subtest and the SPM is reported separately.

Table 4.22. Correlations Between the SPM and the WAIS–III

	SPM	WAIS–III	
	Raw Total Score	Mean	SD
WAIS–III			
VIQ	.49	112.8	13.8
PIQ	.79	111.7	9.2
FSIQ	.64	113.3	12.2
VCI	.55	111.4	12.5
POI	.65	114.1	12.4
WMI	—	—	—
PSI	.25	103.4	11.0
Arithmetic	.32	11.9	2.1
Digit Span	.13	11.2	3.0
Matrix Reasoning	.81	12.6	2.5
SPM			
Mean	50.6		
SD	6.1		

Note. N = 26. All correlations were corrected for the variability of the WAIS–III standardization sample (Guilford & Fruchter, 1978).

The correlation coefficients between the WAIS–III VIQ, PIQ, FSIQ, VCI, and POI scores and the SPM are statistically significant and range from .49 to .79. As expected, the correlations with the PIQ score (.79) and the POI score (.65) are the highest. The correlation with the PSI score is low (.25) and is also expected because the SPM is an untimed, nonverbal reasoning task. The SPM apparently is not highly related to working memory, as indicated by its low correlations with the Arithmetic (.32) and Digit Span (.13) subtests.

The results are very consistent with the previous findings of significant correlations (from the .50s to .70s) between the SPM and the predecessors of the WAIS–III (Burke, 1985; Burke & Bingham, 1969; Desai, 1955; Hall, 1957; B. Levine & Iscoe, 1954; McLaurin & Farrar, 1973; C. G. Watson & Klett, 1974). In addition, Matrix Reasoning has the highest correlations with the SPM (.81) than do the other WAIS–III subtests. This high correlation provides support for the validity of this new subtest of the WAIS–III.

Correlations With the *Stanford–Binet Intelligence Scale—Fourth Edition*

The *Stanford–Binet Intelligence Scale—Fourth Edition* (SB–IV; R. L. Thorndike et al., 1986) and the WAIS–III were administered to a sample of 26 adults. The sample was the same one used for the correlation studies with the SPM (Raven, 1976) previously described.

Table 4.23 reports the corrected correlation coefficients, means, and standard deviations between the WAIS–III IQ and Index scores and the SB–IV Standard Area Scores (SAS) and overall composite score. The correlation coefficients were corrected for the variability of the WAIS–III standardization sample. Additionally, because the Letter–Number Sequencing subtest was not administered to this sample, the WMI score could not be calculated. Data for the individual Arithmetic and Digit Span subtests are reported separately.

The correlation between the WAIS–III FSIQ score and the global SB–IV composite score is .88, a result consistent with studies testing the relationship between the Wechsler scales and the SB–IV (R. L. Thorndike et al., 1986). The result also suggests that the WAIS–III has a strong relationship with the SB–IV, as did the WAIS–R.

The highest correlations occur between the WAIS–III PIQ score and the SB–IV Standard Area Scores, generally ranging in the .80s. The exception is the Short-Term Memory SAS, which has much lower correlations with the WAIS–III IQ scores (range .44–.50). The correlations with the Arithmetic and Digit Span subtests (.34 and .52, respectively) are in a similar range. These data indicate that the WMI of the WAIS–III and the Short-Term Memory Area of the SB–IV do not share an appreciable amount of variance. Another difference between the WAIS–III and the SB–IV occurs with the measures of processing speed. The correlations between the WAIS–III PSI score and the SB–IV scores are very low, ranging from -.01 to .32. These results are expected because the SB–IV does not include a separate measure of processing speed.

Table 4.23. Correlations Between the SB–IV and the WAIS–III

| | SB–IV | | | | | WAIS–III | |
	Verbal Reason.	Visual Reason.	Quantitative Reason.	Short-Term Memory	SB–IV Composite	Mean	SD
WAIS–III							
VIQ	.72	.53	.69	.44	.78	112.8	13.8
PIQ	.81	.82	.83	.48	.89	111.7	9.2
FSIQ	.79	.69	.80	.50	.88	113.3	12.2
VCI	.87	.57	.78	.41	.85	111.4	12.5
POI	.76	.78	.80	.36	.86	114.1	12.4
WMI	—	—	—	—	—	—	—
PSI	-.19	.32	-.01	.06	.07	103.4	11.0
Arithmetic	.18	.48	.54	.34	.51	11.9	2.1
Digit Span	.26	.30	.38	.52	.48	11.2	3.0
SB–IV							
Mean	116.6	110.1	115.5	110.7	114.8		
SD	13.6	12.0	16.7	14.3	12.1		

Note. N = 26. All correlations were corrected for the variability of the WAIS–III standardization sample (Guilford & Fruchter, 1978).

Summary

As expected, there was a high degree of correlation between the WAIS–III IQ scores and the corresponding scores on the WISC–III and WAIS–R. The WAIS–III also demonstrated a high degree of correlation with the SB–IV (R. L. Thorndike et al., 1986). The PIQ of the WAIS–III demonstrated a strong association with the SPM (Raven, 1976). The index-level scores of the WAIS–III correlated highly with the WISC–III Index scores and had a lower correlation with scores on other intelligence tests. This finding suggests that these indexes add unique measures of intellectual functioning not found in the SB–IV or SPM. Significant mean score differences between the WAIS–III and WAIS–R were found, but mean scores on the WAIS–III and the WISC–III were very similar, a result suggesting that these two tests yield similar estimates of intellectual ability.

Convergent Evidence for the WMS–III as a Measure of Memory Functioning

The WMS–III was designed for the assessment of auditory and visual declarative memory abilities and auditory and visual working memory abilities in adults and older adolescents. In part, the development of the WMS–III was based on its predecessors, the WMS and WMS–R. Many of the procedures from these previous versions were retained but updated and expanded to reflect the increased knowledge regarding human memory functioning. Additional procedures were developed in response to criticisms of tasks on the WMS and WMS–R and were based on results of clinical studies of novel memory tasks. The WMS–III was developed to measure memory functioning and, therefore, it was expected to have a moderate to high degree of correlation with other memory tests.

Correlations With the WMS–R

A sample of 207 adults were administered the WMS–R and the WMS–III in counterbalanced order. The mean age was 44.7 years ($SD = 20.6$). The interval between the two testing sessions ranged from 2 to 12 weeks, with a median interval of 32 days. Participants were recruited according to the same methods used to select the standardization sample. The sample had the following composition: 52.2% female and 47.8% male; 76.9% White, 10.1% African American, 10.1% Hispanic, and 2.9% of other racial/ethnic origin. By level of education, the sample had the following representation: 3.4%, ≤8 years; 4.3%, 9–11 years; 31.9%, 12 years; 25.6%, 13–15 years; and 34.8%, ≥16 years.

Table 4.24 presents the correlation coefficients, means, and standard deviations of the sample's performance on the two tests. The correlation coefficients were calculated in a two-step process identical to that described previously in this chapter for the WAIS–III—WAIS–R correlation study. As reviewed in the *WMS–III Administration and Scoring Manual*, a number of substantial changes were implemented in the WMS–III. All of the WMS–III subtests, for example, that contribute to the visual memory indexes are completely different from those in the WMS–R. Because of the substantial number of changes from the WMS–R to the WMS–III, especially in the visually presented memory subtests, it was anticipated that the WMS–III auditorily presented indexes would exhibit higher correlations with the corresponding WMS–R indexes than those between the WMS–R and WMS–III visual indexes.

The correlation coefficients between the WMS–III Auditory Immediate Index and the WMS–R Verbal Memory Index, the WMS–III Visual Immediate Index and the WMS–R Visual Memory Index, and the WMS–III Immediate Memory Index and the WMS–R General Memory Index are .72, .36, and .62, respectively. As expected, summary measures based on visually presented material show lower correlations than those based on auditorily presented material. The WMS–III Working Memory Index correlates highest with the WMS–R Attention/Concentration Index (.64) and relatively lower with the other WMS–R memory indexes, with correlations ranging from .34 (Verbal Memory and Visual Memory indexes) to .38 (Delayed Recall Index).

Table 4.24. Correlations Between the WMS–R and the WMS–III

| | WMS–R Indexes | | | | | WMS–III | |
	Verbal Memory	Visual Memory	General Memory	Attention/ Concentration	Delayed Recall	Mean[a]	SD
WMS–III							
Auditory Immediate	.72	.53	.73	.40	.68	103.3	15.1
Visual Immediate	.33	.36	.36	.15	.40	103.4	15.4
Immediate Memory	.60	.51	.62	.31	.62	104.1	15.9
Auditory Delayed	.68	.49	.69	.33	.67	104.3	15.1
Visual Delayed	.36	.42	.39	.15	.41	103.8	15.7
Aud Rec Delayed	.56	.38	.55	.27	.51	104.6	16.1
General Memory	.65	.54	.67	.30	.65	105.1	15.8
Working Memory	.34	.34	.36	.64	.38	103.3	14.7
WMS–R							
Mean[a]	102.2	104.3	103.4	100.5	104.8		
SD	15.8	15.2	16.4	14.3	15.8		

Note. N = 207. Correlations were computed separately for each order of administration in a counterbalanced design and corrected for the variability of the WMS–III standardization sample (Guilford & Fruchter, 1978).

[a] The Mean values are the average of the means of the two administration orders.

Correlations With the *Children's Memory Scale*

The *Children's Memory Scale* (CMS; M. Cohen, 1997) is an individually administered test of memory functioning for children and adolescents aged 5–16 years. The CMS and the WMS–III normative age ranges overlap at age 16. A sample of 86 adolescents aged 16 were administered the CMS and the WMS–III in a counterbalanced design in order to investigate the interrelationships of these two instruments. The interval between the two testing sessions ranged from 2 to 12 weeks, with a median interval of 30 days.

Participants were recruited according to the same methods used to select the standardization sample. The sample had the following composition: 46.5% female and 53.5% male; 75.6% White, 9.3% African American, 11.6% Hispanic, and 3.5% of other racial/ethnic origin. By parent education level, the sample had the following representation: 3.5%, ≤8 years; 9.3%, 9–11 years; 27.9%, 12 years; 27.9% 13–15 years; and 31.4%, ≥16 years.

It was anticipated that WMS–III auditory indexes would correlate most highly with the CMS auditory (i.e., verbal) indexes. Similarly, the WMS–III visual indexes were expected to correlate most highly with the CMS visual indexes. Finally, the WMS–III Working Memory Index was predicted to correlate most highly with the CMS Attention/Concentration Index. The correlation coefficients were calculated in a two-step process identical to that described previously in this chapter for the WAIS–III—WAIS–R correlation study.

Table 4.25 presents the correlation coefficients, means, and standard deviations of the sample's performance on the two tests. The correlation coefficients between the WMS–III Auditory Immediate and the CMS Verbal Immediate indexes, the WMS–III Visual Immediate and CMS Visual Immediate indexes, the WMS–III Auditory Delayed and the CMS Verbal Delayed indexes, and the WMS–III Visual Delayed and the CMS Visual Delayed indexes are .74, .55, .65, and .26, respectively. The auditory indexes of the WMS–III correlate highest with the corresponding CMS indexes. The WMS–III Visual Immediate Index correlates highest with the CMS Visual Immediate Index; however, the WMS–III Visual Delayed Index correlates highest with the CMS Verbal Delayed Index and next highest with the CMS Visual Delayed Index. This unexpected finding may be due to differences in the content of the WMS–III and CMS visual subtests. Finally, as expected, the WMS–III Working Memory Index correlates highest with the CMS Attention/Concentration Index (.68) and relatively lower with the other CMS indexes, with correlations ranging from .21 (Verbal Recognition Delayed Index) to .48 (Learning Index). These observed patterns and magnitudes of relationships between the CMS and the WMS–III generally provide evidence of convergent and divergent validity and support the notion that the CMS and the WMS–III are measuring similar constructs.

Table 4.25. Correlations Between the CMS and the WMS–III

| | CMS Indexes | | | | | | | | WMS–III[a] | |
	Verbal Immediate	Visual Immediate	Learning	Verbal Delayed	Visual Delayed	Verbal Rec Del	General Memory	Attention/ Concentration	Mean	SD
WMS–III										
Auditory Immediate	.74	.35	.65	.70	.27	.53	.72	.41	95.2	19.6
Visual Immediate	.40	.55	.44	.44	.41	.36	.55	.30	102.7	14.6
Immediate Memory	.70	.50	.66	.70	.40	.56	.76	.44	98.6	17.8
Auditory Delayed	.63	.35	.58	.65	.24	.48	.64	.41	94.7	18.5
Visual Delayed	.35	.46	.40	.41	.26	.36	.46	.17	103.2	14.9
Aud Rec Del	.56	.26	.44	.56	.13	.44	.52	.48	99.5	16.8
General Memory	.63	.43	.59	.66	.26	.52	.67	.43	98.9	17.0
Working Memory	.36	.33	.48	.44	.23	.21	.44	.68	98.4	14.7
CMS										
Mean[a]	98.6	101.0	98.7	98.8	99.1	98.2	99.8	97.9		
SD	21.6	12.6	17.8	17.2	13.7	16.5	18.9	14.8		

Note. N = 86. All correlations were computed separately for each order of administration in a counterbalanced design and corrected for the variability of the WMS–III standardization sample (Guilford & Fruchter, 1978).

[a] The Mean values are the average of the means of the two administration orders. The weighted average was obtained with Fisher's z transformation.

Evidence Based on Test-Criterion Relationships

Assessment of Psychoeducational and Developmental Disorders

The concurrent validity studies that have been presented demonstrate the validity of the WAIS–III and WMS–III as measures of intelligence and memory, respectively. In clinical settings, the measurement of these constructs occurs frequently as part of the assessment of developmental problems, especially those associated with academic performance, in adolescents and young adults. When a diagnosis of specific developmental disorders such as mental retardation and learning disabilities is made, an assessment of intellectual functioning assessment must be obtained (American Psychiatric Association, 1994). A clinically valid test of intelligence should sensitive to these developmental issues. Memory assessment has not been determined to be diagnostic of specific developmental disorders; however, memory testing enables the clinician to determine if specific cognitive limitations are contributing to the individual's difficulties in learning or adaptation. Moreover, in some cases, memory may be a domain of cognitive functioning that is the focus of remediation efforts. Evidence of the validity of the WAIS–III and WMS–III for such applications was obtained from clinical studies of adolescents and adults with developmental disorders and through concurrent assessment of academic skills correlated with intelligence and memory.

For the following studies involving individuals with psychoeducational and developmental disorders, the demographic data and performance data for the WAIS–III are presented in Tables 4.26 and 4.27, respectively. The demographic data and performance data for the WMS–III are presented in Tables 4.28 and 4.29, respectively.

Mental Retardation

According to the definitions of the *DSM–IV*, the American Association on Mental Retardation (1992), and the Developmentally Disabled Assistance and Bill of Rights Act of 1975, mental retardation is a developmental disorder that manifests before age 18. Individuals with mental retardation exhibit significantly subaverage intellectual functioning that exists concurrently with related limitations in 2 or more of the following 10 adaptive skill areas: communication, self-care, home living, social skills, community use, self-direction, health and safety, functional academics, leisure, and work. According to

Table 4.26. Demographic Data of Samples With Psychoeducational and Developmental Disorders for WAIS–III Studies

	Mental Retardation (Mild)	Mental Retardation (Moderate)	ADHD	LD Math	LD Reading	Deafness/ Hearing Deficiencies
N	46	62	30	22	24	30
Age						
Mean	30.8	32.8	19.8	18.0	17.5	36.5
SD	11.7	12.9	2.4	2.0	1.7	17.1
Sex						
Female	54.3	41.0	22.6	31.8	37.5	63.3
Male	45.7	59.0	77.4	68.2	62.5	36.7
Race/Ethnicity						
White	76.1	86.9	93.5	77.3	95.8	96.7
African American		3.3	6.5			
Hispanic	21.7	9.8		18.2	4.2	3.3
Other	2.2			4.5		
Education						
≤8	50.0	90.2	3.2		8.3	6.7
9–11	17.4	1.6	32.3	63.6	58.4	3.3
12	32.6	8.2	29.0	18.2	12.5	43.3
13–15			29.0	9.1	20.8	40.0
≥16			6.5	9.1		6.7

Note. Except for sample size (*N*) and age, data are reported as percentages.

Table 4.27. WAIS–III Performance of Samples With Psychoeducational and Developmental Disorders

	Mental Retardation (Mild)		Mental Retardation (Moderate)		ADHD		LD Math		LD Reading	
Scale/Index	Mean	SD	Mean	SD	Mean	SD	Mean	SD	Mean	SD
VIQ	60.1	5.0	54.7	4.7	104.2	12.4	98.4	9.9	96.7	11.4
PIQ	64.0	5.8	55.3[a]	4.4	100.9	12.8	99.9	10.6	102.1	10.6
FSIQ	58.3	4.8	50.9[a]	4.1	103.0	11.8	99.2	8.2	99.0	10.9
VCI	63.4	6.3	56.8	6.0	105.4	12.3	102.0	11.6	97.9	14.0
POI	66.8	5.6	58.9	5.4	100.9	13.7	102.3	12.1	102.2	11.7
WMI	—	—	—	—	97.1[b]	13.6	89.4[c]	10.2	91.3[d]	11.4
PSI	63.3	4.0	57.8[a]	3.8	93.4	13.5	95.2	11.7	95.6	10.1
N	46		62		30		22		24	

[a] Sample size for these three variables was 61.

[b] Sample size for this variable was 20.

[c] Sample size for this variable was 9.

[d] Sample size for this variable was 18.

Table 4.28. Demographic Data of Samples With Psychoeducational and Developmental Disorders for WMS–III Studies

	ADHD	LD Reading
N	21	18
Age		
Mean	19.2	18.2
SD	1.9	2.1
Sex		
Female	28.6	33.3
Male	71.4	66.7
Race/Ethnicity		
White	71.5	94.4
African American	9.5	
Hispanic		5.6
Other		
Unknown	19.0	
Education		
≤8		4.8
9–11	38.1	11.1
12	23.8	44.4
13–15	33.3	16.7
≥16		27.8

Note. Except for sample size (*N*) and age, data are reported as percentages.

Table 4.29. WMS–III Performance of Samples with Psychoeducational and Developmental Disorders

	ADHD		LD Reading	
	Mean	**SD**	**Mean**	**SD**
Primary Indexes				
Auditory Immediate	94.9	14.8	98.0	14.2
Visual Immediate	92.6	13.5	97.4	11.6
Immediate Memory	92.5	13.6	97.1	13.3
Auditory Delayed	96.7	15.2	92.7	16.8
Visual Delayed	94.6	10.7	98.1	15.4
Auditory Recognition Delayed	97.1	19.9	93.3	17.2
General Memory	95.1	14.3	93.7	16.7
Working Memory	94.1	14.0	91.7	9.6
Auditory Process Composites	Median %ile	%ile Range	Median %ile	%ile Range
Single–Trial Learning	36%	1%–87%	40%	3%–92%
Learning Slope	60%	6%–96%	44%	3%–98%
Retention	55%	1%–91%	22%	2%–91%
Retrieval	65%	1%–99%	42%	5%–97%
N	21		18	

the normal distribution of IQ scores, about 2.3% of adults obtain scores 2 *SD*s below the mean (100). However, the prevalence of mental retardation varies from study to study, ranging from 2.5% to 3.0% of the general population because the diagnosis of mental retardation must take into account both intellectual ability and adaptive functioning (Harrison, 1990; S. A. Richardson & Koller, 1985).

Many studies have been conducted to characterize the performance of individuals with mental retardation on the previous versions of the Wechsler intelligence scales. One method is based on subtest-score profiles. Individuals with mental retardation often exhibit relatively flat score profiles, with the lowest scores obtained on Arithmetic, Vocabulary, and Coding. When Bannatyne's recategorization method was used, individuals with mental retardation tended to show weaknesses on the subtests related to acquired knowledge (Kaufman & Van Hagen, 1977; Naglieri, 1980; Rubin, Goldman, & Rosenfeld, 1985; Rugel, 1974; Silverstein, 1968; Simon & Clopton, 1984). For the WAIS–III study, it was expected that participants with mental retardation would have flat subtest-score profiles (on all except the PSI subtests), with scores from 2 *SD*s to 3 *SD*s below average according to the severity of the disorder. Scores on the PSI subtests were expected to be slightly higher, because previous research has reported that children with mental retardation obtained relatively higher scores on the PSI than on the other indexes (Wechsler, 1991).

The WAIS–III was administered to 108 adults diagnosed as mentally retarded (see Table 4.26 for demographic data). These examinees did not take the WMS–III, nor were they administered the WAIS–III Letter–Number Sequencing subtest. Without this subtest, the WMI score cannot be computed. See Appendix F for the inclusion criteria for participation in this study.

Table 4.27 presents the mean scores and standard deviations for the WAIS–III IQ scales and indexes for the participants with mental retardation. The mean FSIQ score of the participants with mild mental retardation is 58.3, indicating that this group has global impairment. As expected, the impairment is equally distributed across all of the domains of cognitive functioning. The mean VIQ score (60.1) and mean PIQ score (64.0) are more than 2 *SD*s lower than those obtained by the general population. Furthermore, as the severity of the mental retardation increases, the deficits in cognitive functioning increase, as reflected in the WAIS–III scores. The mean VIQ, PIQ, and FSIQ scores of the participants with moderate mental retardation are 54.7, 55.3, and 50.9, respectively. As expected, the variability in the performance of each of these clinical groups is very small. The standard deviations range from 4.1 to 5.8, which are much smaller than those found in the general population (15). These results are very consistent with the previous reports by L. Atkinson (1992), Craft and Kronenberger (1979), and Spruill (1991) for adult participants, and by Wechsler (1991) for children.

For the WAIS–III indexes, impairment again appears to be distributed across the different domains of functioning. The VCI, POI, and PSI scores of the individuals with mild retardation are 63.4, 66.8, and 63.3, respectively. The same pattern is observed in the group with moderate mental retardation, whose mean VCI, POI, and PSI scores are 56.8, 58.9, and 57.8, respectively. The standard deviations of the Index scores range from 3.8 to 6.3 points, which are significantly smaller than those of the general population (15). The generally equal impairment across these three indexes is roughly consistent with the results reported in the WISC–III manual (Wechsler, 1991). However, children with mental retardation performed slightly better on the PSI. Further research is needed to determine if this pattern remains consistent.

On the WAIS–III subtests, both of the groups had the most difficulty on the Arithmetic subtest. This pattern is consistent with previous report that individuals with mental retardation have the most difficulty on the subtests measuring acquired knowledge (Kaufman & Van Hagen, 1977; Naglieri, 1980; Rubin et al., 1985; Rugel, 1974; Silverstein, 1968; Simon & Clopton, 1984). Additionally, both groups performed relatively poorly on the Symbol Search subtest.

Attention-Deficit/Hyperactivity Disorder

Attention-deficit/hyperactivity disorder (ADHD) is a neurodevelopmental disorder characterized by a wide range of chronic problems with inattention. Sometimes hyperactive–impulsive behaviors are also present, but current *DSM–IV* criteria do not require any hyperactive–impulsive symptoms for diagnosis of ADHD. Discussions by several researchers (Denckla, 1993, 1996; Pennington, Bennetto, McAleer, & Roberts, 1996; Pennington & Ozonoff, 1996) suggest that ADHD inattention symptoms overlap considerably with the neuropsychological concepts of working memory and executive function.

In earlier conceptualizations, ADHD was considered a childhood behavior disorder whose symptoms dissipated in adolescence. Mounting evidence from longitudinal studies and other research summarized by Spencer, Biederman, Wilens, and Faraone (1994), however, have indicated that at least 30%–50% of children diagnosed with ADHD continue to maintain significant ADHD symptoms through adolescence and into adulthood. Estimates of the occurrence of ADHD range from 3% to 5% during childhood (American Psychiatric Association, 1994).

Results of neuroimaging studies involving individuals with attention-deficit disorder (ADD) indicate mild abnormalities associated with the frontal lobes, corpus callosum, basal ganglia, and cerebellum (Giedd, Blumenthal, Molloy, & Castellanos, 2001). Asymmetry (right greater than left) of dorsolateral prefrontal cortex activation has been associated with symptom severity and impaired performance on tests of attention (Spalletta et al., 2001). Results of other studies have indicated asymmetry in the frontal lobes, with right less than left, for boys (Baving, Laucht, & Schmidt, 1999; Rubia et al., 1999). Findings of functional asymmetry may relate to the age and sex of the child and to specific tasks used during imaging.

Results of morphometric studies of ADD have found asymmetry of the head of the caudate nucleus (right greater than left) and decreased white matter in the right frontal lobe (Semrud-Clikeman et al., 2000). Caudate asymmetry was associated with symptom severity (Mataro, Garcia-Sanchez, Junque, Estevez-Gonzalez, Pujol, 1997; Semrud-Clikeman et al., 2000) and poorer performance on measures of inhibitory control, whereas deficits in sustained attention were related to decreased white matter in the right hemisphere (Semrud-Clikeman et al., 2000). The association between abnormal brain morphology and behavioral regulation was observed irrespective of diagnosis (Semrud-Clikeman et al., 2000). Results of MRI studies demonstrate that the caudate nucleus decreases in size with normal maturation; however, youth with ADHD do not demonstrate any change in the size of the caudate nucleus and have abnormal right–left symmetry of the caudate (Castellanos et al., 1996; Castellanos et al., 1994).

Traditional IQ scores have not been found useful in discriminating persons with ADHD from a nonclinical population. Yet, comparisons of subtest score patterns on tests of intellectual functioning by individuals with and without ADHD have been found useful in assessing inattention symptoms of ADHD. On the Wechsler scales (e.g., the WISC–III and the WAIS–R), some subtests are more sensitive than others to impairments in attention, working memory, and processing speed, domains that are central to ADHD. Intraindividual comparisons of performance have demonstrated that individuals with ADHD tend to perform more poorly on a cluster of subtests that are concentration sensitive than on verbal or spatial subtests. Prifitera and Dersh (1992) have discussed how such comparisons can be used to increase the convergent validity in diagnostic assessment.

T. E. Brown (1996) reported on a group of 191 adolescents diagnosed with ADHD whose mean concentration index score (indexes are based on Bannatyne's revised recategorization [1974]) was 18 points lower than their mean verbal index score. Of this sample, 66% obtained a concentration index score at least 15 points (1 *SD*) lower than their verbal or spatial index score (whichever was higher); 24.6% had a discrepancy of 30 points (2 *SD*s) or more between those measures. Only 21.9% and 2%, respectively, of the

123

WISC–III standardization sample obtained similar discrepancies (T. E. Brown, 1996).

Using the subtests of the WAIS–R, Biederman et al. (1993) found that adults diagnosed with ADHD obtained significantly lower Freedom From Distractibility Index and FSIQ scores than did those in the control group without ADHD. T. E. Brown (1996) reported on 142 adults diagnosed with ADHD who obtained a mean difference of 22 points between their mean concentration index score (101.1) and mean verbal index score (123.9) on the WAIS–R. Of these, 86.6% obtained concentration index scores at least 1 *SD* lower than their verbal or spatial index scores (whichever was higher), whereas 31% obtained a WAIS–R concentration index score at least 2 *SD*s lower (T. E. Brown, 1996).

The score discrepancies found by T. E. Brown (1996) are much greater than the discrepancies obtained by the WAIS–R standardization sample (20% and 2%, respectively).

In addition, results of neuropsychological studies have indicated that adults diagnosed with attention deficit disorder (ADD) perform more poorly than control participants on list-learning tasks (Holdnack, Moberg, Arnold, Gur, & Gur, 1995; Mungas, 1983). Results of neuropsychological studies with children and adolescents with ADD have shown deficits in vigilance (Barkley, Anastopoulos, Guevremont, & Fletcher, 1991), immediate visual memory (Kataria, Hall, Wong, & Keys, 1992), verbal memory (Barkley et al., 1991; Loge, Staton, & Beatty, 1990), and working memory (Holdnack, Ledbetter, & Cohen, 1996).

For the present study, the WAIS–III was administered to a sample of 30 older adolescents and adults diagnosed with ADHD according to clinical interviews, *DSM–IV* diagnostic criteria, and the *Brown Attention-Deficit Disorder Scales* (T. E. Brown, 1996). Of these participants, 21 also took the WMS–III. (See Tables 4.26 and 4.28 for the demographic data for the WAIS–III and WMS–III samples, respectively, and Appendix F for the inclusion and exclusion criteria for participation in these studies.)

WAIS–III Results

The mean scores and standard deviations of the ADHD sample on the WAIS–III scales and indexes are presented in Table 4.27. Compared to the performance of the WAIS–III standardization sample, the mean intellectual functioning of the sample with ADHD is in the average range, and the mean VIQ–PIQ score difference is not significant.

The sample with ADHD did show significant intraindividual differences in their WAIS–III Index scores. Their mean WMI score is about 8.3 points lower than their mean VCI score, and their mean PSI score is about 7.5 points lower than their mean POI score. About 30% of the sample with ADHD had WMI scores at least 1 *SD* lower than their VCI scores, whereas 13% of the WAIS–III standardization sample obtained such discrepancies. About 26% of the sample with ADHD had PSI scores at least 1 *SD* lower than their POI scores, whereas 14% of the WAIS–III standardization sample had such discrepancies.

For differences between the higher of the VCI or POI score and the lower of the WMI or PSI score, 61.3% of the sample obtained differences of 1 *SD*, and 16.1% obtained differences of 2 *SD*s or more; only 30.5% and 3.5% of the WAIS–III standardization sample, respectively, had such differences. These results are comparable to the findings by T. E. Brown (1996) in his study of the performance of individuals with ADHD on the WAIS–R.

At the subtest level, the data suggest that the ADHD sample performed relatively more poorly on Digit Symbol—Coding, Digit Span, Symbol Search, and Letter–Number Sequencing. These results are consistent with previous findings that individuals with ADHD tend to perform relatively poorly on tasks related to working memory (Holdnack et al., 1996) and on tasks requiring sustained attention and processing speed (Arcia & Gualtieri, 1994). These results are very consistent with those found on the WISC–III (see T. E. Brown, 1996, and Schwean, Saklofske, Yackulic, & Quinn, 1992).

Because the pattern of performance demonstrated on the WAIS–III by individuals with ADHD is somewhat similar to that by individuals with learning disorders, additional measures, such as the *DSM–IV* diagnostic criteria for ADHD, the *Brown Attention-Deficit Disorder Scales* (T. E. Brown, 1996), and a continuous performance measure should be used to determine whether the subtest score patterns are due to ADHD or a learning disorder or both. In addition, because this pattern of subtest scores was obtained by only a majority (not all) of the participants with ADHD, the diagnosis of ADHD should not be made solely on the basis of this score pattern.

WMS–III Results

The performance data for the WMS–III indexes and composites for the sample with ADHD are presented in Table 4.29. As shown, mean index performance ranges from 92.5 (Immediate Memory Index) to 97.1 (Auditory Recognition Delayed Index), and all mean Index scores are in the *average* range. Follow-up analyses were performed on the data from the 21 participants with ADHD and an additional 10 participants with ADHD who were administered only the Logical Memory subtest of the WMS–III. The performance on the immediate recall condition of Logical Memory was first transformed from a scaled score metric to an index metric (i.e., $M = 100$, $SD = 15$)

and was then compared with their Verbal Comprehension Index score of the WAIS–III. For these individuals, the mean difference score (Verbal Comprehension Index score minus Logical Memory score) was 8.5, indicating that their immediate memory performance was lower than their Verbal Comprehension Index; the mean difference score in the WMS–III standardization sample was 0.5. Additionally, the frequencies of the difference scores were evaluated for both the ADHD group and the WMS–III standardization sample. Of the ADHD group, 29% obtained a difference of at least 1 *SD* between these measures (memory lower than IQ), whereas only 15% of the WMS–III standardization sample had such a difference; 10% of the ADHD sample versus 2.1% of the standardization sample obtained a difference of 2 *SD*s between these measures. These percentages of differences are lower than those obtained by Quinlan and Brown (1997), but do show a clear trend of lower verbal memory compared to verbal intellectual functioning.

Learning Disabilities

Learning disability is associated with difficulties in acquiring a specific academic skill despite normal intellectual functioning (American Psychiatric Association, 1994). It is estimated that about 4% of school-aged children have a reading disorder and 1% of school-aged children have a mathematics disorder, whereas pure writing disability is relatively rare. Cognitive and neuroimaging research has increased our understanding of the underlying processes and brain regions associated with developmental reading disorders. Results of research on brain functioning for orthographic tasks suggest multiple posterior brain systems, one involving the temporo-parietal and one involving temporo-occipital brain regions (Pugh et al., 2001). These systems develop at different times, with the dorsal system (temporo-parietal region) relating to phonological and lexical mapping and orthographic representations whereas the late-emerging ventral (temporo-occipital) system appears to enable rapid word-form identification and recognition (Pugh et al., 2001). Individuals with dyslexia may recruit other brain regions, particularly the posterior right hemisphere (Pugh et al., 2000) and left frontal region (Georgiewa et al., 2002; Richards et al., 1999), to perform phonological tasks and to compensate for dominant temporal-lobe dysfunction. During lexical-judgment tasks, individuals with dyslexia displayed activation in orbito-frontal region whereas normally functioning readers activated the middle frontal gyrus on this task (Corina et al., 2001). Research has also focused on the role of the cerebellum in learning disabilities and poor automatization of cognitive tasks (Nicolson, Fawcett, & Dean, 2001).

Morphological studies have focused on the identification of abnormal symmetry of the planum temporale (a region important in the processing and integrating of auditory input) in dyslexia (Frank & Pavlakis, 2001). The results of these studies need to be evaluated carefully in light of research demonstrating that sex and age effects may account for differences observed in morphometric studies of dyslexia (Schultz et al., 1994).

The majority of research on learning disabilities has been conducted with children and adolescents. Some of this work was conducted with the Bannatyne recategorization method (Bannatyne, 1968, 1974). According to this method, the subtests of the Wechsler scales are classified into four categories: conceptual, spatial, sequencing, and acquired knowledge. The performance by individuals with learning disabilities was more frequently found to exhibit a pattern of spatial > conceptual > acquired knowledge > sequencing. Other researchers have proposed an "ACID" profile to characterize the performance by individuals with learning disabilities on the Wechsler intelligence scales (Ackerman, Dykman, & Peters, 1976; Kaufman, 1979; Sandoval, Sassenrath, & Penaloza, 1988). That is, individuals with learning disabilities are more likely to show relative weaknesses on the Arithmetic, Coding, Information, and Digit Span subtests. Studies involving adults with learning disabilities have replicated these findings (Cordoni, O'Donnell, Ramaniah, Kurtz, & Rosenshein, 1981; Katz, Goldstein, Rudisin, & Bailey, 1993; Kender, Greenwood, & Conard, 1985).

With the accumulation of factor analytic studies and the release of the WISC–III in 1991, researchers found similarities between Bannatyne's four-category structure and the ACID profile and the factor structure of the WISC–III. When the WISC–III Index scores are compared, the profiles become striking. Individuals with learning disabilities tend to show relative weaknesses in the domains related to the third and fourth factors (i.e., the WMI and PSI), with scores approximately 0.5–0.67 SDs below average (Prifitera & Dersh, 1992; Wechsler, 1991).

Results of memory studies have also indicated decreased story recall in adults with learning disabilities (Worden, 1986), verbal and visual memory deficits and poorer performance on Digit Span in adolescents with learning disabilities (Ormrod & Lewis, 1985), and working memory deficits in children with learning disabilities (Swanson, 1993; Swanson, Cochran, & Ewers, 1990).

For the present study, 46 adults diagnosed with learning disabilities (24 in reading, 22 in math) were administered the WAIS–III. Of this sample, 18 with learning disabilities in reading were also administered the WMS–III. Participants for this study were recruited from several university centers. See Tables 4.26 and 4.28 for the demographic data for the WAIS–III and WMS–III samples, respectively, and Appendix F for the inclusion criteria for participation.

WAIS–III Results

Table 4.27 provides the mean scores and standard deviations for the WAIS–III IQ scales and indexes for the two groups with learning disabilities (reading and math). The mean IQ scores are all in the *average* range; scores for the group with reading disabilities range from 96.7 to 102.1, and for the group with math disabilities, from 98.4 to 99.9.

The pattern of scores becomes pronounced at the index level. For the group with reading disabilities, the Index scores range from 91.3 to 102.2, and for the group with math disabilities, from 89.4 to 102.3. A striking finding, however, is that the differences between the VCI and WMI scores are 7 and 13 points for the reading and math groups, respectively. Moreover, the VCI scores are at least 15 points higher than the WMI scores for 41.7% of the individuals with reading disabilities, compared to 13% of the WAIS–III standardization sample. The pattern is similar for the nonverbal Index scores. The difference between the POI and PSI scores is about 7 points for both the reading and math groups, and the POI scores are at least 15 points higher than the PSI scores for 30.4% of these individuals, compared to 14% of the WAIS–III standardization sample.

At the subtest level, the performance of both groups on the ACID profile was clearly depressed, with 24% exhibiting a partial ACID profile and 6.5% exhibiting a full ACID profile, proportions that are greater than those in the general population. These results are very consistent with findings from previous research (e.g., Ackerman et al., 1976; Cordoni et al., 1981; Katz et al., 1993; Kaufman, 1979; Kender et al., 1985; Prifitera & Dersh, 1992; Sandoval et al., 1988; Wechsler, 1991) except that the rate of the partial ACID profile found in the current study is a little higher. The results also suggest that the discrepancies between the VCI and WMI scores and between the POI and PSI scores may be more powerful than the ACID profile analysis in characterizing learning disabilities.

WMS–III Results

Table 4.29 presents the WMS–III performance statistics for those participants with reading disabilities. Similarly to the participants with ADHD previously described, the participants with reading disabilities exhibit average memory performance on all WMS–III indexes. The Index scores range from 91.7 (Working Memory Index) to 98.1 (Visual Delayed Index). Follow-up *t* tests were performed to compare the performance on the Primary Indexes by the group with reading disabilities and a control group (matched for age, sex, race/ethnicity, and education). The results of these tests did not reveal any significant differences between mean scores of the two groups ($p < .05$) for any of the WMS–III indexes. However, the differences on the Retention

Composite was statistically significant ($p < .01$) and indicated that the group with reading disabilities performed more poorly than the matched control group. These results suggest that although the group level of performance is in the *average* range, individually, participants with reading disabilities have a higher forgetting rate for auditorily presented stimuli than do the participants in the matched control group.

Hearing Deficiencies

Deafness and hardness of hearing affect language acquisition and the development of verbal skills. Many studies have reported that individuals with hearing deficiencies performed at the average or low average level on the Performance scales of the Wechsler intelligence scales and on other nonverbal instruments, such as Raven's SPM (1976). The VIQ scores of the individuals with hearing deficiencies were about 1 *SD* lower than their PIQ scores (Braden, 1992; Wechsler, 1991). At the subtest level, they usually performed relatively poorly on the Coding or Digit Symbol subtest (Braden, 1990; Pickles, 1966; Sullivan & Schulte, 1992; B. U. Watson, Sullivan, Moeller, & Jensen, 1982).

The Performance scales of the Wechsler intelligence scales are the most preferred instruments for assessing the intellectual functioning of individuals with hearing deficiencies (Braden, 1992; E. S. Levine, 1974; Maller & Braden, 1992; McQuaid & Alovisetti, 1981; Trott, 1984). As a means of evaluating the clinical utility of the WAIS–III with individuals who are have hearing deficiencies, the Standardization Edition of the WAIS–III was translated into American Sign Language (ASL) by Kostrubala and Braden (1997). The quality of translation was ensured by a back-translation procedure (Hambleton, 1994). The WAIS–III was first translated into ASL and then translated back into English by different ASL experts so that the consistency with the English version could be checked. The translation was modified to correct any inconsistencies, and several iterations were made until high consistency was reached.

The ASL translation of the WAIS–III was administered to a sample of 30 individuals with hearing deficiencies, with the following composition: 63% female, 37% male; 97% White, and 3% Hispanic. The participants ranged in age from 18 to 75 years ($M = 36.5$ years, $SD = 17.1$). See Appendix F for the inclusion criteria for participation in this study.

The reliability of the ASL version of the WAIS–III was estimated on the basis of this sample. The average split-half reliability coefficient for the VIQ scale was .93, with a range of .84–.97; for the PIQ scale (excluding Digit Symbol—Coding), .81, with a range of .73–.91; and for the FSIQ scale, .89. All averages were calculated with Fisher's z transformation. Because the sample was relatively small, further reliability studies may be necessary. However, the obtained reliability coefficients are consistent with those reported for the general population.

The means and standard deviations of the WAIS–III subtest scaled scores, IQ scores, and Index scores are reported in Table 4.30. The mean PIQ score (103.2) is in the *average* range, the mean VIQ score (82.7) is in the *low average* range and significantly lower (about 1.37 *SD*) than the mean PIQ score. The standard deviations of the IQ scores are similar to those of the general population. At the index level, both the POI and PSI scores are in the *average* range. The VCI score is in the *low average* range and significantly lower than the POI and PSI scores (about 1.14 *SD* and 1.47 *SD*, respectively). Although the mean subtest scaled scores on all of the Performance subtests were in the *average* range (9.7–10.9), the performance on Digit Symbol—Coding was the lowest (9.7), about 0.67 *SD* below the average on the rest of the Performance subtests. These results are very similar to those reported previously (Braden, 1990, 1992; Pickles, 1966; B. U. Watson et al., 1982; Wechsler, 1991).

Table 4.30. WAIS–III Performance of Individuals With Deafness/Hearing Deficiencies

Scale/Index	Mean	SD
VIQ	82.7	16.8
PIQ	103.2	13.1
FSIQ	90.8	15.2
VCI	81.6	15.7
POI	103.6	12.9
WMI	—	—
PSI	99.8	16.4
N	30	

Summary

The results of these clinical studies reveal that the WAIS–III is differentially sensitive to developmental disorders, as expected. On average, the performance of individuals with moderate mental retardation was below that of those diagnosed with mild mental retardation. The scores for both groups were in the *extremely low* range and dissimilar to scores obtained by individuals with learning disabilities and ADHD, who performed in the *average* range on measures of intellectual functioning. These results indicate that the WAIS–III provides a good estimate of intellectual functioning. The WAIS–III is also sensitive to mild processing weaknesses observed in individuals with psychoeducational difficulties.

The WMS–III is not typically used for diagnosing mental retardation and was not included in the studies of these groups. Performance on the WMS–III by the samples with ADHD and learning disabilities displayed mild weaknesses, particularly, in comparison to their intellectual functioning.

Assessment of Neurological Disorders and Disorders Associated With Dementia

The sensitivity of the WAIS–III and WMS–III to cognitive weaknesses associated with various neurological disorders was assessed. These studies are very important in establishing the sensitivity of the WMS–III to the effects of disorders associated with dementia and amnesia. In general, the results of these studies demonstrate the clinical applicability of the WAIS–III and WMS–III for assessing the effects of neurological disorders and disorders associated with dementia. Zhu, Tulsky, Price, and Chen (2001) derived reliability coefficients and standard errors of measurement for selected clinical groups with neurological disorders.

The demographic characteristics of most of the samples for these special group studies are presented in Table 4.31. The data are presented as mean age and percentages of the samples by sex, race/ethnicity, and education level.

The results of the following studies involving individuals with neurological disorders, except temporal lobe epilepsy, are presented in Table 4.32. The table includes the mean scores and standard deviations for the WAIS–III IQ scales and indexes and the WMS–III Primary Indexes and the median percentile scores and percentile ranges for the WMS–III Auditory Process Composites. The results of the sample with temporal lobe epilepsy are presented later in Table 4.33.

Alzheimer's Disease

Alzheimer's disease is a chronic, progressive neurological disorder that causes a gradual loss of cognitive functions and, as the disease progresses, impairments in social and occupational functioning and eventually death. Alzheimer's disease is the most common form of dementia among older persons (Zec, 1993). Although the causes of Alzheimer's disease are unknown, neuropathological findings include general cortical atrophy of the temporal–parietal and frontal regions of the brain. Other brain regions, such as the hippocampus and amygdala, may be affected by the presence of neuritic plaques (Zec, 1993). The presence of neurofibrillary plaques and tangles detected at autopsy have been associated with abnormalities on mental-status and memory examinations (Fuld, Katzman, Davies, & Terry, 1982).

Table 4.31. Demographic Data of the Samples With Neurological, Alcohol-Related, and Neuropsychiatric Disorders

	Neurological Disorders Groups							Alcohol-Related Disorders		Neuropsychiatric Disorders
						Temporal Lobe Epilepsy				
	Alzheimer's Disease Mild	Huntington's Disease	Parkinson's Disease	Traumatic Brain Injury	Multiple Sclerosis	Left Lobectomy	Right Lobectomy	Chronic Alcohol Abuse	Korsakoff's Syndrome	Schizophrenia
N	35	15	10	22	25	15	12	28	10	42
Age										
Mean	72.2	44.7	71.2	26.9	44.6	32.5	30.5	53.3	61.0	38.2
SD	7.8	12.0	11.5	5.9	9.6	7.8	5.7	10.2	10.8	6.1
Sex										
Female	42.9	66.7	20.0	36.4	84.0	73.3	50.0	3.6		19.0
Male	57.1	33.3	80.0	63.6	16.0	26.7	50.0	96.4	100.0	81.0
Race/Ethnicity										
White	88.6	100.0	80.0	100.0	76.0	93.3	58.3	89.3	100.0	61.9
African American	8.6		10.0		16.0	6.7	33.3	7.1		31.0
Hispanic			10.0				8.3			
Other	2.9				8.0					2.4
Unknown								3.6		4.8
Education										
≤8	2.9							7.1	30.0	4.8
9–11	8.6	6.7		13.6			8.3	14.3	20.0	11.9
12	17.1	33.3	70.0	31.8	32.0	26.7	16.7	32.1	20.0	38.1
13–15	22.9	20.0	10.0	40.9	20.0	60.0	50.0	28.6	30.0	28.6
≥16	48.6	40.0	20.0	13.6	36.0	13.3	25.0	17.9		16.7
Unknown					12.0					

Note. Except for sample size (*N*) and age, data are reported as percentages.

Table 4.32. WAIS–III and WMS–III Performance of Samples With Neurological Disorders

	Alzheimer's Disease Mild		Huntington's Disease		Parkinson's Disease		Traumatic Brain Injury		Multiple Sclerosis[a]	
	Mean	SD	Mean	SD	Mean	SD	Mean	SD	Mean	SD
WAIS–III Scales/Indexes										
VIQ	92.2	13.1	90.9	7.0	94.6	8.3	89.6	12.4		
PIQ	81.7	13.2	78.2	8.9	82.3	12.3	84.5	13.8		
FSIQ	86.6	13.1	84.0	8.2	88.2	10.1	86.5	10.9		
VCI	93.0	12.0	98.4	8.9	96.9	7.3	89.6	12.7		
POI	84.8	12.4	84.9	9.3	84.7	12.1	92.1	15.0		
WMI	87.2	17.3	81.7	10.3	89.6	12.1	89.8	13.1		
PSI	79.6	14.4	69.3	7.8	81.7	10.3	73.4	10.7		
WMS–III Primary Indexes										
Auditory Immediate	68.7	11.0	78.3	13.3	86.0	17.4	89.3	19.3	97.7	14.4
Visual Immediate	70.6	10.9	73.5	7.1	84.7	15.1	74.9	13.9	81.5	14.3
Immediate Memory	62.9	11.4	70.9	11.0	82.3	17.8	78.9	17.7	88.0	15.9
Auditory Delayed	66.1	9.6	83.7	12.5	85.8	17.2	89.6	21.8	92.8	19.1
Visual Delayed	67.5	8.1	71.2	10.5	80.9	13.1	74.3	13.9	82.2	16.6
Auditory Recognition Delayed	65.6	8.6	88.0	9.8	90.0	14.1	93.6	16.6	92.4	14.5
General Memory	60.4	8.9	76.4	10.5	81.8	15.1	81.9	16.5	86.7	17.8
Working Memory	80.4	16.9	83.1	11.1	85.6	13.0	91.9	11.9	94.8	18.2
WMS–III Auditory Process Composites	Median %ile	%ile Range	Median %ile	%ile Range	Median %ile	%ile Range	Median %ile	%ile Range	Median %ile	%ile Range
Single-Trial Learning	3%	1%–52%	14%	1%–44%	18%	1%–44%	29%	1%–95%	36%	3%–95%
Learning Slope	3%	1%–52%	17%	1%–85%	51%	11%–99%	39%	1%–96%	44%	1%–98%
Retention	1%	1%–99%	39%	1%–98%	27%	1%–70%	36%	1%–95%	32%	1%–91%
Retrieval	34%	2%–78%	65%	11%–88%	50%	11%–94%	50%	2%–99%	34%	5%–88%
N	35		15		10		22		25	

[a] Because of sampling constraints, the participants with multiple sclerosis were not administered the WAIS–III.

Alzheimer's disease is associated with diffuse (Alexander, Prohovnik, Stern, & Mayeux, 1994; Almkvist, Bäckman, Basun, & Wahlund, 1993; Brinkman & Braun, 1984; Gfeller & Rankin, 1991; Goldman, Axelrod, Giordani, Foster, & Berent, 1992; McCurry, Fitz, & Teri, 1994; J. J. Ryan, Paolo, Oehlert, & Coker, 1991) and progressive (e.g., American Psychiatric Association, 1994; Lezak, 1995) deterioration of cognitive functions. The primary purpose of memory and intelligence testing of individuals with Alzheimer's disease is to gauge the degree of deterioration against the baseline of premorbid cognitive ability.

Impairment in declarative memory for new information appears early in the course of this disease, and the decline becomes more rapid as the disease advances (Storandt & Hill, 1989; Zec, 1993). Moreover, memory dysfunction in older persons without apparent disease has been found to predict later development of probable Alzheimer's disease (Bondi et al., 1994; Jacobs et al., 1995; Masur, Sliwinski, Lipton, Blau, & Crystal, 1994). Diagnosis of Alzheimer's disease necessarily requires validation of neurocognitive deficits, including memory impairment, through neuropsychological procedures (McKhann et al., 1984).

Increasingly, researchers have focused on studies of individuals who do not meet diagnostic criteria for dementia but who exhibit some form of cognitive impairment (Peterson et al., 2001). Diagnostic issues and group heterogeneity in outcomes hamper research of mild cognitive impairment (Palmer, Wang, Backman, Winblad, & Fratiglioni, 2002; Ritchie, Artero, & Touchon, 2001). Results of neuropsychological studies indicate higher rates of progression to Alzheimer's-type dementia in individuals with mild cognitive deficits (Morris et al., 2001), and memory impairment was found to predict long-term outcomes (Tuooko, Frerichs, & Kristjansson, 2001) and to signal the presence of an underlying disease process (Portin et al., 2001). Imaging research demonstrates reduced volume of the hippocampus and entorhinal cortex in mild cognitive impairment (Du et al., 2001). Early identification of dementia enables clinicians to recommend appropriate medical interventions and aid families in long-term planning.

A sample of 35 individuals clinically diagnosed with probable Alzheimer's disease were administered the WAIS–III and the WMS–III. These individuals were identified in a variety of settings, including a geriatric medical clinic, a dementia diagnostic clinic, a memory disorders clinic, and nursing homes. The diagnosis of probable Alzheimer's disease was made in accordance with the guidelines established by the National Institute of Neurological and Communicative Disorders and Stroke (NINCDS) and the Alzheimer's Disease and Related Disorders Association (ADRDA) Work Group (McKhann et al., 1984). See Table 4.31 for the demographic statistics for this sample and Appendix F for the inclusion and exclusion criteria for participation in this study.

As indicated in Table 4.31, the sample had a significantly higher education level than that of the general population (e.g., 48.6% of the sample had completed at least 4 years of college, and an additional 22.9% had completed some post-high-school education).

For the WAIS–III and WMS–III studies, the participants with probable Alzheimer's disease were expected to exhibit decrements in cognitive functioning on the WAIS–III measures as well as impaired memory functioning on the WMS–III indexes. For this sample, it was also anticipated that memory functioning would be more impaired relative to global intellectual functioning. Because education level and intellectual functioning are related, this group was expected to have average premorbid WAIS–III IQ and Index scores higher than those for the general population. Therefore, results must be interpreted in light of these possible effects. Table 4.32 presents the WAIS–III and WMS–III results of this study.

WAIS–III Results

As the data in Table 4.32 show, all of the mean WAIS–III IQ and Index scores for the sample with probable Alzheimer's disease are lower than the mean scores of the general population. Mean IQ scores are 92.2 (VIQ), 81.7 (PIQ), and 86.6 (FSIQ). As expected, the PIQ score is lower than the mean VIQ score because the verbal scores tend to be somewhat more resilient and less sensitive to the effects of this neurologic condition. Again, in view of the high education level of these examinees, even their current mean VIQ level may still represent a 10-point decrement from their premorbid level.

The Index scores show more differentiation of abilities, ranging from 79.6 for the PSI to 93.0 for the VCI. As expected, the POI and PSI scores show the largest decrements of all of the WAIS–III indexes, with scores of 84.8 and 79.6, respectively.

WMS–III Results

Mean scores on the WMS–III memory indexes range from 60.4 for the General Memory Index to 80.4 for the Working Memory Index (see Table 4.32). With the exception of the performance on the Working Memory Index, mean scores on the indexes are clearly impaired (i.e., scores of 70 or below). The percentages of the sample scoring 70 or below on the Immediate Memory Index and General Memory Index are 71% and 89%, respectively. These rates can be contrasted with the percentages of the sample obtaining scores below 70 on the WAIS–III IQ scales: 9% (VIQ), 17% (PIQ), and 9% (FSIQ). As expected, the group performance on the memory indexes is much lower relative to the WAIS–III performance. The WMS–III Auditory Process Composites provide information for various aspects of learning and memory for auditorily presented stimuli. These composites show that as a group the participants with Alzheimer's disease demonstrate *borderline* to *impaired* recall performance after the first presentation of memory stimuli (Single-Trial Learning); show little, if any, improvement with repeated exposure to the stimuli (Learning Slope); and, at delayed recall, have marked difficulty recalling the limited information that was learned in the immediate condition. Performance on the Retrieval Index does not indicate that these individuals have greater access to previously learned information by recognition than by recall. Thus, as expected, the examinees with Alzheimer's disease demonstrated inefficient encoding and impaired storage of new information without prominent retrieval deficits.

Huntington's Disease

Huntington's disease is a relatively rare, genetically transmitted, neuro-degenerative disorder that produces a characteristic form of dementia and eventually results in death (Brandt & Bylsma, 1993; Brandt & Butters, 1986; Martin & Gusella, 1986). The onset of the disorder is characterized by involuntary movements and cognitive impairments that typically appear during the third or fourth decade of life (Brandt & Bylsma, 1993). The neuropathology of Huntington's disease includes loss of cells in the caudate nucleus. Eventually other basal ganglia structures become involved, and cortical atrophy may occur (Brandt & Bylsma, 1993; Martin & Gusella, 1986).

Most individuals with Huntington's disease experience significant declines in cognitive, motor, and personality functioning. Diagnosis of Huntington's disease at an early age is more common than in the case of Alzheimer's disease (Lezak, 1995). Intellectual performance, however, shows a pattern parallel to that of persons with Alzheimer's and Parkinson's diseases, namely, relatively preserved verbal comprehensive abilities coupled with impaired perceptual organizational abilities (Randolph, Mohr, & Chase, 1993). Attention span is thought to diminish (Brandt & Butters, 1986) in proportion to disease progression (Lezak, 1995). Other neuropsychological symptoms include impairments in learning and memory, spatial reasoning, visual–motor skills, and attention/concentration (Brandt & Butters, 1986).

Results of memory studies of individuals with Huntington's disease have indicated that memory deficits occur early in the course of the disease and become more generalized and severe as the disease progresses (Butters, Sax, Montgomery, & Tarlow, 1978) and that retrieval, rather than storage, deficits are predominant in declarative memory procedures (Butters, Wolfe, Martone, Granholm, & Cermak, 1985). Rates of forgetting may not be as rapid as those for persons with Alzheimer's disease but are faster than those of healthy individuals (Tröster et al., 1993). The issue of impaired versus spared recognition compared to persons with Alzheimer's disease has yet to be resolved; studies support both hypotheses (Brandt, 1992). Studies of memory functioning in persons with Huntington's disease based on the WMS and the WMS–R have provided the following findings: increased intrusion errors on Visual Reproduction compared to healthy individuals (Jacobs, Tröster, Butters, Salmon, & Cermak, 1990), impaired performance on Logical Memory and Visual Reproduction on immediate and delayed trials compared to age-matched individuals (Tröster et al., 1993), lower memory quotient scores for those with moderate to severe symptoms of Huntington's disease (Butters et al., 1985), and impaired logical memory in persons in the early and late stages of Huntington's disease but only impaired Visual Reproduction in persons having the disease for 3 years or longer (Butters et al., 1978).

A sample of 15 participants diagnosed with Huntington's disease and selected from various research centers from across the country completed the WAIS–III and the WMS–III. See Table 4.31 for the demographic data for this sample and Appendix F for the inclusion and exclusion criteria for participation in this study.

It was expected that participants with Huntington's disease would exhibit decrements in overall cognitive functioning, with memory performance being lower relative to intellectual ability. The overall education level of the 15 participants in this group was higher than that of the general population, with 40% having 16 or more years of education and another 20% having 13–15 years. It would be expected that this group's performance on the WAIS–III would be higher than that of the general population if not for the presence of Huntington's disease. Performance on the WAIS–III Verbal subtests (e.g., Vocabulary and Information) was expected to be the least impaired, whereas performance on the PSI subtests (Digit Symbol—Coding and Symbol Search) was expected to be the most impaired. Previous research has indicated that visual–spatial processing skills are particularly susceptible to the effects of Huntington's disease. Therefore, it was hypothesized that the participants would show less severe decrements on the WMS–III auditory indexes and that memory deficits would be characterized by poor encoding and retrieval, with relatively spared storage processes.

WAIS–III Results

The WAIS–III mean scores and standard deviations for the sample with Huntington's disease are presented in Table 4.32. As the data show, the mean IQ scores are significantly lower than average, ranging from 78.2 to 90.9. As expected, performance on the PIQ scale (78.2) is more impaired than performance on the VIQ scale (90.9).

On the WAIS–III indexes, the lowest scores were obtained on the PSI (69.3). Additionally, deficits on the POI (84.9) and the WMI (81.7) are pronounced. Also as expected, the mean score on the VCI (98.4) is relatively intact for this sample (although the performance level may be worse than their premorbid functioning).

The mean scores obtained by this sample are nearly identical to those found by Randolph et al. (1993), who found that individuals with Huntington's disease have significant impairment, relative to the general population, in most intellectual functions, excluding verbal comprehensive abilities.

WMS–III Results

As the data in Table 4.32 show, participants with Huntington's disease obtained mean WMS–III Index scores ranging from 70.9 (Immediate Memory Index) to 88.0 (Auditory Recognition Delayed Index). The obtained index scores mildly support the predictions that performance on tasks with visually presented stimuli would be lower than that on tasks with auditorily presented stimuli. The group obtained Single-Trial Learning and Learning Slope composite median percentile scores of 14% and 17%, respectively. The median Retention Composite percentile score (39%) is significantly higher than that obtained by the sample with mild Alzheimer's disease. This pattern of scores suggests that individuals with Huntington's disease exhibit less severe storage problems than does the sample with Alzheimer's disease. Finally, the Retrieval Composite score (65%) suggests significantly more retrieval difficulty than was noted in the sample with Alzheimer's disease. That is, individuals with Huntington's disease are disproportionately aided by a recognition (versus recall) testing format.

Parkinson's Disease

Parkinson's disease is a disease of involuntary movement characterized by resting tremors, reduced initiation of voluntary movements, shuffling gait, plastic rigidity, and impaired posture (Hoehn & Yahr, 1967; for a complete review see Mahurin, Feher, Nance, Levy, & Pirozzolo, 1993). The average age of onset is in the fifth and sixth decades of life (Hoehn & Yahr, 1967). Parkinson's disease is relatively common among individuals aged 60 and older, occurring in approximately 1% of the population (Schoenberg, 1987). No single cause has been identified; rather, multiple pathological processes have been implicated (Mahurin et al., 1993). Neuropathological processes involve loss of cells in the regions of the substantia nigra and reduced dopamine production (Mahurin et al., 1993).

Impairment of intellectual functioning is often seen in individuals diagnosed with Parkinson's disease, although clinical dementia is found less frequently

(J. A. Cooper, Sagar, Jordan, Harvey, & Sullivan, 1991). Verbal comprehensive abilities are generally preserved, whereas perceptual organizational abilities and speed of information processing tend to be relatively impaired (e.g., Randolph et al., 1993). Randolph et al. found that individuals with Parkinson's disease could be differentiated from those with Alzheimer's or Huntington's disease in terms of absolute levels of intelligence. However, those with Parkinson's disease obtained WAIS–R profiles similar to those of the two other groups, namely, preservation of verbal knowledge coupled with relative impairment on Performance subtests. R. G. Brown and Marsden (1986) postulated that the perceptual organizational deficits frequently observed in individuals with Parkinson's disease are secondary to difficulties in set-shifting. J. A. Cooper et al. (1991) reported executive dysfunction in their sample of respondents with Parkinson's disease as suggested by relatively poor sequencing on Picture Arrangement and forward and backward conditions of Digit Span. Motor deficits are frequently observed, although there is some evidence of dissociation between cognition and motor control in the early stages of the disease (J. A. Cooper et al., 1991).

Results of memory studies of individuals with Parkinson's disease have shown impaired memory span, increased intrusions in delayed recall, and impaired recognition memory, with average rates of forgetting (Massman, Delis, Butters, Levin, & Salmon, 1990). Other results have indicated reduced word-list learning in advanced stages of the disease compared to control-group performance but similar to that of individuals with frontal lobe impairment (Daum et al., 1995). Normal performance on WMS–R Logical Memory passages and selective-reminding tasks but impaired list learning on the *California Verbal Learning Test* (CVLT; Delis, Kramer, Kaplan, & Ober, 1987) have been reported (A. E. Taylor, Saint–Cyr, & Lang, 1990). Memory dysfunction has been thought to relate to dysfunction of frontal–striatal neural networks (A. E. Taylor et al., 1990). Studies have shown that performance by individuals with Parkinson's disease on the WMS or the WMS–R is lower than that of control-group participants (J. A. Cooper et al., 1991; Pirozzolo, Hansch, Mortimer, Webster, & Kuskowski, 1982).

A sample of 10 participants diagnosed with idiopathic Parkinson's disease were administered the WAIS–III and the WMS–III. See Table 4.31 for the demographic data for this sample and Appendix F for the inclusion criteria for participation in this study.

On the WAIS–III, impairment was expected to be most pronounced on the POI and PSI tasks, with little or no impairment on the VCI tasks. The participants with Parkinson's disease were also expected to show decrements in performance on the WMS–III indexes. On both the WAIS–III and the WMS–III measures, performance was predicted to be lower than that of the general population but not impaired to the degree observed in individuals with mild Alzheimer's disease.

Direct comparison in these studies between the groups with Alzheimer's and Huntington's disease is difficult because the latter group had significantly lower education levels, which may reflect much lower premorbid general intelligence. Such comparisons, therefore, are beyond the scope of these studies.

WAIS–III Results

The mean score and standard deviations for the WAIS–III IQ scales and indexes of the sample are presented in Table 4.32. The mean WAIS–III IQ scores are 94.6 (VIQ), 82.3 (PIQ), and 88.2 (FSIQ). As expected, the VIQ score is relatively intact, whereas the PIQ score is relatively lower.

On the WAIS–III indexes, the differences between various types of functioning are more pronounced. The lowest scores were obtained on the POI (84.7) and PSI (81.7). The mean score on the WMI is 89.6, which is *average* to *low average*. In contrast to these scores, the mean VCI score is in the *average* range of functioning (96.9).

Taken together, these results suggest that individuals with Parkinson's disease have relatively spared verbal comprehensive abilities coupled with compromised abilities in speed of perceptual processing, visual–spatial organization, and, to some degree, working memory. The findings are consistent with the pattern of IQ scores and with the relative sparing of verbal comprehensive ability reported by Randolph et al. (1993).

WMS–III Results

As the data in Table 4.32 show, the participants with Parkinson's disease obtained mean WMS–III index scores ranging from 80.9 (Visual Delayed Index) to 90.0 (Auditory Recognition Delayed Index). The Index scores were in the same general range as the WAIS–III PIQ and FSIQ scores. Overall, the WMS–III Index scores are just over 1 *SD* lower than the general population mean, but the extent of memory impairment is much less than that observed in the participants with mild Alzheimer's disease. The median Single-Trial Learning and Learning Slope composite percentile scores are 18% and 51%, respectively. These results suggest that although performance on the initial learning trial is lower than average, these individuals demonstrate performance gains over subsequent trials similar to that of nonimpaired individuals. The median Retention Composite percentile score (27%) indicates slightly higher forgetting rates compared to those of a nonimpaired control group.

Traumatic Brain Injury

Traumatic brain injury (TBI) is a neurological condition of relatively high incidence in adolescence and early ad ulthood (Goldst in & Levin, 1990). Head injuries most commonly occur in individuals between birth and 24 years of age (Annegers, Grabow, Kurland, & Laws, 1980; Kraus et al., 1984).

Traumatic brain injury is highly variable in its long-term effects but can be associated with numerous cognitive impairments (Dikmen, Reitan, & Temkin, 1983). The actual functioning that becomes impaired depends on the site and the severity of the damage. The frontal lobes and anterior temporal lobes are particularly vulnerable to contusions, hemorrhages, and hematomas associated with acceleration and deceleration forces of closed head injury (Mattson & Levin, 1990). Frontal lobe damage is associated primarily with executive dysfunction; in severe injuries, the dysfunction can be quite debilitating because the individual experiences greatly impaired flexibility in problem solving or in adaptability (Lezak, 1995). Other neuropathological processes associated with closed head injury include diffuse damage produced by axonal shearing and stretching, which may especially cause reduced speed of information processing (Adams, Graham, Murray, & Scott, 1982).

Mild head injuries are most commonly associated with attentional deficits (Capruso & Levin, 1992; Lezak, 1995; Shum, McFarland, & Bain, 1994). Speeded performance is also likely to be adversely affected (Bawden, Knights, & Winogron, 1985). However, it is memory dysfunction that is the most common cognitive impairment reported after closed head injury (Capruso & Levin, 1992). In cases of moderate closed head injury, symptoms vary widely, and most individuals continue to experience significant impairment 3 months after injury (Lezak, 1995). Dikmen, Machamer, Winn, and Temkin (1995) found significant impairments one year after injury, but this finding was largely a function of the severity of the injury. Cases of impaired memory performance despite normal intellectual functioning have been documented in individuals with severe closed head injury who were more than 2 years posttrauma (Levin, Goldstein, High, & Eisenberg, 1988). The presence of verbal learning deficits 12 months after head injury was best predicted by occurrence of posttraumatic amnesia, duration of posttraumatic amnesia, and subarachnoid hematoma (Haslam et al., 1994). In older adults, head injury has been associated with impairment in language production and visual and verbal memory functioning (Goldstein et al., 1994).

Reid and Kelly (1993) examined WMS–R profiles of individuals who had closed head injuries and found increased forgetting rates on the Logical Memory and Visual Reproduction subtests. Coma severity, as measured by the *Glasgow Coma Scale* (Jennett & Bond, 1975; Teasdale & Jennett, 1974), was unrelated to WMS–R scores; however, duration of posttraumatic amnesia was negatively correlated with performance on the visual memory indexes (Reid & Kelly, 1993). Group performance on the WMS–R indexes varied from *impaired* performance on the delayed recall indexes to *borderline* performance on the Verbal Memory and General Memory indexes to *low average* performance on visual memory and Attention/Concentration indexes. All mean scores were lower than those of the noninjured control group (Reid & Kelly, 1993). Individuals with severe head injury performed more poorly than did control-group individuals on the Logical Memory and Paired Associates learning tasks of the WMS, with duration of posttraumatic amnesia having predicted the degree of memory impairment (Brooks, 1976). Hippocampal atrophy after severe closed head injury, as determined by magnetic resonance imaging volumetric analysis, predicted decreased memory performance on the WMS–R Logical Memory and Visual Reproduction subtests (Bigler et al., 1996).

A sample of 22 adults who had experienced a moderate to severe single closed head injury were administered the WAIS–III and the WMS–III to ascertain the sensitivity of these tests to memory problems associated with this disorder. Participants were selected from various research centers across the country. See Table 4.31 for the demographic data for this sample and Appendix F for inclusion and exclusion criteria for participation in this study.

It was predicted that the most affected WAIS–III subtests would be the speeded Performance subtests (especially those of the PSI) and the subtests composing the WMI. Verbal functioning was not expected to be as impaired, and no modality-specific deficits were anticipated. It was also hypothesized that individuals with closed head injury would show decrements in memory performance on all WMS–III indexes.

WAIS–III Results

Table 4.32 shows the mean scores and standard deviations for the WAIS–III IQ scales and indexes for the sample with traumatic brain injury. As predicted for individuals with moderately severe head injury, the group exhibited some overall impairment (FSIQ = 86.5). The mean PIQ score (84.5) is slightly lower than the mean VIQ score (89.6), but not significantly lower.

On the WAIS–III indexes, the pattern of relative strengths and weaknesses is clearer, with scores ranging from 73.4 to 92.1. As expected, the lowest score was obtained on the PSI (73.4), a score that is significantly lower than the other Index scores. In contrast to this deficit, performance on the POI is relatively intact, with a mean score of 92.1. These results suggest that tasks requiring rapid processing are significantly impaired relative to spatial tasks for which timing is relatively less important. The mean scores on the VCI (89.6) and WMI (89.8) are from *low average* to *average* and are relatively lower than the scores obtained by the general population.

Taken together, these results suggest that individuals with moderate impairment due to traumatic brain injury have global cognitive deficits but with processing speed being predominantly affected.

WMS–III Results

As the data in Table 4.32 show, the participants with closed head injury exhibit an unexpected pattern of memory performance, with mean WMS–III Index scores ranging from 74.3 (Visual Delayed Index) to 93.6 (Auditory Recognition Delayed Index). Although no modality-specific deficits had been predicted, the participants performed more poorly on the visual memory indexes than on the auditory memory indexes. For example, whereas 18% of the sample received a score below 70 on the Auditory Immediate Index, 38% of the sample received a score in the same range on the Visual Immediate Index. The median WMS–III Auditory Process Composite percentile scores range from 29% (Single-Trial Learning) to 50% (Retrieval); thus, these examinees evidenced mildly reduced encoding and storage but average retrieval skills.

D. C. Fisher, Ledbetter, Cohen, Marmor, and Tulsky (2000) compared the WAIS–III and WMS–III score profiles of patients with mild traumatic brain injury, patients with moderate to severe traumatic brain injury, and a matched control group. The authors reported statistically significant score differences for all of the WAIS–III and WMS–III indexes, with the exception of the Auditory Recognition Delayed Index. The largest effect sizes were observed for the Processing Speed, Visual Immediate, and Visual Delayed Memory indexes. On both the WAIS–III and WMS–III, all index scores for the group with moderate to severe injury were significantly lower than those of the control group. For the group with mild injury, the WAIS–III scores did not differ significantly from those of the control group. On the WMS–III, however, this group performed significantly lower than the control group on the Auditory Immediate, Immediate, Auditory Delayed, Visual Delayed, and General Memory indexes. Fisher et al. concluded that the WMS–III measures are more sensitive to the effects of head injury than are the WAIS–III measures even though the largest effect size was observed on WAIS–III PSI.

Donders, Tulsky, and Zhu (2001) compared WAIS–III performance of 100 patients with traumatic brain injury and a matched control group drawn from the WAIS–III standardization sample. The authors found that two of the three new WAIS–III subtests are sensitive to the effects of head injury.

Although the patients with moderate to severe traumatic brain injury performed more poorly than the control group on Letter–Number Sequencing and Symbol Search, Matrix Reasoning did not differentiate the clinical group from the control group. None of the WAIS–III measures differentiated the group with mild head injury from the control group. Performance by the group with moderate injury was more impaired than performance by the group with mild injury on the same variables. The authors tested logistic regression models to determine if WAIS–III performance could differentiate those with mild injury from those with moderate to severe injury. Symbol Search had the largest effect size, and additional variables did not improve the overall model statistics. A cutoff score of 9 was established to differentiate the two clinical groups. The resulting classification table indicated modest classification ability. The WAIS–III tests are sensitive to the effects of traumatic brain injury. Futher research is needed to enable the determination of injury severity based on WAIS–III scores alone (Donders et al., 2001).

Multiple Sclerosis

Multiple sclerosis (MS) is a relatively common neurological disorder of young and middle adulthood (Hauser, 1994). Neuropathological processes include inflammation, scarring, and demyelination of neurons in the central nervous system, producing dysfunction of conductance in these cells (Hauser, 1994). Differentiated according to two patterns of MS symptomatology, individuals with relapsing–remitting MS demonstrated limited cognitive impairment, whereas those with chronic–progressive MS were diffusely impaired but with memory deficits found only in verbal memory (Heaton, Nelson, Thompson, Burks, & Franklin, 1985). White-matter lesions detected by magnetic resonance imaging have been associated with memory dysfunction in individuals with MS (L. Ryan, Clark, Klonoff, Li, & Paty, 1996), with total lesion area the best predictor of neuropsychological impairment (Swirsky–Sacchetti et al., 1992).

Examinations of memory functioning in individuals with MS have indicated impaired performance on prose recall (Goldstein, McKendall, & Haut, 1992; Grigsby, Ayarbe, Kravcisin, & Busenbark, 1994; Litvan, Grafman, Vendrell, & Martinez, 1988) of the WMS and WMS–R but normal recall for important ideas within the stories (Goldstein et al., 1992); lower WMS MQ scores compared to scores of a control group (Litvan et al., 1988; Rao, Hammeke, McQuillen, Khatri, & Lloyd, 1984); and lower scores on WMS Verbal Paired Associates (Maurelli et al., 1992; Rao et al., 1984), Digit Span Forward and Backward (Grigsby et al., 1994; Krupp, Sliwinski, Masur, Friedberg, & Coyle, 1994), Mental Control (Rao et al., 1984), Visual Reproduction (Rao et al., 1984), and List Learning (Maurelli et al., 1992). Other studies failed to find lower performance on measures of verbal memory (Krupp et al., 1994) or

Digit Span (Litvan et al., 1988). J.S. Fisher (1988) reported three patterns of impaired memory functioning on the WMS–R for individuals with MS. One group exhibited significant, global impairment; the second group had intact working memory and mildly impaired memory and learning; and the third group was relatively unimpaired. Performance by the group with MS on all WMS–R indexes was in the *average* range but in the *high average* range for the matched control group. These results suggest loss of functioning, especially in delayed recall, in the group with MS (J. S. Fisher, 1988). No modality-specific deficits were observed in that study (J. S. Fisher, 1988).

A sample of 25 participants were administered the WMS–III. Because of sampling constraints, data for the WAIS–III were not obtained for this group. See Table 4.31 for the demographic data for this sample and Appendix F for the inclusion criteria for participation in this study.

As a group, the individuals with MS were expected to obtain lower scores on the WMS–III indexes than the general population. Furthermore, it was expected that although a small percentage of the sample would obtain Index scores in the *impaired* range, the overall mean scores would be in the *low average* to *average* range.

As shown in Table 4.32, the mean WMS–III Index scores range from 81.5 (Visual Immediate Index) to 97.7 (Auditory Immediate Index) for the sample with MS. From 10% to 30% of the participants scored below 70 on most of the WMS–III indexes except the Working Memory Index and the Auditory Recognition Delayed Index. Contrary to some studies previously cited, individuals in this sample were more likely to perform in the *impaired* range on visual indexes than on the auditory indexes. As a group, the participants with MS exhibited forgetting rates similar to those exhibited by individuals with Huntington's disease, Parkinson's disease, and traumatic brain injury.

Temporal Lobe Epilepsy

Epilepsy is a relatively common neurological disorder, having a lifetime prevalence rate of approximately 2% (McIntosh, 1992). Surgical resection of the epileptogenic foci is one method for the treatment of intractable seizure disorder (Dichter, 1994).

Hippocampal sclerosis was found in 60% of a sample of individuals with treatment-resistant epilepsy and was related to deficits in recall regardless of hemisphere (McMillan, Powell, Janota, & Polkey, 1987). Patients receiving surgical treatment for left temporal lobe epilepsy tend to perform more poorly after surgery than before surgery and in comparison to individuals not receiving treatment (Chelune, Naugle, Lüders, Sedlak, & Awad, 1993).

Attempts to identify material-specific memory deficits in individuals with right versus left temporal lobe epilepsy or after right or left temporal lobectomy have yielded mixed results. The results of some studies have indicated impaired facial memory (Beardsworth & Zaidel, 1994) and impaired spatial memory (M. L. Smith & Milner, 1989) associated with right temporal lobe epilepsy but not with left temporal lobe epilepsy. Research studies based on the WMS or the WMS–R have provided the following findings: Performance on the Logical Memory subtest was more impaired in examinees with left temporal lobe epilepsy than those with right temporal lobe epilepsy and correlated with left hippocampal neuron loss. The WMS–R has been shown to be sensitive to material-specific deficits after left but not right temporal lobectomy (Naugle et al., 1993).

The WMS–III and some subtests from the WAIS–III (Vocabulary, Similarities, Digit Span, Letter–Number Sequencing, Digit Symbol—Coding, Block Design, and Matrix Reasoning) were administered to a sample of 15 participants with left temporal lobe epilepsy and 12 with right temporal lobe epilepsy, all of whom had undergone hippocampectomy for the treatment of intractable seizure disorder. Participants were selected from various clinical centers across the country. See Table 4.31 for the demographic data for this sample and Appendix F for the inclusion criteria for participation in this study.

Although material-specific deficits after right and left temporal lobectomy have not been consistently reported, it was expected that participants who had undergone left temporal lobectomy would obtain lower scores on tasks with auditorily presented material than on tasks with visually presented materials; it was less certain but also of interest whether participants who had undergone right temporal lobectomy would exhibit the opposite pattern. The mean performance of both groups was expected to be lower than the mean performance of the general population.

WAIS–III Results

As predicted, deficits in intellectual functioning were relevant to the site of the lobectomy (see Table 4.33). For the group of examinees who had a left temporal lobectomy, scores on the WAIS–III subtests that measure verbal comprehension skills (Vocabulary and Similarities) are lower than the general population mean (7.5 and 8.1, respectively). Additionally, the standard deviations are also smaller than those for the general population. The group's scores on tasks requiring fluid reasoning and visual processing show no impairment. For the group with left temporal lobectomy, the results are consistent with previous findings. For the individuals with right temporal lobectomy, the scores on the WAIS–III subtests are close to the mean of the general population, ranging from 8.8 to 10.7. These results are consistent with previous research.

However, because both sample sizes were quite small (i.e., 15 and 12), further research is needed to determine if these results are representative.

WMS–III Results

As the data in Table 4.33 show, the participants with left lobectomy obtained mean WMS–III Index scores ranging from 77.3 (General Memory Index) to 95.4 (Working Memory Index). The participants with right lobectomy obtained mean Index scores ranging from 83.5 (Visual Immediate Index) to 97.8 (Working Memory Index). The mean performance for both groups is lower than the general population mean, and the group with left lobectomy generally show a greater degree of memory impairment than does the group with right lobectomy (e.g., General Memory Index scores are 77.3 and 87.6, for the left lobectomy and right lobectomy groups, respectively).

The general trend of lower scores on auditory tasks than on visual tasks by the participants with left lobectomy was exhibited for both the immediate and the delayed conditions. For the participants with right lobectomy, the opposite pattern was observed, with poorer performance on the visually presented tasks than on the auditorily presented tasks. The median percentile scores for the WMS–III Auditory Process Composites also indicate that the group with left lobectomy performed lower than the group with right lobectomy on the Single-Trial Learning, Learning Slope, and Retention composites. The especially poor Retention score suggests a worse storage deficit (i.e., rapid forgetting over delay interval). On the other hand, performance on the Retrieval Composite is relatively higher for the group with left lobectomy than for the group with right lobectomy, so a retrieval deficit appears to be responsible for some of the problems. This pattern suggests that recognition aids retrieval more for the group with left lobectomy than for the group with right lobectomy.

Additional studies of WMS–III performance by patients diagnosed with left or right temporal lobe epilepsy have been conducted. Doss, Chelune, and Naugle (2000) compared the performance on the published version of the WMS–III and performance on the standardization edition. The standardization edition contained more memory subtests than the published version because some subtests were not included in the published version for psychometric reasons. Doss et al. noted that this shortening of the battery might have affected the quality of the normative data by changing the time between immediate and delayed recall conditions, changing potential interference factors due to the reordering of the test sequences and changing fatigue factors (particularly on Letter–Number Sequencing). For this study, the patients receiving the standardization protocol were those respondents originally documented in the *WAIS–III—WMS–III Technical Manual*. For the comparative sample, the authors administered the published battery to an additional 30 patients. The results indicated no statistically significant differences in performance between the patients receiving the published battery and those receiving the standardization battery. Also, the authors noted that respondents with right temporal lobe epilepsy performed better on auditory measures than on visual memory measures and that respondents with left temporal lobe epilepsy performed better on visual memory measures than on auditory measures. These results confirm the results of the original study (The Psychological Corporation, 1997).

Table 4.33. WAIS–III and WMS–III Performance of Samples With Temporal Lobe Epilepsy

	Left Lobectomy		Right Lobectomy	
	Mean	SD	Mean	SD
WAIS–III Subtests				
Vocabulary	7.5	1.7	8.8	2.1
Similarities	8.1	1.8	10.3	2.4
Digit Span	8.5	2.5	10.5	2.6
Letter–Number Sequencing	9.1	3.4	9.6	3.2
Digit Symbol—Coding	9.4	2.0	9.8	3.0
Block Design	10.4	2.8	10.2	3.2
Matrix Reasoning	10.2	2.5	10.7	3.3
WMS–III Primary Indexes				
Auditory Immediate	77.9	16.3	95.0	11.3
Visual Immediate	86.5	15.4	83.5	9.1
Immediate Memory	78.1	16.2	87.2	10.7
Auditory Delayed	75.4	14.5	93.5	11.9
Visual Delayed	85.3	16.5	84.3	11.7
Auditory Recognition Delayed	83.0	18.5	92.1	15.7
General Memory	77.3	15.1	87.6	12.7
Working Memory	95.4	15.6	97.8	12.9
Auditory Process Composites	Median %ile	%ile Range	Median %ile	%ile Range
Single-Trial Learning	21%	1%–44%	36%	14%–87%
Learning Slope	11%	1%–95%	39%	1%–74%
Retention	2%	1%–39%	36%	1%–95%
Retrieval	65%	11%–99%	42%	5%–78%
N	15		12	

Wilde et al. (2001) further explored the utility of WMS–III profiles in differentiating respondents with right versus left temporal lobe epilepsy. The results of this study confirmed findings from previous studies, specifically better auditory versus visual memory in patients with right temporal lobe epilepsy and the opposite pattern for patients with left temporal lobe epilepsy. Wilde et al. also found that these effects were stronger for delayed versus immediate memory measures. The application of these score differences did not consistently classify patients accurately as belonging to the right or left temporal lobe epilepsy group. The authors concluded that the WMS–III may not be useful in identifying location (right versus left) of seizure foci prior to surgery but may be useful in establishing baseline information for assessment of change after surgery and identification of those at risk for impairment subsequent to surgery (Wilde et al., 2001).

Assessment of Alcohol-Related Disorders

The study of patients with Korsakoff's syndrome is particularly important in establishing the divergent cognitive processes tapped by the WAIS–III and WMS–III. For the following studies involving individuals with alcohol-related disorders, the performance data for the WAIS–III and the WMS–III are presented in Table 4.34.

Table 4.34. WAIS–III and WMS–III Performance of Samples With Alcohol-Related Disorders

	Chronic Alcohol Abuse		Korsakoff's Syndrome	
	Mean	SD	Mean	SD
WAIS–III Scales/Indexes				
VIQ	108.6	12.7	94.5	10.3
PIQ	101.2	14.5	92.2	17.7
FSIQ	106.1	13.5	92.8	13.6
VCI	109.0	11.4	92.7	9.3
POI	102.0	14.0	96.9	15.4
WMI	104.6	12.3	98.4	15.5
PSI	97.7	12.5	88.2	19.3
WMS–III Primary Indexes				
Auditory Immediate	108.0	15.4	73.1	7.8
Visual Immediate	96.0	14.5	67.8	6.8
Immediate Memory	102.5	16.5	64.4	8.2
Auditory Delayed	107.3	15.5	63.5	5.3
Visual Delayed	97.9	13.5	65.4	8.3
Auditory Recognition Delayed	109.6	13.0	64.5	8.0
General Memory	105.2	14.2	57.8	6.7
Working Memory	98.0	9.3	97.8	13.0
Auditory Process Composites	Median %ile	%ile Range	Median %ile	%ile Range
Single-Trial Learning	75%	9%–99%	12%	3%–36%
Learning Slope	52%	1%–95%	3%	1%–34%
Retention	59%	4%–98%	1%	1%–4%
Retrieval	50%	11%–97%	28%	5%–78%
N	28		10	

Chronic Alcohol Abuse

Several essential and associated features characterize alcoholism (American Psychiatric Association, 1994). Alcohol abuse consists of a "maladaptive pattern of [alcohol] use manifested by recurrent and significant adverse consequences related to the repeated use of [alcohol]" (American Psychiatric Association, 1994, p. 182). In addition to maladaptive behaviors, a growing body of research has documented cognitive dysfunction in those who abuse alcohol but who do not have Korsakoff's syndrome.

The neuropsychological effects of chronic alcoholism are unclear. First, there seem to be etiological differences in the causes of alcoholism, different features that are associated with alcoholism, and different risk factors in predicting alcoholism. Some investigators have classified individuals with alcoholism into different types (e.g., Bohman, Cloninger, Sigvardsson, & von Knorring, 1987), with each type associated with differential patterns of intellectual and memory deficits. Others have reported the degree of variability in the neuropsychological effects of chronic alcoholism (Rourke & Løberg, 1996). Still other research has suggested that there may be premorbid cognitive deficits in those who abuse alcohol that may be expressed in increased rates of learning disabilities in their histories (see Rhodes & Jasinski, 1990) or in the higher rates of neuropsychological impairment in individuals at high risk for becoming a substance abuser (see Tarter, Hegedus, Goldstein, Shelly, & Alterman, 1984). The most important variable contributing to the mixed results might be the variety of risk factors that must be accounted for in studies of the relation between cognitive functioning and alcoholism. For instance, these risk factors may include moderator variables such as the tendency toward antisocial personality (e.g., Malloy, Noel, Rogers, Longabaugh, & Beattie, 1989; Schuckit, Smith, Anthenelli, & Irwin, 1993), the number of years of alcohol consumption (C. Ryan & Butters, 1983; Tarter, 1973), and age (Jones & Parsons, 1971; Malloy et al., 1989; Parsons & Farr, 1981; C. Ryan & Butters, 1980). The last factor to be controlled in any study is the length of time since the individual has stopped consuming alcohol. Often, the neuropsychological effects tend to "recover" over time (Ellenberg, Rosenbaum, Goldman, & Whitman, 1980; Ellis & Oscar–Berman, 1989; Glenn & Parsons, 1990) so that the individual tends to return much closer to his or her baseline functioning. Additionally, the number of times the individual has returned to a pattern of alcohol abuse and then stopped the abuse may also be a salient variable in the equation (Glenn, Parsons, Sinha, & Stevens, 1988).

In view of the variables that might play a part in the effects of persistent chronic alcoholism on cognitive functioning, it is not surprising that the results from different studies yield inconsistent patterns. Indeed, some studies of the intellectual functioning of chronic alcohol abusers have indicated average or slightly higher levels of ability (Bowden, Whelan, Long, & Clifford, 1995; Eckardt et al., 1996; Oscar–Berman, Clancy, & Weber, 1993), whereas other studies showed mildly impaired performance (e.g., Rhodes & Jasinski, 1990). The reported intellectual deficits have tended to fall into three domains (Malloy et al., 1989): abstract reasoning, learning and memory, and visual–spatial ability. On the WAIS–R, subtests that may be differentially affected are Block Design, Digit Symbol, and Object Assembly (Ellis & Oscar–Berman, 1989; O'Mahony & Doherty, 1993; Parsons & Farr, 1981). Additionally, Verbal subtests measuring crystallized intelligence (e.g., Vocabulary, Information, and Similarities) are not typically affected by chronic alcoholism (Ellis & Oscar–Berman, 1989; O'Mahony & Doherty, 1993; Rourke & Løberg, 1996; Tamkin & Dolenz, 1990).

The results of studies of alcohol abusers after detoxification have shown impairment on the Logical Memory and Visual Reproduction subtests of the WMS and the WMS–R (O'Mahony & Doherty, 1993, 1996). Using the WMS–R, J. J. Ryan and Lewis (1988) studied memory functioning of alcohol abusers 2–6 weeks after detoxification. Compared to the control participants, the alcohol abusers performed more poorly on all WMS–R indexes and especially on the Digit Span, Logical Memory, and Visual Reproduction subtests (J. J. Ryan & Lewis, 1988). The level of performance of the alcohol abusers was in the *low average* to *average* ranges across indexes, with performance only on the Visual Memory Index in the *low average* range (J. J. Ryan & Lewis, 1988). The observed deficits in memory functioning may be a transient phenomenon. Ellenberg et al. (1980) reported verbal and visual–spatial memory impairment in alcohol abusers within 2 days of detoxification. However, verbal memory deficits remitted quickly, and only a few older, chronic alcohol abusers sustained visual–spatial memory deficits longer than 25 days (Ellenberg et al., 1980). Long-term abstinence has been associated with normal neurocognitive functioning (Reed, Grant, & Rourke, 1992). Although mammillary body shrinkage was found in chronic alcohol abusers without Korsakoff's syndrome, this group did not display poorer memory performance compared to a matched control group (Davila, Shear, Lane, Sullivan, & Pfefferbaum, 1994). Memory impairment may occur only in a subset of chronic alcohol abusers who also have cirrhosis of the liver (Arria et al., 1991) or in those with comorbid antisocial personality disorder (Malloy et al., 1989).

A sample of 28 participants with alcoholism who had recently undergone detoxification and who did not meet diagnostic criteria for Korsakoff's syndrome were administered the WAIS–III and the WMS–III to determine the sensitivity of these tests to cognitive dysfunction and memory in this group. See Table 4.31 for the demographic data for this sample and Appendix F for the inclusion criteria for participation in this study.

The participants with alcoholism were predicted to show variable performance, with their mean level of performance in the *low average* to *average* ranges. Further, their performance on the visual memory indexes was expected to be relatively lower than that on the auditory memory indexes. For the WAIS–III, the PIQ score was expected to be somewhat lower relative to the VIQ score (because of lower scores on the Block Design and Digit Symbol—Coding subtests). However, because the Digit Symbol—Coding and Block Design subtests might be related to speed of information processing, the group's scores on the POI and PSI were predicted to be the lowest of all the WAIS–III Index scores.

WAIS–III Results

The results obtained in the study (see Table 4.34) indicate that all the scores on the WAIS–III obtained by the individuals who had been diagnosed with chronic alcoholism are in the *average* range of functioning. Relative to their Verbal scores, the group's WAIS–III PIQ, POI, and PSI scores are slightly lower, a pattern that was predicted. The PIQ and POI scores are about 0.5 *SD*s below the VIQ and VCI scores. However, the PSI score is significantly lower (about 1 *SD*) than the Verbal scores. The results of this study suggest only very subtle, if any, deficits, but this pattern is in the same direction as those found in previous studies.

WMS–III Results

As the data in Table 4.34 show, the mean performance of this sample on the WMS–III indexes range from 96.0 (Visual Immediate Index) to 109.6 (Auditory Recognition Delayed Index). As expected, the mean performance on all of the indexes is in the *average* range. Also as expected, mean performance on the auditory indexes is relatively higher than mean performance on the visual indexes, although scores on the visual indexes are in the *average* range. Only 7.1% of the sample (i.e., 2 participants) received an Index score below 70, and this occurred on the Visual Immediate Index. This group's performance on the WMS–III is consistent with results reported in the literature.

Korsakoff's Syndrome

Korsakoff's syndrome is a neurological disorder associated with chronic alcoholism, resulting in transient and long-term cognitive deficits (Salmon, Butters, & Heindel, 1993). Acute disturbances in ocular movement, gait, and orientation are reversible with proper treatment. Nutritional deficiencies are believed to be responsible for the development of Korsakoff's syndrome. Long-term cognitive problems may include executive dysfunction, apathy, severe anterograde amnesia, and retrograde amnesia, with relatively intact working memory and overall intellectual functioning (Salmon et al., 1993).

The results of memory studies have indicated that individuals with Korsakoff's syndrome exhibit global impairment in memory compared to individuals with temporal lobe epilepsy and those with non-Korsakoff's alcoholism who may exhibit material- or modality-specific deficits despite average verbal intellectual functioning (Cutting, 1978). Shimamura and Squire (1984) reported impaired associative learning in individuals with Korsakoff's syndrome compared to those with chronic alcoholism in nonpriming conditions. Butters et al. (1988) reported that, on the WMS–R, persons with Korsakoff's syndrome exhibited impaired performance on the Verbal, General, and Delayed Recall indexes, although visual memory was in the *borderline* range and the mean Attention/Concentration Index was *average*.

A sample of 10 participants diagnosed with Korsakoff's syndrome were administered the WAIS–III and the WMS–III to assess the sensitivity of these tests to this amnesic disorder. See Table 4.31 for the demographic data for this sample and Appendix F for the inclusion criteria for participation in this study.

In previous research (e.g., Butters & Cermack, 1980), dramatic differences between scores on intellectual tests and memory tests have been reported for individuals with Korsakoff's syndrome. Therefore, such differences were expected for this study as well. The participants with Korsakoff's syndrome were expected to exhibit relatively intact WAIS–III scores but show *impaired* performance on all of the WMS–III memory indexes, except the Working Memory Index. The level of impairment on these memory indexes was expected to be similar to that of individuals with Alzheimer's disease.

WAIS–III Results

Table 4.34 presents the WAIS–III mean performance data for individuals with Korsakoff's syndrome. As predicted, the WAIS–III scores obtained by these individuals are relatively intact. The mean IQ scores range from 92.2 (PIQ to 94.5 (VIQ). Only the mean PSI score is slightly lower (88.2) but not significantly.

WMS–III Results

Table 4.34 presents the WMS–III mean performance data for the participants with Korsakoff's syndrome. As expected, mean performance on the WMS–III Working Memory Index is in the *average* range (97.8), and mean scores on the other indexes range from 57.8 (General Memory Index) to 73.1 (Auditory Immediate Index). The range of scores on the General Memory Index for the individuals in this sample was 45–66, indicating consistently, severely impaired memory performance. The WMS–III Auditory Process Composites also show a pattern of *impaired* performance for this group. The Single-Trial

Learning Composite median percentile score (12%) shows an overall reduced ability to learn from a single-trial exposure to auditory stimuli. The median Learning Slope Composite percentile score (3%) suggests that these individuals benefit little from repeated exposure to the material to be learned. Also, the material that is learned is quickly forgotten from immediate to delayed conditions, as indicated by the Retention Composite median percentile score of 1%. Finally, the Retrieval Composite percentile score (28%) reveals that these participants were not aided by the recognition format. Their results suggest severely impaired encoding and storage with relatively normal attention, working memory, and retrieval.

Assessment of Neuropsychiatric Disorders— Schizophrenia

For the study involving individuals with schizophrenia, the performance data for the WAIS–III and the WMS–III are presented in Table 4.35.

Table 4.35. WAIS–III and WMS–III Performance of Samples With Schizophrenia

	Mean	SD
WAIS–III Scales/Indexes		
VIQ	88.9	15.2
PIQ	86.2	12.9
FSIQ	86.8	14.8
VCI	93.3	16.4
POI	89.6	13.9
WMI	85.0	15.1
PSI	83.4	11.8
WMS–III Primary Indexes		
Auditory Immediate	83.3	15.6
Visual Immediate	82.3	14.3
Immediate Memory	79.1	15.7
Auditory Delayed	84.4	15.9
Visual Delayed	79.3	14.8
Auditory Recognition Delayed	86.1	14.9
General Memory	79.7	15.8
Working Memory	85.6	13.9
Auditory Process Composites	Median %ile	%ile Range
Single–Trial Learning	9%	1%–96%
Learning Slope	34%	1%–95%
Retention	19%	1%–95%
Retrieval	50%	2%–88%
N	42	

Schizophrenia is a chronic, severe neuropsychiatric disorder characterized by "positive" symptoms, such as hallucinations, delusions, and thought disorders, and by "negative" symptoms, such as alogia, anhedonia, avolition, and flattening of affect (American Psychiatric Association, 1994; Andreasen & Carpenter, 1993). Schizophrenia is a relatively common disorder, having a lifetime prevalence of 0.5%–1% (Andreasen & Carpenter, 1993). Although the causes of schizophrenia remain unknown, the illness is reliably associated with abnormalities of brain structure and physiology as demonstrated by neuroimaging studies (R. E. Gur et al., 1991; Shapiro, 1993). Dysfunction of the temporal–hippocampal region (Arnold, Hyman, Van Hoesen, & Damasio, 1991; Conrad, Abebe, Austin, Forsythe, & Scheibel, 1991) and the frontal cortex (Goldberg, Weinberger, Berman, Pliskin, & Podd, 1987; Seidman et al., 1994; Weinberger, Berman, & Zec, 1986) have been implicated in schizophrenia (Gold et al., 1994; Seidman et al., 1994).

The types of cognitive deficits occurring with schizophrenia are wide ranging. Early work on schizophrenia demonstrated disrupted attention and slowed reaction time (Shakow, 1963). Heaton and Crowley (1981) observed poor performance on a series of tests measuring general intellectual functioning and concluded that individuals with schizophrenia perform at levels characteristic of someone with gross neurological damage. Individuals with chronic schizophrenia have shown deficits in several areas, including abstract reasoning, word fluency, sequential memory, cognitive set-shifting, and attention (Dickerson, Ringel, & Boronow, 1991; Gold et al., 1994; Seidman et al., 1994). Other research has also suggested that these individuals perform poorly on tasks requiring working memory (Gold, Carpenter, Randolph, Goldberg, & Weinberger, 1997).

Although memory dysfunction is not considered a diagnostic criteria of schizophrenia, results of neuropsychological studies have demonstrated significant impairment in memory functioning, especially verbal memory functioning (Saykin et al., 1991). This pattern of deficits has been reported in individuals with first-episode schizophrenia as well as for individuals with chronic schizophrenia (Saykin et al., 1994). This finding suggests that the deficit is not the product of exposure to neuroleptics. Other researchers have reported deficits in visual–spatial memory (Hoff, Riordan, O'Donnell, Morris, & DeLisi, 1992) and in memory for spatial context (Rizzo, Danion, Van Der Linden, Grange, & Rohmer, 1996). Although schizophrenia is a chronic disorder, the severity of neuropsychological deficits, including memory dysfunction, does not appear to be progressive, as it is in dementia (Heaton et al., 1994). It has been suggested that verbal learning deficits associated with schizophrenia appear to be related to difficulties in encoding and retrieving information without significant storage (rapid forgetting) problems (Paulsen et al., 1995).

The results of studies based on the WMS and the WMS–R have indicated impaired or reduced performance on the Logical Memory, Verbal Paired Associates, and Visual Reproduction subtests (Hoff et al., 1992; Saykin et al., 1991).

For the present study, a sample of 42 participants with schizophrenia were administered the WAIS–III and the WMS–III to determine the sensitivity of these tests to individuals diagnosed with schizophrenia. See Table 4.31 for the demographic characteristics of this sample and Appendix F for the inclusion criteria for participation in this study.

It was hypothesized that the participants with schizophrenia would perform in the *low average* to *average* range of functioning on the WAIS–III measures that reflect general intellectual functioning. However, more pronounced deficits and, thus, relatively lower scores would be found on the measures related to working memory and processing speed. Furthermore, these individuals were expected to perform more poorly on all of the WMS–III indexes compared to the general population, with no modality-specific deficits expected.

WAIS–III Results

Table 4.35 presents the WAIS–III mean performance data for the individuals with schizophrenia. As predicted, the WAIS–III mean IQ scores obtained by these individuals are in the *low average* range (86.2–88.9), indicating that these individuals have a relative decrement in functioning compared to the general population. The mean performance on the Index scores match the predictions that had been made. The group's mean scores on the VCI and POI are relatively (though slightly) higher (93.3 and 89.6, respectively) than those on the WMI (85.0) and PSI (83.4). These results support the premise that individuals with schizophrenia will show impairments on tasks requiring attention, processing speed, and working memory.

WMS–III Results

As the data in Table 4.35 show, the mean performance on the WMS–III Primary Indexes ranges from 79.1 (Immediate Memory Index) to 86.1 (Auditory Recognition Delayed Index). The participants with schizophrenia performed in the *low average* to *borderline* ranges on every Primary index. The results do not indicate any trends with regard to auditory or visual modality-specific deficits. These results do indicate that the WMS–III is sensitive to memory deficits observed in previous studies of individuals with schizophrenia. Hawkins (1999) reported that the data provided in the *WAIS–III—WMS–III Technical Manual* (The Psychological Corporation, 1997) suggest mild deficits in new learning, with memory performance similar to intellectual ability, in most cases.

Evidence Based on Relationships With Other Variables

WAIS–III Correlations With Selected External Measures

Table 4.36 provides the demographic data and the sizes of the samples on which the WAIS–III comparison studies were based. The data are presented as mean age and the percentages of each sample by sex, race/ethnicity, and education level. The samples are ordered by groups according to the type of external measure (e.g., cognitive ability). The table also includes the percentages of each sample by clinical diagnostic group because the clinical diagnoses of the participants might have affected the correlational results.

Measures of Academic Achievement

The WIAT–II is the most recent revision of the WIAT. The WIAT–II measures reading, math, writing, and language skills in youth and adults. The expanded normative data set includes norms for ages 4–89 and facilitates the assessment of academic skills through adulthood. The WAIS–III linking sample had the following demographic composition for adolescents: By sex, the sample was 52.9% female and 47.1% male; by race/ethnicity, 66.3% White, 10.6% African American, 18.3% Hispanic, and 4.8% Asian. By parent education level, the sample was 19.2% ≤12 years, 35.6% high school or equivalent, 28.3% some college, and 16.3% college. By geographic region, the sample had the following composition: 35.6% South, 26%. West, 21.2% North Central, and 17.3% Northeast. For college students, the sample was 51.1% female and 48.9% male; by race/ethnicity, 66% White, 15.7% African American, 8.6% Hispanic, and 8.2% Asian. The adult sample was 58% female and 42% male; by race/ethnicity, 72% White, 12% African American, 7% Hispanic, and 2% Asian; by education level, 10% ≤12 years, 40% high school or equivalent, 25% some college, and 15% college; and by geographic region, 54% South, 22% West, 19% North Central, and 5% Northeast.

Table 4.37 presents correlations between WAIS–III FSIQ, VIQ, and PIQ with WIAT–II subtest and composite scores for three groups: 17–19 year-olds, college students, and adults. For the 17–19 year-old group, high positive correlations were observed between the VIQ and FSIQ and most of the WIAT–II composite scores. The PIQ had a moderate correlation with reading and high correlations with math and language skills. For college students, the correlation between academic performance and intellectual ability was not as large, a finding likely due to the homogeneity of the group and resulting restriction

157

Table 4.36. Demographic Data of the Samples for the WAIS–III/External Measures Comparison Studies

	Cognitive Ability						Attention		Memory			
	WAIS-R	WISC-R	SPM	MicroCog	DRS	WMS-R	Trail-Making Test	MicroCog	WMS-R	CVLT	Rey-O	MicroCog
N	88	24	22	16	74	55	56	16	31	19	24	16
Age												
Mean	48.6	18.3	35.7	44.7	58.8	43.1	52.1	44.7	52.6	59.5	54.6	44.7
SD	20.5	4.6	5.0	20.0	14.8	15.9	19.0	20.0	13.8	15.4	17.8	20.0
Sex												
Female	37.5	37.5	22.7	23.5	28.4	36.4	46.4	23.5	12.9	36.8	37.5	23.5
Male	62.5	62.5	77.3	76.5	71.6	63.6	53.6	76.5	87.1	63.2	62.5	76.5
Race/Ethnicity												
White	94.4	75.0	77.3	100.0	90.5	87.3	92.8	100.0	96.8	89.4	100.0	100.0
African American	4.5		22.7		8.1	10.9	5.4		3.2	5.3		
Hispanic	1.1	20.8			1.4	1.8	1.8			5.3		
Other		4.2										
Education												
≤8	8.0	4.2	9.1	5.9	8.1	7.3	3.6	5.9	12.9		12.5	5.9
9–11	5.7	83.3	4.5	53.0	2.7	10.9	3.6	53.0	9.7		4.2	53.0
12	38.6	4.2	22.7	23.5	32.4	25.5	35.6	23.5	29.0	47.4	33.3	23.5
13–15	30.7	8.3	31.8	17.6	24.3	41.8	30.4	17.6	35.5	15.8	25.0	17.6
≥16	17.0		31.9		32.5	14.5	26.8		12.9	36.8	25.0	
Diagnostic Group												
AD (Mild)	16.1			23.5	29.6		26.6	23.5		21.1	16.7	23.5
AD (Moderate)	4.5				4.1		3.6			5.3	4.2	
Traumatic Brain Injury	6.8					5.5	10.7		6.5		12.5	
Depression				5.9	2.7	23.6		5.9			4.2	5.9
Lobectomy–Left						1.8						
Lobectomy–Unspec.						16.4						
Lobectomy–Right	4.5					25.4	5.4					
Chronic Alcoholism	9.1			17.6	27.0	1.8		17.6	42.0	42.0		17.6
Huntington's Disease	11.4			11.8	20.3	16.4	17.9	11.8	3.2		33.2	11.8
Korsakoff's	10.2				1.4				29.0		29.2	
ADHD	6.8	8.0										
LD–Math	4.5	42.1										
LD–Reading	3.4	33.3										
MR (Mild)		8.3										
MR (Moderate)		8.3										
Parkinson's Disease	10.2			17.6	13.5			17.6				17.6
Schizophrenia			100.0	23.6			17.9	23.6	3.2	31.6		23.6
Stroke Right							1.8					
Stroke Left												
Neurotoxin Exposure	12.5				1.4	9.1	16.1		16.1			

Table 4.36. Demographic Data of the Samples for the WAIS–III/External Measures Comparison Studies *(continued)*

	Language				Fine Motor Speed and Dexterity				Spatial Processing			Executive Functioning
	BNT	Controlled Word Association Test	Category Naming Test	Token Test	Finger-Tapping Test	Grooved Pegboard	MicroCog	MicroCog	MicroCog	JOLO	Rey–O	WCST
N	103	51	16	27	22	21	16	16	16	28	27	21
Age												
Mean	54.3	65.6	54.4	68.1	44.8	35.7	44.7	44.7	44.7	55.4	53.0	65.2
SD	19.7	15.2	15.2	10.7	19.1	11.5	20.0	20.0	20.0	19.5	17.8	13.8
Sex												
Female	49.5	37.3	56.2	25.9	68.2	71.4	23.5	23.5	23.5	21.4	40.7	14.3
Male	50.5	62.7	43.8	74.1	31.8	28.6	76.5	76.5	76.5	78.6	59.3	85.7
Race/Ethnicity												
White	89.3	90.1	87.4	81.5	95.5	90.5	100.0	100.0	100.0	82.1	100.0	85.7
African American	7.8	5.9	6.3	14.8	4.5	9.5				17.9		9.5
Hispanic	1.9	2.0	6.3	3.7								4.8
Other	1.0	2.0										
Education												
≤8	5.8	7.8	6.3	11.1			5.9	5.9	5.9	3.6	11.1	4.8
9–11	6.8	5.9		7.4	4.5	9.5				3.6	3.7	4.8
12	32.1	33.3	43.6	37.0	36.4	52.4	53.0	53.0	53.0	35.6	29.6	52.3
13–15	29.1	19.6	18.8	7.4	36.4	28.6	23.5	23.5	23.5	28.6	33.4	4.8
≥16	26.2	33.4	31.3	37.1	22.7	9.5	17.6	17.6	17.6	28.6	22.2	33.3
Diagnostic Group												
AD (Mild)	30.0	52.9	18.8	51.9	13.6		23.5	23.5	23.5	32.2	14.8	33.3
AD (Moderate)	5.8	9.8		11.1	9.1					3.6	3.7	9.5
Traumatic Brain Injury					9.1						11.1	
Depression						9.5	5.9	5.9	5.9	7.1	3.7	
Lobectomy–Left	14.6				9.1	38.1						
Lobectomy–Unspec.	1.0											
Lobectomy–Right	11.7	5.9		3.7	18.2	19.0				17.9		
Chronic Alcoholism	1.9	5.9					17.6	17.6	17.6			
Huntington's Disease	9.7		62.4		4.5		11.8	11.8	11.8		33.4	
Korsakoff's	7.8	2.0			4.5	4.8					25.9	
ADHD							17.6	17.6	17.6			
LD–Math												
LD–Reading												
MR (Mild)												
MR (Moderate)												
Parkinson's Disease	8.7	19.6	18.8	33.3						32.1		47.7
Schizophrenia						4.8	23.6	23.6	23.6	7.1		9.5
Stroke Right												
Stroke Left	1.0											
Neurotoxin Exposure	7.8	3.9			31.9	23.8						

Note. Except for sample size (*N*) and age, data are reported as percentages.

of range. The FSIQ and VIQ had moderate to high positive correlations whereas the PIQ had low to moderate correlations with WIAT–II composite scores. For the adult sample, the FSIQ and VIQ had high correlations with reading and math and moderate correlations with writing and language skills. The PIQ was highly correlated with reading in the adult group. Moderate associations between the PIQ and the other WIAT–II composite scores were observed in the adult group. In general, the correlation between specific WIAT–II subtest scores and IQ scores were lower than the correlations between the WIAT–II composite scores and WAIS–III IQ scores.

The results provide support for the use of the WAIS–III as a predictor of academic functioning. The results lend support for the use of a discrepancy model of IQ compared to achievement based on the WAIS–III and WIAT–II. The correlation between the WAIS–III and the WIAT–II is similar in degree to that reported for the WAIS–III and the WIAT. Clinicians should expect more variability between IQ level and individual WIAT–II subtest performance than is observed for the composite scores. College students may display more variability in IQ–achievement discrepancies compared to adults in general and high-school students (a discussion of discrepancy analysis methodology is discussed in Chapter 5).

Measures of Cognitive Ability

Correlations between the WAIS–III and the other measures of cognitive ability are presented in Table 4.38. The external measures were the IQ scores of the WAIS–R and the WISC–R, the total score of the SPM (Raven, 1976), the Information Processing Accuracy Index of the *MicroCog: Assessment of Cognitive Functioning* (Powell et al., 1993), and the total score of the *Dementia Rating Scale* (DRS; Mattis, 1988). The mean WAIS–III FSIQ scores for the WAIS–R, WISC–R, SPM, MicroCog, and DRS samples were 93.5 (SD = 13.5), 90.8 (SD = 18.1), 93.8 (SD = 16.4), 94.3 (SD = 13.7), and 90.9 (SD = 15.8), respectively.

As the data in Table 4.38 show, the correlations between the WAIS–III IQ and Index scores and the external measures (except between the WAIS–III VCI and the MicroCog) are moderate to high, ranging from .50 to .91. The correlations between the WAIS–III and the WAIS–R range from .50 to .85. The correlations between these two versions are highest when similar scales are compared. The correlation between the WAIS–III VIQ and WAIS–R VIQ is .85, between the PIQ scores, .82, and between the FSIQ scores, .84. Significant, but relatively lower, correlations occur between the WAIS–III VIQ and WAIS–R PIQ scores (.66) and between the WAIS–III PIQ and WAIS–R VIQ scores (.54). The pattern of these correlations, though slightly lower in magnitude than those reported in Table 4.18 for the nonclinical population, provides evidence of convergent and discriminant validity of the WAIS–III.

Table 4.37. Intercorrelations of the WAIS–III IQ Scores and the WIAT–II Subtest and Composite Standard Scores

WAIS–III	WIAT–II Subtests									WIAT–II Composites				
	Word Reading	Numerical Operations	Reading Comprehension	Spelling	Pseudoword Decoding	Math Reasoning	Written Expression	Listening Comprehension	Oral Expression	Reading	Mathematics	Written Language	Oral Language	Total
Ages 17–19 (High School)														
FSIQ	.68	.73	.73	.70	.52	.82	.65	.80	.50	.77	.82	.72	.81	.88
VIQ	.70	.69	.75	.65	.53	.74	.60	.82	.46	.78	.75	.67	.78	.85
PIQ	.47	.64	.51	.60	.40	.76	.61	.58	.50	.57	.75	.66	.71	.79
Mean	99.33	98.51	99.16	99.81	100.46	98.61	98.62	100.03	99.20	99.36	98.40	98.65	98.94	100.40
SD	14.82	16.72	16.40	14.92	14.13	16.87	16.51	15.03	14.48	14.76	17.95	16.70	13.61	15.07
College Students														
FSIQ	.48	.57	.56	.43	.45	.67	.41	.65	.40	.63	.70	.46	.62	.71
VIQ	.52	.50	.55	.45	.47	.62	.38	.66	.34	.66	.64	.44	.61	.68
PIQ	.32	.55	.45	.30	.29	.59	.38	.48	.39	.42	.63	.39	.51	.55
Mean	107.93	112.73	106.45	110.11	102.76	109.36	110.00	106.84	104.40	105.49	112.36	111.51	106.44	109.26
SD	9.61	11.05	10.60	10.75	12.48	10.94	12.64	11.71	13.63	11.02	12.62	14.91	12.76	11.87
Adults														
FSIQ	.66	.82	.76	.66	.69	.78	.62	.73	.49	.86	.82	.63	.67	.86
VIQ	.62	.79	.73	.67	.62	.76	.60	.68	.46	.84	.80	.62	.65	.85
PIQ	.57	.67	.63	.51	.67	.65	.54	.64	.44	.77	.68	.51	.57	.72
Mean	99.40	100.26	97.80	100.59	104.58	100.50	102.16	99.85	98.24	100.08	100.71	101.33	98.31	101.61
SD	12.38	16.27	16.82	13.09	10.44	15.06	14.75	14.18	13.19	12.71	16.27	14.90	12.84	14.19

161

Table 4.38. Correlations Between the WAIS–III and Other Measures of Cognitive Ability

	WAIS–R					WISC–R						SPM		MicroCog Information Processing Accuracy	MicroCog			DRS	
	VIQ	PIQ	FSIQ	Mean	SD	VIQ	PIQ	FSIQ	Mean	SD	TS	Mean	SD		Mean	SD	TS	Mean	SD
WAIS–III																			
VIQ	.85	.66	.83	96.7	11.8	.90	.81	.88	90.7	17.0	.78	97.5	16.2	.59	98.9	13.3	.59	96.4	14.7
PIQ	.54	.82	.73	90.5	15.7	.85	.90	.89	91.9	16.9	.83	90.4	15.2	.77	88.9	13.5	.58	85.3	15.7
FSIQ	.75	.80	.84	93.5	13.5	.91	.88	.91	90.8	18.1	.84	93.8	16.4	.69	94.3	13.7	.61	90.9	15.8
VCI	.79	.60	.76	98.3	12.6	.88	.72	.83	92.5	18.4	.78	102.5	16.4	.28	103.1	14.4	.59	98.5	14.0
POI	.51	.79	.70	93.3	14.3	.80	.88	.85	95.1	16.5	.84	93.9	15.5	.74	92.1	11.8	.55	88.2	13.6
WMI	.61	.55	.64	92.8	14.8	—	—	—	—	—	.61	87.6	16.0	.61	87.9	13.7	.58	90.6	17.3
PSI	.50	.76	.67	85.6	16.8	.65	.77	.71	85.9	16.6	.54	87.4	13.8	.66	84.6	16.2	.56	81.9	16.5
Mean	98.2	93.6	95.9			98.0	98.1	98.5			38.1			88.8			127.9		
SD	12.2	15.1	13.2			24.9	24.0	24.5			13.4			16.8			13.5		
N	88	88	88			24	24	24			22			16			74		

A similar pattern of correlations, yet with higher magnitude, is found between the WAIS–III and the WISC–R (ranging from .71 to .91). The magnitude of these correlations might have been influenced by the composition of the sample (e.g., 16% Mental Retardation and 75% Learning Disability) or by the smaller sample size.

The correlations between the WAIS–III VIQ, PIQ, and FSIQ scores and the SPM are .78, .83, and .84, respectively. These results are consistent with those for a nonclinical sample reported earlier in this chapter and with results of research reported in the literature. In addition, the correlation between the WAIS–III Matrix Reasoning subtest and the SPM was .79, which is also consistent with the results from the nonimpaired sample.

For the most part, the correlations between the WAIS–III IQ and Index scores and the MicroCog are all in the moderate range; the only exception is between the WAIS–III VCI and the MicroCog (.28). The correlations are in the expected range and are higher than those obtained between the WAIS–R and the MicroCog (Powell et al., 1993). Similarly, moderate correlations (ranging from .55 to .61) were obtained between the DRS Total Score and all of the WAIS–III variables.

Measures of Attention and Concentration

The correlations between WAIS–III and a variety of attention and concentration measures were obtained from various clinical groups. The external measures were the Attention/Concentration Index of the WMS–R, the Trail-Making Test (Trails A and Trails B) from the *Halstead–Reitan Neuropsychological Battery* (HRNB; Reitan & Wolfson, 1993), and the Attention/Mental Control Index of the MicroCog (Powell et al., 1993). The correlations, means, and standard deviations for each measure are shown in Table 4.39. (See Table 4.36 for the demographic makeup of the samples.) The mean WAIS–III FSIQ scores of the samples who took the WMS–R, the Trail-Making Test, and the MicroCog were 87.3 ($SD = 17.5$), 90.0 ($SD = 11.8$), and 94.3 ($SD = 13.7$), respectively.

Because the WAIS–III is not a comprehensive measure of attention and concentration, moderate correlations were expected. Of the WAIS–III indexes, the one most related to measures of attention is the WMI, and, therefore, the higher correlations were expected with this variable.

As shown in Table 4.39, the WAIS–III IQ and Index scores have low to moderate correlations with the Attention/Concentration Index of the WMS–R (ranging from .36 to .46). As expected, the exception is the WAIS–III WMI, which has a much higher correlation with this WMS–R index (.66). The magnitude of this result is partly due to the fact that these two indexes share a

Table 4.39. Correlations Between the WAIS–III and Measures of Attention and Concentration

	WMS-R			Trail-Making Test				MicroCog		
	Attention/ Concentration Index	Mean	SD	Trails A	Trails B	Mean	SD	Attention/Mental Control Index	Mean	SD
WAIS–III										
VIQ	.42	87.7	17.9	-.27	-.53	93.6	10.7	.72	98.9	13.3
PIQ	.46	88.9	16.0	-.56	-.65	87.1	14.2	.67	88.9	13.5
FSIQ	.46	87.3	17.5	-.46	-.66	90.0	11.8	.73	94.3	13.7
VCI	.36	91.9	16.1	-.12	-.40	95.9	11.6	.45	103.1	14.4
POI	.46	92.1	14.9	-.53	-.62	90.8	12.4	.58	92.1	11.8
WMI	.66	90.8	16.5	-.37	-.65	89.5	15.7	.65	87.9	13.7
PSI	.38	85.2	14.9	-.49	-.55	81.2	15.4	.60	84.6	16.2
Mean	97.0			56.7	156.2			87.6		
SD	13.9			26.5	92.8			18.6		
N	55			56	56			16		

common subtest (Digit Span). The other external measures (Trails A, Trails B, and MicroCog) generally correlate higher with the WAIS–III WMI than with the other WAIS–III IQ scales and indexes. The WMI correlations with the external measures range from -.37 (Trails A) to .66 (WMS–R Attention/Concentration Index).

The differences between the WAIS–III WMI correlations with the Trail-Making Test (Trails A and Trails B) provide additional evidence of construct validity. For Trails A, the correlation with the WMI is -.37. However, when the complexity of the task is increased, as in Trails B (for which working memory is needed to a much greater extent), the correlation between these two variables is much higher (-.65).

For all three external measures, correlations with the WAIS–III VCI are relatively lower. All of these results provide evidence of concurrent and discriminant validity.

Measures of Memory

The correlations between the WAIS–III and a number of memory measures were obtained. The external measures were the WMS–R memory indexes, the CVLT (Delis et al., 1987), the *Rey–Osterrieth Complex Figure Test* (Rey–O; Rey, 1941, 1959), and the Memory Index of the MicroCog (Powell et al., 1993). The correlations, means, and standard deviations for each measure are shown in Table 4.40. The mean WAIS–III FSIQ scores for the WMS–R, CVLT, Rey–O, and MicroCog external samples were 99.2 (*SD* = 12.8), 86.8 (*SD* = 10.5), 85.5 (*SD* = 11.5), and 94.3 (*SD* = 13.7), respectively.

The WAIS–III IQ scales and indexes were expected to show low to moderate correlations with most of the memory measures. Higher correlations were predicted between measures with the same presentation modality. For instance, the WMS–R Verbal Memory Index was predicted to have higher correlations with the WAIS–III VIQ and VCI scores than with the other IQ and Index scores.

Correlations between the WAIS–III IQ and Index scores and the WMS–R Index scores range from .33 to .77. The VIQ has a relatively high correlation with the Verbal Memory Index (.71) and the Visual Memory Index (.73), whereas the PIQ has a higher correlation with the Visual Memory Index (.65) than with the other indexes. These results are similar to the pattern obtained between the WAIS–III and WMS–III for the normative sample. Similarly, low to moderate correlations were obtained between the WAIS–III and the CVLT scores. However, as expected, relatively higher correlations (.58) were obtained between the WAIS–III VCI and the short-delay recall and long-delay recall variables of the CVLT. Much lower, almost negligible, correlations were obtained between the WAIS–III IQ scores and the memory components of

Table 4.40. Correlations Between the WAIS–III and Measures of Memory

	WMS–R						CVLT					Rey–O					MicroCog		
	Verbal	Visual	General	Delayed	Mean	SD	Trials 1–5	Short Delay	Long Delay	Mean	SD	Direct Copy	Imm Mem	Delayed Mem	Mean	SD	Memory Index	Mean	SD
WAIS–III																			
VIQ	.71	.73	.72	.67	100.7	11.2	.31	.36	.47	92.5	10.3	.43	-.08	-.18	90.3	9.0	.41	98.9	13.3
PIQ	.49	.65	.55	.52	97.3	15.4	.26	.11	.29	82.2	10.8	.45	-.16	-.14	81.9	14.2	.55	88.9	13.5
FSIQ	.67	.77	.71	.67	99.2	12.8	.33	.28	.43	86.8	10.5	.48	-.13	-.16	85.5	11.5	.49	94.3	13.7
VCI	.71	.64	.70	.65	101.9	12.8	.38	.58	.58	95.4	10.1	.27	.05	.01	90.8	9.0	.28	103.1	14.4
POI	.34	.54	.41	.36	99.1	14.6	.29	.16	.30	86.5	9.1	.46	-.03	-.03	88.0	13.9	.51	92.1	11.8
WMI	.33	.56	.40	.34	99.4	13.2	.22	.09	.16	86.3	14.8	.26	-.23	-.34	89.4	16.1	.15	87.9	13.7
PSI	.46	.55	.50	.49	92.7	15.5	.16	-.01	.23	77.4	14.2	.40	-.35	-.37	76.1	17.1	.54	84.6	16.2
Mean	98.7	101.2	98.8	90.2			30.0	-2.3	-2.4			28.8	8.7	6.6			89.4		
SD	18.6	17.9	21.7	26.6			13.7	1.1	1.1			6.5	7.1	6.6			20.4		
N	31	31	31	31			19	19	19			24	24	24			16		

Note. For the CVLT, a *T* score was used for the Trials 1–5 variable, and z scores were used for the short- and long-delay variables.

the Rey–O. These results are predictable because of the complex nature of the Rey–O tasks. The Direct Copy component of the Rey–O is moderately correlated with the WAIS–III IQ scores and is especially related to the optional procedure, Digit Symbol—Copy ($r = .51$). Finally, moderate correlations were obtained between the WAIS–III variables and the MicroCog memory scores.

Correlations between the WAIS–III WMI and the other measures are much lower, ranging from .09 (CVLT short-delay recall) to .40, with the exception of the correlation (.56) with the WMS–R Visual Index. The magnitudes of these correlations tend to be lower than the correlations with the WAIS–III VCI index and are commensurate with the hypothesis that working memory is different from and significantly independent of learning efficiency, episodic memory, and delayed recall.

Measures of Language

The correlations between the WAIS–III and measures of language, along with the means and standard deviations for each measure, are presented in Table 4.41. The external measures were the total score of the *Boston Naming Test* (BNT; E. Kaplan, Goodglass, & Weintraub, 1983), the FAS Total Score (FAS TS) of the Controlled Word Association Test and the Token Test of the *Multilingual Aphasia Examination* (Benton & Hamsher, 1994), and the Animals part of the *Category Naming Test* (Morris et al., 1989). The WAIS–III VIQ and VCI scores were expected to have the highest correlations with all of these measures; correlations with all the other WAIS–III IQ and Index scores would be low to moderate. Also, the WAIS–III verbal indexes were expected to correlate more highly with the external language measures than would the WAIS–III performance indexes. The mean WAIS–III FSIQ scores for the BNT, Controlled Word Association Test, Token Test, and *Category Naming Test* external samples were 84.5 ($SD = 13.9$), 88.4 ($SD = 13.9$), 84.3 ($SD = 11.5$), and 84.4 ($SD = 7.9$), respectively. (See Table 4.36 for the demographic information for these samples.)

As predicted, most of the variables correlate highest with the WAIS–III VCI and VIQ scores. The BNT has moderate correlations with all of the WAIS–III IQ and Index scores, but its highest correlation is with the VCI (.48). Similarly, the Controlled Word Association Test also has moderate correlations with all of the WAIS–III measures, but its highest correlations are with the FSIQ, VIQ, and VCI scores (.59, .61, and .57, respectively). The Token Test, which measures an examinee's ability to follow simple to multistep commands without having to produce a verbal response, has higher correlations with the WAIS–III VIQ (.62) and VCI (.59) than with the other WAIS–III scores. The *Category Naming Test*, a measure of semantic fluency, has its highest correlations with the WAIS–III VIQ and VCI (.55 and .62, respectively).

Table 4.41. Correlations Between the WAIS–III and Measures of Language

	BNT			Controlled Word Association Test			Token Test			Category Naming Test		
	TS	Mean	SD	FAS TS	Mean	SD	TS	Mean	SD	Animals	Mean	SD
WAIS-III												
VIQ	.38	87.3	13.8	.61	93.4	12.7	.62	89.1	11.3	.55	88.8	8.6
PIQ	.42	83.6	14.5	.48	84.1	15.5	.11	80.9	12.7	-.04	81.6	9.5
FSIQ	.44	84.5	13.9	.59	88.4	13.9	.42	84.3	11.5	.36	84.4	7.9
VCI	.48	90.4	12.5	.57	94.5	12.1	.59	90.9	11.9	.62	93.6	11.1
POI	.43	87.5	13.7	.40	86.4	13.7	.12	85.0	11.4	.02	87.0	8.9
WMI	.27	87.1	15.2	.54	89.1	15.5	.42	85.2	14.0	.17	80.4	9.7
PSI	.34	80.4	14.4	.55	82.9	15.8	.12	77.0	10.4	.15	73.7	10.1
Mean	46.8			29.7			39.1			12.0		
SD	11.1			13.7			5.8			2.9		
N	103			51			27			16		

Measures of Fine Motor Speed and Fine Motor Dexterity

The correlations between the WAIS–III and the following measures of fine motor speed and fine motor dexterity were obtained: the average number of taps over five trials for Dominant Hand and Nondominant Hand on the Finger-Tapping Test of the HRNB (Reitan & Wolfson, 1993), time in seconds for Dominant Hand and Nondominant Hand on the *Grooved Pegboard* (Lafayette Instrument Company, 1989), and the Reaction Time Index of the MicroCog (Powell et al., 1993). The correlations, means, and standard deviations for each measure are shown in Table 4.42. The mean WAIS–III FSIQ scores for the Finger-Tapping Test, *Grooved Pegboard*, and MicroCog external samples were 95.2 (*SD* = 13.5), 95.0 (*SD* = 17.2), and 94.3 (*SD* = 13.7), respectively.

The Finger-Tapping Test and *Grooved Pegboard* are measures of simple motor functioning and eye–hand coordination. Dominant-hand and non-dominant-hand scores are reported for each. These measures were predicted to have low to moderate correlations with most of the WAIS–III IQ and Index scores. The Finger-Tapping variables were expected to have the highest correlations with the WAIS–III PSI and to be moderate in magnitude. The correlations with the *Grooved Pegboard* were expected to be somewhat higher because of the increased complexity of the task.

As expected, the Dominant-Hand score of the Finger-Tapping Test correlates moderately with the PSI. Moderate, negative correlations occur between the WAIS–III measures and the *Grooved Pegboard* dominant-hand and non-dominant-hand conditions. The highest correlation is between the WAIS–III PSI and the *Grooved Pegboard* dominant-hand condition. Moderate correlations also occur between all of the WAIS–III IQ and Index scores and the MicroCog Reaction Time Index (range .32–.85). This pattern of correlations is likely because the MicroCog is more complex than the other external measures in this study.

Measures of Spatial Processing

The correlations between WAIS–III and a number of external measures of spatial processing were obtained from several studies. The external measures were the Spatial Processing Index of the MicroCog (Powell et al., 1993), the total score on the *Judgment of Line Orientation* (JOLO; Benton, Hamsher, Varney, & Spreen, 1983), and the Direct Copy condition of the Rey–O (Rey, 1941, 1959). The correlations, means, and standard deviations for each measure are shown in Table 4.43. The mean WAIS–III FSIQ scores for the Micro Cog, JOLO, and Rey–O external samples were 94.3 (*SD* = 13.7), 85.6 (*SD* = 13.2), and 87.0 (*SD* = 11.8), respectively.

Table 4.42. Correlations Between the WAIS–III and Measures of Fine Motor Speed and Fine Motor Dexterity

| | Finger-Tapping Test | | | | Grooved Pegboard | | | | MicroCog | | |
	Dominant Hand	Nondominant Hand	Mean	SD	Dominant Hand	Nondominant Hand	Mean	SD	Reaction Time Index	Mean	SD
WAIS-III											
VIQ	.07	-.11	95.9	9.4	-.40	-.46	93.9	14.7	.65	98.9	13.3
PIQ	.28	.06	94.2	16.5	-.59	-.49	96.7	19.8	.65	88.9	13.5
FSIQ	.22	.02	95.2	13.5	-.54	-.51	95.0	17.2	.69	94.3	13.7
VCI	.07	-.14	96.1	12.3	-.41	-.41	92.9	15.8	.32	103.1	14.4
POI	.09	-.03	94.0	12.0	-.40	-.46	96.6	17.8	.63	92.1	11.8
WMI	—	—	—	—	—	—	—	—	.85	87.9	13.7
PSI	.47	.18	91.2	19.2	-.63	-.41	94.1	17.6	.59	84.6	16.2
Mean	38.8	37.6			93.0	102.9			87.9		
SD	14.1	11.9			35.4	55.7			13.2		
N	22	22			21	21			16		

It was anticipated that WAIS–III IQ and Index scores would be at least moderately correlated with the MicroCog Spatial Processing Index, because spatial processing is related to overall intellectual functioning and this MicroCog index contains components of short-term memory, attention, perception, and spatial processing. A similar pattern was expected with the JOLO, which is a relatively complex task. The Rey–O Direct Copy task involves predominantly constructional processes and perception and would be slightly less related to the verbal scales. Therefore, the WAIS–III PIQ, POI, and PSI scores were expected to show higher correlations with the Rey–O than would the WAIS–III verbal scales.

Correlations between the WAIS–III PIQ, POI, and PSI scores and the Rey–O are in the moderate range but generally higher than the correlations obtained between the WAIS–III verbal scores and the Rey–O. Also, as expected, the MicroCog Spatial Processing Index and the JOLO have moderate correlations with most of the WAIS–III IQ and Index scores.

These results suggest that the WAIS–III IQ scales and indexes are related to other measures of spatial processing. However, as the tasks become more constructional and involve less reasoning, the correlations with the VCI and WMI become lower.

Table 4.43. Correlations Between the WAIS–III and Measures of Spatial Processing

	MicroCog			JOLO			Rey–O		
	Spatial Processing Index	Mean	SD	TS	Mean	SD	Direct Copy	Mean	SD
WAIS–III									
VIQ	.63	98.9	13.3	.54	89.1	12.9	.43	91.5	9.5
PIQ	.65	88.9	13.5	.54	83.7	14.9	.50	83.5	14.2
FSIQ	.67	94.3	13.7	.61	85.6	13.2	.51	87.0	11.8
VCI	.41	103.1	14.4	.61	91.9	12.5	.28	92.6	10.2
POI	.54	92.1	11.8	.55	87.6	13.1	.48	89.2	13.5
WMI	.57	87.9	13.7	.56	87.3	13.5	.27	89.7	15.3
PSI	.63	84.6	16.2	.47	80.4	14.9	.48	78.7	18.3
Mean	87.4			24.9			29.3		
SD	16.5			6.4			6.4		
N	16			28			27		

Measures of Executive Functioning

The correlations between WAIS–III and the *Wisconsin Card Sorting Test* (WCST; Berg, 1948; Grant & Berg, 1948; Heaton, Chelune, Talley, Kay, & Curtiss, 1993) were based on a sample of 21 participants. The WCST is a neuropsychological instrument for assessing problem-solving strategies, cognitive flexibility, and the ability to use feedback in problem solving. The scores obtained on the WCST are number of correct responses, number of categories completed, number of errors, and number of perseverations (cognitive inflexibility or the inability to switch tasks and apply new rules).

It was predicted that two WCST scores, the number correct and number of categories completed, would be more related to general intellectual functioning (FSIQ) and the more fluid, processing tasks of the WAIS–III PIQ and POI than to the other scores on the WAIS–III. These WCST scores were also predicted to be less related to the WAIS–III tasks that require more crystallized, acquired knowledge (e.g., the VCI). Additionally, because the WCST also requires intact working memory (i.e., the examinee must keep track of correct and incorrect responses to complete the task successfully), relatively higher correlations with the WAIS–III WMI were also anticipated. The remaining scores on the WCST, which are associated with impaired performance, total errors and perseverative errors, were expected to have low, negative correlations with all of the WAIS–III indexes. The correlations, means, and standard deviations for each measure are shown in Table 4.44. The mean WAIS–III FSIQ score for the WCST sample was 85.9 (SD = 11.9).

Table 4.44. Correlations Between the WAIS–III and Measures of Executive Functioning

	WCST					
	Total Correct	Categories Completed	Total Errors	Perseverative Errors	Mean	*SD*
WAIS–III						
VIQ	.34	.31	⁻.01	⁻.22	90.7	12.1
PIQ	.42	.39	⁻.19	⁻.23	82.4	13.2
FSIQ	.42	.40	⁻.11	⁻.26	85.9	11.9
VCI	.33	.26	.00	⁻.20	92.8	12.6
POI	.45	.40	⁻.22	⁻.19	86.2	12.3
WMI	.48	.31	.08	⁻.15	85.0	13.2
PSI	.30	.29	⁻.17	⁻.23	78.4	11.3
Mean	57.6	1.6	53.5	34.6		
SD	21.2	1.7	18.0	15.9		
N	21	21	21	21		

As predicted, the highest correlations are between the WCST total number correct score and the WAIS–III FSIQ (.42), PIQ (.42), POI (.45), and WMI (.48) and between the WCST category score and the WAIS–III FSIQ (.40), PIQ (.39), and POI (.40). These correlations support the premise that the WCST correct scores (which reflect an individual's problem-solving strategies and flexibility) would be most related to the WAIS–III general intellectual functioning and perceptual scores. Moreover, the WAIS–III WMI is most related to WCST total number correct (.48).

WMS–III Correlations With Selected External Measures

The correlations between WMS–III indexes and the external measures are based on data from mixed samples of individuals who were clinically diagnosed with various neurological disorders. Table 4.45 presents demographic characteristics for individuals who completed each external measure for the WMS–III comparison studies. The data are presented as mean age and percentages of the samples by sex, race/ethnicity, and education level. The samples are ordered according to the type of external measure (e.g., cognitive ability).

For these comparison studies, if multiple measures from one external instrument were used, then the correlations for those measures are based on the same individuals. In Table 4.46, for example, correlations between the WMS–III and the WAIS–R and the MicroCog (Powell et al., 1993) are reported. For the WAIS–R sample, correlations for the VIQ, PIQ, and FSIQ scores are based on the same individuals. The sample for the Information Processing Accuracy Index of the MicroCog is different from the WAIS–R sample. Relative comparisons between the measures within each test can be made, but because the samples for the WAIS–R and the MicroCog vary greatly in size and are composed of individuals who have different clinical diagnoses, relative comparisons between the WAIS–R and the MicroCog may be misleading. Therefore, to the degree that clinical group composition affects the observed relationships, correlations from test to test may not be comparable.

Table 4.45. Demographic Data of the Samples for the WMS–III/External Measures Comparison Studies

WAIS-III	WAIS-III	Cognitive Ability			Attention				Memory			
		WAIS-R	MicroCog	DRS	WAIS-R	WMS-R	MicroCog	Trail-Making Test	WMS-R	CVLT	MicroCog	Rey-O
N	104	85	14	79	85	55	14	74	51	34	14	17
Age												
Mean	47.8	56.5	52.1	60.8	56.5	43.0	52.1	50.2	43.9	54.5	52.1	50.0
SD	20.6	17.3	19.6	15.4	17.3	15.9	19.6	19.1	16.0	16.8	19.6	18.2
Sex												
Female	41.3	28.2	35.7	29.1	28.2	36.4	35.7	55.4	33.3	52.9	35.7	41.2
Male	57.7	70.6	64.3	68.4	70.6	61.8	64.3	44.6	64.7	47.1	64.3	58.8
Unknown	1.0	1.2		2.5	1.2	1.8			2.0			
Race/Ethnicity												
White	88.5	88.1	100.0	88.6	88.1	85.5	100.0	87.8	88.2	82.4	100.0	100.0
African-American	6.7	7.1		7.6	7.1	10.9		8.1	7.8	11.8		
Hispanic	1.9	2.4		1.3	2.4	1.8		1.4	2.0	2.9		
Other												
Unknown	2.9	2.4		2.5	2.4	1.8		2.7	2.0	2.9		
Education												
≤8	3.9	5.9		7.6	5.9	3.6		1.4	4.0			
9–11	5.8	7.1	7.1	2.5	7.1	10.9	7.1	2.7	9.8	47.1	7.1	5.9
12	35.5	35.1	57.3	27.9	35.1	23.6	57.3	37.7	21.6	20.6	57.3	41.2
13–15	28.8	28.3	14.2	22.7	28.3	36.5	14.2	29.8	35.2	26.4	14.2	23.5
≥16	14.5	16.5	7.1	26.6	16.5	12.7	7.1	21.6	15.7	5.9	7.1	23.5
Unknown	11.5	7.1	14.3	12.7	7.1	12.7	14.3	6.8	13.7		14.3	5.9
Diagnostic Group												
AD (Mild)	14.3	18.8	28.5	31.6	18.8		28.5	21.5		14.7	28.5	5.9
AD (Moderate)	4.8	8.2		6.3	8.2			2.7		5.9		
Traumatic Brain Injury	5.8	7.1		2.5	7.1			8.1	3.9			
Depression						5.5		5.4				
Lobectomy–Left	5.8		14.3			23.6	14.3		23.5		14.3	
Lobectomy–Unspec.	1.0					1.8			2.0			
Lobectomy–Right	6.7	5.9			5.9	16.4		4.1	13.7			
Chronic Alcoholism	7.7	28.2	14.3	25.3	28.2	25.4	14.3		25.5		14.3	
Huntington's Disease	9.6	7.1	14.3	19.0	7.1	1.8	14.3	13.5	2.0		14.3	41.2
Korsakoff's	8.7	9.4		1.3	9.4	16.4			17.6	23.5		23.5
ADHD	5.8											
LD–Math	3.8											
LD–Reading	2.9											
Multiple Sclerosis	3.8							17.6		38.3		11.8
Parkinson's Disease	8.7	11.8		12.7	11.8			13.5		17.6		17.6
Schizophrenia			28.6	1.3		9.1	28.6	1.4	2.0		28.6	
Stroke Left												
Neurotoxin Exposure	10.6	3.5			3.5			12.2	9.8			

Evidence Based on Relationships With Other Variables

Table 4.45. Demographic Data of the Samples for the WMS–III/External Measures Comparison Studies *(continued)*

	Language		Spatial Processing			Executive Functioning	MicroCog	Fine Motor Speed and Dexterity	
	BNT	Controlled Word Association Test	Rey-O	MicroCog	JOLO	WCST	MicroCog	Finger-Tapping Test	Grooved Pegboard
N	107	63	29	14	28	23	14	23	44
Age									
Mean	55.5	63.6	54.8	52.1	55.9	66.7	52.1	45.2	35.9
SD	20.3	17.4	18.3	19.6	20.1	13.5	19.6	20.6	11.3
Sex									
Female	49.5	41.3	41.4	35.7	25.0	13.0	35.7	65.2	75.0
Male	50.5	57.1	58.6	64.3	75.0	87.0	64.3	34.8	25.0
Unknown		1.6							
Race/Ethnicity									
White	87.8	84.1	100.0	100.0	82.1	87.0	100.0	95.7	79.6
African -American	7.5	9.5			17.9	8.7		4.3	18.2
Hispanic	1.9	1.6				4.3			
Other	0.9	1.6							
Unknown	1.9	3.2							2.2
Education									
≤8	5.6	9.5	6.8	7.1	3.6	4.3	7.1		2.3
9–11	5.6	3.2	3.4	57.3	39.3	4.3	57.3	34.8	41.0
12	31.8	31.7	31.0	14.2	32.1	52.5	14.2	43.5	36.3
13–15	29.9	22.3	34.7	7.1	25.0	8.6	7.1	13.0	11.3
≥16	21.5	23.8	20.7	14.3		26.0	14.3	8.7	9.1
Unknown	5.6	9.5	3.4			4.3			
Diagnostic Group									
AD (Mild)	31.0	46.0	17.2	28.5	32.1	30.4	28.5	17.4	
AD (Moderate)	6.5	9.5	6.9			8.7			
Traumatic Brain Injury			10.3					8.7	
Depression			3.4					8.7	4.5
Lobectomy–Left	14.0	1.6		14.3	10.7		14.3	8.7	36.3
Lobectomy–Unspec.	0.9								2.3
Lobectomy–Right	11.2	6.3	6.9		17.9			17.4	13.6
Chronic Alcoholism	1.9	4.8		14.3		8.7	14.3	4.3	
Huntington's Disease	9.3		31.0	14.3			14.3	4.3	2.3
Korsakoff's	7.5	1.6	24.3						
ADHD									
LD–Math									
LD–Reading									
Multiple Sclerosis	0.9	11.1							
Parkinson's Disease	8.4	15.9			32.2	43.5			27.3
Schizophrenia					7.1	8.7	28.6		
Stroke Left	0.9								2.3
Neurotoxin Exposure	7.5	3.2						30.5	11.4

Note. Except for sample size (*N*) and age, data are reported as percentages.

Measures of Cognitive Ability

The correlations between the WMS–III and measures of overall cognitive ability, as well as the means and standard deviations for each measure, are presented in Table 4.46. The external measures were the VIQ, PIQ, and FSIQ scores on the WAIS–R, the Information Processing Accuracy Index of the MicroCog (Powell et al., 1993), and the total score of the DRS (Mattis, 1988). The mean WAIS–III FSIQ scores for the WAIS–R, MicroCog, and DRS external samples were 94.7 (SD = 13.2), 91.3 (SD = 13.2), and 90.9 (SD = 15.8), respectively.

Because of the moderately high correlations between the WMS–III indexes and WAIS–III IQ scales and indexes for standardization participants, correlations of the WMS–III with other measures of general cognitive ability were expected to be in the same general range (i.e., in the .50s and .60s between the WMS–III General Memory Index and overall ability scores) or slightly higher because of the relatively wider range of scores typically observed in clinical populations.

The correlations between the WMS–III indexes and the Microcog and the DRS are in the moderate to high range, as expected. In general, the correlations between the WMS–III indexes and WAIS–R IQ scores are in the moderate range and are somewhat lower than expected. The descriptive statistics and clinical group composition for the WAIS–R sample provide an explanation for the relatively lower correlations for this sample. First, relative to the mean IQ scores, the mean scores for WMS–III indexes are generally 10–15 points lower. Second, the WAIS–R sample is composed of about 23% of individuals with Korsakoff's syndrome or mild Alzheimer's disease. These two groups usually present more memory loss relative to IQ decrements. Consequently, the relatively lower correlations of the WMS–III with the WAIS–R compared to those with the MicroCog and the DRS are expected and provide evidence of divergent validity of the WAIS–III and the WMS–III for this clinical sample. When the participants with Korsakoff's syndrome or Alzheimer's disease were omitted from the sample in a follow-up analyses, the correlation between the WMS–III General Memory Index and WAIS–R FSIQ score was in the expected range (r = .51, p < .001, n = 80).

Table 4.46. Correlations Between the WMS–III and Measures of Cognitive Ability

	WAIS-R					MicroCog				DRS	
	VIQ	PIQ	FSIQ	Mean	SD	Information Processing Accuracy Index	Mean	SD	TS	Mean	SD
WMS–III											
Auditory Immediate	.38	.39	.43	86.0	18.9	.47	85.5	15.0	.62	83.3	22.1
Visual Immediate	.29	.34	.33	82.7	16.5	.70	82.6	9.0	.51	79.3	16.1
Immediate Memory	.38	.41	.42	81.1	19.3	.62	80.9	13.1	.60	77.3	22.3
Auditory Delayed	.25	.26	.28	84.7	19.8	.40	82.1	12.4	.62	83.0	21.7
Visual Delayed	.31	.42	.39	81.0	16.9	.33	83.1	13.3	.57	77.3	16.9
Auditory Recognition Delayed	.30	.29	.32	86.6	21.0	.60	87.1	20.4	.63	84.6	20.8
General Memory	.32	.36	.37	80.7	20.3	.53	80.4	14.6	.65	77.8	22.0
Working Memory	.33	.44	.43	91.9	15.6	.55	88.8	13.7	.61	85.0	15.3
Auditory Process Composites											
Single-Trial Learning	.38	.41	.44			.54			.66		
Learning Slope	.25	.21	.25			-.18			.41		
Retention	.12	.03	.07			.38			.17		
Retrieval	.30	.29	.32			.58			.59		
Mean	97.7	93.1	95.2			84.6			126.9		
SD	11.9	14.6	12.7			14.9			14.1		
N			104				14			79	

Measures of Attention and Concentration

Correlations between the WMS–III and several measures of attention and concentration were obtained for various clinical groups. The external measures were the age-corrected scaled score on the Digit Span subtest of the WAIS–R, the Attention/Concentration Index of the WMS–R, the Attention/ Mental Control Index of the MicroCog (Powell et al., 1993), and Trails A and Trails B (time in seconds) of the HRNB Trail-Making Test (Reitan & Wolfson, 1993). The correlations, means, and standard deviations for each measure are presented in Table 4.46. The mean WAIS–III FSIQ scores for the WAIS–R, WMS–R, MicroCog, and Trail-Making Test external samples were 93.3 (*SD* = 15.0), 97.9 (*SD* = 14.6), 91.3 (*SD* = 13.2), and 90.0 (*SD* = 11.8), respectively.

The WMS–III Working Memory Index was predicted to correlate higher with the external measures of attention and concentration than would the other WMS–III memory indexes.

As the data in Table 4.47 show, the WMS–III Working Memory Index generally correlates much higher with the external measures of attention and concentration than do the other WMS–III indexes. The correlations between the WMS–III Working Memory Index and the external measures range from .48 (WAIS–R Digit Span) to .85 (MicroCog Attention/Mental Control Index). Additional evidence of validity is provided by the pattern of correlations between the WMS–III Working Memory Index and Trails A and Trails B of the Trail-Making Test. The correlation between the WMS–III index and Trails A is -.31. However, when the complexity of the task is increased (and working memory is needed to a much greater extent), as in Trails B, the correlation between these two variables is much higher (-.62). This pattern is similar to the one found between the WAIS–III WMI and Trails A and Trails B.

Table 4.47. Correlations Between the WMS–III and Measures of Attention and Concentration

	WAIS-R			WMS-R			MicroCog			Trail-Making Test			
	Digit Span	Mean	SD	Attention/ Concentration Index	Mean	SD	Attention/ Mental Control Index	Mean	SD	Trails A	Trails B	Mean	SD
WMS–III													
Auditory Immediate	.31	87.3	21.9	.37	90.9	19.0	.52	85.5	15.0	-.09	-.43	86.4	18.2
Visual Immediate	.20	81.5	17.4	.13	86.7	15.8	.72	82.6	9.0	-.23	-.41	79.9	14.3
Immediate Memory	.28	81.2	22.3	.30	86.5	19.0	.67	80.9	13.1	-.16	-.48	79.8	17.5
Auditory Delayed	.28	86.6	22.8	.32	88.1	21.4	.17	82.1	12.4	-.16	-.46	85.5	19.1
Visual Delayed	.33	80.2	18.1	.17	86.3	16.4	.17	83.1	13.3	-.32	-.48	78.4	15.4
Auditory Recognition Delayed	.22	86.9	23.1	.18	92.1	21.9	.43	87.1	20.4	-.18	-.45	88.6	18.7
General Memory	.30	81.4	23.4	.26	86.2	20.8	.31	80.4	14.6	-.24	-.52	80.5	18.5
Working Memory	.48	90.1	15.1	.73	97.9	13.4	.85	88.8	13.7	-.31	-.62	89.1	15.7
Auditory Process Composites													
Single-Trial Learning	.35			.34			.61			-.16	-.48		
Learning Slope	.18			.36			-.16			-.02	-.26		
Retention	.13			.09			-.16			-.07	-.41		
Retrieval	.25			.26			.37			-.18	-.48		
Mean	13.6			97.0			82.2			52.8	143.7		
SD	3.9			13.9			18.4			25.3	88.4		
N	85			55			14			74			

Measures of Memory

Correlations between the WMS–III and a number of other measures of memory were obtained from several clinical groups. These external measures were several indexes of the WMS–R, the CVLT (Delis et al., 1987), the Memory Index of the MicroCog (Powell et al., 1993), and the Rey–O (Rey, 1941, 1959). The correlations, means, and standard deviations for each measure are presented in Table 4.48. The mean WAIS–III FSIQ scores for the WMS–R, CVLT, MicroCog, and Rey–O external samples were 99.2 (SD = 12.8), 86.8 (SD = 10.5), 91.3 (SD = 13.2), and 83.1 (SD = 5.6), respectively.

The WMS–III indexes were expected to have moderate to high correlations with other memory measures. It was also anticipated that the WMS–III Working Memory Index would have lower correlations with the external memory measures than would the other WMS–III indexes. Finally, because the Direct Copy condition of the Rey–O is not a memory task, the correlations with the WMS–III indexes were expected to be very low or negligible.

The correlations between the WMS–III Working Memory Index and the external measures range from .07 (CVLT Long-Delay Free Recall) to .42 (MicroCog Memory Index) and are generally lower than the correlations between the other WMS–III indexes and external measures. The WMS–III auditory memory indexes have relatively high correlations with comparable WMS–R, CVLT, and MicroCog measures. As expected, the WMS–III visual indexes generally correlate lower with the CVLT verbal memory measures than do the WMS–III auditory indexes (the exception is the correlation between the visual memory indexes and the CVLT Long-Delay Free Recall score). However, the correlations between the WMS–III auditory indexes and external measures with visually presented material (e.g., WMS–R and Rey–O) are nearly as high as those of the WMS–III visual indexes. Unexpectedly, the WMS–III Visual Delayed Memory Index is unrelated to both the immediate and delayed measures of the Rey–O. Overall, however, these results are evidence of the convergent validity of the WMS–III. For the indexes with visually presented material, these results are equivocal with respect to convergent and divergent validity of the WMS–III. It should be noted, however, that none of the external measures is generally recognized as representing a "pure" visual memory construct.

Table 4.48. Correlations Between the WMS–III and Other Measures of Memory

	WMS-R						CVLT					MicroCog			Rey-O				
	Verbal	Visual	General	Del	Mean	SD	Trials 1-5	Short Delay	Long Delay	Mean	SD	Memory Index	Mean	SD	Direct Copy	Imm Mem	Del Mem	Mean	SD
WMS-III																			
Aud Imm	.75	.63	.73	.75	91.6	19.2	.71	.52	.40	82.5	17.9	.71	85.5	15.0	-.07	.55	.53	77.1	17.1
Vis Imm	.57	.50	.56	.64	86.5	15.7	.37	.24	.41	75.2	11.2	.52	82.6	9.0	-.23	.55	.54	71.1	8.2
Imm Mem	.75	.64	.73	.78	86.8	19.0	.66	.48	.45	74.6	16.1	.73	80.9	13.1	-.13	.63	.62	68.9	13.8
Aud Del	.70	.61	.70	.77	88.8	21.7	.74	.63	.50	82.4	17.2	.57	82.1	12.4	.03	.54	.61	81.8	18.5
Vis Del	.52	.55	.58	.68	86.1	16.5	.40	.44	.46	74.9	12.2	.30	83.1	13.3	-.15	.14	.22	69.3	10.2
Aud Rec Del	.79	.64	.73	.78	92.7	22.1	.50	.44	.43	85.2	15.3	.54	87.1	20.4	-.09	.64	.58	83.2	20.5
Gen Mem	.74	.67	.74	.83	86.6	21.2	.66	.60	.53	76.5	15.3	.55	80.4	14.6	-.06	.54	.57	73.2	16.6
Wkg Mem	.23	.29	.29	.17	97.6	12.4	.33	.26	.07	85.6	14.2	.42	88.8	13.7	.36	.19	.11	82.7	12.2
Auditory Process Composites																			
Single-Trial Learn	.74	.61	.68	.71			.70	.49	.25			.59			.04	.49	.50		
Learning Slope	.63	.59	.66	.71			.46	.36	.45			.25			-.21	.48	.44		
Retention	.55	.46	.54	.66			.53	.52	.33			.11			.17	.45	.53		
Retrieval	.78	.65	.75	.81			.66	.57	.50			.34			-.03	.62	.62		
Mean	94.0	98.3	95.1	87.6			34.7	-2.1	-2.3			85.6			29.3	11.4	9.7		
SD	17.7	16.5	21.3	23.4			14.5	1.2	1.2			18.8			5.6	6.4	5.5		
N			51						34			14				17			

Note. For the CVLT, a *T* score was used for the Trials 1–5 variable, and *z* scores were used for the short- and long-delay variables.

Measures of Language

Correlations between WMS–III and the total score of the BNT (E. Kaplan et al., 1983) and the FAS Total Score (FAS TS) of the Controlled Word Association Test (Benton & Hamsher, 1994) were obtained. The correlations, means, and standard deviations for each measure are provided in Table 4.49. The mean WAIS–III FSIQ scores for the BNT and Controlled Word Association Test external samples were 88.7 (SD = 13.1) and 88.5 (SD = 14.0), respectively.

The WMS–III indexes were predicted to show low to moderate correlations with the BNT and Controlled Word Association Test. Further, the WMS–III indexes based on auditorily presented material were expected to correlate more highly with the external language measures than would the WMS–III indexes based on visually presented material.

All of the correlations between the WMS–III indexes and the BNT are in the low to moderate range. These correlations range from .25 (Working Memory Index) to .39 (Auditory Immediate Memory and Auditory Recognition Delayed indexes). Correlations of similar magnitude occur between the

Table 4.49. Correlations Between the WMS–III and Measures of Language

	BNT			Controlled Word Association Test		
	TS	Mean	SD	FAS TS	Mean	SD
WMS–III						
Auditory Immediate	.39	78.4	17.2	.38	78.2	18.2
Visual Immediate	.27	78.5	15.1	.21	75.4	14.5
Immediate Memory	.38	73.8	17.7	.33	71.8	18.9
Auditory Delayed	.31	77.4	17.6	.29	76.6	17.8
Visual Delayed	.30	77.0	15.8	.29	73.4	14.8
Aud Rec Del	.39	79.7	19.7	.24	77.1	18.4
General Memory	.36	73.7	18.7	.30	70.9	18.5
Working Memory	.25	88.1	16.4	.50	85.5	15.6
Auditory Process Composites						
Single-Trial Learning	.37			.50		
Learning Slope	.43			.14		
Retention	.16			.18		
Retrieval	.38			.27		
Mean	46.8			31.0		
SD	11.0			13.6		
N		107			63	

WMS–III indexes and the Controlled Word Association Test, ranging from .21 (Visual Immediate Memory Index) to .50 (Working Memory Index). Although the trend is not particularly strong, the WMS–III Auditory Immediate Memory Index correlates more highly with the external language measures than does the WMS–III Visual Immediate Memory Index. This trend, however, is not consistent for the corresponding WMS–III delayed measures.

Measures of Spatial Processing

Correlations between the WMS–III and external measures of spatial processing were obtained. The external measures were the Spatial Processing Index of the MicroCog (Powell et al., 1993), the total score of the JOLO (Benton et al., 1983), and the Direct Copy condition of the Rey–O (Rey, 1941, 1959). The correlations, means, and standard deviations for each measure are provided in Table 4.50. The mean WAIS–III FSIQ scores for the MicroCog, JOLO, and Rey–O external samples were 91.3 (SD = 13.2), 88.7 (SD = 12.3), and 87.0 (SD = 11.8), respectively.

Table 4.50. Correlations Between the WMS–III and Measures of Spatial Processing

	MicroCog			JOLO			Rey–O		
	Spatial Processing						Direct		
	Index	Mean	SD	TS	Mean	SD	Copy	Mean	SD
WMS–III									
Auditory Immediate	.57	85.5	15.0	.30	84.0	16.9	.11	75.8	16.3
Visual Immediate	.71	82.6	9.0	.35	78.3	14.1	-.07	70.5	7.6
Immediate Memory	.69	80.9	13.1	.35	77.3	17.5	.06	67.6	13.6
Auditory Delayed	.31	82.1	12.4	.29	80.5	17.2	.07	77.5	18.3
Visual Delayed	.47	83.1	13.3	.37	75.6	14.3	.01	68.7	9.4
Aud Rec Del	.45	87.1	20.4	.50	82.9	18.4	.05	80.3	19.6
General Memory	.47	80.4	14.6	.41	75.2	17.3	.05	70.2	16.2
Working Memory	.67	88.8	13.7	.26	87.4	16.7	.28	87.2	16.0
Auditory Process Composites									
Single-Trial Learning	.60			.33			.17		
Learning Slope	.39			.27			-.04		
Retention	-.11			.21			.10		
Retrieval	.43			.43			.06		
Mean	87.6			25.9			29.6		
SD	17.7			4.1			6.3		
N		14			28			29	

The WMS–III Visual Immediate Index and Working Memory Index were anticipated to correlate higher with the MicroCog Spatial Processing Index than would the WMS–III auditory memory indexes, because this MicroCog index includes components of short-term visual memory and attention. Low correlations between the WMS–III indexes and the JOLO and Rey–O were expected.

As expected, the WMS–III Visual Immediate Memory Index and Working Memory Index correlate more highly with the MicroCog Spatial Processing Index than do the WMS–III auditory measures. Correlations between the WMS–III indexes, except the Working Memory Index, and the Rey–O are generally very low. Unexpectedly higher correlations occur between the WMS–III indexes and the JOLO. Because of these results, the JOLO total score was correlated with WAIS–III FSIQ score, and a strong relationship was found ($r = .71$, $p < .001$). Correlations between the WMS–III indexes and the JOLO were recomputed, with the effects of FSIQ score controlled. All correlations between the WMS–III indexes and the JOLO were nonsignificant in this follow-up analysis. These results suggest that the relationship between the WMS–III and the JOLO can be explained by a general cognitive decline to which both measures are sensitive. Overall, these data are evidence of the convergent and divergent validity of the WMS–III indexes.

Measures of Executive Functioning

Correlations between the WMS–III and the WCST (Berg, 1948; Grant & Berg, 1948; Heaton et al., 1993), along with the means and standard deviations, are reported in Table 4.51. The mean WAIS–III FSIQ score for the WCST sample was 86.7 ($SD = 11.7$).

The WCST is a neuropsychological instrument for assessing problem-solving strategies, cognitive flexibility, and the ability to use feedback in problem solving. The test requires intact working memory, because the individual must keep track of correct and incorrect responses to complete the task successfully. The WCST score associated with better performance (i.e., the total number of correct responses) was expected to have low, positive correlations with the WMS–III indexes, whereas the WCST scores associated with impaired performance (i.e., total errors and perseverative errors) were expected to have low, negative correlations with the WMS–III indexes. Moreover, the WMS–III Working Memory Index was expected to have the highest correlations with the WCST measures.

Table 4.51. Correlations Between the WMS–III and Measures of Executive Functioning

	WCST				
	Total Correct	Total Errors	Perseverative Errors	Mean	SD
WMS–III					
Auditory Immediate	.33	.06	⁻.01	80.5	17.0
Visual Immediate	.09	.18	.04	77.8	15.6
Immediate Memory	.23	.13	.01	74.7	18.4
Auditory Delayed	.31	⁻.09	⁻.18	78.9	18.1
Visual Delayed	.34	.04	⁻.03	75.3	16.7
Auditory Recognition Delayed	.33	⁻.18	⁻.17	83.0	21.3
General Memory	.37	⁻.07	⁻.14	74.4	20.0
Working Memory	.60	.12	⁻.01	82.0	12.2
Auditory Process Composites					
Single-Trial Learning	.41	⁻.14	⁻.17		
Learning Slope	.39	.06	⁻.12		
Retention	.10	.12	⁻.01		
Retrieval	.34	⁻.15	⁻.19		
Mean	60.5	51.4	32.8		
SD	22.4	18.8	16.4		
N				23	

As predicted, the WMS–III Working Memory Index has the highest correlation with the WCST, but only with the total correct score. As the data in Table 4.51 show, there is a general trend of low, positive correlations between the WMS–III memory indexes and the WCST total correct score and low, negative correlations between the WMS–III and the WCST total errors and perseverative errors.

Measures of Fine Motor Speed and Fine Motor Dexterity

Correlations between the WMS–III and the following measures of fine motor speed and fine motor dexterity were obtained: the Reaction Time Index of the MicroCog (Powell et al., 1993), the average number of taps over five trials for Dominant Hand and Nondominant Hand on the Finger-Tapping Test of the HRNB (Reitan & Wolfson, 1993), and time in seconds for Dominant Hand and Nondominant Hand on the *Grooved Pegboard* (Lafayette Instrument Company, 1989). The correlations, means, and standard deviations for each measure are shown in Table 4.52. The mean WAIS–III FSIQ scores for the MicroCog, Finger-Tapping Test, and *Grooved Pegboard* samples were 91.3 (*SD* = 13.2), 95.7 (*SD* = 11.8), and 90.4 (*SD* = 13.5), respectively.

Table 4.52. Correlations Between the WMS–III and Measures of Fine Motor Speed and Fine Motor Dexterity

	MicroCog Reaction Time Index			Finger-Tapping Test				Grooved Pegboard			
		Mean	SD	Dominant Hand	Nondominant Hand	Mean	SD	Dominant Hand	Nondominant Hand	Mean	SD
WMS–III											
Auditory Immediate	.11	85.5	15.0	-.09	-.20	89.0	19.2	.08	-.13	88.1	15.6
Visual Immediate	.44	82.6	9.0	.21	-.07	82.7	13.5	-.53	-.27	83.0	13.2
Immediate Memory	.24	80.9	13.1	.03	-.16	83.0	18.1	-.24	-.25	82.8	13.3
Auditory Delayed	-.11	82.1	12.4	-.21	-.19	90.2	17.9	.03	-.13	85.4	17.5
Visual Delayed	.02	83.1	13.3	.08	-.09	82.0	14.8	-.42	-.23	83.7	14.0
Aud Rec Del	.14	87.1	20.4	-.06	-.07	95.7	20.5	-.09	-.22	88.2	17.8
General Memory	.03	80.4	14.6	-.09	-.14	86.3	18.8	-.17	-.23	82.7	15.2
Working Memory	.65	88.8	13.7	.08	-.07	95.1	14.6	-.16	-.18	94.2	14.3
Auditory Process Composites											
Single-Trial Learning	.25			-.08	-.10			.04	-.15		
Learning Slope	-.31			.10	-.09			.09	.13		
Retention	-.19			-.19	.00			.11	.07		
Retrieval	.07			-.13	-.12			-.04	-.20		
Mean		83.9		38.0	35.7			93.3	101.6		
SD		13.9		13.1	9.5			36.8	60.0		
N		14			23				44		

Very low correlations between the WMS–III auditory indexes and all of the external measures and moderately low correlations between the WMS–III visual indexes and the external measures were expected.

The WMS–III Working Memory Index shows a strong relationship with the MicroCog Reaction Time Index but is unrelated to the Finger-Tapping Test and *Grooved Pegboard* measures. Additionally, the results show that performance for the Dominant Hand on the *Grooved Pegboard* measure is inversely related to the WMS–III visual memory indexes. These results indicate that the WMS–III memory indexes are generally unrelated to simple and choice reaction time (i.e., MicroCog) and fine motor speed. However, visual memory is related to fine motor dexterity and perceptual motor speed, with those who score higher on WMS–III visual indexes demonstrating faster performance on the *Grooved Pegboard* dominant-hand measure. These correlations provide evidence of convergent and divergent validity.

Demographic Studies

Differential age effects on measures of intellectual functioning have been well documented and have been, in part, the basis for the concepts of "crystallized" and "fluid" abilities. J. J. Ryan, Sattler, and Lopez (2000) evaluated age trends in WAIS–III performance, using procedures employed by Sattler (1992) in evaluating WAIS–R age trends. The analysis revealed relatively stable performance on measures of verbal intellectual abilities across the age span (Ryan, Sattler, et al., 2000). The authors reported that performance on Information was the most stable across age groups whereas performance on Letter–Number Sequencing displayed the most age-related declines. Ryan, Sattler, et al. also found that measures of processing speed showed the strongest age-associated effects and that performance measures in general displayed more age effects than did verbal measures (Ryan, Sattler, et al., 2000). The authors concluded that the observed age trends are evidence that the WAIS–III subtests measure aspects of fluid and crystallized intelligence.

Basso, Harrington, Matson, and Lowery (2000) studied sex effects on performance on the WMS–III Verbal Paired Associates and Faces subtests. Their results indicated significant sex effects for Verbal Paired Associates learning but none for Faces. Basso et al. suggested that male respondents might have obtained lower scores than expected on Verbal Paired Associates because norms are not stratified by sex. The study by Basso et al. was based on a relatively small sample of homogeneous participants. An analysis of the sex effects on Verbal Paired Associates in the standardization sample yielded no significant results at the multivariate level, Wilks' Lambda = .996, $F(4, 1245)$ = 1.12, $p > .05$. Individual measures of delayed cued recall, $F(1, 1248) = 4.5$, $p < .05$) and Verbal Paired Associates learning, $F(1, 1248) = 4.9$, $p < .05$, had a small, statistically significant effect. The average performance for women on the learning trial and the delayed cued recall scaled scores were 10.2 (±3.1), and for men, 9.8 (±2.8). The mean difference is small and not likely to have clinical relevance.

M. Taylor and Heaton (2001) studied comprehensive demographically adjusted (age, education, sex, and race/ethnicity) WAIS–III/WMS–III factor scores. Historically, the IQ and memory scores of the Wechsler scales have been adjusted for age. The authors proposed that the comprehensive demographically adjusted norms improves the accuracy of diagnostic classification for WAIS–III and WMS–III scores. Taylor and Heaton employed sophisticated fractional polynomial regression procedures with the WAIS–III/WMS–III standardization sample and oversample data to create demographically adjusted norms. They explored multiple cut-off criteria and determined that 1.0 SD provided optimal sensitivity and specificity statistics. The number of impaired factor scores also provides useful neurodiagnostic information. Demographically corrected norms are available in the upgraded version of the WAIS–III/WMS–III/WIAT–II scoring assistant software program.

The demographically adjusted norms provide the clinician with an estimate of the examinee's current intellectual and memory performance relative to a homogeneous subgroup similar in age, education level, sex, and race/ethnicity. With demographically adjusted norms, the clinician can determine if the respondent's current cognitive performance is below expectations, given specific background variables. Below-expected performance may indicate the presence of a clinical condition that has affected the examinee's cognitive functioning. Demographically adjusted norms are not intended for the purpose of making judgments regarding intellectual capacity, expected functional capacity, or predicted academic abilities. These norms are useful in the context of a neuropsychological evaluation. They are a means of avoiding overestimation of neuropsychological impairments in some groups (e.g., low educational level) and increasing sensitivity to impairment in other groups (e.g., high educational level). The use of demographically adjusted norms to diagnose a learning disability or mental retardation, to predict an individual's educational abilities or ability to perform a specific job, or to determine if the individual has functional disability would be inappropriate. When using demographically adjusted norms to make judgments regarding acquired neurocognitive impairment, clinicians are encouraged to also consider any other relevant psychosocial information (e.g., all specific education or occupational records) that may be available.

Prediction of Premorbid Intellectual and Memory Functioning

The *Wechsler Test of Adult Reading* (WTAR; The Psychological Corporation, 2001) was developed and co-normed along with the WAIS–III and WMS–III.

The methodology for the development of the WTAR is directly associated with the *National Adult Reading Test* (NART; Nelson, 1982) and the North American counterparts of the NART, *American Version of the National Adult Reading Test* (AMNART; Grober & Sliwinski, 1991) and *North American Adult Reading Test* (NAART; Blair & Spreen, 1989). All of these tests are based on a reading recognition paradigm, which requires no text comprehension or word definition, but only recognition of words that have irregular grapheme-to-phoneme translation. These tests share some item content.

The use of words with irregular pronunciation minimizes the assessment of the *current ability* of the examinee to apply standard pronunciation rules and maximizes the assessment of *previous learning* of the word (Grober & Sliwinski, 1991; Nelson, 1982). Unlike many intellectual and memory abilities, reading recognition is *relatively* stable in the presence of cognitive declines associated with normal aging or brain insult, although it is not impervious to the effects of significant intellectual impairments (see Crawford [1992], Spreen & Strauss [1998], Putnam, Ricker, Ross, & Kurtz [1999] for reviews).

Numerous methodologies have been developed in an attempt to determine intellectual loss or decline. Each of the methodologies has strengths and weaknesses that affect the accuracy and utility of that approach (see Putnam et al., 1999, for a review). The NART methodology has been studied extensively and shown to be an effective method for predicting verbal, performance, and full-scale IQ with enhanced predictive power when demographic variables are used concurrently in prediction equations (Crawford, 1992).

The WTAR manual provides tables of predicted intellectual functioning based on demographic variables and a methodology similar to that developed by Barona, Reynolds, and Chastain (1984).

The WTAR was developed for use in the United States and United Kingdom and provides the clinician a test with decided advantages over other reading tests designed to predict premorbid intellectual functioning.

- The WTAR is normed on a large, nationally representative, stratified sample.

- The WTAR is directly linked to and co-normed with the WAIS–III and WMS–III. Prediction equations are available for WAIS–III Index scores and selected WMS–III Index scores.

- Norms are provided for a wide age range, from late adolescence through late adulthood.

- Validity data from samples with a variety of clinical disorders indicate the utility of WTAR prediction of WAIS–III Index scores and WMS–III memory performance.

- Prediction of WTAR scores based on demographic variables enables the user to better determine whether demographic variables or WTAR plus demographic variables is most appropriate for predicting a respondent's IQ and memory scores.

- Tables provide for easy conversion of WTAR and demographic variables to predicted IQ and memory performance. Scores predicted from WTAR performance alone, demographic variables alone, or WTAR performance plus demographic variables are presented.

The purpose of the WTAR is not for the assessment and diagnosis of developmental reading disorders, as is the WIAT–II, but rather for the estimation of premorbid intellectual and memory abilities. The use of WTAR and demographics predictions of intellectual functioning should not be used as a direct measure of intellectual ability. These measures have not been validated for the purposes of identifying intellectual capacity, prediction of academic potential, identifying mental deficiency or developmental disability, prediction of employability or job performance, or determination of disability status. These measures are valid only for the purposes of estimating an examinee's intellectual status prior to illness or injury.

The demographically adjusted norms and the WTAR are different methods for determining whether an examinee's current performance is consistent with the expected performance of individuals with similar psychosocial backgrounds. The WTAR adds another dimension to this assessment by testing the examinee's current word-reading ability, which has been shown to be relatively insensitive to the effects of brain injury and cognitive decline. The clinician tests the hypothesis: In view of this examinee's psychosocial background (age, education, sex, race/ethnicity) and reading skills, what is the examinee's expected intellectual ability? Is the examinee's current ability level consistent with what is expected based on his or her psychosocial background and reading ability? The clinician is able to determine whether the degree of difference is statistically significant and whether the frequency of the difference is rare or common.

Malingering Studies

Killgore and DellaPietra (2000a) investigated the use of the Logical Memory delayed recognition to detect response bias and possible malingering. The recall trial is presented in a yes/no format, so the examinee has a 50% chance of responding correctly to an item by guessing (Killgore & DellaPietra, 2000a). The authors concluded that the wording of the items and the sequential ordering would result in an examinee's being able to guess the correct answer without any knowledge of the actual story. The authors identified three sources of item bias: yes-saying to proper names, priming of yes responses by previous items of similar content, and nay-saying to unlikely occurrences. On the basis of these hypotheses, Killgore and DellaPietra predicted which items would demonstrate a response bias. They administered the Logical Memory recall trial to a nonclinical control group without having exposed the respondents to the stories. The results generally supported their hypotheses. The authors then administered the items according to standard procedures to a mixed neurological sample to determine if patients who had received the standard protocol also exhibited a higher tendency of endorsing the identified items as well as recall items that did not pull for specific responses. The clinical group obtained higher scores than did the "naíve" control group and a "better-than-chance" level of performance. The results indicated that patients with memory problems had recognized some of the story content. Item-level analysis provided further evidence that presentation of item content resulted in more correct responses than would be expected by chance.

In a second study, Killgore and DellaPietra (2000b) identified six items on the WMS–III Logical Memory subtest that were correctly endorsed above chance levels by a nonclinical group. The subtest was administered to a group of control respondents who were instructed to feign memory impairment and to a mixed clinical group. The authors' purpose was to determine if the six items would discriminate among the three groups: naíve, malingerers, and patients. The six items were entered into a discriminate function analysis, and the results were highly significant, with 98.9% classification accuracy. A computational equation was derived for the six items, and this total score was resubmitted to discriminate analysis. This analysis yielded the same results as the analysis with the items entered individually. Killgore and

DellaPietra used a cutoff score of 136 and below to indicate malingering (subtest scores range from –22 to 226). The cutoff score resulted in 97% sensitivity and 100% specificity in identifying malingerers. The authors suggested that these findings provide initial support for the use of the Logical Memory recall trial in the assessment of malingering versus actual brain injury.

Sequential Assessment

The clinician may be required to assess the functioning of the same patient on more than one occasion for a variety of clinical reasons (e.g., assess change after surgery or cognitive decline), or multiple clinicians might assess the functioning of the same patient using the same instruments (medical–legal cases). Iverson (2001) utilized the test–retest correlations to compute reliable change estimates for the primary WAIS–III and WMS–III index scores in three clinical groups.

Lineweaver and Chelune (2000d) proposed a methodology for evaluating significant changes in WAIS–III and WMS–III scores over time. The methodology assumes practice effects result in non-zero interval changes, influences of measurement error, and regression to the mean. The reliable change index is noted to be limited by assuming a zero change score from Time 1 to Time 2. The authors proposed the use of a regression-based approach that controls for non-zero changes over time and the influences of other variables such as age. The standard error of regression is used as a measure of significant change. The authors illustrated the application of the methodology, providing several case examples.

Other Issues

Since the original publication of the *WAIS–III—WMS–III Technical Manual*, several issues regarding the use of the WAIS–III and the WMS–III have emerged.

Tulsky and Zhu (2000) investigated potential fatigue effects on the normative data for the Letter–Number Sequencing subtest. During standardization, the Letter–Number Sequencing subtest was administered as part of the WMS–III, which was administered in counterbalanced order with the WAIS–III. Tulsky and Zhu compared the performance of participants who were administered Letter–Number Sequencing before completing the WAIS–III to the performance of those completing the subtest after the WAIS–III had been administered. The authors found no performance differences, even for the older age groups.

Zhu and Tulsky (2000) examined all of the WAIS–III and WMS–III subtests and index scores to determine if order of presentation resulted in differences in performance. The authors noted very small effects for Digit Span and Digit Symbol—Coding of the WAIS–III and for Faces II and Logical Memory II of the WMS–III. The effect sizes were very small, a result suggesting that the mean performance on the subtests across administration orders was very similar. This finding indicates that administration order did not invalidate the norms developed for these tasks. The index scores and most subtest scores did not exhibit any significant effects of administration order (Zhu & Tulsky, 2000). The findings from these studies are consistent with those by Doss et al. (2000), who found no differences in performance level between the longer standardization versions and the published versions of the two instruments.

This update of the *WAIS–III—WMS–III Technical Manual* includes a new table of scaled scores for Digit Span Backward (see Appendix E). These norms enable the clinician to determine if the patient has a specific weakness on Digits Backward relative to his or her overall performance on that subtest.

CHAPTER 5

Interpretive Considerations

This chapter focuses on basic interpretive considerations of the WAIS–III and the WMS–III and addresses general interpretive issues concerning selected topics and test scores. The chapter also briefly discusses how some of the new features that have been added and some of the changes from the previous versions of the Wechsler scales might be used in clinical practice.

Results from the WAIS–III and the WMS–III provide important information regarding an individual's neurocognitive functioning, but they should never be interpreted in isolation. Four broad sources of information are typically available to the clinician conducting a psychological or neuropsychological evaluation: medical and psychosocial history, direct behavioral observations, quantitative test scores, and qualitative aspects of test performance. The WAIS–III and the WMS–III provide quantitative and qualitative information that is best interpreted in conjunction with a thorough history and careful clinical observations of the examinee. Results should always be evaluated within the context of the reasons for referral and all known collateral information.

Scores and Descriptive Classifications

Subtest raw scores for the WAIS–III and the WMS–III are transformed to age-corrected subtest scaled scores with a mean of 10 and a standard deviation of 3 (the WMS–III also includes some instances in which raw scores are transformed to percentile ranks). A subtest scaled score of 10 reflects the average performance of a given age group (or the reference group). Scores of 7 and 13 correspond to 1 *SD* below and above the mean, respectively, and scaled scores of 4 and 16 deviate 2 *SD*s from the mean.

The WAIS–III and the WMS–III also yield standard scores based on various composites of subtest scaled scores. The WAIS–III IQ and Index scores and the WMS–III Index scores, both computed as standard scores, also share a common metric for evaluating level of performance. The IQ and Index scores are scaled to a metric with a mean of 100 and a standard deviation of 15 for each age group. A score of 100 on any of these measures defines the average performance of individuals similar in age. Scores of 85 and 115 correspond to 1 *SD* below and above the mean, respectively, whereas scores of 70 and 130 are 2 *SD*s below and above the mean. About 68% of all examinees obtain scores between 85 and 115, about 95% score in the 70–130 range, and nearly all examinees obtain scores between 55 and 145 (3 *SD*s on either side of the mean). The relation of WAIS–III IQ and Index scores and WMS–III Index scores to deviations from the mean and the associated percentile rank equivalents are presented in Table 5.1. Additionally, the WMS–III yields four composite scores that represent various aspects of auditory learning. Scores for these supplemental composites are presented as percentile rank equivalents, which represent an individual's standing compared to the normative group. The descriptive classifications corresponding to the IQ and Index scores for the WAIS–III and the WMS–III are presented in Table 5.2

Use of Confidence Intervals Around Scores

As described in Chapter 3, reporting a score in terms of confidence intervals is a means of expressing the reliability of that test score. Confidence intervals assist the examiner in test interpretation by delineating a range of scores in which the examinee's "true" score most likely falls, and reminds the examiner that the observed score contains measurement error.

Normative Reference Groups

The computation of subtest scaled scores for both the WAIS–III and the WMS–III are based on the performance of examinees in 13 age groups within the standardization samples. With these age-corrected scaled scores, an individual's performance is compared to that of his or her age peers. The age-corrected scaled scores are used to derive the IQ and Index scores. This methodology is consistent with the construction of IQ and Index scores for the WISC–III. The procedure, however, represents a significant departure from the one used to derive subtest scaled scores of the WAIS–R, which are based on the performance of a reference group of individuals aged 20–34 years. This change, however, does not affect the IQ scores because the WAIS–R sums of subtest scaled scores (i.e., based on the reference group's scaled scores) were age-corrected at the IQ score level. The primary difference is that the age correction in the WAIS–III occurs at the subtest scaled-score level rather than at the level of the sums of scaled scores.

Table 5.1. Relation of IQ and Index Scores to Standard Deviations From the Mean and Percentile Rank Equivalents

IQ/Index Score	Number of *SD*s From the Mean	Percentile Rank Equivalent[a]
155	+3⅔	>99.9
150	+3⅓	>99.9
145	+3	99.9
140	+2⅔	99.6
135	+2⅓	99
130	+2	98
125	+1⅔	95
120	+1⅓	91
115	+1	84
110	+⅔	75
105	+⅓	63
100	0 (Mean)	50
95	−⅓	37
90	−⅔	25
85	−1	16
80	−1⅓	9
75	−1⅔	5
70	−2	2
65	−2⅓	1
60	−2⅔	0.4
55	−3	0.1
50	−3⅓	<0.1
45	−3⅔	<0.1

[a] The percentile ranks are theoretical values for a normal distribution.

Table 5.2. Qualitative Descriptions of IQ and Index Scores

Score	Classification	Percent Included in Theoretical Normal Curve
130 and above	Very Superior	2.2
120–129	Superior	6.7
110–119	High Average	16.1
90–109	Average	50.0
80–89	Low Average	16.1
70–79	Borderline	6.7
69 and below	Extremely Low	2.2

The use of age-corrected scaled scores in the WAIS–III is supported by research and empirical data. In terms of brain functioning, young adulthood represents the stage when the brain has reached physical maturation but has not yet been significantly affected by normal, age-related neurodegenerative processes. Analyses of the WAIS–III and WMS–III standardization data reveal that for many tasks, young adults (ages 20–34) obtain the highest scores of any age group across the life span. However, performance on some tasks, such as Vocabulary and Information subtests, increases until 40–50 years of age. Reference-group norms do not account for such changes. The age-corrected subtest scaled scores, on the other hand, reflect an individual's standing in relation to his or her age-matched peers.

Comparisons to a reference group of 20- to 34-year-olds is still possible at the subtest level for the WAIS–III, but such comparisons are considered secondary, or supplementary, for interpretation. For the WMS–III, the addition of optional, reference-group norms is a change from the WMS–R. When subtest score interpretations involve questions about performance relative to that of a younger group, the reference-group norms are appropriate. The reference-group norms might be compared to the age-adjusted norms as a way of highlighting the effects of age, if any, on memory and other cognitive functions.

Level of Performance

In its most straightforward form, level of performance refers to the rank (usually expressed as a scaled or standard score, percentile rank, and descriptive classification) obtained by an individual on a given test in comparison to the performance by an appropriate normative group. For clinical decisions, level of performance is important for estimating the presence and severity of any impairment or presence of a relative strength. For nonclinical settings (e.g., industrial and occupational settings), the emphasis of level of performance is placed more on competency and the patterns of a person's strengths and weaknesses without necessarily implying any type of impairment. Test results can be described in a manner similar to the following example:

> Relative to individuals of comparable age [or, alternatively, of a reference group of younger adults], this individual is currently functioning in the [descriptive classification] (see Table 5.2) range on a standardized measure of [IQ or Index name].

Examiners should keep in mind that IQ and Index scores are estimates of overall functioning in a particular cognitive domain or content area. As such, composite scores should always be evaluated in the context of those measures that contribute to the specific IQ scale or index. The interpretation of an IQ or Index score may be influenced by substantial differences between the subtest scores on which the IQ or Index score is based. Two component subtest scores, one unusually high and one unusually low, for example, will push the Index score toward the arithmetic mean and thus toward the *average* range. Such an *average* score reflects a dramatically different pattern of abilities than does an *average* Index score obtained from two subtest scores that are both in the *average* range. Evaluation of the component scores of IQ and Index scores is important, and the failure to evaluate them can lead to erroneous clinical inferences, especially when such components and the Index scores are interpreted in isolation. As stated in the opening paragraphs of this chapter, the clinical interpretation of the WAIS–III and WMS–III scores should be conducted in the context of the individual's medical and psychosocial history and in consideration of behavioral and other qualitative observations.

WAIS–III

Description of IQ Scores

The VIQ score of the WAIS–III is a measure of acquired knowledge, verbal reasoning, and attention to verbal materials. The items that compose the subtests of this scale, even those included in the Stimulus Booklet, are presented verbally, and the examinee articulates the responses. The VIQ score, apart from some content changes of the scale at the item level, is relatively unchanged from the VIQ score in the WAIS–R.

The PIQ score is a measure of fluid reasoning, spatial processing, attentiveness to detail, and visual–motor integration. The tasks should be fairly novel to the first-time examinee. The PIQ score, apart from some changes of the scale at the item level, is basically similar to the PIQ score of the WAIS–R. In the WAIS–III, however, the impact of bonus points has been reduced. The Object Assembly subtest has been made optional and replaced with Matrix Reasoning, which does not depend on quick performance. With the introduction of Matrix Reasoning, the PIQ score is less speed-dependent and places greater emphasis on abstract, nonverbal reasoning.

The FSIQ score is the overall summary score that estimates an individual's general level of intellectual functioning. It is the aggregate score of the VIQ and PIQ scores and is usually considered to be the score that is most representative of *g*, or global intellectual functioning.

Description of Index Scores

Like the VIQ score, the VCI score of the WAIS–III is a measure of verbal acquired knowledge and verbal reasoning. The items of the subtests that compose this index are presented verbally, and the examinee must articulate the responses. The major difference between this score and the VIQ score is the inclusion of Digit Span, Arithmetic, and Comprehension in the VIQ scale. Because the attentional/working memory subtests, that is, Arithmetic and Digit Span, are not included in the VCI, the index may be conceptualized as a more refined, "purer" measure of verbal comprehension.

The POI score of the WAIS–III is a measure of nonverbal, fluid reasoning, attentiveness to detail, and visual–motor integration. All of the items of the subtests that compose this scale are presented in the Stimulus Booklet; the examinee responds by pointing, building block designs, or indicating a response choice (orally or by pointing). Quick responding is less important on the POI than it is on the PIQ scale because the subtest most related to processing speed (Digit Symbol—Coding) is not included in this index. Moreover, only one of the three subtests of the POI includes bonus points for quick performance. The composition of the POI score makes it a more refined measure of fluid reasoning and visual–spatial problem solving than the PIQ score.

The Working Memory indexes of both the WAIS–III and the WMS–III are highly correlated ($r = .82$). The subtests of both indexes include a range of tasks that require the examinee to attend to information, to hold briefly and process that information in memory, and then to formulate a response. The main difference between the WAIS–III and WMS–III indexes is the inclusion of Arithmetic and Digit Span (verbal tasks) in the WAIS–III index and the inclusion of a nonverbal task (Spatial Span) in the WMS–III. The working memory subtests composing the WAIS–III index include only verbally presented items, whereas the WMS–III index is equally represented by subtests with auditorily and visually presented items.

The PSI score is a measure of the individual's ability to process visual information quickly. Comparisons between the PSI and POI scores can reveal possible effects of time demands on visual–spatial reasoning and problem solving. Research has suggested that the PSI is also highly sensitive to many different neuropsychological conditions (see Chapter 4).

IQ Scores Versus Index Scores

Unlike its predecessors, the WAIS–III provides options for two sets of scores. The examiner should consider these options before deciding which subtests to administer (see Figure 1.1 of the *WAIS–III Administration and Scoring Manual*). When time permits, or the goal is to obtain extensive data about intellectual functioning, all 13 subtests (excluding Object Assembly, which is optional) should be administered. Doing so increases testing time from the WAIS–R administration time by approximately 5 minutes but allows for the computation of both IQ and Index scores. However, the requirements of the clinical situation or time constraints may preclude the administration of all 13 subtests.

The referral question, purpose of testing, and practical issues (such as time constraints) will determine which scores to obtain and which subtests to administer. Some federal and state laws and regulations require IQ scores and the analysis of the discrepancies between those scores. In such cases, the 11 subtests that make up the WAIS–III IQ scores must be administered. Of course, during the testing, the examiner can watch for any patterns in the examinee's performance to determine if the supplementary subtests (or optional subtest) would aid in the interpretation of the results.

Optional Procedures of the WAIS–III

Discrepancies Between Digit Span Forward and Backward

The ability to repeat digits in the order of verbal (forward) presentation is considered a measure of concentration, and the average adult performance is 7 digits recalled, plus or minus 2 (Miller, 1956; Spitz, 1972). This task tends to remain relatively stable with aging in normally functioning men and women (Weintraub & Mesulam, 1985). Orsini et al. (1987) and Benton, Eslinger, and Damasio (1981) have shown that only a small number of older adults (approximately 8%) show decrements in performance. Digit Span Backward, however, is more affected by aging and by impairment. Costa (1975) has shown that a backward verbal digit span in normally functioning adults is generally one less digit than the forward span. However, normally functioning adults over 70 years old show a greater discrepancy, with a significantly shortened backward span (Lezak, 1995).

To assess this effect of aging, E. Kaplan et al. (1991) have developed measures that highlight the differences between the forward and backward tasks of Digit Span. First, the greatest number of digits recalled in the forward task and the greatest number recalled in the backward task can be compared to the performance of the normative sample (see Table B.6 in the *WAIS–III Administration and Scoring Manual*). Second, the difference between the two can be calculated and compared to the performance of the normative sample (see Table B.7 of the *WAIS–III Administration and Scoring Manual*). These two procedures can help the examiner determine if there are attentional deficits, which become more apparent when the two components of Digit Span are broken down. The information can also help the examiner determine if further testing of working memory functioning is warranted. For example, a significant discrepancy score may indicate that the Spatial Span subtest from the WMS–III should be administered. This subtest is the visual analogue of Digit Span and is also related to the working memory construct.

Digit Symbol Optional Procedures

As E. Kaplan et al. (1991) have pointed out, there may be several reasons for poor performance on Digit Symbol—Coding. In addition to tapping processing speed, the subtest is also affected by motor coordination, short-term memory, visual perception, and clerical speed and accuracy. Some of the potential reasons for an examinee's poor performance can be determined by two optional procedures, which were designed to differentiate incidental memory and graphomotor speed.

The first optional procedure, Digit Symbol—Incidental Learning, taps the individual's ability to learn and remember the number–symbol pairing. On the Digit Symbol—Coding subtest, if an individual must continuously check the key before responding to an item, then his or her performance will be considerably impeded. To determine if failure to learn or to remember digit–symbol combinations is affecting performance on the subtest, the examiner can administer Incidental Learning, which includes two tasks. For the first task, Pairing, the examinee is asked to recall the symbols paired with the numbers. For the second task, Free Recall, the examinee must recall the symbols by themselves. As E. Kaplan et al. (1991) pointed out, if the examinee has difficulty remembering (as indicated by a paucity of symbols recalled, incorrect pairing of the numbers and symbols, and confabulations of the symbol), then the possibility of memory impairment should be considered.

The second optional procedure, Digit Symbol—Copy, requires the examinee to copy the symbols without having to match them to numbers. Performance on this task can reveal whether or not the examinee has difficulty writing the symbols (poor graphomotor production and speed).

Normative data for these optional procedures are presented as cumulative percentages for the 13 age groups and the reference group and are included in Appendix A, Table A.11 of the *WAIS–III Administration and Scoring Manual.*

WMS–III

Examiners who are familiar with the WMS–R will notice that the index structure of the WMS–III has changed in a number of ways.

First, the number of indexes has increased from five in the WMS–R to eight in the WMS–III. The WMS–III includes eight Primary Indexes and four Auditory Process Composites. As their label suggests, the Primary Indexes are intended to be the principal scores used to evaluate memory functioning. The Auditory Process Composites are supplementary in nature and can be used to evaluate various processes of memory when stimuli are presented in the auditory modality.

Second, the WMS–III reflects two notable changes in the index nomenclature. Because the same subtest content can be encoded in different ways (e.g., verbal labels can be given to "nonverbal" materials such as figures or pictures), the "verbal" label used in the WMS–R was changed to reflect more accurately the modality of presentation rather than the index content. Therefore, the label "auditory," which is the parallel to "visual," is used instead of "verbal." In some instances, however, the label "verbal" was retained because of historical continuity (e.g., the Verbal Paired Associates subtest dates to the early 1900s). Next, the Attention/Concentration Index of the WMS–R was renamed on the WMS–III to the Working Memory Index. This change reflects the content shift from relatively low-level attentional tasks to relatively high-level working memory tasks. For example, Letter–Number Sequencing (a complex working memory task) replaces the Mental Control subtest on the Working Memory Index.

Third, the WMS–III indexes represent significant revisions of the content of the WMS–R. The two subtests that contribute to the visual memory indexes—Faces and Family Pictures—are new, as is the Letter–Number Sequencing subtest. The Visual Reproduction, Mental Control, and Digit Span subtests were retained in the WMS–III but are now optional subtests. Additionally, whenever possible, delayed recognition tasks were included for comparison with performance on the delayed recall conditions.

Finally, the method of calculating several WMS–III Index scores differs significantly from that used in the WMS–R. The WMS–R Verbal Memory Index and Visual Memory Index are analogous to the WMS–III Auditory Immediate and Visual Immediate indexes. The WMS–R General Memory Index is most similar to the WMS–III Immediate Memory Index. The WMS–III General Memory Index consists of only delayed memory subtests, in sharp contrast to the WMS–R General Memory Index, which is composed of only immediate memory subtests. This conceptual shift from immediate to delayed measures to represent the global memory score (i.e., General Memory) was based on two considerations: First, the relationship between immediate memory and delayed memory is such that adequate performance on delayed subtests warrants the assumption of adequate immediate memory, whereas the reverse is not always true. Second, the delayed memory measures conceptually correspond more closely to real-life or everyday memory demands; thus the ecological validity of delayed measures is likely to be greater.

Primary Indexes

Auditory Immediate and Auditory Delayed Indexes

The Auditory Immediate Index is composed of the Logical Memory I and Verbal Paired Associates I subtests, and its score is calculated as follows:

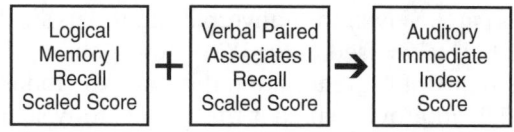

The Auditory Delayed Index is composed of the Logical Memory II and Verbal Paired Associates II subtests, with its score calculated as follows:

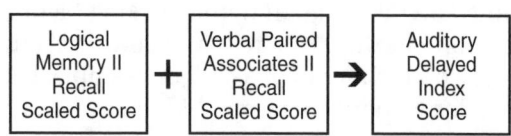

During Logical Memory I, narrative stories are read aloud to the examinee, who is asked to retell them from memory. The Verbal Paired Associates I subtest requires examinees to learn pairs of words that are seemingly unrelated. With the exception of the first story of Logical Memory I, all information to be remembered from these two subtests is presented at least twice. These subtests require the examinee to recall (via free recall) the information later. For Logical Memory II and Verbal Paired Associates II, the delayed conditions, the examinee is asked to recall again the material that was presented in the immediate condition. The immediate and delayed conditions are temporally separated by approximately 25–35 minutes. The Auditory Immediate Index and Auditory Delayed Index scores are calculated by summing the appropriate scaled scores; the subtests that compose each index are thus equally weighted.

These Index scores are measures of memory functioning when stimuli are presented in the auditory modality. Low scores, relative to an individual's intellectual and attentional functioning, may suggest a verbal learning or memory problem. A low score on the delayed index, relative to that on the immediate index, may indicate a high rate of forgetting. The assessment of delayed recall should always be made in the context of the immediate condition because delayed recall (i.e., the amount of information available through recall) depends on the amount of information that was initially acquired. In other words, inferences about an examinee's inability to retain information may be inaccurate if relatively little information is learned initially.

Visual Immediate and Visual Delayed Indexes

The Visual Immediate Index is composed of the Faces I and Family Pictures I subtests, with its score calculated as follows:

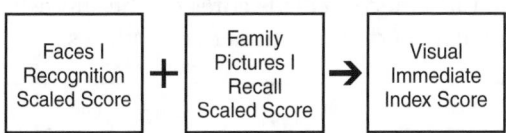

The Visual Delayed Index is composed of the Faces II and Family Pictures II subtests, with its score calculated as follows:

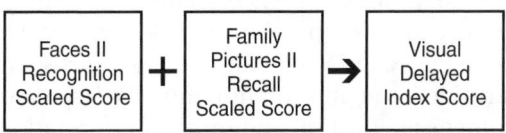

For Faces I, the examinee is initially presented photographs of 24 target faces. The examinee is then presented photographs of 48 faces, including the 24 target faces and 24 new faces. The examinee must identify each face as either a target face or a new one. For Faces II, the examinee is again presented the 24 target faces and 24 different faces and is again asked to identify each face as either a target face or a new one. For Family Pictures I, a family portrait and four subsequent scenes involving the family characters and family dog are shown to the examinee. The examinee is asked to identify who was in each scene and each character's activity and location. Family Pictures II requires the examinee to recall the same information without again seeing the family portrait or the four scenes. The immediate and delayed conditions are temporally separated by approximately 25–35 minutes. As with the auditory indexes, the visual indexes are equally weighted by their component subtests.

The interpretation of scores for the Visual Immediate and Visual Delayed indexes is similar to that of the Auditory Immediate and Auditory Delayed indexes. These Index scores summarize overall memory functioning when information is presented visually. Low scores, relative to an individual's intellectual and attentional functioning, may reflect a memory weakness or impairment when information is presented visually. The interpretation of scores on the Visual Delayed Index should be made in the context of performance on the Visual Immediate Index. It is also important for examiners to keep in mind that the subtests that compose these visual indexes represent both a recognition paradigm (Faces) and a recall paradigm (Family Pictures). Consequently, meaningful differences between the scores on Faces and Family Pictures, with a higher Faces score, may indicate retrieval difficulties.

Immediate Memory Index

The Immediate Memory Index score is calculated by summing, and thus equally weighting, the sums of scaled scores on the subtests that compose the Auditory Immediate and Visual Immediate indexes:

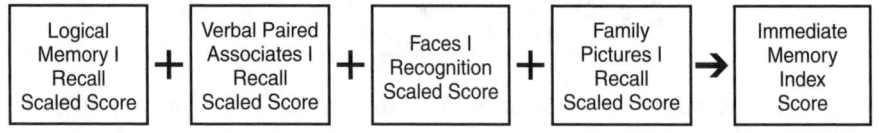

The Immediate Memory Index score is considered the best global indicator of immediate memory functioning. However, differences between the Auditory Immediate Index and Visual Immediate Index scores can be evaluated to determine if the presentation modality (spoken or visual) has affected the examinee's acquisition and recall of information. Low scores, relative to intellectual functioning, attention, or delayed memory, may represent a weakness or deficit in learning or immediate memory.

Auditory Recognition Delayed Index

The Auditory Recognition Delayed Index is composed of the Logical Memory II and Verbal Paired Associates II subtests. This Index score is simply a linear transformation from the Auditory Recognition Delayed Index scaled score (metric of 1–19) to the Auditory Recognition Delayed Index standard score metric:

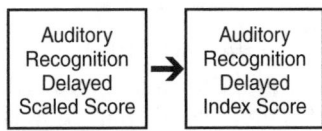

The Auditory Recognition Delayed Index is the recognition counterpart to the Auditory Delayed Index, which incorporates a recall procedure. The Auditory Recognition Delayed Index is formed by adding the recognition raw scores of Logical Memory II and Verbal Paired Associates II and converting that sum first to a scaled score and then to an Index score. The Auditory Recognition Delayed Index score does not represent an equal weighting of the Logical Memory II and Verbal Paired Associates II scores. Compared to Verbal Paired Associates delayed recognition, Logical Memory delayed recognition has greater variance. Therefore, the Auditory Recognition Delayed Index is more heavily weighted in the direction of Logical Memory.

Information retrieval based on recognition is generally easier than retrieval based on free recall. Thus, low scores on the Auditory Delayed Index with relatively better performance on the Auditory Recognition Delayed Index may indicate retrieval difficulties.

General Memory Index

As stated previously, the composition of the General Memory Index of the WMS–III represents a significant departure from the WMS–R. The WMS–III Immediate Memory Index is analogous in composition to the WMS–R General Memory Index because both are measures of *immediate* memory. As shown in the following equation, the WMS–III General Memory Index score represents a global measure of *delayed* memory and is made up of the sum of scaled scores on the subtests that compose the Auditory Delayed Index, the Visual Delayed Index, and the Auditory Recognition Delayed Index:

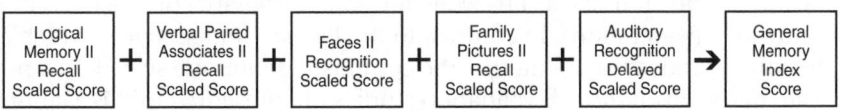

Any differences between the subtest scaled scores that contribute to the General Memory Index score should be considered in its interpretation. To the extent that these component scores are substantially different, the General Memory Index score may not represent a unitary global estimate of memory functioning. The General Memory Index score, however, is considered the best overall measure of the types of abilities that are critical to effective memory in day-to-day tasks (i.e., memory of newly learned information after delays during which intervening cognitive activity occurs).

Working Memory Index

The Working Memory Index of the WMS–III shares a subtest in common with the WAIS–III: Letter–Number Sequencing. The WMS–III Working Memory Index also includes the Spatial Span subtest, whereas the WAIS–III Working Memory Index includes the Arithmetic and Digit Span subtests. As such, the WMS–III Working Memory Index is equally weighted with one auditorily presented task (Letter–Number Sequencing) and one visually presented task (Spatial Span). In contrast, the WAIS–III Working Memory Index is composed of all auditorily presented tasks. The WMS–III Working Memory Index score is calculated as follows:

For nonimpaired individuals (i.e., the standardization sample), the Working Memory indexes of the WMS–III and the WAIS–III correlated very highly ($r = .82$, $p < .001$). The WMS–III Working Memory Index also correlates very highly with the WMS–R Attention/Concentration Index (see Chapter 4 of this Manual).

The Working Memory Index is a measure of complex or high-level attentional tasks that stress the ability to attend to information, to hold and process that information in memory, and to formulate a response based on that information. Low scores relative to overall intellectual functioning may indicate a working memory weakness or impairment.

Auditory Process Composites

The four Auditory Process Composites—Single-Trial Learning, Learning Slope, Retention, and Retrieval—were developed primarily on the basis of theoretical considerations. In contrast to the Primary Index scores, which are scaled on a standard-score metric, the composite scores are scaled on a percentile metric. Even though validation studies are presented in this Manual, scores on these composites should be interpreted cautiously until further validation studies are conducted. Although this Manual presents relevant psychometric data concerning reliability and validity of the composite scores, the clinician should understand the complex nature of these scores (e.g., many are composed of difference scores, ratios, percentages, etc.). For example, the Retention Composite score is a ratio of delayed memory to immediate memory that is converted to a "savings" percentage score.

Moreover, the Retention Composite represents a relative measure of memory retention that controls the level of immediate acquisition. The level of acquisition, however, modifies the interpretation of the Retention Composite score. These conceptual and psychometric complexities should be adequately appreciated by those who interpret the scores from these composites. Due to the nature of the scores, interpretations based on the Auditory Process Composites should be especially cautious, and conclusions confirmed with data from multiple sources.

Single-Trial Learning Composite

The Single-Trial Learning Composite comprises the first trial of both stories of Logical Memory I and the first trial of Verbal Paired Associates I, and its score is calculated as follows:

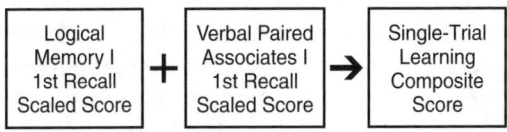

The Single-Trial Learning Composite is very highly correlated with the Auditory Immediate Index. This composite is a measure of recall capacity after a single presentation of material. Low scores, relative to attention and overall intellectual capabilities, may indicate weaknesses or deficits in immediate auditory memory. The Single-Trial Learning Composite also forms the comparison standard for the evaluation of learning through repetition (see the discussion of the Learning Slope Composite next).

Learning Slope Composite

The Learning Slope Composite is a measure of the relative increase from the first trial to the last trial (i.e., last trial score minus first trial score) for Logical Memory I Story B and Verbal Paired Associates I. The score is calculated as follows:

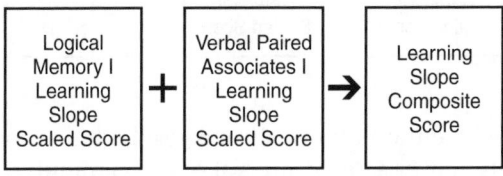

High raw scores, that is, the difference score between the last and first presentation trials, indicate a substantial increase in performance. High Learning Slope Composite scores indicate good learning performance relative to the first trial, whereas low scores indicate a diminished ability to profit from multiple trials. The Learning Slope Composite should always be interpreted in the context of initial performance (i.e., in the context of the Single-Trial Learning Composite score). When initial performance is high, performance cannot improve much over subsequent trials. For example, an individual who recalls 7 of the 8 word pairs in Trial 1 of Verbal Paired Associates I can improve his or her learning-slope score by only 1 raw-score point. Conversely, when initial performance is low, performance on subsequent trials can greatly improve.

Retention Composite

Percent retention scores for the WMS were first proposed by Russell (1975). Retention scores have been found clinically useful in differentiating normally functioning individuals from individuals with dementia (e.g., Welsh, Butters, Hughes, Mohs, & Heyman, 1991) and may be useful in discriminating among various clinical groups (Tröster et al., 1993). Normative percent retention scores for the WMS–R have been reported by Prifitera and Ledbetter (1992). Also, percent retention scores were shown to be significantly related to level of education (Ledbetter & Prifitera, 1993).

The WMS–III Primary Indexes are measures of an individual's immediate and delayed memory relative to a normative sample. Note that although scores on the delayed indexes represent the individual's performance at the delayed point (relative to his or her peers), they do not represent the individual's efficiency in delayed memory relative to his or her own immediate performance. In contrast, the Retention Composite is a measure of delayed free recall relative to the individual's performance in the immediate condition. In effect, the individual is serving as his or her own control. The Retention Composite score is calculated as follows:

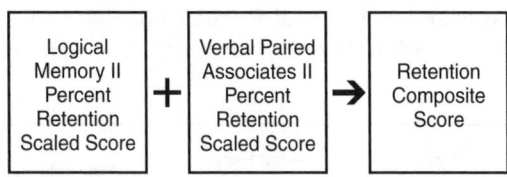

Low scores on the Retention Composite suggest high rates of forgetting of auditory information over a delay interval of 25–35 minutes. An adequate evaluation of the retention of material at delayed recall must be based on at least a minimal immediate score. An evaluation of delayed memory is difficult when initial acquisition is low. Therefore, percent retention scores must always be interpreted in the context of initial acquisition. That is to say, identical percent retention scores for two individuals may be obtained by two very different levels of performance. A retention score of 50%, for example, might be based on the examinee's remembering two Logical Memory I units at immediate recall and one unit at delayed recall. Another examinee's retention score of 50% might be based on his or her remembering 50 units in the immediate condition and 25 units in the delayed condition.

Retrieval Composite

The Retrieval Composite score is calculated by subtracting the average of the Logical Memory II and Verbal Paired Associates II recall scaled scores from the combined Logical Memory II and Verbal Paired Associates II recognition scaled score:

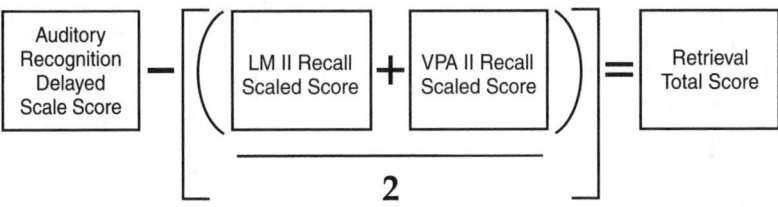

The Retrieval Composite is a measure of the degree to which cuing increases information retrieval beyond the amount of information available through free recall. High scores suggest that more information may be available in the examinee's knowledge base than he or she can access through free, unaided recall; that is, they may suggest that the person has a retrieval problem. Average scores suggest that free recall accesses most or all of the newly learned material. Low scores suggest that recognition is poorer than recall (possibly due to a ceiling effect). Identification errors during recognition memory testing may reflect guessing or may suggest that nontarget stimuli (i.e., foils or distractors) interfere with retrieval and that the examinee has difficulty differentiating accurately between previously presented material and incorrect alternatives.

Subtests

Information and Orientation

Information and Orientation is an optional subtest and does not contribute to the WMS–III Index scores. Findings on this subtest can help the examiner determine the appropriateness of a memory test or the examinee's ability to be validly tested on the more complex and demanding components of the WMS–III. Relatively low scores may be caused by a variety of factors, such as disorientation, aphasia, inattention, poor motivation, or a thought disorder. To the degree that such factors affect test results, interpretation should take

Table 5.3. Frequencies (Cumulative Percentages) of Information and Orientation Total Scores by Age

Total Score						Age Group							
	16-17	18-19	20-24	25-29	30-34	35-44	45-54	55-64	65-69	70-74	75-79	80-84	85-89
14	100	100	100	100	100	100	100	100	100	100	100	100	100
13	27	24	34	30	27	30	34	33	34	41	49	37	59
12	5	4	10	5	8	8	5	10	6	12	19	16	24
11	1			3	1	4	1	5	4	4	10	13	12
10							1	1		1	3	5	5
9										1	3	3	5
8											3	1	5
7											1	1	3
6												1	
5													
4													
3													
2													
1													
0													

these into account. As shown in Table 5.3, individuals in the standardization sample rarely obtained *raw* scores below 10 on Information and Orientation.

Logical Memory

With some differences in the content, administration, and scoring, the WMS, WMS–R, and WMS–III have all included the Logical Memory subtests. The WMS–III Logical Memory subtests contain a new story (i.e., Story B) and revised administration and scoring procedures. The Logical Memory I Total Score is computed by summing the recall units for Story A and the recall units for both trials of Story B. The second trial of Story B was added for two reasons. First, performance on the two recall trials of Story B can be contrasted (i.e., the Learning Slope scaled score can be obtained) to evaluate any deviations from expected change from the first to second trials. Also, the second trial of Story B increases the likelihood that the examinee will "learn" or acquire enough of the material to be remembered later in the delayed condition. This repetition helps to ensure that initial learning is maximized because retention of material can be evaluated only in the context of the material initially learned.

Low scores on the Logical Memory I and II recall measures may suggest deficits or weaknesses in learning of or memory for conceptual material presented in the auditory modality. The supplemental thematic recall scores can be compared to the literal or near-literal recall unit scores. Thematic recall is a measure of the examinee's ability to remember thematic information, which is more general than the specific and literal information that is scored for the Primary Indexes. For example, in the first thematic unit for Story A, the examinee has only to indicate that the story has a female character to receive credit. In contrast, to earn credit for the story recall units, the examinee must identify the character's name. The Logical Memory II percent retention score represents the examinee's retention of material from the immediate condition to the delayed condition.

Verbal Paired Associates

Results from studies of the WMS–R have shown that the hard items on the Verbal Paired Associates tasks correlate more highly with other measures of verbal memory (Macartney–Filgate & Vriezen, 1988) and are more clinically sensitive (Fisher, 1988; Trahan, Larrabee, Quintana, Goethe, & Willingham, 1989) than the easy items. Therefore, revisions of this subtest have included the replacement of overlearned or easily acquired word associations (e.g.,

Baby–Cries) with novel and unrelated word pairs (e.g., *Star–Ladder*). For the WMS–III Verbal Paired Associates, four learning trials of the word-pair list are administered. For the delayed condition (i.e., Verbal Paired Associates II), the examiner reads the first word of each pair, and the examinee provides the second, or "associated," word (i.e., cued recall). For the recognition task, administered after the delayed cued-recall task, the examinee is read a list of 24 word pairs and must identify each word pair either as one presented in the previous conditions or as a new one. Low scores on the Verbal Paired Associates I and II recall measures may suggest deficits or weaknesses in learning or memory for auditory material. In contrast to the material presented in Logical Memory I and II, the stimulus material of Verbal Paired Associates I and II is semantically unrelated. Verbal Paired Associates therefore requires the examinee to organize the material more actively. The Verbal Paired Associates II percent retention score represents the examinee's retention of material from the immediate condition to the delayed condition.

Word Lists

The word list is a familiar paradigm for assessing learning and memory. The WMS–III Word Lists subtest is optional (i.e., none of the Word Lists scores contributes to an Index score). The Word Lists subtest incorporates a full reminding procedure, as in the CVLT (Delis et al., 1987), but unlike the CVLT, the WMS–III subtest does not organize the words into semantic categories.

The Immediate Recall score, which is the sum of List A Trials 1–4, is a measure of immediate recall ability for unstructured material that is repeated during learning. High scores indicate efficient learning and immediate recall, whereas low scores indicate weaknesses or deficits in learning and immediate recall. The Delayed Recall and Delayed Recognition tasks assess information retention and retrieval after a delay of 25–35 minutes. The Word Lists percent retention score is calculated by dividing the Delayed Recall score by the Trial 4 score of Word Lists I and multiplying by 100. This score provides a measure of delayed information-recall efficiency relative to the amount of material previously accessible. Two contrast scores are also calculated: List A Trial 1 versus List B, and List A Trial 4 versus List A Short-Delay Recall. The first contrast score quantifies performance differences on the first trial of each list. The second contrast score indicates whether List A consolidation in memory is adversely affected by the presentation of a word list that is similar in content and structure to the the first list, or whether List B learning is rendered more difficult by prior exposure to List A (proactive interference).

Faces

Faces is a subtest new to the WMS–III and was added because of findings from research with tests using similar paradigms. Results from studies have suggested that memory for faces is sensitive to right hemisphere deficits (Carlesimo & Caltagirone, 1995; Newcombe, de Haan, Ross, & Young, 1989; Schweinberger, Buse, Freeman, Schonle, & Sommer, 1992) and to right temporal lobe and hippocampal lesions. Memory for faces has also been associated with increased right temporal cerebral blood flow (R. C. Gur et al., 1993) and right parietal metabolism (Berardi, Haxby, Grady, & Rapoport, 1991). The memory for faces paradigm has also been found to be sensitive to the effects of right versus left temporal lobe epilepsy in children (Beardsworth & Zaidel, 1994) and adults (Naugle, Chelune, Schuster, Lüders, & Comair, 1994). Low scores on Faces may indicate memory weaknesses or deficits when material is presented visually.

Family Pictures

The recall of stories often involves recall of people, objects, places, and events. The WMS–III Family Pictures subtest was designed to assess recall for scene characters, character activity, and character location. Family Pictures is a new subtest not only to the WMS–III but also to clinical practice and research. Research with tasks that assess similar dimensions have indicated that patients with schizophrenia exhibit impaired spatial location and context (Rizzo et al., 1996). Persons with right hippocampectomy for treatment of temporal lobe epilepsy have been found to exhibit rapid forgetting for spatial location (M. Smith & Milner, 1989). The interpretation of Family Pictures scores should take into account the relative weight the scoring procedure places on the three scoring elements (i.e., memory for character, activity, and location). Scores are character-based; that is, credit for correct activity and location is awarded only in conjunction with scene characters that are correctly identified. Unlike with the Faces subtest, most aspects of Family Pictures can be represented (and presumably encoded) verbally.

Visual Reproduction

Visual reproduction has been related to left hippocampal volume in individuals with traumatic brain injury (Bigler et al., 1996) and to right versus left hippocampal atrophy in female examinees with right hemisphere temporal lobe epilepsy (Trenerry, Jack, Cascino, Sharbrough, & Ivnik, 1996). Results of studies of other versions of this test have indicated that it is not differentially sensitive to right hemisphere lesions (Chelune & Bornstein, 1988; Naugle et al., 1993) but may reveal memory impairment in specific groups (Butters et al., 1988; Fisher, 1988). Research has indicated that performance on visual reproduction subtests may be confounded by constructional dyspraxia in certain clinical groups (Haut et al., 1994) but that visual memory deficits can be detected if these effects are controlled (Haut et al., 1996). Also, experience indicates that this is one of the more difficult and time-consuming WMS and WMS–R subtests to score.

Retained from the WMS and WMS–R, the Visual Reproduction subtest is an optional subtest in the WMS–III. The WMS–III subtest includes two new design cards (A and E); one WMS–R card (Card B) was deleted. In addition to the immediate and delayed recall conditions, the WMS–III Visual Reproduction subtest includes a delayed recognition condition followed by a direct copy task and a discrimination condition. The scoring criteria were also changed on the basis of several studies that compared responses by clinical groups and matched normal control groups. In most cases, the scoring criteria now allow for partial credit.

These changes now allow examiners to make comparisons between delayed recall and recognition. The direct copy score can be compared to the recall measures to assess possible motor-control effects on drawing ability. The discrimination condition can reveal visual–perceptual distortions that might have adversely affected the examinee's learning and memory. Table 5.4 presents the cumulative frequencies for the discrimination condition for each of the 13 standardization age groups. As shown, raw scores below 5 are rare at any age. The Visual Reproduction percent retention score is a measure of the examinee's retention of material over a delay of 25–35 minutes.

Letter–Number Sequencing

The Letter–Number Sequencing subtest is a measure of auditory working memory. The development of this task was based, in part, on the work of Gold et al. (1997). Research has shown that this task is differentially sensitive to a variety of neurocognitive disorders. Also, the ability to perform the task may be spared in individuals with anterograde amnesia (see Gathercole, 1994, and Kopelman, 1994, for a review). The WMS–III Letter–Number Sequencing subtest requires the examinee to order sequentially a series of numbers and letters orally presented in a specified random order. The examinee must first remember the numbers and letters and then reorganize the numbers into ascending order and the letters into alphabetical order.

Spatial Span

Spatial Span is the visual analogue of the Digit Span subtest. Previous versions of spatial span tasks include those designed by Corsi (1972) and by E. Kaplan et al. (1991). Administration is similar to that of the WMS–R subtest except that a three-dimensional board is used rather than the two-dimensional card. The WMS–III Spatial Span Board is a modification

Table 5.4. Frequencies (Cumulative Percentages) of Visual Reproduction Discrimination Total Scores by Age

Total Score	Age Group														
	16–17	18–19	20–24	25–29	30–34	35–44	45–54	55–64	65–69	70–74	75–79	80–84	85–89
7	100	100	100	100	100	100	100	100	100	100	100	100	100
6	22	18	19	24	18	22	21	29	36	42	39	32	63
5	4		2	3	1	1	2	9	7	6	7	9	29
4									1	1		5	11
3												1	3
2													
1													
0													

of the one designed by E. Kaplan et al. (1991). Spatial Span taps the examinee's ability to hold a visual–spatial sequence of events in working memory.

Digit Span

Digit Span is now an optional subtest on the WMS–III and does not contribute to any of the indexes. The Digit Span subtest is composed of Digit Span Forward and Digit Span Backward, which, as noted by E. Kaplan et al. (1991), may tap different functions. Digit Span Forward is a measure of focused attention, whereas Digit Span Backward demands more effort from working memory. Because Digit Span is optional, normative information only for the combined Digit Span Forward and Digit Span Backward is reported. (For information on evaluating discrepancies between Digit Span Forward and Digit Span Backward, see the discussion of this subtest in the WAIS–III section.)

Mental Control

The Mental Control subtest of WMS–III is also optional and does not contribute to any of the indexes. The WMS–III version reflects expanded content and changes in the scoring criteria. This subtest is a measure of the examinee's ability to retrieve overlearned information and to mentally process information. For example, the examinee is asked to say the alphabet and to perform novel multitasking skills, such as alternately saying the days of the week and counting by sixes. Subtest scores reflect both accuracy and speed. Bonus points are awarded for quick, perfect performance.

Patterns and Profiles of Performance

Historically, two primary schools of thought have addressed issues of interscale variations that are commonly used in the interpretation of test scores. Spearman (1904, 1932/1970) argued that most cognitive abilities (e.g., those measured by most WAIS–III and WMS–III subtests) should be approximately equal and reflect a general cognitive factor, or g. In contrast, E. L. Thorndike, Lay, and Dean (1909) argued that "scatter" or ability differences (e.g., subtest-to-subtest or index-to-index) are the norm in healthy individuals. Thorndike et al.'s arguments should caution clinicians not to overinterpret ability differences or scatter. An excellent discussion of these issues can be found in Matarazzo (1990). A brief description of examining intrascore variations, or "score scatter," in the WAIS–III and the WMS–III is presented here.

Performance on the WAIS–III and the WMS–III can be interpreted in terms of the patterns of an examinee's various scores. Comparing an individual's functioning in one cognitive area to his or her functioning in another area can generate hypotheses about spared and impaired cognitive abilities. These ability comparisons are based on pairwise statistical comparisons between IQ and Index scores, which can help the examiner identify potentially meaningful patterns of strengths and weaknesses, a process that is important in describing functional impairment and for planning rehabilitation protocols.

The most appropriate use of profile analyses is the generation of hypotheses that are, in turn, either corroborated or refuted by other evaluation results, background information, direct behavioral observations, or additional evaluation. Profile analyses occur mostly at the IQ and Index score levels and are based on statistically significant differences between these scores and the clinically important frequency (or base rate) of the score differences in the standardization sample (Matarazzo, 1990). Interpretations based on profile analysis are often stated in a manner similar to the following example:

> This individual demonstrated a [mild, moderate, severe] weakness in [name or description of the IQ or Index] relative to [name or description of the other IQ or Index]. The discrepancy is [both statistically significant and rare in nonimpaired persons, or statistically significant but not uncommon in normally functioning persons].

Although statistically significant pairwise differences occur in many impaired populations, the same ability differences may also occur frequently in the normally functioning population (Matarazzo, 1990). Therefore, it is critical for the examiner to know the frequency of discrepancies between scores in the WAIS–III and WMS–III standardization samples (e.g., see Matarazzo & Herman, 1985, for a discussion of this issue pertaining to the WAIS–R). Base-rate information provides a basis for estimating the rarity or commonness of the examinee's obtained difference within the normal adult population.

A discrepancy that is statistically significant yet frequent in the standardization sample probably reflects normal variations in an individual's abilities. In contrast, a discrepancy that is both statistically significant and rare in the standardization sample could represent a meaningful and substantial decrease in at least one of the abilities being compared. All relevant explanations should be considered, including the possibility that the ability is impaired due to brain dysfunction. In general, the larger the discrepancy and the less frequent its occurrence, the less likely it can be explained as normal variation.

The following example illustrates the possible interpretation of a statistically significant *and* infrequent difference between two scores:

A 74-year-old, high-school-educated female examinee with no prior history of neurologic or psychiatric difficulty obtained a VIQ–PIQ score difference of +33 points. This difference is statistically significant at the $p < .05$ level, and the base rate for this occurrence is 0.5%, meaning that a difference of this magnitude occurred in less than 1% of the standardization sample. Because of the statistical significance and high infrequency of this difference in the general population, an appropriate hypothesis might be that this individual's nonverbal intellectual functioning is impaired relative to her verbal intellectual functioning.

The next example illustrates the possible interpretation of a statistically significant *but* frequent difference between two scores:

A 20-year-old, male college student with no history of neurologic, psychiatric, or academic difficulties obtained an Immediate Memory Index score that was 16 points higher than his Working Memory Index score. This difference is statistically significant at the $p < .05$ level and occurred in approximately 29% of the standardization sample. Although this difference is statistically significant, it occurs with such frequency (i.e., nearly 1 of 3 individuals obtained this difference) in the general population that it is neither unusual nor, in and of itself, indicative of impairment. In the absence of other evidence, this discrepancy does not necessarily indicate a deficit in working memory relative to immediate memory.

The following descriptions of selected WAIS–III and WMS–III differences are suggested interpretive guidelines for comparing selected pairs of scores. Several other interpretations might be possible in addition to the ones suggested here. Any interpretation should always be considered an hypothesis to be evaluated in the context of a thorough clinical evaluation.

WAIS–III Discrepancy Analyses

Several types of discrepancy scores can be calculated within the WAIS–III. They can be obtained at the subtest level, the IQ level (i.e., differences between VIQ and PIQ scores), and the index level. Discrepancy scores can also be obtained across test batteries. WAIS–III and WMS–III discrepancy scores are provided in this Manual (see Appendixes B and C) and can be recorded on the WMS–III Record Form. Discrepancies between the WAIS–III and the WIAT–II achievement scores can also be calculated for examinees aged 16–19 and recorded on the WIAT–II Record Form. The tables for these discrepancy analyses are listed in Appendixes B and C.

Subtest Score Patterns and Discrepancies

Most individuals have areas of relative cognitive strengths and weaknesses. It is, in fact, very uncommon for a "normal" person to function at the same level in every ability area.

The WAIS–III Record Form provides a section for determining the individual's strengths and weaknesses at the subtest level. These strengths and weaknesses are calculated in terms of the Full Scale or in terms of the Verbal and Performance scales. The examiner must choose whether to use a mean score of all the subtests that were administered (the overall global mean) or to use the mean scores of the Verbal and Performance subtests. If the latter method is used, the mean of all of the Verbal subtests administered is the base against which each Verbal subtest score is compared, and the mean score of all Performance subtests administered is the base against which each Performance subtest score is compared. Table B.3 in the *WAIS–III Administration and Scoring Manual* includes both the significance of the difference (at .05 and .15 levels) as well as the differences obtained by various percentages of the normative sample. Using this frequency data, the examiner can decide how rare the obtained difference is in a normative sample.

IQ Score and Index Score Discrepancies

In constructing the IQ scores for the Wechsler–Bellevue, Wechsler (1939) placed most of the emphasis on the FSIQ score and believed that an examinee's FSIQ score is always an average of the person's performance on all of the subtests (Wechsler, 1944). However, Wechsler realized that occasions arose when the VIQ and PIQ scores must be viewed separately, usually for persons "with special disabilities who need special consideration" (Wechsler, 1944, p. 138).

Since the publication of the Wechsler–Bellevue, the VIQ–PIQ difference score has become a more common method of determining when to modify the interpretation of an FSIQ score and to examine the VIQ and PIQ scores separately. With the publication of the WAIS–R in 1981, Wechsler included a table to show the minimum differences between the VIQ and PIQ scores required for significance at the .15 and .05 levels of confidence for each age group. Generally, a difference score of 10 points was required at the .05 level, and a difference of 7 points at the .15 level. These values became "rules of thumb," and clinicians started applying them clinically with their examinees.

Matarazzo and Herman (1985) first documented how frequently these differences occurred in the WAIS–R standardization sample and that a relatively large difference may not be rare in the general population. They demonstrated the need for examining statistical significance as well as clinical meaningfulness (base rates) and cautioned the clinician against overinterpretation of VIQ–PIQ score differences. When comparing discrepancy scores, the examiner must review other variables (e.g., the psychosocial history, education level) in addition to the statistical significance and clinical meaningfulness of the test scores. When a significant and meaningful difference is found, psychologists might interpret the FSIQ score differently, in a way that reflects these differences. A variety of detailed interpretation schemes has been suggested to explain meaningful differences (e,g., Kaufman, 1990, 1994; Sattler, 1992).

In addition to the VIQ–PIQ score differences, the WAIS–III includes normative discrepancy information on all possible pairs of Index scores. The VCI–POI score comparison is similar to the VIQ–PIQ score comparison except that Arithmetic, Digit Span, and Comprehension are not included in the VCI, and Digit Symbol—Coding and Picture Arrangement are not included in the POI. The VCI–POI discrepancy score may be useful for testing hypotheses about the effect of these excluded subtests on the respective VIQ and PIQ scores. For instance, if the examiner suspects that the examinee has relatively lower ability on tasks requiring attention, working memory, or processing speed, which would affect VIQ and PIQ scores, he or she can examine Verbal and Performance differences using the VCI–POI comparison, for which these abilities are not emphasized.

The VCI–WMI score comparison can reveal differences between the individual's capacity to hold and process information in memory and his or her acquired knowledge and verbal reasoning skills. Similarly, the POI–PSI score difference can reveal differences between an individual's visual–spatial and fluid reasoning skills and his or her ability to process information quickly. Because the subtests that compose the VCI and WMI are all verbal and the subtests that compose the POI and PSI are nonverbal, these discrepancy comparisons may provide meaningful information.

Tables B.1 and B.2 of the *WAIS–III Administration and Scoring Manual* provide the statistical significance and frequency data necessary for analyzing these various discrepancy scores. Because Matarazzo and Herman (1985) have demonstrated that frequencies of score differences can vary by ability level, the frequencies of differences for various levels of FSIQ scores are provided in Appendix D of this Manual. The user is cautioned, however, that when an individual has a neuropsychological disorder or condition that may affect cognitive functioning, the individual's current ability level may be lower than his or her premorbid functioning (see Heaton et al., 1978; Parsons & Prigatano, 1978). In such a case, the frequencies of differences by levels of FSIQ score reported in the tables may be misleading and should be used with caution.

Directional Discrepancy Scores

The *WAIS–III Administration and Scoring Manual* presents cumulative frequencies for composite-score discrepancies irrespective of the direction of the difference (Table B.2). For example, if VIQ minus PIQ equals –10, the value reported in the frequency table is 10. It is not possible to determine how often the VIQ will be greater than the PIQ or vice versa; however, it is possible to know how often the VIQ and PIQ differ by 10. The cumulative frequencies provide an estimate of the base rate that the degree of difference in performance is observed in the general population. This method of computing discrepancy scores presumes the clinician has no a priori hypotheses regarding the clinical profile of the respondent. Tulsky, Zhu, and Vasquez (1998) reported that the use of discrepancy scores that do not indicate the direction of the difference may overestimate the frequency of the difference score when the clinician has specific expectations regarding the relationship among the IQ measures. For instance, the clinician may expect that for an examinee diagnosed with Huntington's chorea the PIQ will be lower than the VIQ due to relatively preserved verbal versus visual–perceptual skills in this clinical group (see Table 4.31 of this manual). Tulsky et al. (1998) reported that the distribution of difference scores was normally distributed and presented a methodology for approximating the cumulative frequency of directional discrepancies for WAIS–III IQ and Index scores. Sattler and Ryan (1999) applied this methodology to the WAIS–III IQ and index scores, making the frequencies available to clinicians. Tulsky, Rolfhus, and Zhu (2000) evaluated the accuracy of the methodology for estimating the base rates for directional discrepancies. The results of the study indicated a close approximation of estimated versus actual directional discrepancy score base rates (Tulsky et al., 2000). The cumulative frequencies for the actual directional discrepancies are presented in the article. Clinicians should use the standard discrepancy tables for evaluations for which they have no expectations regarding the performance of the examinee, as will be the case most of the time. In situations where the examine already has a diagnosis, suspected condition (e.g., dementia), or known medical condition and the clinician expects the examinee to display higher or lower scores on specific measures, then the examiner should use the new directional discrepancy tables. The tables of directional discrepancy-score base rates for the WAIS–III IQ and Index scores (Table D.6) and the WMS–III Index scores (Table D.7) are provided in Appendix D of this manual.

Other Score Discrepancies

The introduction of new indexes and the co-norming and codevelopment of the WAIS–III and the WMS–III have made possible the comparison of a variety of scores, at both the subtest and index levels. Because these comparisons are new, their clinical utility and meaning are speculative. They are, however, fertile ground for research and clinical investigations and may prove to be meaningful and important. These score differences should be interpreted cautiously until further research establishes their meaning, validity, and diagnostic utility. Providing a detailed, systematic, and "complete" method of protocol analysis is beyond the scope of this Manual (see Kaufman, 1990, 1994, and Sattler, 1992, for detailed guides on interpretation strategies for other Wechsler intelligence measures). Nevertheless, examiners are advised against taking a "shotgun" approach to interpretation (Kaufman, 1994). Until more experience has been accumulated and research performed, the examiner should have a clear reason for calculating a difference score, and that reason should be based on the examinee's history, the referral question, behavioral observations, and other test results. It should also be remembered that a difference between two scores may be clinically meaningful for one individual, whereas the same difference for another individual may not be.

WMS–III Discrepancy Analyses

Primary Index Score Comparisons

Immediate Versus Delayed Indexes

The comparisons between immediate, or short-term, memory and delayed, or long-term, memory are perhaps the most common in memory assessment. Relevant WMS–III comparisons include those between the Immediate Memory Index and the General Memory Index, for an analysis of global differences, and between the Auditory Immediate and Auditory Delayed indexes and between the Visual Immediate and Visual Delayed indexes, for an analysis of modality-specific differences. Low delayed performance relative to immediate memory performance (considered in the context of intellectual functioning and attentional abilities) may indicate weaknesses or deficits in the examinee's ability to retain previously learned material.

Auditory Versus Visual Indexes

Differences in performance on the auditory and visual indexes (i.e., Auditory Immediate versus Visual Immediate and Auditory Delayed versus Visual Delayed) may indicate lifelong strengths and weaknesses or acquired deficits in memory processes when information is presented in different modalities.

Other cognitive abilities (e.g., attentional abilities, receptive and expressive language abilities, perceptual organizational abilities, and vocabulary and articulation) may also influence differences in auditory and visual presentation.

Working Memory Versus Immediate Memory Indexes

The Working Memory Index score can be compared to the Auditory Immediate Index, Visual Immediate Index, and Immediate Memory Index scores as a means of evaluating possible differences between complex attentional abilities and the acquisition and encoding processes (i.e., learning and memory), which depend on attention. A low Working Memory Index score in the context of a low Immediate Memory Index score and relatively higher intellectual functioning may indicate that attentional abilities are affecting the examinee's ability to learn the material initially.

Auditory Delayed Index Versus Auditory Recognition Delayed Index

The comparison between scores on the Auditory Delayed Index and Auditory Recognition Delayed Index is essentially a comparison between delayed recall and delayed recognition. A profile of scores in which performance is adequate in the immediate conditions but low in both delayed recall and recognition conditions suggests that the examinee was not able to retain previously learned information over an interval of 25–35 minutes. Because retrieval through recall is more demanding than retrieval through recognition, a low Auditory Delayed Index score relative to the Auditory Recognition Delayed Index score may suggest some type of retrieval weakness or deficit. Again, it is important for the examiner to consider all recall–recognition comparisons in the context of initial learning.

Auditory Process Composite Score Comparisons

Single-Trial Learning Composite Versus Learning Slope Composite

A low Single-Trial Learning Composite score relative to the Learning Slope Composite score suggests that although the examinee's immediate auditory memory may appear to be weak or impaired (possibly due to anxiety—check measures of attention and working memory), memory improves over multiple learning trials. Low scores on both the Single-Trial Learning Composite and the Learning Slope Composite suggest immediate memory difficulties and a decreased capacity to learn from subsequent learning trials. Comparisons between the Single-Trial Learning Composite and the Learning Slope Composite scores should not be made when the Single-Trial Learning Composite score is very high. When the Single-Trial Learning Composite score is relatively high (i.e., the examinee has learned much or most of the material on the first trial), performance cannot improve much.

Retention Composite Versus Auditory Delayed Index

A comparison between the Retention Composite and Auditory Delayed Index highlights the difference between intraexaminee and interexaminee comparisons. A high Retention Composite score in the context of a low Auditory Delayed Index score indicates that the examinee's delayed recall performance is low compared to that of the normative group (interexaminee comparison). This pattern of scores also indicates, however, that the examinee could later recall the information, at a similar level of performance, that was learned during the immediate condition (intraexaminee comparison). This examinee would also be expected to have a poor Immediate Auditory Index score, confirming weak learning but adequate retention. In this case, a relatively good recognition score (compared to the Auditory Delayed Index score) would suggest an additional retrieval weakness.

Differences Between the WAIS–III and the WMS–III

Discrepancies between intelligence and memory are sometimes used to evaluate memory functioning. With this approach, learning and memory are assumed to be underlying components of general intellectual ability and, as such, to be significantly related to the examinee's performance on tests of intellectual functioning. Because of the relatively high intercorrelations between intellectual functioning and memory (see Chapter 4), the examinee's IQ scores become an index or estimate of his or her probable level of memory ability. Discrepancies between the estimated memory performance based on IQ scores and the examinee's actual memory performance form the basis for the discrepancy analysis. The discrepancy score then provides a global indication of whether or not the examinee's ability to learn and remember new material is commensurate with what would be expected on the basis of his of her intellectual functioning.

Some researchers have proposed that a discrepancy in which IQ scores are appreciably higher than memory scores may be suggestive of an acquired memory impairment (Milner, 1975; Prigatano, 1974; Quadfasel & Pruyser, 1955). Others (e.g., Butters, 1986) have argued that IQ–memory discrepancies may not be sensitive to various patterns of memory deficits that are observed in particular clinical populations. Bornstein, Chelune, and Prifitera (1989) compared the base rates (frequencies) of IQ–memory score discrepancies obtained by a mixed clinical sample diagnosed with memory impairment and by the WMS–R standardization sample. Their results indicated that the discrepancy between the FSIQ score and the Delayed Memory Index score has some clinical utility. Specifically, a discrepancy of 15 points was obtained by only 10% of the standardization sample but by about 33% of the clinical sample. Bornstein et al. noted, however, that the direct interpretation of the IQ–memory score discrepancy may be confounded by other factors. They correctly pointed out that the IQ–memory score discrepancy does not take into account overall level of performance, estimates of premorbid abilities, or the possible effects of neurological disorders and other specific neurocognitive functions on intellectual and memory functioning. An examinee with dementia, for example, might have experienced a global cognitive decline, that is, across a broad spectrum of many abilities that includes memory. In this instance, a low IQ–memory score discrepancy does not indicate the absence of a memory deficit but, rather, indicates only that the examinee's level of memory performance, relative to global cognitive abilities, is commensurate (i.e., low). Alternatively, the examinee's level of memory performance may indeed be in the *impaired* range. The IQ–memory score discrepancy, therefore, should always be interpreted in the context of current level of intellectual and memory functioning and estimated or known premorbid functioning. To the extent that an examinee's overall intellectual functioning has remained relatively stable, a large discrepancy score in which the IQ score is greater than the memory score suggests a more focal memory impairment or weakness in the context of relatively intact overall abilities. In other instances in which both intellectual functioning and memory decline, the absence of a significant discrepancy is consistent with global neurocognitive impairment, where memory is one of many cognitive abilities that have declined.

The interpretation of differences between intellectual and memory functioning follows the same logic and methodology as used in the interpretation of ability–achievement discrepancies. (The specific criteria and rationale for evaluating these global ability–achievement differences can be found in The Psychological Corporation, 1992, and later in this chapter.) An essential criterion for the appropriateness of score comparisons is the comparability of the normative data for the two test measures. They must be highly comparable or the same. Because the WAIS–III and the WMS–III were co-normed, direct comparsions based on the same normative data can be made.

Two methods of discrepancy analysis are offered for WAIS–III and WMS–III comparisons: the simple-difference method and the predicted-difference method. Although both methods are presented, the predicted-difference method is generally preferred because of two primary considerations. The formula for the predicted-difference method not only takes into account the reliabilities and the correlations between the two measures but also corrects for regression to the mean.

In general, the FSIQ score should be used as the best estimate of intellectual ability. However, if the difference between an examinee's VIQ and PIQ scores is 10 points or more ($p < .05$), the higher of these two IQ scores could be used instead of the FSIQ score as the best estimate of intellectual ability. Furthermore, the General Memory Index score is usually the best estimate of an examinee's memory functioning. In some cases, however the direct interpretation of the General Memory Index score may be obscured by significant differences between component subtest scores. For example, if the difference between auditory and visual subtest scores is significant and meaningful, the modality-specific Index scores may be more appropriate than the General Memory Index score (i.e., the concept of "overall" memory becomes less meaningful in this case). This Manual provides discrepancy-score tables for comparing the WAIS–III VIQ, PIQ, and FSIQ scores and the WMS–III Primary Index scores.

Simple-Difference Method

With the simple-difference method, a WMS–III Primary Index score (usually the General Memory Index score) is subtracted from the WAIS–III IQ score (usually the FSIQ score). This method is sometimes selected because it is easy to explain to examinees, families, or other health professionals. However, as Braden and Weiss (1988) pointed out, the simple subtraction of standard scores assumes a perfect correlation between the two scores. Further, unless the simple difference is tested for statistical significance, measurement error is also ignored.

The proper use of the simple-difference method requires the examiner to determine first if the difference is statistically significant, and if it is, to determine how frequently a difference of its size occurred in the standardization sample (Berk, 1984). These two steps should be familiar because they are the same ones used to interpret the difference between WISC–III VIQ and PIQ scores (Wechsler, 1991).

First, the statistical significance of the difference between two scores accounts for measurement error and allows the examiner to conclude if the difference is a "real" or a "chance" occurrence. That is, the difference must be of sufficient size to minimize the probability that it has occurred because of unreliability in the measures. Formulas for determining the statistical significance of simple differences are identical to those for calculating the ability–achievement difference scores (The Psychological Corporation, 1992;

also see Reynolds, 1985, 1990) and were used for the construction of the tables in Appendix C. Tables C.1–C.3 provide the differences between the WAIS–III FSIQ, VIQ, and PIQ scores and WMS–III Primary Index scores required for statistical significance at the .05 and .01 levels. The difference score (calculated according to the steps in Chapter 3 of the *WMS–III Administration and Scoring Manual*) must be equal to or greater than the listed value to be statistically significant. For example, for a 63-year-old individual, an FSIQ–General Memory Index score difference of 11 is statistically significant at the .05 level because the difference is greater than 10.2, the listed value (Table C.1). This score difference, however, is not statistically significant at the .01 level because it is less than 13.4, the listed value for this age group.

The second consideration for interpreting the difference between two scores is the frequency of that difference within the general population. That is, the difference must be of a magnitude that is relatively rare in the sample that links the two measures (i.e., the co-normative sample of the WAIS–III and the WMS–III). Even though a difference is statistically significant, it may occur frequently. Tables C.4–C.6 list the differences between the WAIS–III FSIQ, VIQ, and PIQ scores and the WMS–III Primary Index scores obtained by various percentages of the standardization sample. It is important to note that Tables C.4–C.6 present percentages of the standardization sample who obtained WMS–III Index scores lower than their IQ scores. For example, an FSIQ–General Memory Index score difference of 28 points occurred in 2% of the WAIS–III—WMS–III standardization sample (Table C.4), indicating that it is quite rare to obtain a discrepancy of this size in the general population.

Predicted-Difference Method

Shepard (1980) was one of the first to advocate a predicted-difference method based on the correlation between the two variables. For discrepancies between ability and memory, the ability score is used in a regression equation to calculate a predicted memory score. The prediction formula used for the discrepancies between WAIS–III and WMS–III scores is identical to the ability–achievement formula used by The Psychological Corporation (1992). One noteworthy limitation of the predicted-difference method is that when correlations between measures are low, the range of predicted scores is restricted. Berk (1984) summarized the disadvantages of the predicted method, pointing out the limitations of imperfect correlations (discrepancies are due to prediction error as well as true differences).

The predicted-difference method is based on the difference between the memory score predicted from the IQ score and the memory score actually obtained by the examinee. As with the simple-difference method, in order for differences to be meaningful, the difference score should be statistically significant and rare. Tables B.1–B.3 provide the estimated (predicted) WMS–III Primary Index scores based on the WAIS–III FSIQ, VIQ, and PIQ scores, respectively, for all ages. In Table B.1, for example, the General Memory Index score predicted from an FSIQ score of 87 obtained by a 63-year-old individual is 92. This score is subtracted from the General Memory Index score obtained by the examinee. This difference is the discrepancy score. Tables B.4–B.6 provide the differences between predicted and obtained Primary Index scores for the FSIQ, VIQ, and PIQ scores required for significance at the .05 and .01 levels. The discrepancy score must be equal to or greater than the listed value for the relevant age group to be statistically significant. For the 63-year-old examinee who obtained an FSIQ score of 87, according to Table B.4, a discrepancy score of 17 is significant at the .05 level but not at the .01 level. The frequency of the discrepancy score is then determined. Tables B.7–B.9 provide the percentages of the standardization sample who obtained various discrepancy scores. It is important to note that Tables B.7–B.9 present percentages of the standardization sample who obtained WMS–III Index scores lower than their predicted WMS–III Index scores. Table B.7, for example, indicates that a difference between the predicted (i.e., from the FSIQ) General Memory Index score and the actual General Memory Index score of 8 points was obtained by 25% of the WAIS–III—WMS–III standardization sample, whereas a difference of 27 points was obtained by 1%–2% of the sample.

Differences Between the WAIS–III and the WIAT–II

The WAIS–III provides a means of comparing an individual's general intellectual ability level to his or her level of academic achievement. Comparisons between intellectual ability and academic achievement have served as a primary criterion in determining the presence of specific learning disabilities since the enactment of the Education for All Handicapped Children Act of 1975.

Two methods for comparing intellectual ability and academic achievement are presented: the simple-difference method and the predicted-difference method (the *WIAT–II Examiner's Manual* provides the rationale for choosing these methods and the statistical procedures involved.) The method for analyzing and interpreting ability–achievement discrepancies is very similar to the one used for the VIQ–PIQ score discrepancies discussed earlier.

Simple-Difference Method

With the simple-difference method, a WIAT–II standard score is subtracted from the IQ score. This method is often selected because it is easy to explain to parents and school board members.

Table C.7 reports the minimum differences between WAIS–III FSIQ, VIQ, PIQ, VCI, and POI scores and WIAT–II subtest or composite standard scores required for significance at the .05 and .01 levels. The differences between WAIS–III IQ and Index scores and WIAT–II subtest and composite standard scores obtained by various percentages of the linking sample are provided in Tables C.8–C.12. The percentages represent the portions of the samples who obtained WIAT–II scores lower than IQ scores.

Predicted-Difference Method

The predicted-achievement method takes into account the reliability of the ability and achievement scales as well as the correlations between them. Thus, the interpretations based on this method should be more accurate than those based on the simple-difference method. Tables B.10–B.14 provide predicted WIAT–II subtest and composite scores based on the WAIS–III FSIQ, VIQ, PIQ, VCI, and POI scores. The discrepancies between the predicted and observed achievement scores required for significance at .05 and .01 levels are listed in Table B.15. Tables B.16–B.20 report the differences between predicted and observed achievement scores obtained by various percentages of the linking sample. The percentages represent the portions of the sample who obtained WIAT–II scores lower than IQ scores.

Intercorrelation Tables for the WAIS–III and the WMS–III

Table A.1. Intercorrelations of WAIS–III Subtest Scaled Scores and Sums of Scaled Scores for IQ Scales and Indexes: Ages 16–17 Years

Subtest/Scale/Index	V	S	A	DS	I	C	LN	PC	CD	BD	MR	PA	SS	OA	Verbal	Perf.	Full	VC	PO	WM	PS
V															.87		.82	.90			
S	.63														.76		.71	.84			
A	.55	.45													.77		.73			.82	
DS	.37	.26	.46												.59		.57			.85	
I	.73	.59	.58	.31											.82		.78	.88			
C	.72	.57	.48	.36	.59										.80		.74				
LN	.32	.33	.56	.61	.34	.35														.86	
PC	.43	.34	.27	.31	.42	.38	.32									.74	.63		.78		
CD	.45	.30	.46	.31	.38	.33	.35	.34								.62	.59				.91
BD	.46	.47	.50	.38	.48	.42	.38	.51	.31							.77	.72		.86		
MR	.48	.45	.50	.37	.49	.43	.29	.38	.32	.59						.76	.71		.81		
PA	.41	.31	.29	.26	.39	.40	.10	.39	.23	.36	.43					.68	.59				
SS	.45	.40	.49	.42	.41	.29	.34	.45	.64	.44	.39	.29									.90
OA	.44	.40	.34	.26	.36	.35	.00	.46	.23	.59	.44	.32	.49			.72					
Verbal	.79	.64	.64	.43	.73	.70	.57	.46	.49	.59	.59	.45	.54	.47			.95	.93	.67	.73	.56
Perf.	.62	.52	.57	.46	.61	.55	.44	.56	.39	.61	.59	.47	.62	.57			.91	.67	.93	.50	.69
Full	.77	.63	.66	.48	.72	.68	.57	.54	.49	.65	.64	.49	.62	.55				.88	.84	.70	.66
VC	.76	.66	.60	.36	.73	.72	.38	.45	.43	.54	.54	.42	.48	.45					.63	.44	.50
PO	.56	.52	.52	.43	.57	.50	.42	.50	.40	.66	.56	.48	.52	.61						.49	.51
WM	.41	.36	.61	.64	.36	.39	.67	.31	.40	.48	.36	.11	.44	.11							.46
PS	.50	.38	.53	.41	.44	.34	.38	.43	.64	.41	.39	.29	.64	.40							
Mean	10.0	10.1	10.0	10.0	9.9	9.9	10.0	9.9	10.0	9.9	9.9	10.2	10.1	10.0	59.8	49.9	109.8	29.9	29.8	30.7	20.1
SD	3.0	3.0	3.2	2.9	3.0	2.9	2.8	2.9	3.0	2.9	2.9	3.0	2.9	3.0	13.8	10.5	22.6	7.8	7.1	7.1	5.4

Table A.2. Intercorrelations of WAIS–III Subtest Scaled Scores and Sums of Scaled Scores for IQ Scales and Indexes: Ages 18–19 Years

Subtest/Scale/Index	V	S	A	DS	I	C	LN	PC	CD	BD	MR	PA	SS	OA	Verbal	Perf.	Full	VC	PO	WM	PS
V															.89		.84	.92			
S	.73														.86		.81	.90			
A	.68	.61													.83		.82			.84	
DS	.47	.46	.59												.67		.66			.89	
I	.76	.69	.62	.37											.84		.80	.90			
C	.75	.71	.59	.41	.68										.84		.80				
LN	.49	.47	.57	.65	.45	.40														.87	
PC	.34	.35	.38	.26	.40	.33	.41									.66	.55		.72		
CD	.46	.35	.48	.35	.40	.40	.38	.30								.64	.59				.91
BD	.51	.58	.62	.46	.39	.55	.36	.40	.31							.77	.74		.84		
MR	.52	.54	.59	.52	.47	.51	.63	.33	.39	.59						.79	.75		.81		
PA	.53	.49	.42	.37	.56	.48	.57	.33	.30	.46	.50					.72	.67				
SS	.49	.50	.52	.41	.44	.44	.42	.41	.66	.50	.45	.32									.91
OA	.49	.51	.49	.39	.43	.49	.33	.43	.35	.63	.44	.39	.47								
Verbal	.83	.78	.75	.53	.76	.76	.62	.42	.49	.65	.65	.58	.57	.57		.78	.96	.95	.72	.80	.58
Perf.	.66	.65	.70	.55	.64	.63	.63	.45	.43	.61	.63	.54	.65	.63			.92	.72	.93	.69	.71
Full	.80	.76	.77	.57	.75	.75	.67	.46	.50	.68	.68	.60	.64	.63				.91	.86	.81	.67
VC	.81	.76	.70	.48	.78	.79	.52	.40	.44	.58	.57	.58	.53	.53					.65	.61	.53
PO	.58	.62	.67	.52	.57	.58	.56	.41	.42	.61	.55	.54	.57	.64						.66	.54
WM	.62	.54	.68	.74	.50	.54	.67	.47	.35	.49	.66	.55	.47	.39							.47
PS	.52	.47	.55	.42	.45	.46	.46	.39	.66	.44	.46	.34	.66	.45							
Mean	10.1	10.2	10.2	10.0	10.1	10.2	10.0	9.9	9.9	10.1	10.2	9.9	10.1	10.2	60.7	50.1	110.8	30.3	30.2	30.2	20.0
SD	3.0	3.1	3.1	3.0	3.0	2.9	3.5	2.9	3.0	3.0	3.0	2.9	3.1	3.0	14.8	10.6	24.0	8.2	7.1	8.0	5.5

Table A.3. Intercorrelations of WAIS–III Subtest Scaled Scores and Sums of Scaled Scores for IQ Scales and Indexes: Ages 20–24 Years

Subtest/Scale/Index	V	S	A	DS	I	C	LN	PC	CD	BD	MR	PA	SS	OA	Verbal	Perf.	Full	VC	PO	WM	PS
V															.89		.83	.93			
S	.77														.84		.79	.90			
A	.62	.55													.81		.81			.87	
DS	.43	.38	.59												.63		.64			.83	
I	.77	.68	.59	.38											.85		.79	.90			
C	.72	.70	.56	.26	.70										.81		.75				
LN	.38	.32	.56	.70	.34	.25														.88	
PC	.45	.46	.45	.38	.39	.35	.44									.75	.66		.79		
CD	.33	.31	.38	.45	.30	.25	.31	.35								.63	.54				.90
BD	.55	.48	.66	.48	.50	.49	.48	.48	.32							.79	.76		.86		
MR	.55	.49	.67	.52	.52	.52	.44	.52	.39	.66						.83	.79		.87		
PA	.46	.50	.42	.25	.53	.46	.29	.45	.25	.47	.50					.72	.66				
SS	.48	.44	.57	.49	.46	.44	.48	.47	.61	.58	.51	.43									.90
OA	.58	.52	.55	.35	.49	.50	.26	.51	.22	.66	.56	.43	.55								
Verbal	.83	.76	.72	.48	.78	.72	.53	.52	.42	.65	.67	.54	.60	.62		.76	.95	.95	.73	.74	.56
Perf.	.63	.60	.70	.56	.60	.56	.51	.60	.41	.64	.70	.54	.70	.64			.92	.67	.94	.67	.74
Full	.78	.73	.76	.56	.74	.69	.57	.58	.44	.70	.73	.58	.68	.67				.88	.88	.77	.68
VC	.84	.77	.65	.44	.77	.78	.38	.48	.34	.56	.57	.55	.51	.58					.64	.53	.47
PO	.62	.57	.71	.55	.56	.55	.53	.55	.42	.65	.69	.56	.62	.69						.68	.58
WM	.51	.44	.61	.72	.50	.40	.71	.53	.44	.62	.61	.36	.62	.40							.59
PS	.45	.42	.53	.53	.42	.38	.44	.46	.61	.50	.50	.38	.61	.43							
Mean	10.0	9.9	10.0	10.2	9.8	10.1	10.0	9.9	10.1	10.1	10.0	10.1	10.0	9.9	59.9	50.2	110.1	29.7	30.0	30.0	20.1
SD	3.0	3.0	3.1	3.0	3.0	3.0	2.8	2.9	3.1	3.1	3.0	3.1	3.1	3.2	14.7	11.3	24.4	8.3	7.6	7.3	5.6

Table A.4. Intercorrelations of WAIS–III Subtest Scaled Scores and Sums of Scaled Scores for IQ Scales and Indexes: Ages 25–29 Years

Subtest/Scale/Index	V	S	A	DS	I	C	LN	PC	CD	BD	MR	PA	SS	OA	Verbal	Perf.	Full	VC	PO	WM	PS
V															.91		.85	.94			
S	.77														.85		.79	.89			
A	.66	.61													.83		.82			.82	
DS	.57	.50	.58												.73		.70			.83	
I	.80	.69	.69	.48											.86		.80	.91			
C	.78	.71	.66	.51	.68										.86		.81				
LN	.63	.48	.54	.56	.58	.55														.85	
PC	.38	.36	.42	.30	.38	.42	.26									.74	.62		.81		
CD	.40	.34	.41	.37	.31	.36	.34	.34								.63	.56				.92
BD	.51	.47	.59	.50	.47	.48	.43	.52	.34							.79	.73		.85		
MR	.54	.53	.60	.51	.54	.52	.42	.49	.37	.50						.80	.76		.84		
PA	.56	.48	.52	.42	.54	.55	.60	.49	.39	.48	.50					.77	.73		.59		
SS	.46	.47	.58	.46	.47	.47	.63	.40	.70	.50	.53	.47									.92
OA	.39	.44	.46	.34	.36	.46	.51	.49	.28	.66	.57	.45	.49								
Verbal	.86	.78	.75	.61	.79	.80	.68	.45	.43	.60	.64	.61	.58	.49		.73	.95	.96	.68	.87	.41
Perf.	.64	.58	.68	.56	.60	.62	.71	.57	.43	.66	.66	.61	.70	.65			.91	.67	.93	.72	.55
Full	.81	.73	.78	.63	.75	.77	.75	.53	.46	.67	.70	.66	.68	.60				.89	.84	.88	.67
VC	.86	.77	.72	.57	.79	.79	.62	.41	.38	.53	.59	.58	.51	.44					.61	.74	.49
PO	.57	.54	.65	.52	.56	.57	.67	.56	.39	.66	.63	.59	.57	.69						.68	.52
WM	.71	.57	.61	.62	.71	.66	.63	.37	.47	.65	.65	.52	.56	.55							.55
PS	.47	.44	.54	.45	.43	.45	.49	.36	.70	.46	.49	.47	.70	.41							
Mean	10.0	9.9	10.2	10.0	10.0	10.2	10.3	10.3	9.9	10.3	10.1	10.1	10.1	10.1	60.4	50.7	111.1	30.0	30.8	30.2	20.0
SD	3.0	3.0	3.0	3.1	3.1	2.9	3.2	3.1	3.0	2.9	3.1	3.1	3.0	3.2	15.1	11.4	24.7	8.3	7.6	7.4	5.5

Table A.5. Intercorrelations of WAIS–III Subtest Scaled Scores and Sums of Scaled Scores for IQ Scales and Indexes: Ages 30–34 Years

Subtest/Scale/Index	V	S	A	DS	I	C	LN	PC	CD	BD	MR	PA	SS	OA	Verbal	Perf.	Full	VC	PO	WM	PS
V															.89		.85	.93			
S	.77														.86		.81	.91			
A	.63	.58													.81		.81			.85	
DS	.38	.35	.55												.61		.59			.85	
I	.79	.74	.64	.40											.88		.83	.92			
C	.77	.73	.57	.34	.70										.84		.81				
LN	.54	.48	.60	.61	.40	.45														.86	
PC	.52	.49	.43	.36	.43	.48	.47									.75	.67		.82		
CD	.36	.31	.43	.30	.34	.39	.34	.23								.59	.52				.88
BD	.53	.50	.59	.39	.53	.51	.47	.56	.34							.80	.74		.84		
MR	.56	.47	.68	.47	.55	.54	.48	.46	.30	.52						.76	.74		.80		
PA	.63	.63	.49	.28	.61	.57	.42	.54	.28	.56	.53					.79	.75				
SS	.43	.38	.46	.42	.42	.37	.44	.41	.53	.53	.38	.42									.87
OA	.44	.48	.42	.28	.42	.45	.43	.57	.24	.63	.46	.60	.47								
Verbal	.83	.78	.72	.47	.81	.76	.63	.56	.43	.62	.67	.66	.51	.51							
Perf.	.70	.65	.71	.49	.66	.68	.59	.59	.36	.67	.60	.64	.62	.67	.80						
Full	.81	.76	.76	.50	.78	.76	.65	.60	.43	.67	.68	.69	.58	.61	.96	.93					
VC	.84	.80	.67	.41	.81	.80	.52	.52	.36	.56	.57	.68	.44	.49	.95	.73	.90				
PO	.65	.59	.69	.49	.61	.62	.58	.59	.35	.63	.56	.66	.54	.67	.75	.94	.87	.67			
WM	.61	.58	.66	.67	.53	.53	.67	.49	.41	.56	.68	.44	.47	.46	.81	.70	.81	.62	.71		
PS	.45	.39	.51	.41	.43	.44	.45	.36	.53	.49	.39	.40	.53	.41	.54	.69	.63	.46	.50	.52	
Mean	10.1	10.1	9.8	10.1	10.0	10.2	9.8	9.8	10.0	10.2	10.0	10.0	10.2	10.1	60.3	50.1	110.3	30.2	30.0	30.0	20.2
SD	3.1	3.0	3.1	2.9	3.1	3.1	3.2	2.9	3.0	2.9	2.9	3.0	2.9	3.2	14.9	10.9	24.5	8.5	7.2	8.0	5.2

Table A.6. Intercorrelations of WAIS–III Subtest Scaled Scores and Sums of Scaled Scores for IQ Scales and Indexes: Ages 35–44 Years

Subtest/ Scale/ Index	V	S	A	DS	I	C	LN	PC	CD	BD	MR	PA	SS	OA	Verbal	Perf.	Full	VC	PO	WM	PS
V															.89		.85	.93			
S	.75														.84		.79	.90			
A	.60	.55													.80		.78			.82	
DS	.41	.39	.52												.63		.58			.87	
I	.77	.69	.63	.40											.86		.80	.90			
C	.79	.70	.55	.36	.70										.84		.81				
LN	.49	.62	.63	.56	.57	.43														.85	
PC	.48	.44	.38	.25	.39	.44	.29									.77	.66		.83		
CD	.42	.37	.38	.33	.30	.36	.34	.39								.66	.58				.89
BD	.50	.41	.55	.29	.45	.50	.44	.54	.44							.81	.72		.85		
MR	.56	.55	.62	.39	.53	.55	.48	.52	.37	.64						.80	.78		.85		
PA	.55	.53	.47	.33	.57	.53	.51	.43	.32	.45	.50					.72	.71				
SS	.49	.43	.47	.31	.42	.40	.42	.45	.59	.50	.49	.31									.90
OA	.44	.43	.39	.14	.38	.43	.32	.51	.39	.66	.55	.38	.44								
Verbal	.83	.76	.69	.49	.79	.76	.70	.49	.44	.56	.66	.61	.52	.46		.74	.95	.95	.67	.85	.54
Perf.	.67	.61	.64	.42	.59	.63	.54	.61	.47	.69	.67	.54	.62	.66			.91	.69	.94	.59	.72
Full	.81	.74	.72	.49	.75	.76	.68	.57	.49	.65	.72	.64	.60	.58				.90	.85	.79	.66
VC	.83	.77	.65	.44	.78	.80	.62	.48	.40	.50	.60	.60	.49	.46					.63	.66	.50
PO	.61	.56	.61	.37	.54	.59	.48	.58	.47	.68	.66	.54	.57	.68						.57	.58
WM	.55	.57	.66	.60	.64	.46	.69	.34	.30	.46	.63	.53	.36	.26							.37
PS	.51	.45	.48	.36	.41	.43	.43	.47	.59	.53	.48	.35	.59	.47							
Mean	9.9	10.0	9.8	10.1	10.0	10.0	10.0	10.1	10.1	10.3	10.1	10.1	10.1	10.0	59.7	50.7	110.4	29.8	30.5	29.7	20.2
SD	3.0	3.0	3.3	3.0	3.0	3.0	2.8	3.2	2.9	2.9	3.0	3.1	3.0	2.9	14.9	11.3	24.4	8.2	7.7	8.1	5.2

Table A.7. Intercorrelations of WAIS–III Subtest Scaled Scores and Sums of Scaled Scores for IQ Scales and Indexes: Ages 45–54 Years

Subtest/Scale/Index	V	S	A	DS	I	C	LN	PC	CD	BD	MR	PA	SS	OA	Verbal	Perf.	Full	VC	PO	WM	PS
V															.88		.84	.92			
S	.76														.84		.82	.90			
A	.58	.57													.80		.78			.79	
DS	.43	.36	.45												.62		.56			.82	
I	.75	.69	.65	.37											.85		.82	.89			
C	.75	.71	.60	.40	.70										.86		.81				
LN	.42	.45	.47	.60	.44	.42														.85	
PC	.54	.52	.48	.30	.54	.51	.46									.78	.72		.82		
CD	.41	.36	.43	.32	.34	.44	.49	.45								.71	.61				.92
BD	.57	.63	.59	.34	.59	.53	.47	.50	.47							.82	.78		.84		
MR	.64	.68	.60	.35	.62	.60	.43	.58	.49	.63						.83	.82		.87		
PA	.54	.51	.49	.28	.54	.50	.27	.55	.41	.62	.59					.81	.73				
SS	.50	.47	.56	.35	.45	.52	.50	.53	.70	.58	.50	.48									.92
OA	.53	.54	.47	.29	.50	.44	.42	.56	.38	.66	.59	.53	.51								
Verbal	.81	.76	.69	.47	.78	.78	.58	.60	.48	.67	.72	.59	.59	.57		.77	.95	.95	.79	.81	.58
Perf.	.68	.69	.66	.40	.67	.65	.55	.64	.55	.70	.72	.68	.70	.69			.93	.75	.96	.66	.77
Full	.80	.77	.72	.46	.77	.77	.61	.65	.53	.73	.77	.66	.68	.66				.91	.91	.80	.70
VC	.82	.77	.66	.42	.77	.79	.48	.59	.41	.66	.71	.59	.52	.58					.78	.64	.50
PO	.69	.72	.66	.39	.69	.65	.55	.60	.56	.64	.70	.69	.63	.71						.67	.65
WM	.57	.57	.51	.61	.61	.57	.63	.48	.46	.60	.57	.40	.59	.43							.58
PS	.49	.45	.53	.37	.43	.52	.54	.53	.70	.57	.54	.48	.70	.48							
Mean	9.9	10.1	10.0	10.0	10.0	9.9	10.3	10.1	10.1	10.0	10.1	10.1	10.1	10.0	60.0	50.4	110.4	30.1	30.3	30.8	20.1
SD	3.0	3.0	3.3	3.0	3.0	3.0	3.2	3.0	2.9	3.0	3.0	3.0	2.9	3.0	14.8	11.8	25.0	8.2	7.6	7.4	5.4

Table A.8. Intercorrelations of Subtest Scaled Scores and Sums of Scaled Scores for IQ Scales and Indexes By Age: Ages 55–64 Years

Subtest/Scale/Index	V	S	A	DS	I	C	LN	PC	CD	BD	MR	PA	SS	OA	Verbal	Perf.	Full	VC	PO	WM	PS
V															.89		.85	.93			
S	.77														.86		.83	.91			
A	.61	.61													.82		.79			.81	
DS	.53	.50	.57												.72		.66			.76	
I	.79	.74	.65	.48											.87		.84				
C	.78	.70	.66	.50	.72										.87		.83	.92			
LN	.64	.48	.58	.58	.59	.57											.71			.88	
PC	.53	.51	.45	.40	.50	.53	.41									.78	.62		.83		
CD	.51	.44	.42	.34	.42	.41	.51	.41								.69	.69				.92
BD	.44	.48	.51	.37	.48	.48	.43	.52	.39							.77	.82		.84		
MR	.60	.64	.63	.46	.65	.61	.52	.57	.48	.60						.84	.74		.86		
PA	.60	.59	.46	.39	.60	.55	.38	.51	.38	.49	.62					.78					
SS	.56	.55	.57	.45	.57	.57	.50	.54	.69	.53	.55	.53									.92
OA	.46	.53	.40	.31	.44	.52	.29	.59	.41	.61	.57	.52	.52								
Verbal	.83	.79	.73	.59	.81	.80	.70	.58	.51	.55	.72	.63	.65	.53		.77	.96	.95	.73	.86	.63
Perf.	.70	.69	.64	.51	.69	.67	.60	.64	.51	.63	.74	.64	.74	.70			.92	.75	.95	.65	.78
Full	.82	.79	.73	.58	.80	.79	.70	.64	.54	.62	.77	.68	.73	.64				.92	.88	.82	.73
VC	.84	.80	.68	.54	.81	.80	.62	.56	.50	.51	.69	.65	.61	.52					.69	.73	.60
PO	.63	.64	.63	.48	.65	.64	.55	.61	.50	.63	.67	.64	.64	.70						.63	.62
WM	.72	.63	.55	.54	.66	.64	.69	.47	.48	.50	.58	.41	.55	.35							.57
PS	.59	.54	.54	.43	.54	.53	.56	.51	.69	.50	.56	.49	.69	.51							
Mean	9.9	10.0	10.0	10.0	10.0	10.1	10.2	10.1	9.9	10.1	9.9	10.1	10.1	10.0	60.0	50.0	110.0	29.9	30.0	30.0	19.9
SD	3.0	3.0	3.4	3.2	3.1	3.0	3.1	3.1	3.1	3.0	3.0	3.1	3.0	3.0	15.6	11.8	25.8	8.4	7.6	7.2	5.7

Table A.9. Intercorrelations of WAIS–III Subtest Scaled Scores and Sums of Scaled Scores for IQ Scales and Indexes: Ages 65–69 Years

Subtest/Scale/Index	V	S	A	DS	I	C	LN	PC	CD	BD	MR	PA	SS	OA	Verbal	Perf.	Full	VC	PO	WM	PS
V															.91		.88	.94			
S	.81														.89		.87	.92			
A	.69	.71													.86		.83			.81	
DS	.51	.48	.59												.68		.63			.83	
I	.82	.75	.70	.50											.89		.82	.92			
C	.81	.77	.66	.41	.78										.87		.85				
LN	.66	.60	.55	.60	.59	.51														.86	
PC	.62	.65	.53	.55	.55	.66	.42									.81	.77		.85		
CD	.57	.57	.54	.35	.47	.48	.53	.54								.76	.71				.93
BD	.55	.58	.59	.39	.56	.59	.41	.51	.65							.83	.76		.87		
MR	.60	.64	.64	.38	.49	.61	.45	.61	.51	.56						.82	.79		.86		
PA	.57	.53	.53	.48	.52	.53	.51	.58	.50	.58	.58					.80	.72		.66		
SS	.58	.62	.63	.32	.49	.55	.49	.57	.73	.59	.60	.55									.93
OA	.48	.52	.44	.47	.40	.50	.33	.59	.52	.68	.55	.58	.59								
Verbal	.86	.83	.78	.56	.84	.81	.70	.66	.59	.62	.69	.58	.66	.52		.78	.96	.97	.77	.87	.67
Perf.	.72	.74	.70	.48	.63	.71	.61	.69	.62	.73	.70	.67	.77	.72			.93	.75	.95	.66	.83
Full	.84	.84	.79	.55	.78	.81	.71	.71	.64	.70	.74	.65	.75	.64				.92	.90	.83	.78
VC	.87	.82	.75	.53	.82	.85	.67	.65	.58	.58	.65	.57	.62	.50					.73	.75	.64
PO	.69	.73	.68	.47	.61	.72	.52	.65	.60	.71	.68	.66	.70	.71						.66	.70
WM	.71	.69	.58	.62	.68	.61	.67	.42	.51	.48	.60	.48	.58	.31							.60
PS	.62	.64	.63	.46	.53	.56	.56	.60	.73	.61	.59	.58	.73	.60							
Mean	10.0	10.0	9.9	9.9	10.0	10.0	10.0	10.1	9.9	9.9	10.0	10.0	10.0	10.0	59.9	49.9	109.8	30.0	30.0	30.1	19.9
SD	3.1	3.1	3.3	3.0	3.2	3.2	3.1	3.1	3.2	3.0	3.1	3.2	3.0	3.0	16.0	12.5	27.0	8.7	7.9	7.6	5.8

Table A.10. Intercorrelations of WAIS–III Subtest Scaled Scores and Sums of Scaled Scores for IQ Scales and Indexes: Ages 70–74 Years

Subtest/Scale/Index	V	S	A	DS	I	C	LN	PC	CD	BD	MR	PA	SS	OA	Verbal	Perf.	Full	VC	PO	WM	PS
V															.89		.85	.93			
S	.78														.83		.82	.90			
A	.60	.51													.79		.76			.82	
DS	.44	.29	.48												.61		.53			.76	
I	.75	.68	.65	.37											.86		.83	.89			
C	.74	.73	.57	.38	.73										.86		.83				
LN	.52	.36	.61	.42	.50	.46														.85	
PC	.53	.59	.41	.20	.52	.54	.44									.79	.71		.83		
CD	.45	.43	.43	.27	.41	.43	.40	.45								.70	.63				.90
BD	.53	.58	.51	.24	.52	.53	.46	.59	.47							.83	.75		.87		
MR	.56	.53	.60	.38	.58	.56	.60	.52	.42	.61						.79	.76		.84		
PA	.56	.58	.42	.31	.55	.56	.36	.50	.32	.53	.50					.74	.71				
SS	.53	.54	.49	.34	.55	.58	.56	.55	.59	.56	.53	.53									.88
OA	.47	.51	.36	.23	.47	.49	.32	.56	.43	.64	.50	.60	.48								
Verbal	.83	.74	.69	.45	.79	.79	.61	.58	.50	.60	.62	.62	.63	.52		.77	.95	.95	.73	.77	.63
Perf.	.68	.71	.62	.36	.67	.68	.61	.66	.51	.71	.65	.58	.72	.71			.93	.76	.95	.63	.79
Full	.81	.77	.70	.44	.78	.78	.64	.65	.54	.69	.70	.64	.71	.64				.92	.88	.75	.75
VC	.84	.78	.65	.40	.76	.81	.51	.60	.48	.60	.61	.62	.59	.53					.72	.57	.60
PO	.64	.67	.60	.32	.64	.64	.61	.61	.53	.69	.63	.60	.65	.67						.64	.66
WM	.58	.41	.62	.47	.54	.55	.61	.47	.38	.44	.66	.36	.53	.27							.51
PS	.54	.54	.52	.34	.54	.56	.55	.56	.59	.57	.53	.47	.59	.51							
Mean	10.2	10.2	10.1	10.1	10.0	9.9	9.9	10.1	10.2	10.1	10.0	10.0	10.0	10.0	60.3	50.3	110.6	30.3	30.1	29.9	20.3
SD	2.9	2.9	2.9	2.9	2.9	3.1	3.4	2.9	3.2	2.9	2.9	3.0	3.0	3.0	14.3	11.5	24.3	7.9	7.4	7.5	5.5

Table A.11. Intercorrelations of WAIS–III Subtest Scaled Scores and Sums of Scaled Scores for IQ Scales and Indexes: Ages 75–79 Years

Subtest/Scale/Index	V	S	A	DS	I	C	LN	PC	CD	BD	MR	PA	SS	OA	Verbal	Perf.	Full	VC	PO	WM	PS
V		.77	.49	.55	.77	.73	.50	.39	.43	.41	.38	.45	.33	.35	.88		.81	.92			
S			.56	.52	.77	.72	.55	.51	.48	.50	.45	.51	.49	.45	.88		.86	.92			
A				.50	.58	.53	.44	.28	.29	.39	.36	.34	.43	.25	.74		.68			.81	
DS					.47	.43	.38	.33	.47	.36	.41	.40	.47	.27	.70		.69			.77	
I						.75	.46	.42	.38	.43	.41	.51	.40	.33	.88		.83	.92			
C							.48	.42	.32	.43	.37	.38	.32	.40	.84		.77				
LN								.33	.53	.45	.38	.38	.58	.43			.64			.78	
PC									.43	.49	.34	.43	.45	.52		.75	.62		.77		
CD										.42	.32	.39	.64	.31		.69	.62				.89
BD											.50	.42	.47	.53		.78	.68		.84		
MR												.45	.38	.36		.70	.62		.77		
PA													.41	.45							
SS														.38		.73	.67				.92
OA																					
Verbal	.81	.82	.63	.58	.82	.77	.56	.48	.48	.51	.48	.53	.49	.42		.68	.94	.96	.62	.87	.54
Perf.	.56	.67	.46	.54	.59	.53	.57	.57	.52	.62	.51	.54	.65	.59			.89	.66	.93	.69	.74
Full	.75	.82	.60	.61	.78	.72	.61	.56	.54	.60	.54	.58	.61	.53				.90	.82	.86	.68
VC	.82	.82	.59	.56	.82	.80	.55	.48	.47	.48	.45	.53	.44	.41					.59	.78	.50
PO	.49	.61	.43	.46	.53	.51	.50	.48	.49	.61	.49	.52	.54	.59						.62	.57
WM	.73	.73	.55	.69	.69	.70	.48	.41	.56	.50	.55	.50	.55	.45							.60
PS	.42	.53	.40	.52	.43	.35	.60	.49	.64	.49	.38	.47	.64	.38							
Mean	10.2	10.1	10.3	10.0	10.1	10.2	10.0	10.0	9.9	10.2	10.2	9.9	10.0	10.0	60.9	50.1	111.0	30.4	30.3	30.2	19.9
SD	3.1	3.0	2.9	2.8	2.9	2.8	2.9	3.0	2.7	2.9	2.9	3.0	3.1	3.0	14.4	10.6	23.0	8.2	7.0	6.7	5.3

Table A.12. Intercorrelations of WAIS–III Subtest Scaled Scores and Sums of Scaled Scores for IQ Scales and Indexes: Ages 80–84 Years

Subtest/Scale/Index	V	S	A	DS	I	C	LN	PC	CD	BD	MR	PA	SS	OA	Verbal	Perf.	Full	VC	PO	WM	PS
V															.90		.85	.94			
S	.80														.86		.83	.91			
A	.61	.61													.81		.76			.84	
DS	.43	.40	.44												.60		.53			.81	
I	.78	.71	.62	.29											.84		.77	.90			
C	.74	.65	.60	.35	.69										.83		.79				
LN	.50	.52	.55	.57	.49	.56														.86	
PC	.45	.47	.38	.27	.44	.44	.62									.78	.68		.81		
CD	.47	.48	.42	.41	.36	.35	.55	.46								.74	.67				.91
BD	.46	.50	.50	.14	.35	.45	.37	.50	.48							.78	.66		.84		
MR	.54	.55	.41	.27	.48	.55	.46	.50	.45	.60						.79	.74		.84		
PA	.54	.50	.50	.31	.48	.51	.43	.55	.49	.43	.52					.78	.73				
SS	.47	.44	.48	.43	.34	.39	.64	.54	.66	.54	.47	.45									.91
OA	.26	.27	.23	.11	.21	.33	.15	.52	.26	.49	.36	.33	.35								
Verbal	.85	.79	.71	.45	.77	.75	.65	.51	.51	.48	.60	.58	.53	.29		.69	.94	.95	.63	.85	.57
Perf.	.63	.64	.56	.36	.55	.59	.63	.64	.59	.64	.66	.63	.69	.51			.90	.66	.94	.67	.78
Full	.81	.78	.69	.44	.72	.73	.69	.61	.59	.58	.68	.66	.65	.42				.89	.84	.84	.72
VC	.85	.80	.67	.41	.78	.76	.55	.50	.48	.47	.57	.55	.46	.27					.62	.68	.51
PO	.58	.61	.51	.27	.51	.58	.57	.56	.56	.63	.64	.61	.62	.55						.61	.65
WM	.64	.66	.61	.63	.58	.67	.64	.61	.57	.38	.56	.49	.65	.21							.67
PS	.51	.51	.49	.46	.39	.40	.65	.55	.66	.56	.51	.51	.66	.34							
Mean	10.1	9.9	10.1	10.2	10.1	10.1	9.9	9.9	9.8	9.8	9.8	10.0	10.1	10.0	60.5	49.3	109.8	30.1	29.6	30.8	19.9
SD	3.0	3.0	3.3	2.8	2.8	2.9	3.4	3.0	3.0	3.0	2.9	3.0	3.0	3.0	14.4	11.5	23.8	8.0	7.4	7.9	5.4

Table A.13. Intercorrelations of WAIS–III Subtest Scaled Scores and Sums of Scaled Scores for IQ Scales and Indexes: Ages 85–89 Years

Subtest/Scale/Index	V	S	A	DS	I	C	LN	PC	CD	BD	MR	PA	SS	OA	Verbal	Perf.	Full	VC	PO	WM	PS
V															.86		.79	.90			
S	.70														.81		.79	.88			
A	.46	.39													.69		.67			.81	
DS	.35	.31	.42												.60		.53			.82	
I	.70	.64	.54	.33											.83		.82	.87			
C	.71	.63	.39	.39	.62										.81		.74				
LN	.28	.23	.46	.49	.31	.27														.81	
PC	.44	.49	.28	.19	.56	.48	.23									.76	.68		.78		
CD	.43	.46	.49	.33	.49	.31	.47	.46								.76	.69				.92
BD	.48	.52	.42	.32	.46	.44	.22	.45	.48							.78	.72		.83		
MR	.40	.46	.45	.23	.42	.38	.24	.37	.41	.52						.70	.64		.78		
PA	.47	.53	.42	.32	.63	.48	.21	.55	.50	.49	.39					.78	.74				
SS	.42	.52	.43	.27	.48	.32	.41	.51	.71	.57	.41	.54									.93
OA	.39	.49	.18	.08	.37	.44	-.09	.38	.23	.44	.40	.35	.31								
Verbal	.77	.70	.55	.44	.74	.71	.42	.53	.55	.58	.51	.62	.53	.43		.74	.94	.94	.68	.74	.58
Perf.	.59	.65	.54	.37	.68	.55	.36	.60	.60	.63	.54	.63	.73	.47			.92	.72	.94	.58	.80
Full	.73	.73	.59	.43	.77	.68	.42	.60	.61	.64	.56	.67	.67	.48				.90	.85	.72	.73
VC	.77	.73	.52	.37	.73	.73	.31	.56	.52	.55	.48	.61	.53	.47	.94	.72	.90		.67	.54	.57
PO	.56	.62	.48	.31	.60	.54	.29	.47	.57	.59	.52	.60	.63	.51	.68	.94	.85	.67		.52	.65
WM	.44	.45	.57	.59	.57	.50	.55	.37	.59	.42	.47	.43	.44	.14	.74	.58	.72	.54	.52		.55
PS	.46	.54	.49	.33	.53	.34	.46	.53	.71	.57	.44	.56	.71	.29	.58	.80	.73	.57	.65	.55	
Mean	10.0	10.0	10.1	10.1	10.0	10.1	10.1	10.0	9.9	9.8	10.1	9.9	10.0	10.0	60.2	49.7	109.9	30.0	29.9	30.2	19.8
SD	3.0	2.9	2.7	2.8	2.8	2.8	3.0	3.0	3.0	2.9	2.7	3.1	3.1	3.1	13.1	11.1	22.5	7.7	6.8	7.1	5.6

Table A.14. Intercorrelations of WMS–III Primary Subtest Scaled Scores: Ages 16–17 Years

Subtest	LM I Recall	Faces I Recog	VPA I Recall	Fam Pic I Recall	L–N Sequencing	Spatial Span	LM II Recall	Faces II Recog	VPA II Recall	Fam Pic II Recall	Aud Rec Del
LM I Recall											
Faces I Recognition	-.16										
VPA I Recall	.15	-.18									
Fam Pic I Recall	.28	.25	.11								
L–N Sequencing	.34	-.21	.25	-.10							
Spatial Span	.26	-.04	.04	.09	.40						
LM II Recall	.84	-.02	.13	.33	.32	.23					
Faces II Recognition	-.31	.70	-.13	.20	-.17	.06	-.18				
VPA II Recall	.08	-.03	.69	.06	.31	.03	.17	.10			
Fam Pic II Recall	.28	.27	.17	.94	-.13	.11	.33	.20	.07		
Auditory Recognition Del	.59	.06	.16	.17	.22	.32	.62	-.01	.24	.20	
Mean	9.9	10.0	10.0	10.0	10.0	10.3	10.0	10.0	9.9	9.9	10.0
SD	3.0	3.1	3.1	3.0	2.8	2.7	3.0	3.0	3.0	3.0	2.9

Table A.15. Intercorrelations of WMS–III Primary Subtest Scaled Scores: Ages 18–19 Years

Subtest	LM I Recall	Faces I Recog	VPA I Recall	Fam Pic I Recall	L–N Sequencing	Spatial Span	LM II Recall	Faces II Recog	VPA II Recall	Fam Pic II Recall	Aud Rec Del
LM I Recall											
Faces I Recognition	.18										
VPA I Recall	.68	.37									
Fam Pic I Recall	.30	.21	.16								
L–N Sequencing	.44	.09	.37	.37							
Spatial Span	.32	.16	.38	.26	.58						
LM II Recall	.84	.19	.70	.28	.42	.36					
Faces II Recognition	.18	.75	.35	.26	.19	.14	.19				
VPA II Recall	.48	.30	.78	.08	.26	.21	.47	.31			
Fam Pic II Recall	.37	.28	.24	.89	.43	.34	.37	.30	.15		
Auditory Recognition Del	.65	.15	.44	.28	.30	.22	.60	.19	.37	.38	
Mean	10.1	10.0	10.0	10.0	10.0	9.7	10.0	10.0	10.0	9.9	10.1
SD	3.0	3.1	3.1	2.7	3.5	3.1	3.0	3.0	2.9	2.8	2.8

Table A.16. Intercorrelations of WMS–III Primary Subtest Scaled Scores: Ages 20–24 Years

Subtest	LM I Recall	Faces I Recog	VPA I Recall	Fam Pic I Recall	L–N Sequencing	Spatial Span	LM II Recall	Faces II Recog	VPA II Recall	Fam Pic II Recall	Aud Rec Del
LM I Recall											
Faces I Recognition	.25										
VPA I Recall	.42	.33									
Fam Pic I Recall	.48	.41	.26								
L–N Sequencing	.29	.07	.32	.12							
Spatial Span	.16	-.04	.23	.17	.50						
LM II Recall	.84	.35	.56	.45	.35	.14					
Faces II Recognition	.33	.69	.48	.38	.21	.03	.40				
VPA II Recall	.35	.24	.73	.28	.27	.33	.43	.28			
Fam Pic II Recall	.51	.47	.33	.96	.15	.22	.49	.41	.40		
Auditory Recognition Del	.66	.28	.46	.28	.33	-.03	.68	.43	.21	.28	
Mean	10.0	10.0	10.0	9.9	10.0	10.0	10.1	10.0	10.0	10.0	10.0
SD	3.1	3.0	3.0	3.1	2.8	2.9	3.1	3.1	2.9	3.2	3.0

Table A.17. Intercorrelations of WMS–III Primary Subtest Scaled Scores: Ages 25–29 Years

Subtest	LM I Recall	Faces I Recog	VPA I Recall	Fam Pic I Recall	L–N Sequencing	Spatial Span	LM II Recall	Faces II Recog	VPA II Recall	Fam Pic II Recall	Aud Rec Del
LM I Recall											
Faces I Recognition	.04										
VPA I Recall	.66	-.03									
Fam Pic I Recall	.35	.12	.15								
L–N Sequencing	.41	.12	.47	.10							
Spatial Span	.14	.14	.20	.26	.51						
LM II Recall	.85	.17	.66	.30	.36	.17					
Faces II Recognition	.16	.78	.08	.16	.27	.19	.25				
VPA II Recall	.57	.08	.83	.23	.38	.18	.58	.17			
Fam Pic II Recall	.37	.09	.16	.92	.13	.33	.30	.14	.28		
Auditory Recognition Del	.76	.08	.61	.35	.24	.20	.73	.13	.46	.36	
Mean	9.8	9.9	10.0	10.3	10.1	10.3	9.8	10.0	10.1	10.1	9.8
SD	2.9	2.9	3.0	3.2	3.2	3.0	3.1	3.1	3.1	3.1	3.2

Table A.18. Intercorrelations of WMS–III Primary Subtest Scaled Scores: Ages 30–34 Years

Subtest	LM I Recall	Faces I Recog	VPA I Recall	Fam Pic I Recall	L–N Sequencing	Spatial Span	LM II Recall	Faces II Recog	VPA II Recall	Fam Pic II Recall	Aud Rec Del
LM I Recall											
Faces I Recognition	.07										
VPA I Recall	.55	.22									
Fam Pic I Recall	.38	.25	.36								
L–N Sequencing	.43	.15	.52	.31							
Spatial Span	.28	.13	.35	.29	.50						
LM II Recall	.89	.07	.56	.39	.37	.29					
Faces II Recognition	.11	.71	.27	.19	.21	.17	.09				
VPA II Recall	.54	.19	.83	.44	.54	.36	.55	.24			
Fam Pic II Recall	.41	.24	.34	.94	.31	.28	.41	.18	.43		
Auditory Recognition Del	.69	.16	.43	.33	.31	.24	.73	.17	.41	.34	
Mean	10.3	10.2	9.9	9.9	9.8	10.0	10.2	10.1	10.1	9.8	10.4
SD	3.0	3.1	3.0	3.0	3.2	3.1	3.0	3.0	3.1	3.2	2.8

Table A.19. Intercorrelations of WMS–III Primary Subtest Scaled Scores: Ages 35–44 Years

Subtest	LM I Recall	Faces I Recog	VPA I Recall	Fam Pic I Recall	L–N Sequencing	Spatial Span	LM II Recall	Faces II Recog	VPA II Recall	Fam Pic II Recall	Aud Rec Del
LM I Recall											
Faces I Recognition	.08										
VPA I Recall	.36	.29									
Fam Pic I Recall	.26	.27	.40								
L–N Sequencing	.46	.10	.44	.42							
Spatial Span	.25	.18	.23	.39	.40						
LM II Recall	.88	.15	.46	.35	.55	.35					
Faces II Recognition	.20	.75	.25	.24	.24	.16	.21				
VPA II Recall	.34	.26	.88	.47	.52	.32	.42	.24			
Fam Pic II Recall	.30	.25	.41	.94	.42	.41	.42	.21	.46		
Auditory Recognition Del	.72	.16	.53	.36	.50	.43	.73	.24	.52	.42	
Mean	10.4	10.0	10.1	10.1	10.0	10.0	10.4	10.1	10.4	10.3	10.1
SD	2.8	3.1	3.1	2.9	2.8	2.9	2.8	3.0	3.0	2.9	3.2

Table A.20. Intercorrelations of WMS–III Primary Subtest Scaled Scores: Ages 45–54 Years

Subtest	LM I Recall	Faces I Recog	VPA I Recall	Fam Pic I Recall	L–N Sequencing	Spatial Span	LM II Recall	Faces II Recog	VPA II Recall	Fam Pic II Recall	Aud Rec Del
LM I Recall											
Faces I Recognition	.30										
VPA I Recall	.52	.19									
Fam Pic I Recall	.47	.30	.39								
L–N Sequencing	.33	.22	.28	.35							
Spatial Span	.36	.18	.33	.18	.32						
LM II Recall	.89	.31	.55	.44	.30	.35					
Faces II Recognition	.29	.70	.18	.35	.29	.16	.34				
VPA II Recall	.52	.24	.88	.34	.28	.27	.53	.16			
Fam Pic II Recall	.54	.33	.41	.90	.33	.22	.54	.31	.32		
Auditory Recognition Del	.77	.13	.36	.33	.25	.31	.72	.12	.41	.37	
Mean	10.0	10.0	10.0	10.0	10.3	10.0	10.0	10.0	9.9	10.1	10.0
SD	3.1	3.1	3.0	3.0	3.2	2.9	3.1	3.0	3.0	3.2	2.9

Table A.21. Intercorrelations of WMS–III Primary Subtest Scaled Scores: Ages 55–64 Years

Subtest	LM I Recall	Faces I Recog	VPA I Recall	Fam Pic I Recall	L–N Sequencing	Spatial Span	LM II Recall	Faces II Recog	VPA II Recall	Fam Pic II Recall	Aud Rec Del
LM I Recall											
Faces I Recognition	.10										
VPA I Recall	.42	.34									
Fam Pic I Recall	.30	.40	.44								
L–N Sequencing	.43	.23	.30	.26							
Spatial Span	.40	.26	.24	.26	.48						
LM II Recall	.83	.27	.53	.45	.44	.36					
Faces II Recognition	.06	.56	.37	.38	.21	.23	.27				
VPA II Recall	.30	.32	.83	.39	.28	.18	.43	.34			
Fam Pic II Recall	.29	.31	.43	.91	.27	.20	.42	.27	.40		
Auditory Recognition Del	.72	.13	.54	.30	.43	.36	.68	.22	.43	.29	
Mean	10.0	10.0	10.0	10.0	10.2	10.0	10.0	10.0	9.9	10.0	10.0
SD	2.9	3.1	3.1	3.1	3.1	2.9	3.1	2.9	3.0	3.0	3.1

Table A.22. Intercorrelations of WMS–III Primary Subtest Scaled Scores: Ages 65–69 Years

Subtest	LM I Recall	Faces I Recog	VPA I Recall	Fam Pic I Recall	L–N Sequencing	Spatial Span	LM II Recall	Faces II Recog	VPA II Recall	Fam Pic II Recall	Aud Rec Del
LM I Recall											
Faces I Recognition	.24										
VPA I Recall	.61	.17									
Fam Pic I Recall	.62	.20	.57								
L–N Sequencing	.51	-.02	.40	.37							
Spatial Span	.33	-.01	.26	.31	.43						
LM II Recall	.85	.25	.49	.51	.37	.29					
Faces II Recognition	.29	.69	.28	.23	.12	.13	.31				
VPA II Recall	.52	.15	.81	.50	.39	.26	.49	.29			
Fam Pic II Recall	.59	.21	.57	.92	.40	.36	.50	.23	.53		
Auditory Recognition Del	.68	.20	.46	.48	.55	.32	.62	.21	.50	.52	
Mean	9.9	10.0	10.0	10.0	10.0	10.1	9.9	10.1	10.0	10.1	10.0
SD	3.1	2.8	3.0	3.0	3.1	3.1	3.1	2.9	3.0	3.1	3.0

Table A.23. Intercorrelations of WMS–III Primary Subtest Scaled Scores: Ages 70–74 Years

Subtest	LM I Recall	Faces I Recog	VPA I Recall	Fam Pic I Recall	L–N Sequencing	Spatial Span	LM II Recall	Faces II Recog	VPA II Recall	Fam Pic II Recall	Aud Rec Del
LM I Recall											
Faces I Recognition	.02										
VPA I Recall	.47	.02									
Fam Pic I Recall	.39	.26	.39								
L–N Sequencing	.54	.21	.37	.38							
Spatial Span	.28	.25	.18	.36	.54						
LM II Recall	.81	.04	.41	.53	.51	.25					
Faces II Recognition	.07	.59	.01	.17	.23	.11	.08				
VPA II Recall	.47	.10	.81	.35	.39	.24	.43	.10			
Fam Pic II Recall	.41	.24	.41	.89	.39	.35	.51	.19	.42		
Auditory Recognition Del	.68	.05	.46	.28	.44	.29	.54	.16	.53	.31	
Mean	10.0	10.0	10.0	10.0	9.9	9.7	10.1	10.0	10.0	10.1	9.9
SD	3.0	3.2	3.0	3.1	3.4	3.1	2.9	2.9	3.1	3.1	2.9

Table A.24. Intercorrelations of WMS–III Primary Subtest Scaled Scores: Ages 75–79 Years

Subtest	LM I Recall	Faces I Recog	VPA I Recall	Fam Pic I Recall	L–N Sequencing	Spatial Span	LM II Recall	Faces II Recog	VPA II Recall	Fam Pic II Recall	Aud Rec Del
LM I Recall											
Faces I Recognition	.21										
VPA I Recall	.61	.25									
Fam Pic I Recall	.48	.41	.40								
L–N Sequencing	.35	.33	.35	.39							
Spatial Span	.20	.13	.22	.19	.31						
LM II Recall	.82	.36	.66	.61	.50	.27					
Faces II Recognition	.26	.60	.31	.45	.29	.20	.45				
VPA II Recall	.40	.24	.86	.26	.35	.20	.51	.29			
Fam Pic II Recall	.39	.35	.38	.89	.40	.21	.55	.38	.27		
Auditory Recognition Del	.69	.33	.63	.46	.47	.11	.79	.35	.53	.43	
Mean	10.0	10.0	10.0	10.0	10.0	10.2	10.0	10.0	10.0	10.0	10.0
SD	3.0	2.9	3.1	3.1	2.9	2.9	3.1	3.0	3.0	3.0	3.1

Table A.25. Intercorrelations of WMS–III Primary Subtest Scaled Scores: Ages 80–84 Years

Subtest	LM I Recall	Faces I Recog	VPA I Recall	Fam Pic I Recall	L–N Sequencing	Spatial Span	LM II Recall	Faces II Recog	VPA II Recall	Fam Pic II Recall	Aud Rec Del
LM I Recall											
Faces I Recognition	.34										
VPA I Recall	.53	.32									
Fam Pic I Recall	.47	.52	.48								
L–N Sequencing	.53	.31	.25	.43							
Spatial Span	.30	.11	-.02	.16	.46						
LM II Recall	.83	.28	.51	.48	.47	.24					
Faces II Recognition	.15	.61	.23	.51	.37	.14	.16				
VPA II Recall	.58	.40	.87	.49	.33	.00	.62	.24			
Fam Pic II Recall	.54	.48	.51	.92	.45	.26	.54	.45	.54		
Auditory Recognition Del	.75	.47	.56	.55	.63	.29	.69	.28	.59	.57	
Mean	10.0	10.0	10.0	10.0	9.9	10.0	10.0	10.0	10.0	10.0	10.0
SD	2.9	3.1	3.0	3.0	3.4	3.2	2.9	3.1	3.1	3.1	3.0

Table A.26. Intercorrelations of WMS–III Primary Subtest Scaled Scores: *Ages 85–89 Years*

Subtest	LM I Recall	Faces I Recog	VPA I Recall	Fam Pic I Recall	L–N Sequencing	Spatial Span	LM II Recall	Faces II Recog	VPA II Recall	Fam Pic II Recall	Aud Rec Del
LM I Recall											
Faces I Recognition	.22										
VPA I Recall	.27	.02									
Fam Pic I Recall	.50	.43	.29								
L–N Sequencing	.18	.15	.19	.12							
Spatial Span	.31	.26	-.15	.04	.39						
LM II Recall	.90	.26	.29	.60	.07	.20					
Faces II Recognition	.22	.55	.03	.43	.10	.29	.29				
VPA II Recall	.42	.03	.77	.34	.20	-.04	.41	.14			
Fam Pic II Recall	.61	.40	.28	.85	.08	.19	.72	.40	.40		
Auditory Recognition Del	.73	.22	.34	.45	.10	.28	.72	.32	.51	.53	
Mean	10.0	10.0	10.0	10.1	10.2	9.9	10.0	10.0	10.1	10.0	10.0
SD	3.2	3.0	3.0	3.1	3.0	3.0	3.1	3.0	3.0	3.1	3.1

Table A.27. Intercorrelations of WMS–III Indexes and Composites: Ages 16–17 Years

| | Primary Indexes | | | | | | | | Auditory Process Composites | | | |
	Aud Imm	Vis Imm	Imm Mem	Aud Del	Vis Del	Aud Rec Del	Gen Mem	Wkg Mem	Single-Trial Learning	Learning Slope	Retention	Retrieval
Primary Indexes												
Auditory Immediate												
Visual Immediate	.02											
Immediate Memory	.70	.73										
Auditory Delayed	.75	.14	.61									
Visual Delayed	.01	.87	.63	.14								
Auditory Recognition Delayed	.47	.11	.40	.55	.10							
General Memory	.56	.59	.81	.79	.65	.68						
Working Memory	.35	-.10	.17	.35	-.05	.36	.26					
Auditory Process Composites												
Single-Trial Learning	.94	.00	.64	.60	.00	.47	.47	.28				
Learning Slope	-.37	.00	-.25	.01	-.04	-.05	-.03	.05	-.55			
Retention	.34	.30	.45	.76	.31	.38	.70	.16	.22	-.06		
Retrieval	-.07	.05	-.02	-.21	.03	.68	.13	.08	.05	-.07	-.21	
Mean	19.9	20.0	39.9	19.9	19.9	10.0	49.8	20.3	19.9	20.0	20.0	0.2
SD	4.6	4.8	6.7	4.6	4.6	2.9	8.7	4.6	4.6	4.1	4.9	2.7

Table A.28. Intercorrelations of WMS–III Indexes and Composites: Ages 18–19 Years

	Primary Indexes								Auditory Process Composites			
	Aud Imm	Vis Imm	Imm Mem	Aud Del	Vis Del	Aud Rec Del	Gen Mem	Wkg Mem	Single-Trial Learning	Learning Slope	Retention	Retrieval
Primary Indexes												
Auditory Immediate												
Visual Immediate	.36											
Immediate Memory	.86	.78										
Auditory Delayed	.89	.32	.77									
Visual Delayed	.39	.86	.72	.37								
Auditory Recognition Delayed	.59	.28	.55	.55	.34							
General Memory	.81	.65	.89	.84	.76	.72						
Working Memory	.47	.31	.48	.42	.38	.31	.48					
Auditory Process Composites												
Single-Trial Learning	.94	.31	.79	.78	.33	.54	.71	.44				
Learning Slope	-.10	.01	-.06	.10	.02	-.05	.05	-.03	-.35			
Retention	.45	.27	.45	.75	.30	.30	.61	.31	.32	.11		
Retrieval	-.20	-.03	-.15	-.34	.01	.58	.00	-.06	-.15	-.16	-.38	
Mean	20.1	19.9	40.0	19.9	19.9	10.1	49.9	19.7	20.0	20.2	19.8	0.2
SD	5.6	4.5	8.4	5.0	4.7	2.8	9.9	5.9	5.4	4.1	4.4	2.7

Table A.29. Intercorrelations of WMS–III Indexes and Composites: Ages 20–24 Years

	Primary Indexes								Auditory Process Composites			
	Aud Imm	Vis Imm	Imm Mem	Aud Del	Vis Del	Aud Rec Del	Gen Mem	Wkg Mem	Single-Trial Learning	Learning Slope	Retention	Retrieval
Primary Indexes												
Auditory Immediate												
Visual Immediate	.47											
Immediate Memory	.86	.86										
Auditory Delayed	.87	.47	.78									
Visual Delayed	.58	.89	.86	.55								
Auditory Recognition Delayed	.63	.32	.55	.49	.38							
General Memory	.86	.73	.93	.87	.85	.66						
Working Memory	.34	.11	.26	.37	.21	.09	.32					
Auditory Process Composites												
Single-Trial Learning	.92	.36	.75	.75	.48	.62	.75	.29				
Learning Slope	-.02	.08	.03	.19	.07	-.07	.09	.14	-.32			
Retention	.43	.35	.46	.70	.32	.13	.53	.32	.38	-.03		
Retrieval	-.06	-.06	-.07	-.32	-.04	.62	.00	-.14	.07	-.32	-.42	
Mean	19.9	19.9	39.8	20.1	20.0	10.0	50.0	20.0	20.1	20.2	20.0	-0.1
SD	5.2	5.2	8.8	5.1	5.3	3.0	11.1	4.9	4.9	4.7	4.6	3.0

Table A.30. Intercorrelations of WMS–III Indexes and Composites: Ages 25–29 Years

	Primary Indexes								Auditory Process Composites			
	Aud Imm	Vis Imm	Imm Mem	Aud Del	Vis Del	Aud Rec Del	Gen Mem	Wkg Mem	Single-Trial Learning	Learning Slope	Retention	Retrieval
Primary Indexes												
Auditory Immediate												
Visual Immediate	.20											
Immediate Memory	.82	.73										
Auditory Delayed	.90	.30	.81									
Visual Delayed	.28	.87	.71	.37								
Auditory Recognition Delayed	.74	.34	.72	.67	.34							
General Memory	.81	.62	.93	.88	.72	.78						
Working Memory	.39	.24	.41	.36	.35	.20	.41					
Auditory Process Composites												
Single-Trial Learning	.89	.15	.71	.77	.23	.65	.71	.34				
Learning Slope	.20	.08	.19	.29	.16	.10	.24	.20	-.13			
Retention	.63	.44	.70	.86	.48	.51	.80	.25	.54	.10		
Retrieval	-.01	.05	.03	-.23	.00	.53	.05	-.06	.07	-.21	-.32	
Mean	19.7	20.1	39.9	19.9	20.1	9.8	49.7	20.3	19.8	19.3	19.5	-0.2
SD	5.4	4.5	7.7	5.5	4.7	3.2	10.7	5.4	4.9	4.1	5.3	2.7

263

Table A.31. Intercorrelations of WMS–III Indexes and Composites: Ages 30–34 Years

	Primary Indexes								Auditory Process Composites			
	Aud Imm	Vis Imm	Imm Mem	Aud Del	Vis Del	Aud Rec Del	Gen Mem	Wkg Mem	Single-Trial Learning	Learning Slope	Retention	Retrieval
Primary Indexes												
Auditory Immediate												
Visual Immediate	.37											
Immediate Memory	.84	.81										
Auditory Delayed	.91	.39	.80									
Visual Delayed	.42	.86	.76	.44								
Auditory Recognition Delayed	.66	.34	.61	.69	.35							
General Memory	.82	.68	.91	.88	.77	.77						
Working Memory	.52	.32	.51	.51	.37	.34	.51					
Auditory Process Composites												
Single-Trial Learning	.86	.31	.72	.74	.35	.59	.69	.43				
Learning Slope	.31	.12	.26	.38	.11	.22	.30	.30	-.12			
Retention	.46	.28	.45	.72	.29	.42	.59	.28	.41	.07		
Retrieval	-.29	-.07	-.22	-.38	-.09	.36	-.12	-.22	-.14	-.21	-.39	
Mean	20.2	20.1	40.3	20.3	19.9	10.4	50.7	19.8	20.4	20.1	19.9	0.3
SD	5.3	4.8	8.3	5.3	4.8	2.8	10.4	5.5	4.9	5.0	4.6	2.5

Table A.32. Intercorrelations of WMS–III Indexes and Composites: Ages 35–44 Years

	Primary Indexes								Auditory Process Composites			
	Aud Imm	Vis Imm	Imm Mem	Aud Del	Vis Del	Aud Rec Del	Gen Mem	Wkg Mem	Single-Trial Learning	Learning Slope	Retention	Retrieval
Primary Indexes												
Auditory Immediate												
Visual Immediate	.39											
Immediate Memory	.84	.83										
Auditory Delayed	.92	.45	.82									
Visual Delayed	.45	.88	.79	.51								
Auditory Recognition Delayed	.73	.31	.62	.73	.41							
General Memory	.84	.68	.91	.90	.79	.80						
Working Memory	.50	.40	.54	.61	.47	.55	.65					
Auditory Process Composites												
Single-Trial Learning	.90	.35	.75	.81	.38	.68	.75	.39				
Learning Slope	.20	.21	.24	.31	.28	.15	.28	.31	-.13			
Retention	.50	.36	.52	.70	.36	.43	.61	.51	.46	.04		
Retrieval	.08	-.01	.04	-.03	.07	.59	.21	.14	.17	-.25	-.13	
Mean	20.5	20.1	40.6	20.8	20.4	10.1	51.3	20.1	20.3	20.3	20.9	-0.3
SD	4.9	4.8	8.0	4.9	4.6	3.2	10.6	4.8	4.8	4.1	4.3	2.4

Table A.33. Intercorrelations of WMS–III Indexes and Composites: Ages 45–54 Years

	Primary Indexes								Auditory Process Composites			
	Aud Imm	Vis Imm	Imm Mem	Aud Del	Vis Del	Aud Rec Del	Gen Mem	Wkg Mem	Single-Trial Learning	Learning Slope	Retention	Retrieval
Primary Indexes												
Auditory Immediate												
Visual Immediate	.48											
Immediate Memory	.87	.85										
Auditory Delayed	.93	.47	.83									
Visual Delayed	.51	.87	.79	.49								
Auditory Recognition Delayed	.65	.28	.55	.64	.32							
General Memory	.87	.71	.92	.89	.78	.72						
Working Memory	.46	.36	.48	.42	.38	.41	.48					
Auditory Process Composites												
Single-Trial Learning	.91	.46	.80	.79	.47	.57	.76	.47				
Learning Slope	.32	.26	.34	.45	.24	.22	.39	.16	.00			
Retention	.70	.21	.54	.83	.20	.47	.63	.31	.58	.27		
Retrieval	-.21	-.16	-.22	-.28	-.15	.49	-.06	-.04	-.15	-.23	-.30	
Mean	19.9	20.0	39.9	19.9	20.2	10.0	50.0	20.3	20.1	20.3	20.0	0.0
SD	5.3	5.0	8.8	5.3	5.0	2.9	10.7	4.9	4.9	4.8	4.4	2.6

Table A.34. Intercorrelations of WMS–III Indexes and Composites: Ages 55–64 Years

| | Primary Indexes | | | | | | | | Auditory Process Composites | | | |
	Aud Imm	Vis Imm	Imm Mem	Aud Del	Vis Del	Aud Rec Del	Gen Mem	Wkg Mem	Single-Trial Learning	Learning Slope	Retention	Retrieval
Primary Indexes												
Auditory Immediate												
Visual Immediate	.42											
Immediate Memory	.84	.84										
Auditory Delayed	.87	.50	.82									
Visual Delayed	.44	.81	.74	.53								
Auditory Recognition Delayed	.77	.28	.62	.68	.35							
General Memory	.83	.67	.89	.91	.79	.77						
Working Memory	.47	.35	.49	.44	.33	.46	.49					
Auditory Process Composites												
Single-Trial Learning	.87	.38	.74	.73	.38	.66	.71	.47				
Learning Slope	.09	.07	.09	.18	.16	.04	.17	-.03	-.33			
Retention	.56	.40	.57	.81	.45	.42	.71	.29	.47	.03		
Retrieval	.04	-.20	-.10	-.21	-.14	.55	.01	.14	.08	-.16	-.33	
Mean	20.0	19.9	39.9	19.9	20.1	10.0	49.9	20.2	20.0	20.0	19.9	0.0
SD	5.1	5.2	8.7	5.2	4.7	3.1	10.7	5.2	5.2	5.0	4.5	2.6

Table A.35. Intercorrelations of WMS–III Indexes and Composites: Ages 65–69 Years

	Primary Indexes								Auditory Process Composites			
	Aud Imm	Vis Imm	Imm Mem	Aud Del	Vis Del	Aud Rec Del	Gen Mem	Wkg Mem	Single-Trial Learning	Learning Slope	Retention	Retrieval
Primary Indexes												
Auditory Immediate												
Visual Immediate	.59											
Immediate Memory	.91	.87										
Auditory Delayed	.86	.54	.80									
Visual Delayed	.63	.85	.82	.61								
Auditory Recognition Delayed	.61	.43	.59	.61	.47							
General Memory	.85	.74	.89	.91	.84	.75						
Working Memory	.50	.26	.44	.45	.39	.52	.52					
Auditory Process Composites												
Single-Trial Learning	.93	.51	.83	.80	.55	.57	.77	.46				
Learning Slope	.38	.33	.40	.37	.39	.23	.41	.22	.12			
Retention	.51	.26	.45	.81	.34	.39	.65	.30	.47	.12		
Retrieval	-.15	-.05	-.12	-.29	-.09	.56	-.03	.15	-.14	-.10	-.36	
Mean	19.9	19.9	39.9	19.9	20.2	10.0	50.1	20.0	20.0	19.9	20.0	0.1
SD	5.5	4.5	8.9	5.3	4.7	3.0	11.1	5.2	5.4	3.8	4.9	2.6

Table A.36. Intercorrelations of WMS–III Indexes and Composites: Ages 70–74 Years

	Primary Indexes								Auditory Process Composites			
	Aud Imm	Vis Imm	Imm Mem	Aud Del	Vis Del	Aud Rec Del	Gen Mem	Wkg Mem	Single-Trial Learning	Learning Slope	Retention	Retrieval
Primary Indexes												
Auditory Immediate												
Visual Immediate	.29											
Immediate Memory	.81	.80										
Auditory Delayed	.86	.37	.77									
Visual Delayed	.35	.77	.69	.43								
Auditory Recognition Delayed	.66	.23	.56	.62	.32							
General Memory	.78	.59	.86	.88	.76	.73						
Working Memory	.46	.43	.55	.48	.40	.45	.54					
Auditory Process Composites												
Single-Trial Learning	.88	.22	.69	.69	.26	.53	.61	.43				
Learning Slope	.43	.21	.40	.51	.33	.40	.52	.18	.12			
Retention	.50	.32	.52	.79	.35	.31	.65	.34	.34	.21		
Retrieval	-.10	-.12	-.14	-.28	-.07	.52	-.01	.01	-.09	-.05	-.42	
Mean	20.1	19.9	40.0	20.1	20.2	9.9	50.2	19.5	20.1	20.1	20.0	-0.1
SD	5.1	5.0	8.1	5.0	4.6	2.9	10.1	5.7	4.8	4.1	4.4	2.6

Table A.37. Intercorrelations of WMS–III Indexes and Composites: Ages 75–79 Years

	Primary Indexes								Auditory Process Composites			
	Aud Imm	Vis Imm	Imm Mem	Aud Del	Vis Del	Aud Rec Del	Gen Mem	Wkg Mem	Single-Trial Learning	Learning Slope	Retention	Retrieval
Primary Indexes												
Auditory Immediate												
Visual Immediate	.45											
Immediate Memory	.86	.84										
Auditory Delayed	.88	.51	.82									
Visual Delayed	.45	.83	.74	.54								
Auditory Recognition Delayed	.74	.49	.73	.78	.51							
General Memory	.80	.72	.90	.91	.81	.84						
Working Memory	.39	.38	.45	.47	.41	.37	.49					
Auditory Process Composites												
Single-Trial Learning	.90	.41	.78	.73	.38	.63	.68	.26				
Learning Slope	.45	.36	.48	.58	.41	.48	.57	.33	.15			
Retention	.54	.38	.54	.82	.42	.61	.71	.44	.40	.40		
Retrieval	-.02	.06	.02	-.14	.03	.44	.09	-.08	.00	-.05	-.20	
Mean	20.0	20.0	39.9	20.0	20.0	10.0	50.0	20.1	19.9	20.4	20.0	0.0
SD	5.4	5.0	8.9	5.3	5.0	3.1	11.4	4.7	5.2	4.3	5.1	2.2

Table A.38. Intercorrelations of WMS–III Indexes and Composites: Ages 80–84 Years

	Primary Indexes								Auditory Process Composites			
	Aud Imm	Vis Imm	Imm Mem	Aud Del	Vis Del	Aud Rec Del	Gen Mem	Wkg Mem	Single-Trial Learning	Learning Slope	Retention	Retrieval
Primary Indexes												
Auditory Immediate												
Visual Immediate	.53											
Immediate Memory	.87	.88										
Auditory Delayed	.89	.52	.81									
Visual Delayed	.48	.85	.76	.48								
Auditory Recognition Delayed	.75	.58	.76	.70	.51							
General Memory	.83	.79	.93	.88	.81	.82						
Working Memory	.36	.34	.40	.34	.42	.55	.50					
Auditory Process Composites												
Single-Trial Learning	.91	.49	.79	.81	.42	.70	.77	.35				
Learning Slope	.53	.26	.45	.51	.27	.42	.46	.20	.27			
Retention	.50	.41	.52	.76	.42	.38	.66	.23	.47	.17		
Retrieval	-.06	.16	.06	-.25	.08	.49	.05	.31	.01	-.09	-.38	
Mean	20.0	20.0	40.0	20.0	20.1	10.0	50.0	19.8	20.0	19.8	20.2	0.0
SD	5.2	5.3	9.2	5.4	5.2	3.0	11.5	5.6	4.8	4.2	4.9	2.4

Table A.39. Intercorrelations of WMS–III Indexes and Composites: Ages 85–89 Years

	Primary Indexes								Auditory Process Composites			
	Aud Imm	Vis Imm	Imm Mem	Aud Del	Vis Del	Aud Rec Del	Gen Mem	Wkg Mem	Single-Trial Learning	Learning Slope	Retention	Retrieval
Primary Indexes												
Auditory Immediate												
Visual Immediate	.39											
Immediate Memory	.83	.84										
Auditory Delayed	.89	.44	.79									
Visual Delayed	.43	.79	.74	.55								
Auditory Recognition Delayed	.67	.36	.61	.71	.45							
General Memory	.78	.66	.86	.89	.84	.78						
Working Memory	.20	.20	.24	.16	.24	.24	.24					
Auditory Process Composites												
Single-Trial Learning	.78	.44	.72	.71	.45	.54	.67	.10				
Learning Slope	.60	.07	.39	.51	.15	.41	.39	.30	.12			
Retention	.59	.42	.60	.79	.49	.55	.72	.11	.64	.06		
Retrieval	-.12	.01	-.06	-.17	.05	.49	.09	.12	-.07	-.09	-.17	
Mean	20.0	20.1	40.1	20.1	19.9	10.0	50.0	20.1	20.0	20.1	20.0	-0.1
SD	4.9	5.1	8.4	5.1	5.1	3.1	11.4	5.0	4.3	5.2	5.0	2.3

Table A.40. WMS–III Intercorrelations of Primary and Supplemental Subtest Scaled Scores: Ages 16–29 Years

Subtest	LM I Recall	LM I Them	Faces I Recog	VPA I Recall	Fam Pic I Recall	WL I Recall	VR I Recall	L–N Sequencing	Spatial Span	Spatial Span Fwd	Spatial Span Bkwd	Mental Control	Digit Span
LM I Thematic	.81												
Faces I Recognition	.08	.07											
VPA I Recall	.48	.43	.12										
Fam Pic I Recall	.35	.28	.25	.17									
WL I Recall	.45	.36	.14	.53	.30								
VR I Recall	.39	.30	.18	.37	.26	.40							
L–N Sequencing	.37	.31	.02	.35	.13	.34	.43						
Spatial Span	.22	.21	.06	.22	.20	.20	.40	.50					
Spatial Span Forward	.20	.19	.04	.19	.17	.16	.33	.45	.86				
Spatial Span Backward	.18	.19	.05	.19	.18	.21	.37	.39	.82	.46			
Mental Control	.28	.24	.10	.26	.19	.29	.33	.37	.37	.28	.36		
Digit Span	.30	.25	.11	.20	.15	.24	.36	.63	.42	.36	.36	.40	
LM II Recall	.84	.70	.17	.51	.34	.48	.39	.36	.23	.19	.21	.25	.26
LM II Thematic	.75	.75	.13	.41	.25	.38	.28	.26	.20	.16	.20	.17	.17
Faces II Recognition	.09	.07	.73	.20	.17	.19	.22	.13	.11	.09	.09	.16	.12
VPA II Recall	.37	.31	.15	.76	.27	.47	.39	.31	.19	.16	.18	.27	.19
Auditory Recognition Del	.66	.52	.14	.42	.15	.45	.31	.27	.17	.19	.12	.22	.22
Fam Pic II Recall	.38	.33	.28	.23	.93	.35	.34	.15	.25	.21	.22	.21	.15
WL II Recall	.47	.32	.20	.46	.27	.62	.40	.30	.19	.12	.21	.29	.23
WL II Recognition	.36	.27	.18	.28	.23	.46	.26	.25	.08	.04	.10	.21	.16
VR II Recall	.38	.24	.15	.41	.25	.42	.59	.39	.30	.26	.26	.30	.34
VR II Recognition	.33	.23	.12	.35	.23	.31	.56	.41	.46	.41	.38	.34	.32
VR II Copy	.16	.11	.00	.23	.18	.28	.50	.33	.29	.21	.31	.25	.24
Mean	9.9	9.9	10.0	10.0	10.0	10.0	10.0	10.0	10.1	10.0	10.0	9.4	10.1
SD	3.0	3.0	3.0	3.1	3.0	3.0	3.0	3.1	3.0	3.0	3.1	2.8	2.9

Table A.40. WMS–III Intercorrelations of Primary and Supplemental Subtest Scaled Scores: Ages 16–29 Years *(continued)*

Subtest	LM II Recall	LM II Them	Faces II Recog	VPA II Recall	Aud Rec Del	Fam Pic I Recall	WL II Recall	WL II Recall	VR II Recall	VR II Recog	VR II Copy
LM I Thematic											
Faces I Recognition											
VPA I Recall											
Fam Pic I Recall											
WL I Recall											
VR I Recall											
L–N Sequencing											
Spatial Span											
Spatial Span Forward											
Spatial Span Backward											
Mental Control											
Digit Span											
LM II Recall											
LM II Thematic	.83										
Faces II Recognition	.17	.08									
VPA II Recall	.42	.31	.21								
Auditory Recognition Del	.66	.54	.19	.32							
Fam Pic II Recall	.37	.30	.27	.23	.30						
WL II Recall	.53	.35	.19	.49	.42	.32					
WL II Recognition	.39	.31	.14	.31	.31	.26	.57				
VR II Recall	.39	.24	.24	.43	.38	.29	.46	.30			
VR II Recognition	.33	.27	.22	.30	.27	.28	.30	.20	.52		
VR II Copy	.14	.11	.07	.28	.16	.21	.19	.13	.43	.37	
Mean	9.9	9.9	10.0	10.0	10.0	10.0	10.0	10.0	10.0	10.0	10.0
SD	3.0	3.1	3.0	3.0	3.0	3.0	3.0	3.0	3.1	3.0	3.1

Table A.41. WMS–III Intercorrelations of Primary and Supplemental Subtest Scaled Scores: Ages 30–64 Years

Subtest	LM I Recall	LM I Them	Faces I Recog	VPA I Recall	Fam Pic I Recall	WL I Recall	VR I Recall	L–N Sequencing	Spatial Span	Spatial Span Fwd	Spatial Span Bkwd	Mental Control	Digit Span
LM I Thematic	.83												
Faces I Recognition	.14	.13											
VPA I Recall	.46	.39	.26										
Fam Pic I Recall	.35	.37	.31	.40									
WL I Recall	.54	.45	.24	.52	.34								
VR I Recall	.39	.30	.23	.44	.35	.37							
L–N Sequencing	.41	.29	.17	.38	.33	.38	.42						
Spatial Span	.32	.22	.19	.29	.28	.25	.45	.43					
Spatial Span Forward	.21	.17	.17	.17	.18	.17	.31	.35	.82				
Spatial Span Backward	.31	.18	.17	.27	.24	.24	.43	.35	.84	.44			
Mental Control	.44	.30	.20	.25	.24	.37	.28	.53	.37	.27	.35		
Digit Span	.28	.19	.13	.29	.24	.30	.31	.58	.37	.31	.32	.47	
LM II Recall	.87	.77	.20	.52	.41	.55	.40	.41	.34	.23	.32	.39	.28
LM II Thematic	.78	.83	.13	.41	.37	.45	.32	.34	.25	.16	.23	.31	.22
Faces II Recognition	.17	.13	.68	.27	.29	.30	.27	.24	.18	.17	.14	.22	.22
VPA II Recall	.43	.37	.25	.85	.41	.49	.41	.40	.28	.16	.28	.28	.25
Auditory Recognition Del	.72	.61	.15	.47	.33	.46	.35	.37	.34	.21	.33	.40	.28
Fam Pic II Recall	.39	.40	.28	.40	.92	.34	.36	.33	.28	.21	.21	.23	.24
WL II Recall	.48	.42	.20	.51	.39	.59	.35	.34	.27	.19	.24	.24	.18
WL II Recognition	.41	.37	.23	.47	.35	.60	.30	.25	.16	.09	.16	.29	.15
VR II Recall	.31	.23	.20	.35	.34	.35	.65	.39	.35	.26	.33	.19	.25
VR II Recognition	.37	.30	.23	.42	.44	.37	.67	.42	.44	.34	.37	.31	.37
VR II Copy	.26	.17	.12	.17	.16	.31	.41	.28	.21	.19	.19	.22	.23
Mean	10.1	10.2	10.0	10.0	10.0	10.0	10.0	10.1	10.0	10.0	10.0	9.4	10.1
SD	3.0	3.1	3.1	3.0	3.0	3.1	3.0	3.1	2.9	2.9	3.0	2.8	2.9

Table A.41. WMS–III Intercorrelations of Primary and Supplemental Subtest Scaled Scores: Ages 30–64 Years (continued)

Subtest	LM II Recall	LM II Them	Faces II Recog	VPA II Recall	Aud Rec Del	Fam Pic I Recall	WL II Recall	WL II Recog	VR II Recall	VR II Recog	VR II Copy
LM I Thematic											
Faces I Recognition											
VPA I Recall											
Fam Pic I Recall											
WL I Recall											
VR I Recall											
L–N Sequencing											
Spatial Span											
Spatial Span Forward											
Spatial Span Backward											
Mental Control											
Digit Span											
LM II Recall											
LM II Thematic	.85										
Faces II Recognition	.23	.12									
VPA II Recall	.48	.40	.25								
Auditory Recognition Del	.71	.57	.19	.44							
Fam Pic II Recall	.45	.40	.24	.40	.35						
WL II Recall	.54	.44	.30	.50	.42	.39					
WL II Recognition	.48	.39	.29	.49	.44	.34	.56				
VR II Recall	.37	.27	.29	.37	.31	.36	.44	.33			
VR II Recognition	.39	.33	.24	.42	.40	.43	.37	.27	.65		
VR II Copy	.22	.24	.11	.18	.19	.14	.23	.26	.38	.38	
Mean	10.1	10.1	10.1	10.1	10.1	10.1	10.0	10.0	10.0	10.0	10.0
SD	3.0	3.0	3.0	3.0	3.0	3.1	3.0	3.1	3.1	3.0	3.0

Table A.42. WMS–III Intercorrelations of Primary and Supplemental Subtest Scaled Scores: Ages 65–89 Years

Subtest	LM I Recall	LM I Them	Faces I Recog	VPA I Recall	Fam Pic I Recall	WL I Recall	VR I Recall	L-N Sequencing	Spatial Span	Spatial Span Fwd	Spatial Span Bkwd	Mental Control	Digit Span
LM I Thematic	.84												
Faces I Recognition	.19	.20											
VPA I Recall	.51	.42	.15										
Fam Pic I Recall	.49	.44	.35	.43									
WL I Recall	.52	.39	.23	.52	.39								
VR I Recall	.38	.34	.21	.36	.45	.35							
L-N Sequencing	.43	.31	.20	.32	.35	.42	.34						
Spatial Span	.28	.18	.15	.12	.22	.19	.32	.43					
Spatial Span Forward	.23	.14	.11	.08	.14	.16	.20	.36	.82				
Spatial Span Backward	.27	.19	.14	.13	.25	.20	.35	.38	.83	.40			
Mental Control	.34	.23	.07	.17	.16	.23	.15	.43	.29	.19	.32		
Digit Span	.29	.23	.10	.18	.16	.20	.21	.48	.42	.32	.37	.42	
LM II Recall	.84	.73	.23	.48	.55	.49	.40	.40	.25	.22	.23	.23	.24
LM II Thematic	.77	.78	.21	.42	.47	.44	.36	.34	.20	.17	.18	.22	.22
Faces II Recognition	.20	.18	.61	.18	.35	.21	.32	.22	.17	.11	.17	.09	.11
VPA II Recall	.47	.38	.18	.83	.38	.53	.38	.34	.15	.09	.18	.14	.18
Auditory Recognition Del	.70	.56	.25	.50	.44	.52	.35	.45	.25	.22	.23	.25	.28
Fam Pic II Recall	.50	.44	.33	.44	.89	.45	.44	.35	.28	.18	.31	.18	.19
WL II Recall	.33	.24	.17	.35	.29	.49	.17	.21	.09	.16	.06	.09	.05
WL II Recognition	.43	.32	.21	.45	.33	.60	.26	.35	.13	.13	.12	.15	.12
VR II Recall	.31	.27	.22	.34	.41	.37	.62	.29	.20	.15	.22	.11	.09
VR II Recognition	.35	.26	.23	.41	.37	.35	.65	.35	.31	.23	.30	.19	.17
VR II Copy	.24	.21	.23	.21	.30	.26	.44	.33	.30	.21	.28	.16	.20
Mean	10.0	10.0	10.0	10.0	10.0	10.0	10.1	10.0	10.0	10.0	10.0	9.6	10.1
SD	3.0	3.0	3.0	3.0	3.0	3.0	3.0	3.2	3.0	3.0	3.0	2.7	2.9

Table A.42. WMS–III Intercorrelations of Primary and Supplemental Subtest Scaled Scores: Ages 65–89 Years *(continued)*

Subtest	LM II Recall	LM II Them	Faces II Recog	VPA II Recall	Aud Rec Del	Fam Pic I Recall	WL II Recall	WL II Recall	VR II Recall	VR II Recog	VR II Copy
LM I Thematic											
Faces I Recognition											
VPA I Recall											
Fam Pic I Recall											
WL I Recall											
VR I Recall											
L–N Sequencing											
Spatial Span											
Spatial Span Forward											
Spatial Span Backward											
Mental Control											
Digit Span											
LM II Recall											
LM II Thematic	.88										
Faces II Recognition	.26	.26									
VPA II Recall	.49	.43	.21								
Auditory Recognition Del	.67	.59	.26	.53							
Fam Pic II Recall	.56	.49	.32	.43	.47						
WL II Recall	.37	.27	.11	.36	.38	.30					
WL II Recognition	.45	.36	.20	.48	.49	.36	.60				
VR II Recall	.39	.33	.28	.35	.32	.42	.33	.25			
VR II Recognition	.36	.32	.33	.41	.41	.37	.29	.35	.57		
VR II Copy	.22	.22	.25	.24	.30	.32	.13	.24	.27	.36	
Mean	10.0	10.0	10.0	10.0	10.0	10.1	10.0	10.0	10.0	10.0	10.0
SD	3.0	3.0	3.0	3.0	3.0	3.1	3.1	3.0	3.0	3.0	3.0

Discrepancy Score Tables Based on Predicted-Difference Method

Table B.1. WMS–III Index Scores Predicted From WAIS–III FSIQ
Scores: All Ages

WAIS–III FSIQ	Aud Imm	Vis Imm	Imm Mem	Aud Del	Vis Del	Aud Rec Del	Gen Mem	Wkg Mem	WAIS–III FSIQ
45	68	80	69	69	77	73	67	63	45
46	68	81	69	69	77	74	68	63	46
47	69	81	70	70	78	74	68	64	47
48	69	81	70	70	78	75	69	65	48
49	70	82	71	71	79	75	69	65	49
50	71	82	72	72	79	76	70	66	50
51	71	82	72	72	79	76	71	67	51
52	72	83	73	73	80	76	71	67	52
53	72	83	73	73	80	77	72	68	53
54	73	83	74	74	81	77	72	69	54
55	73	84	74	74	81	78	73	69	55
56	74	84	75	75	82	78	74	70	56
57	75	85	75	75	82	79	74	71	57
58	75	85	76	76	82	79	75	71	58
59	76	85	77	77	83	80	75	72	59
60	76	86	77	77	83	80	76	73	60
61	77	86	78	78	84	81	77	73	61
62	78	86	78	78	84	81	77	74	62
63	78	87	79	79	84	82	78	75	63
64	79	87	79	79	85	82	78	76	64
65	79	87	80	80	85	83	79	76	65
66	80	88	81	81	86	83	80	77	66
67	81	88	81	81	86	84	80	78	67
68	81	88	82	82	87	84	81	78	68
69	82	89	82	82	87	85	81	79	69
70	82	89	83	83	87	85	82	80	70
71	83	90	83	83	88	86	83	80	71
72	83	90	84	84	88	86	83	81	72
73	84	90	85	85	89	87	84	82	73
74	85	91	85	85	89	87	84	82	74
75	85	91	86	86	90	88	85	83	75
76	86	91	86	86	90	88	86	84	76
77	86	92	87	87	90	89	86	84	77
78	87	92	87	87	91	89	87	85	78
79	88	92	88	88	91	90	87	86	79
80	88	93	89	89	92	90	88	86	80
81	89	93	89	89	92	91	89	87	81
82	89	94	90	90	92	91	89	88	82
83	90	94	90	90	93	92	90	88	83
84	91	94	91	91	93	92	90	89	84
85	91	95	91	91	94	93	91	90	85
86	92	95	92	92	94	93	92	90	86
87	92	95	93	93	95	94	92	91	87
88	93	96	93	93	95	94	93	92	88
89	94	96	94	94	95	95	93	93	89
90	94	96	94	94	96	95	94	93	90
91	95	97	95	95	96	96	95	94	91
92	95	97	95	95	97	96	95	95	92
93	96	97	96	96	97	97	96	95	93
94	96	98	97	97	97	97	96	96	94
95	97	98	97	97	98	98	97	97	95
96	98	99	98	98	98	98	98	97	96
97	98	99	98	98	99	99	98	98	97
98	99	99	99	99	99	99	99	99	98
99	99	100	99	99	100	100	99	99	99

Table B.1. WMS–III Index Scores Predicted From WAIS–III FSIQ Scores: All Ages *(continued)*

WAIS–III FSIQ	Aud Imm	Vis Imm	Imm Mem	Aud Del	Vis Del	Aud Rec Del	Gen Mem	Wkg Mem	WAIS–III FSIQ
100	100	100	100	100	100	100	100	100	100
101	101	100	101	101	100	100	101	101	101
102	101	101	101	101	101	101	101	101	102
103	102	101	102	102	101	101	102	102	103
104	102	101	102	102	102	102	102	103	104
105	103	102	103	103	102	102	103	103	105
106	104	102	103	103	103	103	104	104	106
107	104	103	104	104	103	103	104	105	107
108	105	103	105	105	103	104	105	105	108
109	105	103	105	105	104	104	105	106	109
110	106	104	106	106	104	105	106	107	110
111	106	104	106	106	105	105	107	107	111
112	107	104	107	107	105	106	107	108	112
113	108	105	107	107	105	106	108	109	113
114	108	105	108	108	106	107	108	110	114
115	109	105	109	109	106	107	109	110	115
116	109	106	109	109	107	108	110	111	116
117	110	106	110	110	107	108	110	112	117
118	111	106	110	110	108	109	111	112	118
119	111	107	111	111	108	109	111	113	119
120	112	107	111	111	108	110	112	114	120
121	112	108	112	112	109	110	113	114	121
122	113	108	113	113	109	111	113	115	122
123	114	108	113	113	110	111	114	116	123
124	114	109	114	114	110	112	114	116	124
125	115	109	114	114	111	112	115	117	125
126	115	109	115	115	111	113	116	118	126
127	116	110	115	115	111	113	116	118	127
128	117	110	116	116	112	114	117	119	128
129	117	110	117	117	112	114	117	120	129
130	118	111	117	117	113	115	118	120	130
131	118	111	118	118	113	115	119	121	131
132	119	112	118	118	113	116	119	122	132
133	119	112	119	119	114	116	120	122	133
134	120	112	119	119	114	117	120	123	134
135	121	113	120	120	115	117	121	124	135
136	121	113	121	121	115	118	122	124	136
137	122	113	121	121	116	118	122	125	137
138	122	114	122	122	116	119	123	126	138
139	123	114	122	122	116	119	123	127	139
140	124	114	123	123	117	120	124	127	140
141	124	115	123	123	117	120	125	128	141
142	125	115	124	124	118	121	125	129	142
143	125	115	125	125	118	121	126	129	143
144	126	116	125	125	118	122	126	130	144
145	127	116	126	126	119	122	127	131	145
146	127	117	126	126	119	123	128	131	146
147	128	117	127	127	120	123	128	132	147
148	128	117	127	127	120	124	129	133	148
149	129	118	128	128	121	124	129	133	149
150	130	118	129	129	121	125	130	134	150
151	130	118	129	129	121	125	131	135	151
152	131	119	130	130	122	125	131	135	152
153	131	119	130	130	122	126	132	136	153
154	132	119	131	131	123	126	132	137	154
155	132	120	131	131	123	127	133	137	155

Table B.2. WMS–III Index Scores Predicted From WAIS–III VIQ Scores: All Ages

WAIS–III VIQ	Aud Imm	Vis Imm	Imm Mem	Aud Del	Vis Del	Aud Rec Del	Gen Mem	Wkg Mem	WAIS–III VIQ
48	70	84	72	72	82	76	71	68	48
49	70	85	73	72	82	76	71	68	49
50	71	85	74	73	83	77	72	69	50
51	72	85	74	74	83	77	73	70	51
52	72	86	75	74	83	77	73	70	52
53	73	86	75	75	84	78	74	71	53
54	73	86	76	75	84	78	74	71	54
55	74	87	76	76	84	79	75	72	55
56	74	87	77	76	85	79	75	73	56
57	75	87	77	77	85	80	76	73	57
58	76	87	78	77	85	80	76	74	58
59	76	88	78	78	86	81	77	75	59
60	77	88	79	78	86	81	78	75	60
61	77	88	79	79	86	82	78	76	61
62	78	89	80	79	87	82	79	76	62
63	79	89	80	80	87	83	79	77	63
64	79	89	81	81	87	83	80	78	64
65	80	90	81	81	88	84	80	78	65
66	80	90	82	82	88	84	81	79	66
67	81	90	83	82	88	84	82	80	67
68	81	90	83	83	89	85	82	80	68
69	82	91	84	83	89	85	83	81	69
70	83	91	84	84	90	86	83	81	70
71	83	91	85	84	90	86	84	82	71
72	84	92	85	85	90	87	84	83	72
73	84	92	86	85	91	87	85	83	73
74	85	92	86	86	91	88	85	84	74
75	86	93	87	87	91	88	86	85	75
76	86	93	87	87	92	89	87	85	76
77	87	93	88	88	92	89	87	86	77
78	87	93	88	88	92	90	88	86	78
79	88	94	89	89	93	90	88	87	79
80	88	94	89	89	93	91	89	88	80
81	89	94	90	90	93	91	89	88	81
82	90	95	90	90	94	92	90	89	82
83	90	95	91	91	94	92	90	89	83
84	91	95	92	91	94	92	91	90	84
85	91	96	92	92	95	93	92	91	85
86	92	96	93	92	95	93	92	91	86
87	92	96	93	93	95	94	93	92	87
88	93	96	94	94	96	94	93	93	88
89	94	97	94	94	96	95	94	93	89
90	94	97	95	95	97	95	94	94	90
91	95	97	95	95	97	96	95	94	91
92	95	98	96	96	97	96	96	95	92
93	96	98	96	96	98	97	96	96	93
94	97	98	97	97	98	97	97	96	94
95	97	99	97	97	98	98	97	97	95
96	98	99	98	98	99	98	98	98	96
97	98	99	98	98	99	99	98	98	97
98	99	99	99	99	99	99	99	99	98
99	99	100	99	99	100	100	99	99	99
100	100	100	100	100	100	100	100	100	100
101	101	100	101	101	100	101	101	101	101
102	101	101	101	101	101	101	101	101	102

Table B.2. WMS–III Index Scores Predicted From WAIS–III VIQ Scores: All Ages *(continued)*

WAIS–III VIQ	Aud Imm	Vis Imm	Imm Mem	Aud Del	Vis Del	Aud Re Del	Gen Mem	Wkg Mem	WAIS–III VIQ
103	102	101	102	102	101	102	102	102	103
104	102	101	102	102	101	102	102	102	104
105	103	102	103	103	102	103	103	103	105
106	103	102	103	103	102	103	103	104	106
107	104	102	104	104	102	104	104	104	107
108	105	102	104	104	103	104	104	105	108
109	105	103	105	105	103	105	105	106	109
110	106	103	105	105	104	105	106	106	110
111	106	103	106	106	104	106	106	107	111
112	107	104	106	106	104	106	107	107	112
113	108	104	107	107	105	107	107	108	113
114	108	104	107	108	105	108	108	109	114
115	109	105	108	108	105	108	108	109	115
116	109	105	108	109	106	109	109	110	116
117	110	105	109	109	106	109	110	111	117
118	110	105	110	110	106	110	110	111	118
119	111	106	110	110	107	110	111	112	119
120	112	106	111	111	107	111	111	112	120
121	112	106	111	111	107	111	112	113	121
122	113	107	112	112	108	112	112	114	122
123	113	107	112	112	108	112	113	114	123
124	114	107	113	113	108	113	113	115	124
125	115	108	113	114	109	114	114	116	125
126	115	108	114	114	109	114	115	116	126
127	116	108	114	115	109	115	115	117	127
128	116	108	115	115	110	115	116	117	128
129	117	109	115	116	110	116	116	118	129
130	117	109	116	116	111	116	117	119	130
131	118	109	116	117	111	117	117	119	131
132	119	110	117	117	111	117	118	120	132
133	119	110	117	118	112	118	118	120	133
134	120	110	118	118	112	118	119	121	134
135	120	111	119	119	112	119	120	122	135
136	121	111	119	119	113	119	120	122	136
137	121	111	120	120	113	120	121	123	137
138	122	111	120	121	113	121	121	124	138
139	123	112	121	121	114	121	122	124	139
140	123	112	121	122	114	122	122	125	140
141	124	112	122	122	114	122	123	125	141
142	124	113	122	123	115	123	124	126	142
143	125	113	123	123	115	123	124	127	143
144	126	113	123	124	115	124	125	127	144
145	126	114	124	124	116	124	125	128	145
146	127	114	124	125	116	125	126	129	146
147	127	114	125	125	116	125	126	129	147
148	128	114	125	126	117	126	127	130	148
149	128	115	126	126	117	126	127	130	149
150	129	115	127	127	118	127	128	131	150
151	130	115	127	128	118	128	129	132	151
152	130	116	128	128	118	128	129	132	152
153	131	116	128	129	119	129	130	133	153
154	131	116	129	129	119	129	130	133	154
155	132	117	129	130	119	130	131	134	155

Table B.3. WMS–III Index Scores Predicted From WAIS–III PIQ Scores: All Ages

WAIS–III PIQ	Aud Imm	Vis Imm	Imm Mem	Aud Del	Vis Del	Aud Rec Del	Gen Mem	Wkg Mem	WAIS–III PIQ
47	72	79	71	74	77	77	70	66	47
48	73	80	72	74	77	77	71	66	48
49	73	80	72	75	78	78	71	67	49
50	74	81	73	75	78	78	72	68	50
51	75	81	74	76	78	78	73	68	51
52	75	81	74	76	79	79	73	69	52
53	76	82	75	77	79	79	74	69	53
54	76	82	75	77	80	80	74	70	54
55	77	82	76	78	80	80	75	71	55
56	77	83	76	78	81	81	75	71	56
57	78	83	77	79	81	81	76	72	57
58	78	84	77	79	82	82	76	73	58
59	79	84	78	80	82	82	77	73	59
60	79	84	78	80	82	82	78	74	60
61	80	85	79	81	83	83	78	75	61
62	80	85	79	81	83	83	79	75	62
63	81	86	80	82	84	84	79	76	63
64	81	86	81	82	84	84	80	77	64
65	82	86	81	83	85	85	80	77	65
66	82	87	82	83	85	85	81	78	66
67	83	87	82	84	85	85	82	79	67
68	83	88	83	84	86	86	82	79	68
69	84	88	83	85	86	86	83	80	69
70	84	88	84	85	87	87	83	81	70
71	85	89	84	86	87	87	84	81	71
72	85	89	85	86	88	88	84	82	72
73	86	89	85	87	88	88	85	82	73
74	86	90	86	87	89	89	85	83	74
75	87	90	87	88	89	89	86	84	75
76	88	91	87	88	89	89	87	84	76
77	88	91	88	89	90	90	87	85	77
78	89	91	88	89	90	90	88	86	78
79	89	92	89	90	91	91	88	86	79
80	90	92	89	90	91	91	89	87	80
81	90	93	90	91	92	92	89	88	81
82	91	93	90	91	92	92	90	88	82
83	91	93	91	92	93	93	90	89	83
84	92	94	91	92	93	93	91	90	84
85	92	94	92	93	93	93	92	90	85
86	93	95	92	93	94	94	92	91	86
87	93	95	93	94	94	94	93	92	87
88	94	95	94	94	95	95	93	92	88
89	94	96	94	95	95	95	94	93	89
90	95	96	95	95	96	96	94	94	90
91	95	96	95	96	96	96	95	94	91
92	96	97	96	96	96	96	96	95	92
93	96	97	96	97	97	97	96	95	93
94	97	98	97	97	97	97	97	96	94
95	97	98	97	98	98	98	97	97	95
96	98	98	98	98	98	98	98	97	96
97	98	99	98	99	99	99	98	98	97
98	99	99	99	99	99	99	99	99	98
99	99	100	99	100	100	100	99	99	99
100	100	100	100	100	100	100	100	100	100
101	101	100	101	101	100	100	101	101	101
102	101	101	101	101	101	101	101	101	102

Table B.3. WMS–III Index Scores Predicted From WAIS–III PIQ Scores: All Ages *(continued)*

WAIS–III PIQ	Aud Imm	Vis Imm	Imm Mem	Aud Del	Vis Del	Aud Rec Del	Gen Mem	Wkg Mem	WAIS–III PIQ
103	102	101	102	102	101	101	102	102	103
104	102	102	102	102	102	102	102	103	104
105	103	102	103	103	102	102	103	103	105
106	103	102	103	103	103	103	103	104	106
107	104	103	104	104	103	103	104	105	107
108	104	103	104	104	104	104	104	105	108
109	105	104	105	105	104	104	105	106	109
110	105	104	105	105	104	104	106	107	110
111	106	104	106	106	105	105	106	107	111
112	106	105	106	106	105	105	107	108	112
113	107	105	107	107	106	106	107	108	113
114	107	105	108	107	106	106	108	109	114
115	108	106	108	108	107	107	108	110	115
116	108	106	109	108	107	107	109	110	116
117	109	107	109	109	107	107	110	111	117
118	109	107	110	109	108	108	110	112	118
119	110	107	110	110	108	108	111	112	119
120	110	108	111	110	109	109	111	113	120
121	111	108	111	111	109	109	112	114	121
122	111	109	112	111	110	110	112	114	122
123	112	109	112	112	110	110	113	115	123
124	112	109	113	112	111	111	113	116	124
125	113	110	114	113	111	111	114	116	125
126	114	110	114	113	111	111	115	117	126
127	114	111	115	114	112	112	115	118	127
128	115	111	115	114	112	112	116	118	128
129	115	111	116	115	113	113	116	119	129
130	116	112	116	115	113	113	117	120	130
131	116	112	117	116	114	114	117	120	131
132	117	112	117	116	114	114	118	121	132
133	117	113	118	117	115	115	118	121	133
134	118	113	118	117	115	115	119	122	134
135	118	114	119	118	115	115	120	123	135
136	119	114	119	118	116	116	120	123	136
137	119	114	120	119	116	116	121	124	137
138	120	115	121	119	117	117	121	125	138
139	120	115	121	120	117	117	122	125	139
140	121	116	122	120	118	118	122	126	140
141	121	116	122	121	118	118	123	127	141
142	122	116	123	121	118	118	124	127	142
143	122	117	123	122	119	119	124	128	143
144	123	117	124	122	119	119	125	129	144
145	123	118	124	123	120	120	125	129	145
146	124	118	125	123	120	120	126	130	146
147	124	118	125	124	121	121	126	131	147
148	125	119	126	124	121	121	127	131	148
149	125	119	126	125	122	122	127	132	149
150	126	120	127	125	122	122	128	133	150
151	127	120	128	126	122	122	129	133	151
152	127	120	128	126	123	123	129	134	152
153	128	121	129	127	123	123	130	134	153
154	128	121	129	127	124	124	130	135	154
155	129	121	130	128	124	124	131	136	155

Table B.4. Differences Between Predicted and Obtained WMS–III Index Scores Required for Statistical Significance by Age (Predicted-Difference Method—WAIS–III FSIQ)

WMS-III Index	Significance Level	Mean All Ages	Age Group												
			16–17	18–19	20–24	25–29	30–34	35–44	45–54	55–64	65–69	70–74	75–79	80–84	85–89
Auditory Immediate	.05	16.9	16.2	15.5	16.2	16.6	15.8	13.7	17.3	16.9	17.1	17.3	15.6	20.0	20.9
	.01	21.5	20.5	19.7	20.6	21.3	20.2	17.4	22.2	21.6	21.9	22.1	19.9	25.8	26.9
Visual Immediate	.05	16.6	18.8	16.1	16.8	19.1	17.3	17.5	16.0	16.9	15.9	15.5	13.7	16.1	16.2
	.01	20.9	23.7	20.2	21.1	24.1	21.8	22.1	20.2	21.2	19.8	19.3	17.0	20.2	20.3
Immediate Memory	.05	16.4	18.6	14.9	16.3	17.7	15.1	15.0	16.4	17.1	17.3	15.3	13.0	18.1	18.1
	.01	20.8	23.6	18.9	20.7	22.6	19.3	19.0	20.9	21.8	22.1	19.3	16.3	23.2	23.1
Auditory Delayed	.05	14.7	12.0	12.4	13.7	15.6	14.7	11.2	15.6	13.7	15.3	16.2	14.7	18.7	17.6
	.01	18.5	14.6	15.3	17.1	19.6	18.5	13.9	19.7	17.1	19.2	20.4	18.5	23.9	22.2
Visual Delayed	.05	16.1	18.1	16.4	15.7	17.2	14.9	17.5	16.9	16.1	14.9	15.4	15.2	15.2	16.0
	.01	20.2	22.7	20.6	19.8	21.6	18.7	22.2	21.4	20.1	18.5	19.2	18.9	19.0	20.1
Auditory Recognition Delayed	.05	12.7	12.5	10.3	14.2	15.0	13.3	9.3	12.5	10.9	13.1	11.5	12.7	14.3	15.9
	.01	15.5	15.1	12.1	17.6	18.6	16.2	11.0	15.1	13.0	16.1	13.8	15.6	17.8	19.9
General Memory	.05	15.6	16.3	12.7	15.2	16.9	14.6	13.1	16.0	15.2	16.3	15.4	15.3	17.5	18.4
	.01	19.8	20.5	15.9	19.4	21.5	18.4	16.5	20.3	19.2	20.7	19.5	19.5	22.4	23.5
Working Memory	.05	11.9	12.5	12.7	13.9	9.1	11.8	10.2	11.9	12.0	11.1	11.8	11.2	11.8	14.7
	.01	14.7	15.5	15.9	17.4	11.0	14.7	12.4	14.7	15.0	13.5	14.7	13.6	14.7	18.4

Table B.5. Differences Between Predicted and Obtained WMS–III Index Scores Required for Statistical Significance by Age (Predicted-Difference Method—WAIS–III VIQ)

WMS-III Index	Significance Level	Mean All Ages	16–17	18–19	20–24	25–29	30–34	35–44	45–54	55–64	65–69	70–74	75–79	80–84	85–89
Auditory	.05	17.1	16.7	15.8	15.8	16.9	15.0	13.5	18.5	17.9	17.1	17.0	17.4	19.5	21.0
Immediate	.01	21.8	21.2	20.1	20.1	21.7	19.2	17.1	23.7	23.0	21.9	21.6	22.3	25.1	27.0
Visual	.05	17.3	18.7	16.0	17.7	19.3	17.3	18.4	16.3	17.5	16.8	16.6	14.6	16.9	18.3
Immediate	.01	21.7	23.6	20.0	22.3	24.5	21.9	23.3	20.6	22.0	21.0	20.8	18.1	21.3	23.2
Immediate	.05	17.2	19.0	14.9	17.0	18.5	15.0	15.8	17.2	18.2	18.4	16.2	14.9	18.4	19.8
Memory	.01	21.9	24.1	18.9	21.6	23.7	19.0	20.1	22.0	23.2	23.6	20.5	18.9	23.5	25.3
Auditory	.05	15.2	12.5	12.9	14.3	15.9	14.1	11.7	16.6	14.8	15.3	16.5	16.0	18.4	18.1
Delayed	.01	19.0	15.3	16.0	17.8	20.0	17.7	14.6	21.0	18.5	19.2	20.8	20.3	23.4	23.0
Visual	.05	16.9	18.0	16.4	16.5	17.7	15.2	18.4	17.6	17.0	16.6	16.6	16.0	16.2	17.7
Delayed	.01	21.3	22.6	20.6	20.8	22.3	19.0	23.3	22.3	21.4	20.8	20.8	20.0	20.3	22.5
Auditory Recognition	.05	13.0	13.7	10.1	13.3	15.7	13.0	9.7	13.0	12.0	12.8	11.6	13.5	13.9	16.7
Delayed	.01	15.9	16.6	11.9	16.4	19.6	15.8	11.5	15.8	14.4	15.6	14.0	16.6	17.2	20.9
General	.05	16.5	17.4	13.0	15.6	18.0	14.4	14.1	17.2	16.7	17.1	16.6	16.7	17.6	19.8
Memory	.01	20.9	21.9	16.2	19.8	22.9	18.2	17.9	21.9	21.2	21.8	21.1	21.3	22.5	25.4
Working	.05	13.3	13.8	15.2	15.3	12.7	13.4	10.7	13.5	12.9	11.9	13.3	13.0	12.8	15.0
Memory	.01	16.6	17.1	19.2	19.3	15.9	16.8	13.1	16.8	16.1	14.6	16.7	16.0	16.0	18.9

Table B.6. Differences Between Predicted and Obtained WMS–III Index Scores Required for Statistical Significance by Age (Predicted-Difference Method—WAIS–III PIQ)

WMS-III Index	Significance Level	Mean All Ages	16–17	18–19	20–24	25–29	30–34	35–44	45–54	55–64	65–69	70–74	75–79	80–84	85–89
Auditory Immediate	.05	18.0	17.4	17.3	17.7	18.4	18.2	15.8	16.7	16.9	19.1	18.5	15.4	21.3	21.3
	.01	23.0	22.0	22.1	22.6	23.6	23.3	20.1	21.3	21.5	24.5	23.6	19.6	27.5	27.3
Visual Immediate	.05	16.2	18.9	16.8	16.1	18.7	17.6	16.9	16.6	16.6	14.9	14.1	14.0	15.5	13.2
	.01	20.2	23.9	21.0	20.2	23.7	22.2	21.3	20.9	20.8	18.5	17.5	17.3	19.4	16.4
Immediate Memory	.05	16.7	18.6	16.9	16.5	17.9	17.1	15.4	16.2	16.7	17.7	15.1	13.2	18.4	16.6
	.01	21.2	23.6	21.5	21.0	22.9	21.8	19.5	20.6	21.3	22.5	19.1	16.6	23.6	21.1
Auditory Delayed	.05	15.7	13.6	13.9	14.5	16.6	16.7	13.6	15.2	13.8	16.9	16.7	14.9	19.7	17.5
	.01	19.7	16.7	17.3	18.1	21.0	21.1	17.0	19.2	17.3	21.3	21.0	18.8	25.1	22.1
Visual Delayed	.05	15.7	18.0	16.9	15.7	16.9	15.5	17.4	16.9	15.3	13.6	13.5	15.0	14.8	14.0
	.01	19.6	22.5	21.2	19.7	21.2	19.3	22.0	21.4	19.1	16.9	16.7	18.6	18.5	17.5
Auditory Recognition Delayed	.05	13.4	12.0	11.7	15.9	14.8	14.0	11.1	12.4	10.7	14.8	12.5	13.4	15.5	15.6
	.01	16.4	14.4	14.0	19.9	18.4	17.2	13.3	15.0	12.7	18.2	15.2	16.5	19.3	19.5
General Memory	.05	16.0	16.1	14.7	16.2	17.1	16.5	14.4	15.6	14.8	17.3	14.8	15.5	18.3	17.2
	.01	20.3	20.2	18.4	20.6	21.8	21.0	18.2	19.8	18.6	22.0	18.6	19.6	23.3	21.9
Working Memory	.05	12.4	13.3	12.3	13.5	8.5	11.6	11.4	12.0	13.5	12.8	11.6	11.5	13.2	16.0
	.01	15.4	16.5	15.3	16.9	10.2	14.4	14.0	14.7	16.9	15.9	14.4	14.0	16.5	20.2

Table B.7. Frequencies (Cumulative Percentages) of Differences Between Predicted and Obtained WMS–III Index Scores: All Ages (Predicted-Difference Method—WAIS–III FSIQ)

WMS–III Primary Index	Percentage								
	25	20	15	10	5	4	3	2	1
Auditory Immediate	8	11	13	16	20	21	23	25	28
Visual Immediate	10	12	15	18	23	24	27	29	32
Immediate Memory	8	10	13	17	21	22	24	26	28
Auditory Delayed	8	10	13	16	20	22	25	27	32
Visual Delayed	9	11	14	17	22	24	25	28	34
Auditory Recog Delayed	9	11	14	17	21	24	25	27	30
General Memory	8	10	12	15	20	21	24	25	29
Working Memory	8	9	11	14	17	18	19	21	24

Table B.8. Frequencies (Cumulative Percentages) of Differences Between Predicted and Obtained WMS–III Index Scores: All Ages (Predicted-Difference Method—WAIS–III VIQ)

WMS–III Primary Index	Percentage								
	25	20	15	10	5	4	3	2	1
Auditory Immediate	9	11	14	16	21	22	23	25	27
Visual Immediate	10	13	15	19	23	25	27	30	33
Immediate Memory	8	11	14	17	22	23	24	27	30
Auditory Delayed	8	11	13	17	21	23	26	27	31
Visual Delayed	10	11	14	17	23	25	27	30	33
Auditory Recog Delayed	10	12	14	17	21	23	26	28	32
General Memory	8	11	13	16	21	23	25	26	31
Working Memory	9	10	12	15	18	19	20	23	26

Table B.9. Frequencies (Cumulative Percentages) of Differences Between Predicted and Obtained WMS–III Index Scores: All Ages (Predicted-Difference Method—WAIS–III PIQ)

WMS–III Primary Index	Percentage								
	25	20	15	10	5	4	3	2	1
Auditory Immediate	9	11	13	16	21	22	24	26	31
Visual Immediate	10	12	14	18	22	24	26	29	31
Immediate Memory	9	11	13	16	21	23	24	26	30
Auditory Delayed	9	11	14	17	21	23	26	28	32
Visual Delayed	9	11	14	17	22	24	26	28	31
Auditory Recog Delayed	9	12	14	17	22	23	25	27	31
General Memory	8	11	13	15	20	22	23	24	29
Working Memory	8	10	12	14	18	19	20	21	25

Note. Percentages for Tables B.7–B.9 represent the portions of the sample who obtained WMS–III Index scores lower than their predicted WMS–III Index scores by the specified amount or more.

Table B.10. WIAT–II Subtest and Composite Standard Scores Predicted From WAIS–III FSIQ Scores

Ages 16:0–19:11 (High School)

| | Subtest Standard Scores | | | | | | | | | Composite Standard Scores | | | | | |
FSIQ Score	WRD	NO	RC	SP	PD	MR	WE	LC	OE	RD	MA	WL	OL	Total	FSIQ Score
40															40
41															41
42															42
43															43
44															44
45	62	59	63	63	68	56	68	58	73	59	55	63	57	53	45
46	63	60	64	64	68	57	68	59	74	60	56	64	58	54	46
47	63	61	64	65	69	57	69	59	74	61	57	64	59	55	47
48	64	61	65	65	70	58	69	60	75	62	58	65	60	56	48
49	65	62	66	66	70	59	70	61	75	62	59	66	60	56	49
50	65	63	66	67	71	60	71	62	76	63	59	66	61	57	50
51	66	63	67	67	71	61	71	62	76	64	60	67	62	58	51
52	67	64	68	68	72	61	72	63	77	65	61	68	63	59	52
53	67	65	68	69	73	62	72	64	77	65	62	68	64	60	53
54	68	66	69	69	73	63	73	65	78	66	63	69	64	61	54
55	69	66	70	70	74	64	73	65	78	67	63	70	65	62	55
56	69	67	70	71	74	65	74	66	78	67	64	70	66	62	56
57	70	68	71	71	75	65	75	67	79	68	65	71	67	63	57
58	71	69	72	72	75	66	75	68	79	69	66	72	67	64	58
59	72	69	72	73	76	67	76	69	80	70	67	72	68	65	59
60	72	70	73	73	77	68	76	69	80	70	67	73	69	66	60
61	73	71	74	74	77	69	77	70	81	71	68	74	70	67	61
62	74	72	74	75	78	69	78	71	81	72	69	74	71	68	62
63	74	72	75	75	78	70	78	72	82	73	70	75	71	68	63
64	75	73	76	76	79	71	79	72	82	73	71	76	72	69	64
65	76	74	76	77	80	72	79	73	83	74	72	76	73	70	65
66	76	75	77	77	80	73	80	74	83	75	72	77	74	71	66
67	77	75	78	78	81	74	81	75	84	76	73	78	74	72	67
68	78	76	78	79	81	74	81	75	84	76	74	78	75	73	68
69	78	77	79	79	82	75	82	76	85	77	75	79	76	73	69
70	79	78	80	80	82	76	82	77	85	78	76	80	77	74	70
71	80	78	80	81	83	77	83	78	86	79	76	80	77	75	71
72	81	79	81	81	84	78	84	79	86	79	77	81	78	76	72
73	81	80	82	82	84	78	84	79	87	80	78	82	79	77	73
74	82	81	82	83	85	79	85	80	87	81	79	83	80	78	74
75	83	81	83	83	85	80	85	81	88	82	80	83	81	79	75
76	83	82	84	84	86	81	86	82	88	82	80	84	81	79	76
77	84	83	84	85	87	82	86	82	89	83	81	85	82	80	77
78	85	84	85	85	87	82	87	83	89	84	82	85	83	81	78
79	85	84	86	86	88	83	88	84	90	84	83	86	84	82	79
80	86	85	87	87	88	84	88	85	90	85	84	87	84	83	80
81	87	86	87	87	89	85	89	85	91	86	85	87	85	84	81
82	88	87	88	88	89	86	89	86	91	87	85	88	86	85	82
83	88	87	89	89	90	86	90	87	92	87	86	89	87	85	83
84	89	88	89	89	91	87	91	88	92	88	87	89	88	86	84
85	90	89	90	90	91	88	91	88	93	89	88	90	88	87	85
86	90	90	91	91	92	89	92	89	93	90	89	91	89	88	86
87	91	90	91	91	92	90	92	90	94	90	89	91	90	89	87
88	92	91	92	92	93	90	93	91	94	91	90	92	91	90	88
89	92	92	93	93	94	91	94	92	95	92	91	93	91	91	89
90	93	93	93	93	94	92	94	92	95	93	92	93	92	91	90
91	94	93	94	94	95	93	95	93	96	93	93	94	93	92	91
92	94	94	95	95	95	94	95	94	96	94	93	95	94	93	92
93	95	95	95	95	96	94	96	95	97	95	94	95	95	94	93
94	96	96	96	96	96	95	96	95	97	96	95	96	95	95	94
95	97	96	97	97	97	96	97	96	98	96	96	97	96	96	95
96	97	97	97	97	98	97	98	97	98	97	97	97	97	97	96
97	98	98	98	98	98	98	98	98	99	98	98	98	98	97	97
98	99	99	99	99	99	98	99	98	99	99	98	99	98	98	98
99	99	99	99	99	99	99	99	99	100	99	99	99	99	99	99
100	100	100	100	100	100	100	100	100	100	100	100	100	100	100	100

Table B.10. WIAT–II Subtest and Composite Standard Scores Predicted From WAIS–III FSIQ Scores (continued)

Ages 16:0–19:11 (High School)

FSIQ Score	Subtest Standard Scores									Composite Standard Scores					FSIQ Score
	WRD	NO	RC	SP	PD	MR	WE	LC	OE	RD	MA	WL	OL	Total	
101	101	101	101	101	101	101	101	101	100	101	101	101	101	101	101
102	101	101	101	101	101	102	101	102	101	101	102	101	102	102	102
103	102	102	102	102	102	102	102	102	101	102	102	102	102	103	103
104	103	103	103	103	102	103	102	103	102	103	103	103	103	103	104
105	103	104	103	103	103	104	103	104	102	104	104	103	104	104	105
106	104	104	104	104	104	105	104	105	103	104	105	104	105	105	106
107	105	105	105	105	104	106	104	105	103	105	106	105	105	106	107
108	106	106	105	105	105	106	105	106	104	106	107	105	106	107	108
109	106	107	106	106	105	107	105	107	104	107	107	106	107	108	109
110	107	107	107	107	106	108	106	108	105	107	108	107	108	109	110
111	108	108	107	107	106	109	106	108	105	108	109	107	109	109	111
112	108	109	108	108	107	110	107	109	106	109	110	108	109	110	112
113	109	110	109	109	108	110	108	110	106	110	111	109	110	111	113
114	110	110	109	109	108	111	108	111	107	110	111	109	111	112	114
115	110	111	110	110	109	112	109	112	107	111	112	110	112	113	115
116	111	112	111	111	109	113	109	112	108	112	113	111	112	114	116
117	112	113	111	111	110	114	110	113	108	113	114	111	113	115	117
118	112	113	112	112	111	114	111	114	109	113	115	112	114	115	118
119	113	114	113	113	111	115	111	115	109	114	115	113	115	116	119
120	114	115	113	113	112	116	112	115	110	115	116	113	116	117	120
121	115	116	114	114	112	117	112	116	110	116	117	114	116	118	121
122	115	116	115	115	113	118	113	117	111	116	118	115	117	119	122
123	116	117	116	115	113	118	114	118	111	117	119	115	118	120	123
124	117	118	116	116	114	119	114	118	112	118	120	116	119	121	124
125	117	119	117	117	115	120	115	119	112	118	120	117	119	121	125
126	118	119	118	117	115	121	115	120	113	119	121	117	120	122	126
127	119	120	118	118	116	122	116	121	113	120	122	118	121	123	127
128	119	121	119	119	116	122	116	121	114	121	123	119	122	124	128
129	120	122	120	119	117	123	117	122	114	121	124	120	123	125	129
130	121	122	120	120	118	124	118	123	115	122	124	120	123	126	130
131	122	123	121	121	118	125	118	124	115	123	125	121	124	127	131
132	122	124	122	121	119	126	119	125	116	124	126	122	125	127	132
133	123	125	122	122	119	126	119	125	116	124	127	122	126	128	133
134	124	125	123	123	120	127	120	126	117	125	128	123	126	129	134
135	124	126	124	123	120	128	121	127	117	126	128	124	127	130	135
136	125	127	124	124	121	129	121	128	118	127	129	124	128	131	136
137	126	128	125	125	122	130	122	128	118	127	130	125	129	132	137
138	126	128	126	125	122	131	122	129	119	128	131	126	129	132	138
139	127	129	126	126	123	131	123	130	119	129	132	126	130	133	139
140	128	130	127	127	123	132	124	131	120	130	133	127	131	134	140
141	128	131	128	127	124	133	124	131	120	130	133	128	132	135	141
142	129	131	128	128	125	134	125	132	121	131	134	128	133	136	142
143	130	132	129	129	125	135	125	133	121	132	135	129	133	137	143
144	131	133	130	129	126	135	126	134	122	133	136	130	134	138	144
145	131	134	130	130	126	136	127	135	122	133	137	130	135	138	145
146	132	134	131	131	127	137	127	135	122	134	137	131	136	139	146
147	133	135	132	131	127	138	128	136	123	135	138	132	136	140	147
148	133	136	132	132	128	139	128	137	123	135	139	132	137	141	148
149	134	137	133	133	129	139	129	138	124	136	140	133	138	142	149
150	135	137	134	133	129	140	129	138	124	137	141	134	139	143	150
151	135	138	134	134	130	141	130	139	125	138	141	134	140	144	151
152	136	139	135	135	130	142	131	140	125	138	142	135	140	144	152
153	137	139	136	135	131	143	131	141	126	139	143	136	141	145	153
154	137	140	136	136	132	143	132	141	126	140	144	136	142	146	154
155	138	141	137	137	132	144	132	142	127	141	145	137	143	147	155
156															156
157															157
158															158
159															159
160															160

Note. Based on the correlations between the WIAT–II standard scores and the WAIS–III FSIQ across the four age ranges. Presented in the order shown in the table, the average correlations for the nine WIAT–II subtests are .69, .75, .67, .67, .59, .80, .59, .77, and .49, and the average correlations for the five WIAT–II composites are .74, .81, .67, .78, and .86.

WRD = Word Reading
NO = Numerical Operations
RC = Reading Comprehension
SP = Spelling

PD = Pseudoword Decoding
MR = Math Reasoning
WE = Written Expression
LC = Listening Comprehension

OE = Oral Expression
RD = Reading
MA = Mathematics
WL = Written Language

OL = Oral Language

Table B.10. WIAT–II Subtest and Composite Standard Scores Predicted From WAIS–III FSIQ Scores *(continued)*

College Students

FSIQ Score	WRD	NO	RC	SP	PD	MR	WE	LC	OE	RD	MA	WL	OL	Total	FSIQ Score
	Subtest Standard Scores									**Composite Standard Scores**					
40															40
41															41
42															42
43															43
44															44
45	74	69	69	77	75	63	77	65	78	65	62	75	66	61	45
46	74	69	70	77	76	64	78	65	78	66	62	75	66	62	46
47	75	70	70	77	76	64	78	66	79	67	63	75	67	63	47
48	75	70	71	78	77	65	79	66	79	67	64	76	68	63	48
49	76	71	71	78	77	66	79	67	80	68	64	76	68	64	49
50	76	71	72	79	78	66	79	68	80	68	65	77	69	65	50
51	77	72	73	79	78	67	80	68	80	69	66	77	69	65	51
52	77	73	73	80	79	68	80	69	81	70	66	78	70	66	52
53	78	73	74	80	79	68	81	70	81	70	67	78	71	67	53
54	78	74	74	80	79	69	81	70	82	71	68	79	71	68	54
55	79	74	75	81	80	70	81	71	82	72	69	79	72	68	55
56	79	75	75	81	80	70	82	72	82	72	69	80	73	69	56
57	79	75	76	82	81	71	82	72	83	73	70	80	73	70	57
58	80	76	77	82	81	72	83	73	83	73	71	81	74	70	58
59	80	77	77	83	82	72	83	74	84	74	71	81	74	71	59
60	81	77	78	83	82	73	83	74	84	75	72	81	75	72	60
61	81	78	78	83	83	74	84	75	84	75	73	82	76	72	61
62	82	78	79	84	83	75	84	75	85	76	73	82	76	73	62
63	82	79	79	84	83	75	85	76	85	77	74	83	77	74	63
64	83	79	80	85	84	76	85	77	86	77	75	83	78	75	64
65	83	80	80	85	84	77	86	77	86	78	76	84	78	75	65
66	84	81	81	86	85	77	86	78	86	79	76	84	79	76	66
67	84	81	82	86	85	78	86	79	87	79	77	85	79	77	67
68	85	82	82	86	86	79	87	79	87	80	78	85	80	77	68
69	85	82	83	87	86	79	87	80	88	80	78	86	81	78	69
70	86	83	83	87	87	80	88	81	88	81	79	86	81	79	70
71	86	83	84	88	87	81	88	81	88	82	80	87	82	80	71
72	87	84	84	88	87	81	88	82	89	82	80	87	83	80	72
73	87	85	85	89	88	82	89	83	89	83	81	87	83	81	73
74	88	85	85	89	88	83	89	83	90	84	82	88	84	82	74
75	88	86	86	89	89	83	90	84	90	84	83	88	84	82	75
76	89	86	87	90	89	84	90	85	90	85	83	89	85	83	76
77	89	87	87	90	90	85	91	85	91	85	84	89	86	84	77
78	90	87	88	91	90	85	91	86	91	86	85	90	86	84	78
79	90	88	88	91	91	86	91	86	92	87	85	90	87	85	79
80	90	89	89	92	91	87	92	87	92	87	86	91	88	86	80
81	91	89	89	92	92	87	92	88	92	88	87	91	88	87	81
82	91	90	90	92	92	88	93	88	93	89	87	92	89	87	82
83	92	90	90	93	92	89	93	89	93	89	88	92	89	88	83
84	92	91	91	93	93	89	93	90	94	90	89	93	90	89	84
85	93	91	92	94	93	90	94	90	94	91	90	93	91	89	85
86	93	92	92	94	94	91	94	91	94	91	90	94	91	90	86
87	94	93	93	94	94	91	95	92	95	92	91	94	92	91	87
88	94	93	93	95	95	92	95	92	95	92	92	94	93	92	88
89	95	94	94	95	95	93	95	93	96	93	92	95	93	92	89
90	95	94	94	96	96	93	96	94	96	94	93	95	94	93	90
91	96	95	95	96	96	94	96	94	96	94	94	96	94	94	91
92	96	95	96	97	96	95	97	95	97	95	94	96	95	94	92
93	97	96	96	97	97	95	97	95	97	96	95	97	96	95	93
94	97	97	97	97	97	96	98	96	98	96	96	97	96	96	94
95	98	97	97	98	98	97	98	97	98	97	97	98	97	96	95
96	98	98	98	98	98	97	98	97	98	97	97	98	98	97	96
97	99	98	98	99	99	98	99	98	99	98	98	99	98	98	97
98	99	99	99	99	99	99	99	99	99	99	99	99	99	99	98
99	100	99	99	100	100	99	100	99	100	99	99	100	99	99	99
100	100	100	100	100	100	100	100	100	100	100	100	100	100	100	100

Table B.10. WIAT–II Subtest and Composite Standard Scores Predicted From WAIS–III FSIQ Scores *(continued)*

College Students

FSIQ Score	\<Subtest Standard Scores\> WRD	NO	RC	SP	PD	MR	WE	LC	OE	\<Composite Standard Scores\> RD	MA	WL	OL	Total	FSIQ Score
101	100	101	101	100	100	101	100	101	100	101	101	100	101	101	101
102	101	101	101	101	101	101	101	101	101	101	101	101	101	101	102
103	101	102	102	101	101	102	101	102	101	102	102	101	102	102	103
104	102	102	102	102	102	103	102	103	102	103	103	102	102	103	104
105	102	103	103	102	102	103	102	103	102	103	103	102	103	104	105
106	103	103	103	103	103	104	102	104	102	104	104	103	104	104	106
107	103	104	104	103	103	105	103	105	103	104	105	103	104	105	107
108	104	105	104	103	104	105	103	105	103	105	106	104	105	106	108
109	104	105	105	104	104	106	104	106	104	106	106	104	106	106	109
110	105	106	106	104	104	107	104	106	104	106	107	105	106	107	110
111	105	106	106	105	105	107	105	107	104	107	108	105	107	108	111
112	106	107	107	105	105	108	105	108	105	108	108	106	107	108	112
113	106	107	107	106	106	109	105	108	105	108	109	106	108	109	113
114	107	108	108	106	106	109	106	109	106	109	110	106	109	110	114
115	107	109	108	106	107	110	106	110	106	109	110	107	109	111	115
116	108	109	109	107	107	111	107	110	106	110	111	107	110	111	116
117	108	110	110	107	108	111	107	111	107	111	112	108	111	112	117
118	109	110	110	108	108	112	107	112	107	111	113	108	111	113	118
119	109	111	111	108	108	113	108	112	108	112	113	109	112	113	119
120	110	111	111	109	109	113	108	113	108	113	114	109	112	114	120
121	110	112	112	109	109	114	109	114	108	113	115	110	113	115	121
122	110	113	112	109	110	115	109	114	109	114	115	110	114	116	122
123	111	113	113	110	110	115	109	115	109	115	116	111	114	116	123
124	111	114	113	110	111	116	110	115	110	115	117	111	115	117	124
125	112	114	114	111	111	117	110	116	110	116	117	112	116	118	125
126	112	115	115	111	112	117	111	117	110	116	118	112	116	118	126
127	113	115	115	111	112	118	111	117	111	117	119	113	117	119	127
128	113	116	116	112	113	119	112	118	111	118	120	113	117	120	128
129	114	117	116	112	113	119	112	119	112	118	120	113	118	120	129
130	114	117	117	113	113	120	112	119	112	119	121	114	119	121	130
131	115	118	117	113	114	121	113	120	112	120	122	114	119	122	131
132	115	118	118	114	114	121	113	121	113	120	122	115	120	123	132
133	116	119	118	114	115	122	114	121	113	121	123	115	121	123	133
134	116	119	119	114	115	123	114	122	114	121	124	116	121	124	134
135	117	120	120	115	116	123	114	123	114	122	124	116	122	125	135
136	117	121	120	115	116	124	115	123	114	123	125	117	122	125	136
137	118	121	121	116	117	125	115	124	115	123	126	117	123	126	137
138	118	122	121	116	117	125	116	125	115	124	127	118	124	127	138
139	119	122	122	117	117	126	116	125	116	125	127	118	124	128	139
140	119	123	122	117	118	127	117	126	116	125	128	119	125	128	140
141	120	123	123	117	118	128	117	126	117	126	129	119	126	129	141
142	120	124	123	118	119	128	117	127	117	127	129	119	126	130	142
143	121	125	124	118	119	129	118	128	117	127	130	120	127	130	143
144	121	125	125	119	120	130	118	128	118	128	131	120	127	131	144
145	121	126	125	119	120	130	119	129	118	128	131	121	128	132	145
146	122	126	126	120	121	131	119	130	118	129	132	121	129	132	146
147	122	127	126	120	121	132	119	130	119	130	133	122	129	133	147
148	123	127	127	120	121	132	120	131	119	130	134	122	130	134	148
149	123	128	127	121	122	133	120	132	120	131	134	123	131	135	149
150	124	129	128	121	122	134	121	132	120	132	135	123	131	135	150
151	124	129	129	122	123	134	121	133	120	132	136	124	132	136	151
152	125	130	129	122	123	135	121	134	121	133	136	124	132	137	152
153	125	130	130	123	124	136	122	134	121	133	137	125	133	137	153
154	126	131	130	123	124	136	122	135	122	134	138	125	134	138	154
155	126	131	131	123	125	137	123	135	122	135	138	125	134	139	155
156															156
157															157
158															158
159															159
160															160

Note. Based on the correlations between the WIAT–II standard scores and the WAIS–III FSIQ. Presented in the order shown in the table, the correlations for the nine WIAT–II subtests are .48, .57, .56, .43, .45, .67, .41, .65, and .40, and the correlations for the five WIAT–II composites are .63, .70, .46, .62, and .71.

WRD = Word Reading
NO = Numerical Operations
RC = Reading Comprehension
SP = Spelling

PD = Pseudoword Decoding
MR = Math Reasoning
WE = Written Expression
LC = Listening Comprehension

OE = Oral Expression
RD = Reading
MA = Mathematics
WL = Written Language

OL = Oral Language

Table B.10. WIAT–II Subtest and Composite Standard Scores Predicted From WAIS–III FSIQ Scores (continued)

Adults

FSIQ Score	Subtest Standard Scores									Composite Standard Scores					FSIQ Score
	WRD	NO	RC	SP	PD	MR	WE	LC	OE	RD	MA	WL	OL	Total	
40															40
41															41
42															42
43															43
44															44
45	64	55	58	64	62	57	66	60	73	52	55	66	63	53	45
46	64	56	59	64	63	58	67	61	74	53	56	66	64	54	46
47	65	57	60	65	63	58	67	61	74	54	57	67	64	55	47
48	66	57	61	66	64	59	68	62	75	55	57	67	65	56	48
49	66	58	61	66	65	60	69	63	75	56	58	68	66	56	49
50	67	59	62	67	66	61	69	64	76	57	59	69	67	57	50
51	68	60	63	68	66	62	70	64	76	58	60	69	67	58	51
52	68	61	64	68	67	62	70	65	77	59	61	70	68	59	52
53	69	62	64	69	68	63	71	66	77	59	62	71	69	60	53
54	70	62	65	70	68	64	72	66	78	60	62	71	69	61	54
55	70	63	66	70	69	65	72	67	78	61	63	72	70	62	55
56	71	64	67	71	70	66	73	68	79	62	64	72	71	62	56
57	72	65	67	72	70	66	73	69	79	63	65	73	71	63	57
58	72	66	68	72	71	67	74	69	80	64	66	74	72	64	58
59	73	66	69	73	72	68	75	70	80	65	66	74	73	65	59
60	74	67	70	74	72	69	75	71	81	65	67	75	73	66	60
61	74	68	70	74	73	69	76	72	81	66	68	76	74	67	61
62	75	69	71	75	74	70	77	72	82	67	69	76	75	68	62
63	76	70	72	76	75	71	77	73	82	68	70	77	75	68	63
64	76	71	73	76	75	72	78	74	83	69	71	77	76	69	64
65	77	71	74	77	76	73	78	74	83	70	71	78	77	70	65
66	78	72	74	77	77	73	79	75	83	71	72	79	77	71	66
67	78	73	75	78	77	74	80	76	84	71	73	79	78	72	67
68	79	74	76	79	78	75	80	77	84	72	74	80	79	73	68
69	80	75	77	79	79	76	81	77	85	73	75	81	79	73	69
70	80	75	77	80	79	76	81	78	85	74	75	81	80	74	70
71	81	76	78	81	80	77	82	79	86	75	76	82	81	75	71
72	81	77	79	81	81	78	83	80	86	76	77	82	81	76	72
73	82	78	80	82	81	79	83	80	87	77	78	83	82	77	73
74	83	79	80	83	82	80	84	81	87	78	79	84	83	78	74
75	83	80	81	83	83	80	85	82	88	78	80	84	83	79	75
76	84	80	82	84	83	81	85	83	88	79	80	85	84	79	76
77	85	81	83	85	84	82	86	83	89	80	81	86	85	80	77
78	85	82	83	85	85	83	86	84	89	81	82	86	85	81	78
79	86	83	84	86	86	84	87	85	90	82	83	87	86	82	79
80	87	84	85	87	86	84	88	85	90	83	84	87	87	83	80
81	87	84	86	87	87	85	88	86	91	84	84	88	87	84	81
82	88	85	86	88	88	86	89	87	91	84	85	89	88	85	82
83	89	86	87	89	88	87	90	88	92	85	86	89	89	85	83
84	89	87	88	89	89	87	90	88	92	86	87	90	89	86	84
85	90	88	89	90	90	88	91	89	93	87	88	91	90	87	85
86	91	89	89	91	90	89	91	90	93	88	89	91	91	88	86
87	91	89	90	91	91	90	92	91	94	89	89	92	91	89	87
88	92	90	91	92	92	91	93	91	94	90	90	92	92	90	88
89	93	91	92	93	92	91	93	92	95	90	91	93	93	91	89
90	93	92	92	93	93	92	94	93	95	91	92	94	93	91	90
91	94	93	93	94	94	93	94	93	96	92	93	94	94	92	91
92	95	93	94	95	94	94	95	94	96	93	93	95	95	93	92
93	95	94	95	95	95	95	96	95	97	94	94	96	95	94	93
94	96	95	95	96	96	95	96	96	97	95	95	96	96	95	94
95	97	96	96	97	97	96	97	96	98	96	96	97	97	96	95
96	97	97	97	97	97	97	98	97	98	97	97	97	97	97	96
97	98	98	98	98	98	98	98	98	99	97	98	98	98	97	97
98	99	98	98	99	99	99	99	99	99	98	98	99	99	98	98
99	99	99	99	99	99	99	99	99	100	99	99	99	99	99	99
100	100	100	100	100	100	100	100	100	100	100	100	100	100	100	100

Table B.10. WIAT–II Subtest and Composite Standard Scores Predicted From WAIS–III FSIQ Scores *(continued)*

Adults

FSIQ Score			Subtest Standard Scores									Composite Standard Scores			FSIQ Score
FSIQ Score	WRD	NO	RC	SP	PD	MR	WE	LC	OE	RD	MA	WL	OL	Total	FSIQ Score
101	101	101	101	101	101	101	101	101	100	101	101	101	101	101	101
102	101	102	102	101	101	102	101	101	101	102	102	101	101	102	102
103	102	102	102	102	102	102	102	102	101	103	102	102	102	103	103
104	103	103	103	103	103	103	102	103	102	103	103	103	103	103	104
105	103	104	104	103	103	104	103	104	102	104	104	103	103	104	105
106	104	105	105	104	104	105	104	104	103	105	105	104	104	105	106
107	105	106	105	105	105	105	104	105	103	106	106	104	105	106	107
108	105	107	106	105	106	106	105	106	104	107	107	105	105	107	108
109	106	107	107	106	106	107	106	107	104	108	107	106	106	108	109
110	107	108	108	107	107	108	106	107	105	109	108	106	107	109	110
111	107	109	108	107	108	109	107	108	105	110	109	107	107	109	111
112	108	110	109	108	108	109	107	109	106	110	110	108	108	110	112
113	109	111	110	109	109	110	108	109	106	111	111	108	109	111	113
114	109	111	111	109	110	111	109	110	107	112	111	109	109	112	114
115	110	112	111	110	110	112	109	111	107	113	112	109	110	113	115
116	111	113	112	111	111	113	110	112	108	114	113	110	111	114	116
117	111	114	113	111	112	113	110	112	108	115	114	111	111	115	117
118	112	115	114	112	112	114	111	113	109	116	115	111	112	115	118
119	113	116	114	113	113	115	112	114	109	116	116	112	113	116	119
120	113	116	115	113	114	116	112	115	110	117	116	113	113	117	120
121	114	117	116	114	114	116	113	115	110	118	117	113	114	118	121
122	115	118	117	115	115	117	114	116	111	119	118	114	115	119	122
123	115	119	117	115	116	118	114	117	111	120	119	114	115	120	123
124	116	120	118	116	117	119	115	117	112	121	120	115	116	121	124
125	117	120	119	117	117	120	115	118	112	122	120	116	117	121	125
126	117	121	120	117	118	120	116	119	113	122	121	116	117	122	126
127	118	122	120	118	119	121	117	120	113	123	122	117	118	123	127
128	119	123	121	119	119	122	117	120	114	124	123	118	119	124	128
129	119	124	122	119	120	123	118	121	114	125	124	118	119	125	129
130	120	125	123	120	121	124	119	122	115	126	125	119	120	126	130
131	120	125	123	121	121	124	119	123	115	127	125	119	121	127	131
132	121	126	124	121	122	125	120	123	116	128	126	120	121	127	132
133	122	127	125	122	123	126	120	124	116	129	127	121	122	128	133
134	122	128	126	123	123	127	121	125	117	129	128	121	123	129	134
135	123	129	126	123	124	127	122	126	117	130	129	122	123	130	135
136	124	129	127	124	125	128	122	126	117	131	129	123	124	131	136
137	124	130	128	124	125	129	123	127	118	132	130	123	125	132	137
138	125	131	129	125	126	130	123	128	118	133	131	124	125	132	138
139	126	132	130	126	127	131	124	128	119	134	132	124	126	133	139
140	126	133	130	126	128	131	125	129	119	135	133	125	127	134	140
141	127	134	131	127	128	132	125	130	120	135	134	126	127	135	141
142	128	134	132	128	129	133	126	131	120	136	134	126	128	136	142
143	128	135	133	128	130	134	127	131	121	137	135	127	129	137	143
144	129	136	133	129	130	134	127	132	121	138	136	128	129	138	144
145	130	137	134	130	131	135	128	133	122	139	137	128	130	138	145
146	130	138	135	130	132	136	128	134	122	140	138	129	131	139	146
147	131	138	136	131	132	137	129	134	123	141	138	129	131	140	147
148	132	139	136	132	133	138	130	135	123	141	139	130	132	141	148
149	132	140	137	132	134	138	130	136	124	142	140	131	133	142	149
150	133	141	138	133	134	139	131	136	124	143	141	131	134	143	150
151	134	142	139	134	135	140	131	137	125	144	142	132	134	144	151
152	134	143	139	134	136	141	132	138	125	145	143	133	135	144	152
153	135	143	140	135	137	142	133	139	126	146	143	133	136	145	153
154	136	144	141	136	137	142	133	139	126	147	144	134	136	146	154
155	136	145	142	136	138	143	134	140	127	148	145	134	137	147	155
156															156
157															157
158															158
159															159
160															160

Note. Based on the correlations between the WIAT–II standard scores and the WAIS–III FSIQ. Presented in the order shown in the table, the correlations for the nine WIAT–II subtests are .66, .82, .76, .66, .69, .78, .62, .73, and .49, and the correlations for the five WIAT–II composites are .86, .82, .63, .67, and .86.

WRD = Word Reading
NO = Numerical Operations
RC = Reading Comprehension
SP = Spelling

PD = Pseudoword Decoding
MR = Math Reasoning
WE = Written Expression
LC = Listening Comprehension

OE = Oral Expression
RD = Reading
MA = Mathematics
WL = Written Language

OL = Oral Language

Table B.11. WIAT–II Subtest and Composite Standard Scores Predicted From WAIS–III VIQ Scores

Ages 16:0–19:11 (High School)

| | Subtest Standard Scores | | | | | | | | | | Composite Standard Scores | | | | | |
VIQ Score	WRD	NO	RC	SP	PD	MR	WE	LC	OE	RD	MA	WL	OL	Total	VIQ Score
40															40
41															41
42															42
43															43
44															44
45															45
46															46
47															47
48	63	63	62	66	69	62	70	58	77	60	61	66	60	57	48
49	63	64	63	67	69	63	71	59	77	60	62	67	61	58	49
50	64	65	64	68	70	64	71	60	78	61	63	67	62	59	50
51	65	66	65	68	70	64	72	60	78	62	63	68	62	60	51
52	66	66	65	69	71	65	73	61	79	63	64	69	63	60	52
53	66	67	66	70	72	66	73	62	79	63	65	69	64	61	53
54	67	68	67	70	72	67	74	63	80	64	66	70	65	62	54
55	68	68	67	71	73	67	74	64	80	65	66	71	65	63	55
56	68	69	68	72	73	68	75	64	81	66	67	71	66	64	56
57	69	70	69	72	74	69	75	65	81	67	68	72	67	64	57
58	70	70	70	73	75	69	76	66	81	67	69	73	68	65	58
59	71	71	70	74	75	70	77	67	82	68	69	73	68	66	59
60	71	72	71	74	76	71	77	68	82	69	70	74	69	67	60
61	72	73	72	75	76	72	78	68	83	70	71	74	70	68	61
62	73	73	72	75	77	72	78	69	83	70	72	75	71	69	62
63	73	74	73	76	78	73	79	70	84	71	72	76	72	69	63
64	74	75	74	77	78	74	79	71	84	72	73	76	72	70	64
65	75	75	75	77	79	75	80	72	84	73	74	77	73	71	65
66	76	76	75	78	79	75	81	73	85	74	75	78	74	72	66
67	76	77	76	79	80	76	81	73	85	74	75	78	75	73	67
68	77	78	77	79	81	77	82	74	86	76	76	79	75	74	68
69	78	78	78	80	81	77	82	75	86	76	77	80	76	74	69
70	78	79	78	81	82	78	83	76	87	77	78	80	77	75	70
71	79	80	79	81	82	79	83	77	87	77	78	81	78	76	71
72	80	80	80	82	83	80	84	77	88	78	79	82	78	77	72
73	81	81	80	83	84	80	85	78	88	79	80	82	79	78	73
74	81	82	81	83	84	81	85	79	88	80	81	83	80	79	74
75	82	82	82	84	85	82	86	80	89	81	81	84	81	79	75
76	83	83	83	84	86	83	86	81	89	81	82	84	82	80	76
77	84	84	83	85	86	83	87	81	90	82	83	85	82	81	77
78	84	85	84	86	87	84	87	82	90	83	84	86	83	82	78
79	85	85	85	86	87	85	88	83	91	84	84	86	84	83	79
80	86	86	86	87	88	85	89	84	91	84	85	87	85	83	80
81	86	87	86	88	89	86	89	85	92	85	86	88	85	84	81
82	87	87	87	88	89	87	90	85	92	86	87	88	86	85	82
83	88	88	88	89	90	88	90	86	92	87	87	89	87	86	83
84	89	89	88	90	90	88	91	87	93	88	88	90	88	87	84
85	89	89	89	90	91	89	91	88	93	88	89	90	88	88	85
86	90	90	90	91	92	90	92	89	94	89	90	91	89	88	86
87	91	91	91	92	92	91	93	89	94	90	90	91	90	89	87
88	91	92	91	92	93	91	93	90	95	91	91	92	91	90	88
89	92	92	92	93	93	92	94	91	95	91	92	93	92	91	89
90	93	93	93	94	94	93	94	92	96	92	93	93	92	92	90
91	94	94	93	94	95	93	95	93	96	93	93	94	93	93	91
92	94	94	94	95	95	94	95	94	96	94	94	95	94	93	92
93	95	95	95	95	96	95	96	94	97	95	95	95	95	94	93
94	96	96	96	96	96	96	97	95	97	95	96	96	95	95	94
95	96	96	96	97	97	96	97	96	98	96	96	97	96	96	95
96	97	97	97	97	98	97	98	97	98	97	97	97	97	97	96
97	98	98	98	98	98	98	98	98	99	98	98	98	98	98	97
98	99	99	99	99	99	99	99	98	99	99	99	99	98	98	98
99	99	99	99	99	99	99	99	99	100	99	99	99	99	99	99
100	100	100	100	100	100	100	100	100	100	100	100	100	100	100	100

Table B.11. WIAT–II Subtest and Composite Standard Scores Predicted From WAIS–III VIQ Scores *(continued)*

Ages 16:0–19:11 (High School)

VIQ Score	Subtest Standard Scores									Composite Standard Scores					VIQ Score
	WRD	NO	RC	SP	PD	MR	WE	LC	OE	RD	MA	WL	OL	Total	
101	101	101	101	101	101	101	101	101	100	101	101	101	101	101	101
102	101	101	101	101	101	101	101	102	101	102	101	101	102	102	102
103	102	102	102	102	102	102	102	102	101	102	102	102	102	102	103
104	103	103	103	103	102	103	102	103	102	103	103	103	103	103	104
105	104	104	104	103	103	104	103	104	102	104	104	103	104	104	105
106	104	104	104	104	104	104	103	105	103	105	104	104	105	105	106
107	105	105	105	105	104	105	104	106	103	105	105	105	105	106	107
108	106	106	106	105	105	106	105	106	104	106	106	105	106	107	108
109	106	106	107	106	105	107	105	107	104	107	107	106	107	107	109
110	107	107	107	106	106	107	106	108	104	108	107	107	108	108	110
111	108	108	108	107	107	108	106	109	105	109	108	107	108	109	111
112	109	108	109	108	107	109	107	110	105	109	109	108	109	110	112
113	109	109	109	108	108	109	107	111	106	110	110	109	110	111	113
114	110	110	110	109	108	110	108	111	106	111	110	109	111	112	114
115	111	111	111	110	109	111	109	112	107	112	111	110	112	112	115
116	111	111	112	110	110	112	109	113	107	112	112	110	112	113	116
117	112	112	112	111	110	112	110	114	108	113	113	111	113	114	117
118	113	113	113	112	111	113	110	115	108	114	113	112	114	115	118
119	114	113	114	112	111	114	111	115	108	115	114	112	115	116	119
120	114	114	114	113	112	115	111	116	109	116	115	113	115	117	120
121	115	115	115	114	113	115	112	117	109	116	116	114	116	117	121
122	116	115	116	114	113	116	113	118	110	117	116	114	117	118	122
123	116	116	117	115	114	117	113	119	110	118	117	115	118	119	123
124	117	117	117	116	114	117	114	119	111	119	118	116	118	120	124
125	118	118	118	116	115	118	114	120	111	119	119	116	119	121	125
126	119	118	119	117	116	119	115	121	112	120	119	117	120	121	126
127	119	119	120	117	116	120	115	122	112	121	120	118	121	122	127
128	120	120	120	118	117	120	116	123	112	122	121	118	122	123	128
129	121	120	121	119	118	121	117	123	113	123	122	119	122	124	129
130	122	121	122	119	118	122	117	124	113	123	122	120	123	125	130
131	122	122	122	120	119	123	118	125	114	124	123	120	124	126	131
132	123	122	123	121	119	123	118	126	114	125	124	121	125	126	132
133	124	123	124	121	120	124	119	127	115	126	125	122	125	127	133
134	124	124	125	122	121	125	119	127	115	126	125	122	126	128	134
135	125	125	125	123	121	125	120	128	116	127	126	123	127	129	135
136	126	125	126	123	122	126	121	129	116	128	127	124	128	130	136
137	127	126	127	124	122	127	121	130	116	129	128	124	128	131	137
138	127	127	128	125	123	128	122	131	117	130	128	125	129	131	138
139	128	127	128	125	124	128	122	132	117	130	129	126	130	132	139
140	129	128	129	126	124	129	123	132	118	131	130	126	131	133	140
141	129	129	130	126	125	130	123	133	118	132	131	127	132	134	141
142	130	130	130	127	125	131	124	134	119	133	131	127	132	135	142
143	131	130	131	128	126	131	125	135	119	133	132	128	133	136	143
144	132	131	132	128	127	132	125	136	119	134	133	129	134	136	144
145	132	132	133	129	127	133	126	136	120	135	134	129	135	137	145
146	133	132	133	130	128	133	126	137	120	136	134	130	135	138	146
147	134	133	134	130	128	134	127	138	121	137	135	131	136	139	147
148	134	134	135	131	129	135	127	139	121	137	136	131	137	140	148
149	135	134	135	132	130	136	128	140	122	138	137	132	138	140	149
150	136	135	136	132	130	136	129	140	122	139	137	133	138	141	150
151	137	136	137	133	131	137	129	141	123	140	138	133	139	142	151
152	137	137	138	134	131	138	130	142	123	140	139	134	140	143	152
153	138	137	138	134	132	139	130	143	123	141	140	135	141	144	153
154	139	138	139	135	133	139	131	144	124	142	140	135	142	145	154
155	139	139	140	136	133	140	131	144	124	143	141	136	142	145	155
156															156
157															157
158															158
159															159
160															160

Note. Based on the correlations between the WIAT–II standard scores and the WAIS–III VIQ across the four age ranges. Presented in the order shown in the table, the average correlations for the nine WIAT–II subtests are .72, .70, .72, .65, .60, .73, .57, .81, and .44, and the average correlations for the five WIAT–II composites are .78, .75, .65, .77, and .83.

WRD = Word Reading
NO = Numerical Operations
RC = Reading Comprehension
SP = Spelling

PD = Pseudoword Decoding
MR = Math Reasoning
WE = Written Expression
LC = Listening Comprehension

OE = Oral Expression
RD = Reading
MA = Mathematics
WL = Written Language

OL = Oral Language

Table B.11. WIAT–II Subtest and Composite Standard Scores Predicted From WAIS–III VIQ Scores *(continued)*

College Students

VIQ Score	WRD	NO	RC	SP	PD	MR	WE	LC	OE	RD	MA	WL	OL	Total	VIQ Score
40															40
41															41
42															42
43															43
44															44
45															45
46															46
47															47
48	73	74	71	77	75	68	80	65	82	65	67	77	68	64	48
49	73	74	72	77	76	68	81	66	83	66	68	77	69	65	49
50	74	75	72	78	76	69	81	67	83	67	68	78	70	66	50
51	74	75	73	78	77	70	81	67	83	67	69	78	70	66	51
52	75	76	73	78	77	70	82	68	84	68	69	79	71	67	52
53	75	76	74	79	78	71	82	69	84	69	70	79	71	68	53
54	76	77	75	79	78	71	83	69	84	69	71	80	72	69	54
55	76	77	75	80	79	72	83	70	85	70	71	80	73	69	55
56	77	78	76	80	79	73	83	71	85	71	72	80	73	70	56
57	78	78	76	81	80	73	84	71	85	71	73	81	74	71	57
58	78	79	77	81	80	74	84	72	86	72	73	81	74	71	58
59	79	79	77	82	81	75	84	73	86	73	74	82	75	72	59
60	79	80	78	82	81	75	85	73	86	73	75	82	76	73	60
61	80	80	78	82	82	76	85	74	87	74	75	83	76	73	61
62	80	81	79	83	82	76	86	75	87	75	76	83	77	74	62
63	81	81	80	83	82	77	86	75	87	75	76	84	77	75	63
64	81	82	80	84	83	78	86	76	88	76	77	84	78	75	64
65	82	82	81	84	83	78	87	77	88	77	78	84	79	76	65
66	82	83	81	85	84	79	87	77	88	77	78	85	79	77	66
67	83	83	82	85	84	80	87	78	89	78	79	85	80	77	67
68	83	84	82	86	85	80	88	79	89	79	80	86	80	78	68
69	84	84	83	86	85	81	88	79	89	79	80	86	81	79	69
70	84	85	83	87	86	81	89	80	90	80	81	87	82	79	70
71	85	85	84	87	86	82	89	81	90	81	82	87	82	80	71
72	85	86	85	87	87	83	89	81	90	81	82	88	83	81	72
73	86	86	85	88	87	83	90	82	91	82	83	88	84	82	73
74	86	87	86	88	88	84	90	83	91	83	83	88	84	82	74
75	87	87	86	89	88	84	91	83	91	83	84	89	85	83	75
76	87	88	87	89	89	85	91	84	92	84	85	89	85	84	76
77	88	88	87	90	89	86	91	85	92	85	85	90	86	84	77
78	88	89	88	90	90	86	92	85	92	85	86	90	87	85	78
79	89	89	88	91	90	87	92	86	93	86	87	91	87	86	79
80	90	90	89	91	91	88	92	87	93	87	87	91	88	86	80
81	90	90	89	91	91	88	93	87	94	87	88	92	88	87	81
82	91	91	90	92	91	89	93	88	94	88	89	92	89	88	82
83	91	91	91	92	92	89	94	89	94	89	89	92	90	88	83
84	92	92	91	93	92	90	94	89	95	89	90	93	90	89	84
85	92	92	92	93	93	91	94	90	95	90	90	93	91	90	85
86	93	93	92	94	93	91	95	91	95	91	91	94	91	90	86
87	93	93	93	94	94	92	95	91	96	91	92	94	92	91	87
88	94	94	93	95	94	93	95	92	96	92	92	95	93	92	88
89	94	94	94	95	95	93	96	93	96	93	93	95	93	92	89
90	95	95	94	96	95	94	96	93	97	93	94	96	94	93	90
91	95	95	95	96	96	94	97	94	97	94	94	96	95	94	91
92	96	96	96	96	96	95	97	95	97	95	95	96	95	95	92
93	96	96	96	97	97	96	97	95	98	95	96	97	96	95	93
94	97	97	97	97	97	96	98	96	98	96	96	97	96	96	94
95	97	97	97	98	98	97	98	97	98	97	97	98	97	97	95
96	98	98	98	98	98	98	98	97	99	97	97	98	98	98	96
97	98	98	98	99	99	98	99	98	99	98	98	99	98	98	97
98	99	99	99	99	99	99	99	99	99	99	99	99	99	99	98
99	99	99	99	100	100	99	100	99	100	99	99	100	99	99	99
100	100	100	100	100	100	100	100	100	100	100	100	100	100	100	100

Table B.11. WIAT–II Subtest and Composite Standard Scores Predicted From WAIS–III VIQ Scores (continued)

College Students

VIQ Score	Subtest Standard Scores									Composite Standard Scores					VIQ Score
	WRD	NO	RC	SP	PD	MR	WE	LC	OE	RD	MA	WL	OL	Total	
101	101	101	101	100	100	101	100	101	100	101	101	100	101	101	101
102	101	101	101	101	101	101	101	101	101	101	101	101	101	101	102
103	102	102	102	101	101	102	101	102	101	102	102	101	102	102	103
104	102	102	102	102	102	102	102	103	101	103	103	102	102	103	104
105	103	103	103	102	102	103	102	103	102	103	103	102	103	103	105
106	103	103	103	103	103	104	102	104	102	104	104	103	104	104	106
107	104	104	104	103	103	104	103	105	102	105	104	103	104	105	107
108	104	104	104	104	104	105	103	105	103	105	105	104	105	105	108
109	105	105	105	104	104	106	103	106	103	106	106	104	105	106	109
110	105	105	106	105	105	106	104	107	103	107	106	104	106	107	110
111	106	106	106	105	105	107	104	107	104	107	107	105	107	108	111
112	106	106	107	105	106	107	105	108	104	108	108	105	107	108	112
113	107	107	107	106	106	108	105	109	104	109	108	106	108	109	113
114	107	107	108	106	107	109	105	109	105	109	109	106	109	110	114
115	108	108	108	107	107	109	106	110	105	110	110	107	109	110	115
116	108	108	109	107	108	110	106	111	105	111	110	107	110	111	116
117	109	109	109	108	108	111	106	111	106	111	111	108	110	112	117
118	109	109	110	108	109	111	107	112	106	112	111	108	111	112	118
119	110	110	111	109	109	112	107	113	106	113	112	108	112	113	119
120	110	110	111	109	109	112	108	113	107	113	113	109	112	114	120
121	111	111	112	109	110	113	108	114	107	114	113	109	113	114	121
122	112	111	112	110	110	114	108	115	108	115	114	110	113	115	122
123	112	112	113	110	111	114	109	115	108	115	115	110	114	116	123
124	113	112	113	111	111	115	109	116	108	116	115	111	115	116	124
125	113	113	114	111	112	116	109	117	109	117	116	111	115	117	125
126	114	113	114	112	112	116	110	117	109	117	117	112	116	118	126
127	114	114	115	112	113	117	110	118	109	118	117	112	116	118	127
128	115	114	115	113	113	117	111	119	110	119	118	112	117	119	128
129	115	115	116	113	114	118	111	119	110	119	118	113	118	120	129
130	116	115	117	114	114	119	111	120	110	120	119	113	118	121	130
131	116	116	117	114	115	119	112	121	111	121	120	114	119	121	131
132	117	116	118	114	115	120	112	121	111	121	120	114	120	122	132
133	117	117	118	115	116	120	113	122	111	122	121	115	120	123	133
134	118	117	119	115	116	121	113	123	112	123	122	115	121	123	134
135	118	118	119	116	117	122	113	123	112	123	122	116	121	124	135
136	119	118	120	116	117	122	114	124	112	124	123	116	122	125	136
137	119	119	120	117	118	123	114	125	113	125	124	116	123	125	137
138	120	119	121	117	118	124	114	125	113	125	124	117	123	126	138
139	120	120	122	118	118	124	115	126	113	126	125	117	124	127	139
140	121	120	122	118	119	125	115	127	114	127	125	118	124	127	140
141	121	121	123	118	119	125	116	127	114	127	126	118	125	128	141
142	122	121	123	119	120	126	116	128	114	128	127	119	126	129	142
143	122	122	124	119	120	127	116	129	115	129	127	119	126	129	143
144	123	122	124	120	121	127	117	129	115	129	128	120	127	130	144
145	124	123	125	120	121	128	117	130	115	130	129	120	127	131	145
146	124	123	125	121	122	129	117	131	116	131	129	120	128	131	146
147	125	124	126	121	122	129	118	131	116	131	130	121	129	132	147
148	125	124	127	122	123	130	118	132	116	132	131	121	129	133	148
149	126	125	127	122	123	130	119	133	117	133	131	122	130	134	149
150	126	125	128	123	124	131	119	133	117	133	132	122	131	134	150
151	127	126	128	123	124	132	119	134	117	134	132	123	131	135	151
152	127	126	129	123	125	132	120	135	118	135	133	123	132	136	152
153	128	127	129	124	125	133	120	135	118	135	134	124	132	136	153
154	128	127	130	124	126	134	120	136	118	136	134	124	133	137	154
155	129	128	130	125	126	134	121	137	119	137	135	124	134	138	155
156															156
157															157
158															158
159															159
160															160

Note. Based on the correlations between the WIAT–II standard scores and the WAIS–III VIQ. Presented in the order shown in the table, the correlations for the nine WIAT–II subtests are .52, .50, .55, .45, .47, .62, .38, .66, and .34, and the correlations for the five WIAT–II composites are .66, .64, .44, .61, and .68.

WRD = Word Reading
NO = Numerical Operations
RC = Reading Comprehension
SP = Spelling

PD = Pseudoword Decoding
MR = Math Reasoning
WE = Written Expression
LC = Listening Comprehension

OE = Oral Expression
RD = Reading
MA = Mathematics
WL = Written Language

OL = Oral Language

Table B.11. WIAT–II Subtest and Composite Standard Scores Predicted From WAIS–III VIQ Scores (continued)

Adults

VIQ Score	Subtest Standard Scores									Composite Standard Scores					VIQ Score
	WRD	NO	RC	SP	PD	MR	WE	LC	OE	RD	MA	WL	OL	Total	
40															40
41															41
42															42
43															43
44															44
45															45
46															46
47															47
48	68	59	62	65	68	60	69	64	76	56	59	68	66	56	48
49	68	60	63	66	68	61	70	65	77	57	59	68	67	57	49
50	69	60	63	67	69	62	70	66	77	58	60	69	68	57	50
51	70	61	64	67	70	63	71	67	78	59	61	70	68	58	51
52	70	62	65	68	70	64	71	67	78	60	62	70	69	59	52
53	71	63	66	69	71	64	72	68	78	60	63	71	70	60	53
54	72	63	66	69	71	65	73	69	79	61	63	72	70	61	54
55	72	64	67	70	72	66	73	69	79	62	64	72	71	62	55
56	73	65	68	71	73	67	74	70	80	63	65	73	72	63	56
57	73	66	68	71	73	67	74	71	80	64	66	73	72	63	57
58	74	67	69	72	74	68	75	71	81	65	67	74	73	64	58
59	75	67	70	73	75	69	76	72	81	66	67	75	74	65	59
60	75	68	71	73	75	70	76	73	82	66	68	75	74	66	60
61	76	69	71	74	76	70	77	73	82	67	69	76	75	67	61
62	77	70	72	75	76	71	77	74	83	68	70	77	75	68	62
63	77	71	73	75	77	72	78	75	83	69	71	77	76	69	63
64	78	71	74	76	78	73	79	75	83	70	71	78	77	69	64
65	78	72	74	77	78	73	79	76	84	71	72	78	77	70	65
66	79	73	75	77	79	74	80	77	84	71	73	79	78	71	66
67	80	74	76	78	80	75	80	77	85	72	74	80	79	72	67
68	80	75	77	79	80	76	81	78	85	73	75	80	79	73	68
69	81	75	77	79	81	76	82	79	86	74	75	81	80	74	69
70	81	76	78	80	81	77	82	80	86	75	76	81	81	74	70
71	82	77	79	81	82	78	83	80	87	76	77	82	81	75	71
72	83	78	79	81	83	79	83	81	87	76	78	83	82	76	72
73	83	79	80	82	83	79	84	82	88	77	79	83	83	77	73
74	84	79	81	83	84	80	85	82	88	78	79	84	83	78	74
75	85	80	82	83	84	81	85	83	89	79	80	85	84	79	75
76	85	81	82	84	85	82	86	84	89	80	81	85	85	80	76
77	86	82	83	85	86	83	86	84	89	81	82	86	85	80	77
78	86	83	84	85	86	83	87	85	90	81	83	86	86	81	78
79	87	83	85	86	87	84	88	86	90	82	83	87	86	82	79
80	88	84	85	87	88	85	88	86	91	83	84	88	87	83	80
81	88	85	86	87	88	86	89	87	91	84	85	88	88	84	81
82	89	86	87	88	89	86	89	88	92	85	86	89	88	85	82
83	89	87	88	89	89	87	90	88	92	86	86	89	89	86	83
84	90	87	88	89	90	88	90	89	93	87	87	90	90	86	84
85	91	88	89	90	91	89	91	90	93	87	88	91	90	87	85
86	91	89	90	91	91	89	92	90	94	88	89	91	91	88	86
87	92	90	90	91	92	90	92	91	94	89	90	92	92	89	87
88	93	90	91	92	93	91	93	92	94	90	90	93	92	90	88
89	93	91	92	93	93	92	93	92	95	91	91	93	93	91	89
90	94	92	93	93	94	92	94	93	95	92	92	94	94	91	90
91	94	93	93	94	94	93	95	94	96	92	93	94	94	92	91
92	95	94	94	95	95	94	95	95	96	93	94	95	95	93	92
93	96	94	95	95	96	95	96	95	97	94	94	96	95	94	93
94	96	95	96	96	96	95	96	96	97	95	95	96	96	95	94
95	97	96	96	97	97	96	97	97	98	96	96	97	97	96	95
96	98	97	97	97	98	97	98	97	98	97	97	98	97	97	96
97	98	98	98	98	98	98	98	98	99	97	98	98	98	97	97
98	99	98	99	99	99	98	99	99	99	98	98	99	99	98	98
99	99	99	99	99	99	99	99	99	100	99	99	99	99	99	99
100	100	100	100	100	100	100	100	100	100	100	100	100	100	100	100

Table B.11. WIAT–II Subtest and Composite Standard Scores Predicted From WAIS–III VIQ Scores (continued)

Adults

VIQ Score	Subtest Standard Scores									Composite Standard Scores					VIQ Score
	WRD	NO	RC	SP	PD	MR	WE	LC	OE	RD	MA	WL	OL	Total	
101	101	101	101	101	101	101	101	101	100	101	101	101	101	101	101
102	101	102	101	101	101	102	101	101	101	102	102	101	101	102	102
103	102	102	102	102	102	102	102	102	101	103	102	102	102	103	103
104	102	103	103	103	102	103	102	103	102	103	103	102	103	103	104
105	103	104	104	103	103	104	103	103	102	104	104	103	103	104	105
106	104	105	104	104	104	105	104	104	103	105	105	104	104	105	106
107	104	106	105	105	104	105	104	105	103	106	106	104	105	106	107
108	105	106	106	105	105	106	105	105	104	107	106	105	105	107	108
109	106	107	107	106	106	107	105	106	104	108	107	106	106	108	109
110	106	108	107	107	106	108	106	107	105	108	108	106	106	109	110
111	107	109	108	107	107	108	107	108	105	109	109	107	107	109	111
112	107	110	109	108	107	109	107	108	106	110	110	107	108	110	112
113	108	110	110	109	108	110	108	109	106	111	110	108	108	111	113
114	109	111	110	109	109	111	108	110	106	112	111	109	109	112	114
115	109	112	111	110	109	111	109	110	107	113	112	109	110	113	115
116	110	113	112	111	110	112	110	111	107	113	113	110	110	114	116
117	111	113	112	111	111	113	110	112	108	114	114	111	111	114	117
118	111	114	113	112	111	114	111	112	108	115	114	111	112	115	118
119	112	115	114	113	112	114	111	113	109	116	115	112	112	116	119
120	112	116	115	113	112	115	112	114	109	117	116	112	113	117	120
121	113	117	115	114	113	116	112	114	110	118	117	113	114	118	121
122	114	117	116	115	114	117	113	115	110	119	117	114	114	119	122
123	114	118	117	115	114	117	114	116	111	119	118	114	115	120	123
124	115	119	118	116	115	118	114	116	111	120	119	115	115	120	124
125	115	120	118	117	116	119	115	117	111	121	120	115	116	121	125
126	116	121	119	117	116	120	115	118	112	122	121	116	117	122	126
127	117	121	120	118	117	121	116	118	112	123	121	117	117	123	127
128	117	122	121	119	117	121	117	119	113	124	122	117	118	124	128
129	118	123	121	119	118	122	117	120	113	124	123	118	119	125	129
130	119	124	122	120	119	123	118	120	114	125	124	119	119	126	130
131	119	125	123	121	119	124	118	121	114	126	125	119	120	126	131
132	120	125	123	121	120	124	119	122	115	127	125	120	121	127	132
133	120	126	124	122	120	125	120	123	115	128	126	120	121	128	133
134	121	127	125	123	121	126	120	123	116	129	127	121	122	129	134
135	122	128	126	123	122	127	121	124	116	129	128	122	123	130	135
136	122	129	126	124	122	127	121	125	117	130	129	122	123	131	136
137	123	129	127	125	123	128	122	125	117	131	129	123	124	131	137
138	123	130	128	125	124	129	123	126	117	132	130	123	125	132	138
139	124	131	129	126	124	130	123	127	118	133	131	124	125	133	139
140	125	132	129	127	125	130	124	127	118	134	132	125	126	134	140
141	125	133	130	127	125	131	124	128	119	134	133	125	126	135	141
142	126	133	131	128	126	132	125	129	119	135	133	126	127	136	142
143	127	134	132	129	127	133	126	129	120	136	134	127	128	137	143
144	127	135	132	129	127	133	126	130	120	137	135	127	128	137	144
145	128	136	133	130	128	134	127	131	121	138	136	128	129	138	145
146	128	137	134	131	129	135	127	131	121	139	137	128	130	139	146
147	129	137	134	131	129	136	128	132	122	140	137	129	130	140	147
148	130	138	135	132	130	136	129	133	122	140	138	130	131	141	148
149	130	139	136	133	130	137	129	133	122	141	139	130	132	142	149
150	131	140	137	133	131	138	130	134	123	142	140	131	132	143	150
151	132	140	137	134	132	139	130	135	123	143	141	132	133	143	151
152	132	141	138	135	132	140	131	136	124	144	141	132	134	144	152
153	133	142	139	135	133	140	132	136	124	145	142	133	134	145	153
154	133	143	140	136	134	141	132	137	125	145	143	133	135	146	154
155	134	144	140	137	134	142	133	138	125	146	144	134	135	147	155
156															156
157															157
158															158
159															159
160															160

Note. Based on the correlations between the WIAT–II standard scores and the WAIS–III VIQ. Presented in the order shown in the table, the correlations for the nine WIAT–II subtests are .62, .79, .73, .67, .62, .76, .60, .68, and .46, and the correlations for the five WIAT–II composites are .84, .80, .62, .65, and .85.

WRD = Word Reading
NO = Numerical Operations
RC = Reading Comprehension
SP = Spelling

PD = Pseudoword Decoding
MR = Math Reasoning
WE = Written Expression
LC = Listening Comprehension

OE = Oral Expression
RD = Reading
MA = Mathematics
WL = Written Language

OL = Oral Language

Table B.12. WIAT–II Subtest and Composite Standard Scores Predicted From WAIS–III PIQ Scores

Ages 16:0–19:11 (High School)

| | Subtest Standard Scores | | | | | | | | | Composite Standard Scores | | | | | |
PIQ Score	WRD	NO	RC	SP	PD	MR	WE	LC	OE	RD	MA	WL	OL	Total	PIQ Score
40															40
41															41
42															42
43															43
44															44
45															45
46															46
47	75	67	78	72	77	62	74	73	75	74	62	71	66	62	47
48	75	67	79	73	78	63	75	74	75	74	63	71	67	62	48
49	76	68	79	73	78	64	75	74	76	75	64	72	68	63	49
50	76	69	80	74	79	64	76	75	76	75	64	73	68	64	50
51	77	69	80	74	79	65	76	75	77	76	65	73	69	65	51
52	77	70	80	75	79	66	77	76	77	76	66	74	70	65	52
53	78	71	81	75	80	66	77	76	78	77	66	74	70	66	53
54	78	71	81	76	80	67	78	77	78	77	67	75	71	67	54
55	79	72	82	76	81	68	78	77	79	78	68	75	72	68	55
56	79	72	82	77	81	69	79	78	79	78	69	76	72	68	56
57	80	73	82	78	82	69	79	78	80	79	69	76	73	69	57
58	80	74	83	78	82	70	80	79	80	79	70	77	73	70	58
59	80	74	83	79	82	71	80	79	81	80	71	77	74	70	59
60	81	75	84	79	83	71	81	80	81	80	71	78	75	71	60
61	81	76	84	80	83	72	81	80	82	81	72	79	75	72	61
62	82	76	84	80	84	73	82	81	82	81	73	79	76	73	62
63	82	77	85	81	84	74	82	81	82	82	74	80	77	73	63
64	83	77	85	81	85	74	83	82	83	82	74	80	77	74	64
65	83	78	86	82	85	75	83	82	83	83	75	81	78	75	65
66	84	79	86	82	85	76	83	83	84	83	76	81	78	75	66
67	84	79	86	83	86	76	84	83	84	84	76	82	79	76	67
68	85	80	87	83	86	77	84	84	85	84	77	82	80	77	68
69	85	81	87	84	87	78	85	84	85	85	78	83	80	78	69
70	86	81	88	84	87	79	85	85	86	85	79	84	81	78	70
71	86	82	88	85	88	79	86	85	86	86	79	84	82	79	71
72	87	82	89	85	88	80	86	86	87	86	80	85	82	80	72
73	87	83	89	86	88	81	87	86	87	87	81	85	83	81	73
74	88	84	89	86	89	81	87	87	88	87	81	86	84	81	74
75	88	84	90	87	89	82	88	87	88	88	82	86	84	82	75
76	89	85	90	87	90	83	88	88	89	88	83	87	85	83	76
77	89	86	91	88	90	84	89	88	89	89	84	87	85	83	77
78	90	86	91	88	91	84	89	89	90	89	84	88	86	84	78
79	90	87	91	89	91	85	90	89	90	90	85	88	87	85	79
80	90	87	92	90	91	86	90	90	91	90	86	89	87	86	80
81	91	88	92	90	92	86	91	90	91	91	86	90	88	86	81
82	91	89	93	91	92	87	91	91	91	91	87	90	89	87	82
83	92	89	93	91	93	88	92	91	92	92	88	91	89	88	83
84	92	90	93	92	93	89	92	92	92	92	89	91	90	88	84
85	93	91	94	92	94	89	93	92	93	93	89	92	91	89	85
86	93	91	94	93	94	90	93	93	93	93	90	92	91	90	86
87	94	92	95	93	94	91	94	93	94	94	91	93	92	91	87
88	94	92	95	94	95	91	94	94	94	94	91	93	92	91	88
89	95	93	95	94	95	92	95	94	95	95	92	94	93	92	89
90	95	94	96	95	96	93	95	95	95	95	93	95	94	93	90
91	96	94	96	95	96	94	96	95	96	96	94	95	94	94	91
92	96	95	97	96	97	94	96	96	96	96	94	96	95	94	92
93	97	96	97	96	97	95	97	96	97	97	95	96	96	95	93
94	97	96	98	97	97	96	97	97	97	97	96	97	96	96	94
95	98	97	98	97	98	96	98	97	98	98	96	97	97	96	95
96	98	97	98	98	98	97	98	98	98	98	97	98	97	97	96
97	99	98	99	98	99	98	99	98	99	99	98	98	98	98	97
98	99	99	99	99	99	99	99	99	99	99	99	99	99	99	98
99	100	99	100	99	100	99	100	99	100	100	99	99	99	99	99
100	100	100	100	100	100	100	100	100	100	100	100	100	100	100	100

Table B.12. WIAT–II Subtest and Composite Standard Scores Predicted From WAIS–III PIQ Scores *(continued)*

Ages 16:0–19:11 (High School)

	Subtest Standard Scores									Composite Standard Scores					
PIQ Score	WRD	NO	RC	SP	PD	MR	WE	LC	OE	RD	MA	WL	OL	Total	PIQ Score
101	100	101	100	101	100	101	100	101	100	100	101	101	101	101	101
102	101	101	101	101	101	101	101	101	101	101	101	101	101	101	102
103	101	102	101	102	101	102	101	102	101	101	102	102	102	102	103
104	102	103	102	102	102	103	102	102	102	102	103	102	103	103	104
105	102	103	102	103	102	104	102	103	102	102	104	103	103	104	105
106	103	104	102	103	103	104	103	103	103	103	104	103	104	104	106
107	103	104	103	104	103	105	103	104	103	103	105	104	104	105	107
108	104	105	103	104	103	106	104	104	104	104	106	104	105	106	108
109	104	106	104	105	104	106	104	105	104	104	106	105	106	106	109
110	105	106	104	105	104	107	105	105	105	105	107	106	106	107	110
111	105	107	105	106	105	108	105	106	105	105	108	106	107	108	111
112	106	108	105	106	105	109	106	106	106	106	109	107	108	109	112
113	106	108	105	107	106	109	106	107	106	106	109	107	108	109	113
114	107	109	106	107	106	110	107	107	107	107	110	108	109	110	114
115	107	109	106	108	106	111	107	108	107	107	111	108	109	111	115
116	108	110	107	108	107	111	108	108	108	108	111	109	110	112	116
117	108	111	107	109	107	112	108	109	108	108	112	109	111	112	117
118	109	111	107	109	108	113	109	109	109	109	113	110	111	113	118
119	109	112	108	110	108	114	109	110	109	109	114	110	112	114	119
120	110	113	108	110	109	114	110	110	109	110	114	111	113	114	120
121	110	113	109	111	109	115	110	111	110	110	115	112	113	115	121
122	110	114	109	112	109	116	111	111	110	111	116	112	114	116	122
123	111	114	109	112	110	116	111	112	111	111	116	113	115	117	123
124	111	115	110	113	110	117	112	112	111	112	117	113	115	117	124
125	112	116	110	113	111	118	112	113	112	112	118	114	116	118	125
126	112	116	111	114	111	119	113	113	112	113	119	114	116	119	126
127	113	117	111	114	112	119	113	114	113	113	119	115	117	119	127
128	113	118	111	115	112	120	114	114	113	114	120	115	118	120	128
129	114	118	112	115	112	121	114	115	114	114	121	116	118	121	129
130	114	119	112	116	113	121	115	115	114	115	121	117	119	122	130
131	115	119	113	116	113	122	115	116	115	115	122	117	120	122	131
132	115	120	113	117	114	123	116	116	115	116	123	118	120	123	132
133	116	121	114	117	114	124	116	117	116	116	124	118	121	124	133
134	116	121	114	118	115	124	117	117	116	117	124	119	122	125	134
135	117	122	114	118	115	125	117	118	117	117	125	119	122	125	135
136	117	123	115	119	115	126	117	118	117	118	126	120	123	126	136
137	118	123	115	119	116	126	118	119	118	118	126	120	123	127	137
138	118	124	116	120	116	127	118	119	118	119	127	121	124	127	138
139	119	124	116	120	117	128	119	120	118	119	128	121	125	128	139
140	119	125	116	121	117	129	119	120	119	120	129	122	125	129	140
141	120	126	117	121	118	129	120	121	119	120	129	123	127	130	141
142	120	126	117	122	118	130	120	121	120	121	130	123	127	130	142
143	120	127	118	122	118	131	121	122	120	121	131	124	127	131	143
144	121	128	118	123	119	131	121	122	121	122	131	124	128	132	144
145	121	128	118	124	119	132	122	123	121	122	132	125	128	132	145
146	122	129	119	124	120	133	122	123	122	123	133	125	129	133	146
147	122	129	119	125	120	134	123	124	122	123	134	126	130	134	147
148	123	130	120	125	121	134	123	124	123	124	134	126	130	135	148
149	123	131	120	126	121	135	124	125	123	124	135	127	131	135	149
150	124	131	121	126	121	136	124	125	124	125	136	128	132	136	150
151	124	132	121	127	122	136	125	126	124	125	136	128	132	137	151
152	125	133	121	127	122	137	125	126	125	126	137	129	133	138	152
153	125	133	122	128	123	138	126	127	125	126	138	129	134	138	153
154	126	134	122	128	123	139	126	127	126	127	139	130	134	139	154
155	126	134	123	129	124	139	127	128	126	127	139	130	135	140	155
156															156
157															157
158															158
159															159
160															160

Note. Based on the correlations between the WIAT–II standard scores and the WAIS–III PIQ across the four age ranges. Presented in the order shown in the table, the average correlations for the nine WIAT–II subtests are .48, .63, .41, .52, .43, .72, .49, .50, and .47, and the average correlations for the five WIAT–II composites are .49, .72, .55, .63, and .72.

WRD = Word Reading
NO = Numerical Operations
RC = Reading Comprehension
SP = Spelling

PD = Pseudoword Decoding
MR = Math Reasoning
WE = Written Expression
LC = Listening Comprehension

OE = Oral Expression
RD = Reading
MA = Mathematics
WL = Written Language

OL = Oral Language

Table B.12. WIAT–II Subtest and Composite Standard Scores Predicted From WAIS–III PIQ Scores *(continued)*

College Students

PIQ Score	Subtest Standard Scores									Composite Standard Scores					PIQ Score
	WRD	NO	RC	SP	PD	MR	WE	LC	OE	RD	MA	WL	OL	Total	
40															40
41															41
42															42
43															43
44															44
45															45
46															46
47	83	71	76	84	85	69	80	74	79	78	67	79	73	71	47
48	84	71	77	84	85	69	81	75	80	78	67	80	74	71	48
49	84	72	77	84	85	70	81	75	80	78	68	80	74	72	49
50	84	72	78	85	86	70	81	76	80	79	69	81	75	72	50
51	85	73	78	85	86	71	82	76	81	79	69	81	75	73	51
52	85	74	78	85	86	71	82	77	81	80	70	81	76	73	52
53	85	74	79	86	86	72	82	77	82	80	70	82	76	74	53
54	86	75	79	86	87	73	83	78	82	81	71	82	77	75	54
55	86	75	80	86	87	73	83	78	82	81	72	82	77	75	55
56	86	76	80	87	87	74	84	79	83	81	72	83	78	76	56
57	86	76	81	87	88	74	84	79	83	82	73	83	78	76	57
58	87	77	81	87	88	75	84	80	84	82	74	84	79	77	58
59	87	77	82	88	88	76	85	80	84	83	74	84	79	77	59
60	87	78	82	88	88	76	85	81	84	83	75	84	80	78	60
61	88	78	82	88	89	77	85	81	85	84	75	85	80	78	61
62	88	79	83	88	89	77	86	82	85	84	76	85	81	79	62
63	88	80	83	89	89	78	86	82	86	84	77	86	81	80	63
64	89	80	84	89	90	79	87	83	86	85	77	86	82	80	64
65	89	81	84	89	90	79	87	83	86	85	78	86	82	81	65
66	89	81	85	90	90	80	87	84	87	86	79	87	83	81	66
67	90	82	85	90	90	80	88	84	87	86	79	87	83	82	67
68	90	82	86	90	91	81	88	85	87	86	80	88	84	82	68
69	90	83	86	91	91	82	88	85	88	87	81	88	84	83	69
70	91	83	87	91	91	82	89	86	88	87	81	88	85	83	70
71	91	84	87	91	92	83	89	86	89	88	82	89	85	84	71
72	91	85	87	91	92	83	90	87	89	88	82	89	86	85	72
73	91	85	88	92	92	84	90	87	89	89	83	89	86	85	73
74	92	86	88	92	93	85	90	87	90	89	84	90	87	86	74
75	92	86	89	92	93	85	91	88	90	89	84	90	87	86	75
76	92	87	89	93	93	86	91	88	91	90	85	91	88	87	76
77	93	87	90	93	93	86	91	89	91	90	86	91	88	87	77
78	93	88	90	93	94	87	92	89	91	91	86	91	89	88	78
79	93	88	91	94	94	88	92	90	92	91	87	92	89	88	79
80	94	89	91	94	94	88	93	90	92	92	87	92	90	89	80
81	94	90	91	94	95	89	93	91	93	92	88	93	90	89	81
82	94	90	92	95	95	89	93	91	93	92	89	93	91	90	82
83	95	91	92	95	95	90	94	92	93	93	89	93	91	91	83
84	95	91	93	95	95	90	94	92	94	93	90	94	92	91	84
85	95	92	93	95	96	91	94	93	94	94	91	94	92	92	85
86	96	92	94	96	96	92	95	93	95	94	91	95	93	92	86
87	96	93	94	96	96	92	95	94	95	95	92	95	93	93	87
88	96	93	95	96	97	93	96	94	95	95	92	95	94	93	88
89	97	94	95	97	97	93	96	95	96	95	93	96	94	94	89
90	97	94	96	97	97	94	96	95	96	96	94	96	95	94	90
91	97	95	96	97	97	95	97	96	96	96	94	96	95	95	91
92	97	96	96	98	98	95	97	96	97	97	95	97	96	96	92
93	98	96	97	98	98	96	97	97	97	97	96	97	96	96	93
94	98	97	97	98	98	96	98	97	98	97	96	98	97	97	94
95	98	97	98	98	99	97	98	98	98	98	97	98	97	97	95
96	99	98	98	99	99	98	99	98	98	98	97	98	98	98	96
97	99	98	99	99	99	98	99	99	99	99	98	99	98	98	97
98	99	99	99	99	99	99	99	99	99	99	99	99	99	99	98
99	100	99	100	100	100	99	100	100	100	100	99	100	99	99	99
100	100	100	100	100	100	100	100	100	100	100	100	100	100	100	100

Table B.12. WIAT–II Subtest and Composite Standard Scores Predicted From WAIS–III PIQ Scores (continued)

College Students

PIQ Score	Subtest Standard Scores									Composite Standard Scores					PIQ Score
	WRD	NO	RC	SP	PD	MR	WE	LC	OE	RD	MA	WL	OL	Total	
101	100	101	100	100	100	101	100	100	100	100	101	100	101	101	101
102	101	101	101	101	101	101	101	101	101	101	101	101	101	101	102
103	101	102	101	101	101	102	101	101	101	101	102	101	102	102	103
104	101	102	102	101	101	102	102	102	102	102	103	102	102	102	104
105	102	103	102	102	101	103	102	102	102	102	103	102	103	103	105
106	102	103	103	102	102	104	102	103	102	103	104	102	103	103	106
107	102	104	103	102	102	104	103	103	103	103	104	103	104	104	107
108	103	104	104	102	102	105	103	104	103	103	105	103	104	104	108
109	103	105	104	103	103	105	103	104	104	104	106	104	105	105	109
110	103	106	105	103	103	106	104	105	104	104	106	104	105	106	110
111	103	106	105	103	103	107	104	105	104	105	107	104	106	106	111
112	104	107	105	104	103	107	105	106	105	105	108	105	106	107	112
113	104	107	106	104	104	108	105	106	105	105	108	105	107	107	113
114	104	108	106	104	104	108	105	107	105	106	109	105	107	108	114
115	105	108	107	105	104	109	106	107	106	106	109	106	108	108	115
116	105	109	107	105	105	110	106	108	106	107	110	106	108	109	116
117	105	109	108	105	105	110	106	108	107	107	111	107	109	109	117
118	106	110	108	105	105	111	107	109	107	108	111	107	109	110	118
119	106	110	109	106	105	111	107	109	107	108	112	107	110	111	119
120	106	111	109	106	106	112	108	110	108	108	113	108	110	111	120
121	107	112	109	106	106	112	108	110	108	109	113	108	111	112	121
122	107	112	110	107	106	113	108	111	109	109	114	109	111	112	122
123	107	113	110	107	107	114	109	111	109	110	114	109	112	113	123
124	108	113	111	107	107	114	109	112	109	110	115	109	112	113	124
125	108	114	111	108	107	115	109	112	110	111	116	110	113	114	125
126	108	114	112	108	107	115	110	113	110	111	116	110	113	114	126
127	109	115	112	108	108	116	110	113	111	111	117	111	114	115	127
128	109	115	113	109	108	117	111	113	111	112	118	111	114	115	128
129	109	116	113	109	108	117	111	114	111	112	118	111	115	116	129
130	109	117	114	109	109	118	111	114	112	113	119	112	115	117	130
131	110	117	114	109	109	118	112	115	112	113	119	112	116	117	131
132	110	118	114	110	109	119	112	115	113	114	120	112	116	118	132
133	110	118	115	110	110	120	112	116	113	114	121	113	117	118	133
134	111	119	115	110	110	120	113	116	113	114	121	113	117	119	134
135	111	119	116	111	110	121	113	117	114	115	122	114	118	119	135
136	111	120	116	111	110	121	114	117	114	115	123	114	118	120	136
137	112	120	117	111	111	122	114	118	114	116	123	114	119	120	137
138	112	121	117	112	111	123	114	118	115	116	124	115	119	121	138
139	112	122	118	112	111	123	115	119	115	116	125	115	120	122	139
140	113	122	118	112	112	124	115	119	116	117	125	116	120	122	140
141	113	123	118	112	112	124	115	120	116	117	126	116	121	123	141
142	113	123	119	113	112	125	116	120	116	118	126	116	121	123	142
143	114	124	119	113	112	126	116	121	117	118	127	117	122	124	143
144	114	124	120	113	113	126	117	121	117	119	128	117	122	124	144
145	114	125	120	114	113	127	117	122	118	119	128	118	123	125	145
146	114	125	121	114	113	127	117	122	118	119	129	118	123	125	146
147	115	126	121	114	114	128	118	123	118	120	130	118	124	126	147
148	115	126	122	115	114	129	118	123	119	120	130	119	124	127	148
149	115	127	122	115	114	129	118	124	119	121	131	119	125	127	149
150	116	128	123	115	114	130	119	124	120	121	131	119	125	128	150
151	116	128	123	116	115	130	119	125	120	122	132	120	126	128	151
152	116	129	123	116	115	131	120	125	120	122	133	120	126	129	152
153	117	129	124	116	115	131	120	126	121	122	133	121	127	129	153
154	117	130	124	116	116	132	120	126	121	123	134	121	127	130	154
155	117	130	125	117	116	133	121	127	122	123	135	121	128	130	155
156															156
157															157
158															158
159															159
160															160

Note. Based on the correlations between the WIAT–II standard scores and the WAIS–III PIQ. Presented in the order shown in the table, the correlations for the nine WIAT–II subtests are .32, .55, .45, .30, .29, .59, .38, .48, and .39, and the correlations for the five WIAT–II composites are .42, .63, .39, .51, and .55.

WRD = Word Reading
NO = Numerical Operations
RC = Reading Comprehension
SP = Spelling

PD = Pseudoword Decoding
MR = Math Reasoning
WE = Written Expression
LC = Listening Comprehension

OE = Oral Expression
RD = Reading
MA = Mathematics
WL = Written Language

OL = Oral Language

Table B.12. WIAT–II Subtest and Composite Standard Scores Predicted From WAIS–III PIQ Scores (continued)

Adults

PIQ Score	Subtest Standard Scores									Composite Standard Scores					PIQ Score
	WRD	NO	RC	SP	PD	MR	WE	LC	OE	RD	MA	WL	OL	Total	
40															40
41															41
42															42
43															43
44															44
45															45
46															46
47	70	64	67	73	65	65	72	66	77	59	64	73	70	62	47
48	70	65	67	73	65	66	72	67	77	60	65	73	71	63	48
49	71	66	68	74	66	67	73	67	78	61	66	74	71	64	49
50	71	66	68	74	67	67	73	68	78	62	66	74	72	64	50
51	72	67	69	75	67	68	74	69	79	62	67	75	72	65	51
52	72	68	70	75	68	69	74	69	79	63	68	75	73	66	52
53	73	68	70	76	69	69	75	70	80	64	68	76	73	66	53
54	74	69	71	76	69	70	75	71	80	65	69	76	74	67	54
55	74	70	72	77	70	71	76	71	80	65	70	77	75	68	55
56	75	70	72	77	71	71	76	72	81	66	70	77	75	69	56
57	75	71	73	78	71	72	77	72	81	67	71	78	76	69	57
58	76	72	73	78	72	73	78	73	82	68	72	78	76	70	58
59	76	72	74	79	73	73	78	74	82	68	72	79	77	71	59
60	77	73	75	80	73	74	79	74	83	69	73	79	77	71	60
61	78	74	75	80	74	75	79	75	83	70	74	80	78	72	61
62	78	74	76	81	75	75	80	76	83	71	74	81	79	73	62
63	79	75	77	81	75	76	80	76	84	72	75	81	79	74	63
64	79	76	77	82	76	77	81	77	84	72	76	82	80	74	64
65	80	76	78	82	77	77	81	78	85	73	76	82	80	75	65
66	80	77	79	83	77	78	82	78	85	74	77	83	81	76	66
67	81	78	79	83	78	78	82	79	86	75	78	83	81	76	67
68	82	78	80	84	79	79	83	80	86	75	78	84	82	77	68
69	82	79	80	84	79	80	83	80	86	76	79	84	82	78	69
70	83	80	81	85	80	80	84	81	87	77	80	85	83	79	70
71	83	80	82	85	81	81	84	81	87	78	80	85	84	79	71
72	84	81	82	86	81	82	85	82	88	78	81	86	84	80	72
73	85	82	83	86	82	82	86	83	88	79	82	86	85	81	73
74	85	83	84	87	83	83	86	83	89	80	82	87	85	81	74
75	86	83	84	87	83	84	87	84	89	81	83	87	86	82	75
76	86	84	85	88	84	84	87	85	90	82	84	88	86	83	76
77	87	85	85	88	85	85	88	85	90	82	84	88	87	84	77
78	87	85	86	89	85	86	88	86	90	83	85	89	88	84	78
79	88	86	87	89	86	86	89	87	91	84	86	89	88	85	79
80	89	87	87	90	87	87	89	87	91	85	87	90	89	86	80
81	89	87	88	90	87	88	90	88	92	85	87	90	89	86	81
82	90	88	89	91	88	88	90	88	92	86	88	91	90	87	82
83	90	89	89	91	89	89	91	89	93	87	89	91	90	88	83
84	91	89	90	92	89	90	91	90	93	88	89	92	91	89	84
85	91	90	91	92	90	90	92	90	93	88	90	92	92	89	85
86	92	91	91	93	91	91	93	91	94	89	91	93	92	90	86
87	93	91	92	93	91	92	93	92	94	90	91	93	93	91	87
88	93	92	92	94	92	92	94	92	95	91	92	94	93	91	88
89	94	93	93	94	93	93	94	93	95	92	93	94	94	92	89
90	94	93	94	95	93	93	95	94	96	92	93	95	94	93	90
91	95	94	94	95	94	94	95	94	96	93	94	95	95	94	91
92	95	95	95	96	95	95	96	95	97	94	95	96	95	94	92
93	96	95	96	96	95	95	96	96	97	95	95	96	96	95	93
94	97	96	96	97	96	96	97	96	97	95	96	97	97	96	94
95	97	97	97	97	97	97	97	97	98	96	97	97	97	96	95
96	98	97	97	98	97	97	98	97	98	97	97	98	98	97	96
97	98	98	98	98	98	98	98	98	99	98	98	98	98	98	97
98	99	99	99	99	99	99	99	99	99	99	99	99	99	99	98
99	99	99	99	99	99	99	99	99	100	99	99	99	99	99	99
100	100	100	100	100	100	100	100	100	100	100	100	100	100	100	100

Table B.12. WIAT–II Subtest and Composite Standard Scores Predicted From WAIS–III PIQ Scores *(continued)*

Adults

PIQ Score	Subtest Standard Scores									Composite Standard Scores					PIQ Score
	WRD	NO	RC	SP	PD	MR	WE	LC	OE	RD	MA	WL	OL	Total	
101	101	101	101	101	101	101	101	101	100	101	101	101	101	101	101
102	101	101	101	101	101	101	101	101	101	102	101	101	101	101	102
103	102	102	102	102	102	102	102	102	101	102	102	102	102	102	103
104	102	103	103	102	103	103	102	103	102	103	103	102	102	103	104
105	103	103	103	103	103	103	103	103	102	104	103	103	103	104	105
106	103	104	104	103	104	104	103	104	103	105	104	103	103	104	106
107	104	105	104	104	105	105	104	104	103	105	105	104	104	105	107
108	105	105	105	104	105	105	104	105	103	106	105	104	105	106	108
109	105	106	106	105	106	106	105	106	104	107	106	105	105	106	109
110	106	107	106	105	107	107	105	106	104	108	107	105	106	107	110
111	106	107	107	106	107	107	106	107	105	108	107	106	106	108	111
112	107	108	108	106	108	108	106	108	105	109	108	106	107	109	112
113	107	109	108	107	109	108	107	108	106	110	109	107	107	109	113
114	108	109	109	107	109	109	107	109	106	111	109	107	108	110	114
115	109	110	109	108	110	110	108	110	107	112	110	108	108	111	115
116	109	111	110	108	111	110	109	110	107	112	111	108	109	111	116
117	110	111	111	109	111	111	109	111	107	113	111	109	110	112	117
118	110	112	111	109	112	112	110	112	108	114	112	109	110	113	118
119	111	113	112	110	113	112	110	112	108	115	113	110	111	114	119
120	111	113	113	110	113	113	111	113	109	115	114	110	111	114	120
121	112	114	113	111	114	114	111	113	109	116	114	111	112	115	121
122	113	115	114	111	115	114	112	114	110	117	115	111	112	116	122
123	113	115	115	112	115	115	112	115	110	118	116	112	113	116	123
124	114	116	115	112	116	116	113	115	110	118	116	112	114	117	124
125	114	117	116	113	117	116	113	116	111	119	117	113	114	118	125
126	115	117	116	113	117	117	114	117	111	120	118	113	115	119	126
127	115	118	117	114	118	118	114	117	112	121	118	114	115	119	127
128	116	119	118	114	119	118	115	118	112	122	119	114	116	120	128
129	117	120	118	115	119	119	116	119	113	122	120	115	116	121	129
130	117	120	119	115	120	120	116	119	113	123	120	115	117	121	130
131	118	121	120	116	121	120	117	120	114	124	121	116	118	122	131
132	118	122	120	116	121	121	117	120	114	125	122	116	118	123	132
133	119	122	121	117	122	122	118	121	114	125	122	117	119	124	133
134	120	123	121	117	123	122	118	122	115	126	123	117	119	124	134
135	120	124	122	118	123	123	119	122	115	127	124	118	120	125	135
136	121	124	123	118	124	123	119	123	116	128	124	118	120	126	136
137	121	125	123	119	125	124	120	124	116	128	125	119	121	126	137
138	122	126	124	119	125	125	120	124	117	129	126	119	121	127	138
139	122	126	125	120	126	125	121	125	117	130	126	120	122	128	139
140	123	127	125	120	127	126	121	126	117	131	127	121	123	129	140
141	124	128	126	121	127	127	122	126	118	132	128	121	123	129	141
142	124	128	127	122	128	127	122	127	118	132	128	122	124	130	142
143	125	129	127	122	129	128	123	128	119	133	129	122	124	131	143
144	125	130	128	123	129	129	124	128	119	134	130	123	125	131	144
145	126	130	128	123	130	129	124	129	120	135	130	123	125	132	145
146	126	131	129	124	131	130	125	129	120	135	131	124	126	133	146
147	127	132	130	124	131	131	125	130	120	136	132	124	127	134	147
148	128	132	130	125	132	131	126	131	121	137	132	125	127	134	148
149	128	133	131	125	133	132	126	131	121	138	133	125	128	135	149
150	129	134	132	126	133	133	127	132	122	139	134	126	128	136	150
151	129	134	132	126	134	133	127	133	122	139	134	126	129	136	151
152	130	135	133	127	135	134	128	133	123	140	135	127	129	137	152
153	130	136	133	127	135	135	128	134	123	141	136	127	130	138	153
154	131	136	134	128	136	135	129	135	124	142	136	128	131	139	154
155	132	137	135	128	137	136	129	135	124	142	137	128	131	139	155
156															156
157															157
158															158
159															159
160															160

Note. Based on the correlations between the WIAT–II standard scores and the WAIS–III PIQ. Presented in the order shown in the table, the correlations for the nine WIAT–II subtests are .57, .67, .63, .51, .67, .65, .54, .64, and .44, and the correlations for the five WIAT–II composites are .77, .68, .51, .57, and .72.

WRD = Word Reading
NO = Numerical Operations
RC = Reading Comprehension
SP = Spelling

PD = Pseudoword Decoding
MR = Math Reasoning
WE = Written Expression
LC = Listening Comprehension

OE = Oral Expression
RD = Reading
MA = Mathematics
WL = Written Language

OL = Oral Language

Table B.13. WIAT–II Subtest and Composite Standard Scores Predicted From WAIS–III VCI Scores

Ages 16:0–19:11 (High School)

VCI Score	WRD	NO	RC	SP	PD	MR	WE	LC	OE	RD	MA	WL	OL	Total	VCI Score
						Subtest Standard Scores						Composite Standard Scores			
40															40
41															41
42															42
43															43
44															44
45															45
46															46
47															47
48															48
49															49
50	65	69	65	71	73	69	74	60	79	63	67	70	63	62	50
51	66	69	66	71	73	69	74	61	79	64	68	71	64	63	51
52	66	70	66	72	74	70	75	62	80	65	69	71	65	64	52
53	67	70	67	73	75	71	75	63	80	65	69	72	65	65	53
54	68	71	68	73	75	71	76	63	81	66	70	72	66	65	54
55	68	72	69	74	76	72	77	64	81	67	71	73	67	66	55
56	69	72	69	74	76	73	77	65	82	68	71	74	68	67	56
57	70	73	70	75	77	73	78	66	82	68	72	74	68	68	57
58	71	74	71	75	77	74	78	67	82	69	73	75	69	68	58
59	71	74	71	76	78	74	79	67	83	70	73	75	70	69	59
60	72	75	72	77	78	75	79	68	83	71	74	76	70	70	60
61	73	75	73	77	79	76	80	69	84	71	74	77	71	71	61
62	73	76	73	78	79	76	80	70	84	72	75	77	72	71	62
63	74	77	74	78	80	77	81	71	84	73	76	78	73	72	63
64	75	77	75	79	81	78	81	71	85	74	76	78	73	73	64
65	75	78	76	80	81	78	82	72	85	74	77	79	74	74	65
66	76	79	76	80	82	79	82	73	86	75	78	80	75	74	66
67	77	79	77	81	82	79	83	74	86	76	78	80	76	75	67
68	78	80	78	81	83	80	83	75	87	76	79	81	76	76	68
69	78	80	78	82	83	81	84	75	87	77	80	81	77	77	69
70	79	81	79	82	84	81	84	76	87	78	80	82	78	77	70
71	80	82	80	83	84	82	85	77	88	79	81	83	79	78	71
72	80	82	80	84	85	83	85	78	88	79	82	83	79	79	72
73	81	83	81	84	85	83	86	79	89	80	82	84	80	80	73
74	82	84	82	85	86	84	86	79	89	81	83	84	81	80	74
75	82	84	83	85	86	84	87	80	90	82	84	85	82	81	75
76	83	85	83	86	87	85	87	81	90	82	84	86	82	82	76
77	84	86	84	87	88	86	88	82	90	83	85	86	83	83	77
78	85	86	85	87	88	86	89	83	91	84	86	87	84	83	78
79	85	87	85	88	89	87	89	83	91	85	86	87	85	84	79
80	86	87	86	88	89	88	90	84	92	85	87	88	85	85	80
81	87	88	87	89	90	88	90	85	92	86	88	89	86	86	81
82	87	89	87	89	90	89	91	86	92	87	88	89	87	86	82
83	88	89	88	90	91	89	91	86	93	88	89	90	87	87	83
84	89	90	89	91	91	90	92	87	93	88	90	90	88	88	84
85	89	91	90	91	92	91	92	88	94	89	90	91	89	89	85
86	90	91	90	92	92	91	93	89	94	90	91	92	90	89	86
87	91	92	91	92	93	92	93	90	95	90	91	92	90	90	87
88	92	92	92	93	94	93	94	90	95	91	92	93	91	91	88
89	92	93	92	94	94	93	94	91	95	92	93	93	92	92	89
90	93	94	93	94	95	94	95	92	96	93	93	94	93	92	90
91	94	94	94	95	95	94	95	93	96	93	94	95	93	93	91
92	94	95	94	95	96	95	96	94	97	94	95	95	94	94	92
93	95	96	95	96	96	96	96	94	97	95	95	96	95	95	93
94	96	96	96	96	97	96	97	95	97	96	96	96	96	95	94
95	96	97	97	97	97	97	97	96	98	96	97	97	96	96	95
96	97	97	97	98	98	98	98	97	98	97	97	98	97	97	96
97	98	98	98	98	98	98	98	98	99	98	98	98	98	98	97
98	99	99	99	99	99	99	99	98	99	99	99	99	99	98	98
99	99	99	99	99	99	99	99	99	100	99	99	99	99	99	99
100	100	100	100	100	100	100	100	100	100	100	100	100	100	100	100

Table B.13. WIAT–II Subtest and Composite Standard Scores Predicted From WAIS–III VCI Scores *(continued)*

Ages 16:0–19:11 (High School)

	Subtest Standard Scores									Composite Standard Scores					
VCI Score	WRD	NO	RC	SP	PD	MR	WE	LC	OE	RD	MA	WL	OL	Total	VCI Score
101	101	101	101	101	101	101	101	101	100	101	101	101	101	101	101
102	101	101	101	101	101	101	101	102	101	101	101	101	101	102	102
103	102	102	102	102	102	102	102	102	101	102	102	102	102	102	103
104	103	103	103	102	102	102	102	103	102	103	103	102	103	103	104
105	104	103	103	103	103	103	103	104	102	104	103	103	104	104	105
106	104	104	104	104	103	104	103	105	103	104	104	104	104	105	106
107	105	104	105	104	104	104	104	106	103	105	105	104	105	105	107
108	106	105	106	105	104	105	104	106	103	106	105	105	106	106	108
109	106	106	106	105	105	106	105	107	104	107	106	105	107	107	109
110	107	106	107	106	105	106	105	108	104	107	107	106	107	108	110
111	108	107	108	106	106	107	106	109	105	108	107	107	108	108	111
112	108	108	108	107	106	107	106	110	105	109	108	107	109	109	112
113	109	108	109	108	107	108	107	110	105	110	109	108	110	110	113
114	110	109	110	108	108	109	107	111	106	110	109	108	110	111	114
115	111	109	110	108	108	109	108	112	106	111	110	109	111	111	115
116	111	110	111	109	109	110	108	113	107	112	110	110	112	112	116
117	112	111	112	110	109	111	109	114	107	112	111	110	113	113	117
118	113	111	113	111	110	111	109	114	108	113	112	111	113	114	118
119	113	112	113	111	110	112	110	115	108	114	112	111	114	114	119
120	114	113	114	112	111	112	110	116	108	115	113	112	115	115	120
121	115	113	115	112	111	113	111	117	109	115	114	113	115	116	121
122	115	114	115	113	112	114	111	117	109	116	114	113	116	117	122
123	116	114	116	113	112	114	112	118	110	117	115	114	117	117	123
124	117	115	117	114	113	115	113	119	110	118	116	114	118	118	124
125	118	116	117	115	114	116	113	120	110	118	116	115	118	119	125
126	118	116	118	115	114	116	114	121	111	119	117	116	119	120	126
127	119	117	119	116	115	117	114	121	111	120	118	116	120	120	127
128	120	118	120	116	115	117	115	122	112	121	118	117	121	121	128
129	120	118	120	117	116	118	115	123	112	121	119	117	121	122	129
130	121	119	121	118	116	119	116	124	113	122	120	118	122	123	130
131	122	120	122	118	117	119	116	125	113	123	120	119	123	123	131
132	122	120	122	119	117	120	117	125	113	124	121	119	124	124	132
133	123	121	123	119	118	121	117	126	114	124	122	120	124	125	133
134	124	121	124	120	118	121	118	127	114	125	122	120	125	126	134
135	125	122	124	120	119	122	118	128	115	126	123	121	126	126	135
136	125	123	125	121	119	122	119	129	115	126	124	122	127	127	136
137	126	123	126	122	120	123	119	129	116	127	124	122	127	128	137
138	127	124	127	122	121	124	120	130	116	128	125	123	128	129	138
139	127	125	127	123	121	124	120	131	116	129	126	123	129	129	139
140	128	125	128	123	122	125	121	132	117	129	126	124	130	130	140
141	129	126	129	124	122	126	121	133	117	130	127	125	130	131	141
142	129	126	129	125	123	126	122	133	118	131	127	125	131	132	142
143	130	127	130	125	123	127	122	134	118	132	128	126	132	132	143
144	131	128	131	126	124	127	123	135	118	132	129	126	132	133	144
145	132	128	131	126	124	128	123	136	119	133	129	127	133	134	145
146	132	129	132	127	125	129	124	137	119	134	130	128	134	135	146
147	133	130	133	127	125	129	125	137	120	135	131	128	135	135	147
148	134	130	134	128	126	130	125	138	120	135	131	129	135	136	148
149	134	131	134	129	127	131	126	139	121	136	132	129	136	137	149
150	135	132	135	129	127	131	126	140	121	137	133	130	137	138	150
151															151
152															152
153															153
154															154
155															155
156															156
157															157
158															158
159															159
160															160

Note. Based on the correlations between the WIAT–II standard scores and the WAIS–III VCI across the four age ranges. Presented in the order shown in the table, the average correlations for the nine WIAT–II subtests are .70, .63, .70, .59, .54, .62, .52, .80, and .42, and the average correlations for the five WIAT–II composites are .74, .65, .60, .74, and .75.

WRD = Word Reading
NO = Numerical Operations
RC = Reading Comprehension
SP = Spelling

PD = Pseudoword Decoding
MR = Math Reasoning
WE = Written Expression
LC = Listening Comprehension

OE = Oral Expression
RD = Reading
MA = Mathematics
WL = Written Language

OL = Oral Language

Table B.13. WIAT–II Subtest and Composite Standard Scores Predicted From WAIS–III VCI Scores *(continued)*

College Students

VCI Score	Subtest Standard Scores										Composite Standard Scores					VCI Score
	WRD	NO	RC	SP	PD	MR	WE	LC	OE		RD	MA	WL	OL	Total	
40																40
41																41
42																42
43																43
44																44
45																45
46																46
47																47
48																48
49																49
50	76	79	74	80	79	75	83	68	86		70	74	80	73	70	50
51	77	80	74	80	80	75	83	69	87		70	74	81	73	70	51
52	77	80	75	81	80	76	83	69	87		71	75	81	74	71	52
53	78	80	75	81	80	76	84	70	87		72	75	81	74	71	53
54	78	81	76	81	81	77	84	71	88		72	76	82	75	72	54
55	79	81	76	82	81	77	84	71	88		73	76	82	75	73	55
56	79	82	77	82	82	78	85	72	88		73	77	83	76	73	56
57	80	82	78	83	82	78	85	73	88		74	77	83	77	74	57
58	80	82	78	83	83	79	86	73	89		75	78	83	77	75	58
59	81	83	79	83	83	79	86	74	89		75	78	84	78	75	59
60	81	83	79	84	83	80	86	74	89		76	79	84	78	76	60
61	82	84	80	84	84	80	87	75	89		76	80	85	79	76	61
62	82	84	80	85	84	81	87	76	90		77	80	85	79	77	62
63	82	85	81	85	85	81	87	76	90		78	81	85	80	78	63
64	83	85	81	85	85	82	88	77	90		78	81	86	80	78	64
65	83	85	82	86	85	82	88	78	91		79	82	86	81	79	65
66	84	86	82	86	86	83	88	78	91		79	82	87	81	79	66
67	84	86	83	87	86	83	89	79	91		80	83	87	82	80	67
68	85	87	83	87	87	84	89	80	91		81	83	87	83	81	68
69	85	87	84	88	87	84	89	80	92		81	84	88	83	81	69
70	86	87	84	88	88	85	90	81	92		82	84	88	84	82	70
71	86	88	85	88	88	85	90	81	92		83	85	88	84	82	71
72	87	88	85	89	88	86	90	82	92		83	85	89	85	83	72
73	87	89	86	89	89	86	91	83	93		84	86	89	85	84	73
74	88	89	86	90	89	87	91	83	93		84	86	90	86	84	74
75	88	90	87	90	90	87	91	84	93		85	87	90	86	85	75
76	89	90	87	90	90	88	92	85	93		86	87	90	87	85	76
77	89	90	88	91	90	88	92	85	94		86	88	91	87	86	77
78	90	91	88	91	91	89	92	86	94		87	88	91	88	87	78
79	90	91	89	92	91	89	93	87	94		87	89	92	89	87	79
80	91	92	90	92	92	90	93	87	95		88	90	92	89	88	80
81	91	92	90	92	92	90	93	88	95		89	90	92	90	88	81
82	91	92	91	93	93	91	94	88	95		89	91	93	90	89	82
83	92	93	91	93	93	91	94	89	95		90	91	93	91	90	83
84	92	93	92	94	93	92	94	90	96		90	92	94	91	90	84
85	93	94	92	94	94	92	95	90	96		91	92	94	92	91	85
86	93	94	93	94	94	93	95	91	96		92	93	94	92	92	86
87	94	95	93	95	95	93	96	92	96		92	93	95	93	92	87
88	94	95	94	95	95	94	96	92	97		93	94	95	93	93	88
89	95	95	94	96	95	94	96	93	97		93	94	96	94	93	89
90	95	96	95	96	96	95	97	94	97		94	95	96	95	94	90
91	96	96	95	96	96	95	97	94	98		95	95	96	95	95	91
92	96	97	96	97	97	96	97	95	98		95	96	97	96	95	92
93	97	97	96	97	97	96	98	96	98		96	96	97	96	96	93
94	97	97	97	98	98	97	98	96	98		96	97	98	97	96	94
95	98	98	97	98	98	97	98	97	99		97	97	98	97	97	95
96	98	98	98	98	98	98	99	97	99		98	98	98	98	98	96
97	99	99	98	99	99	98	99	98	99		98	98	99	98	97	97
98	99	99	99	99	99	99	99	99	99		99	99	99	99	99	98
99	100	100	99	100	100	99	100	99	100		99	99	100	99	99	99
100	100	100	100	100	100	100	100	100	100		100	100	100	100	100	100

Table B.13. WIAT–II Subtest and Composite Standard Scores Predicted From WAIS–III VCI Scores *(continued)*

College Students

	Subtest Standard Scores									Composite Standard Scores					
VCI Score	WRD	NO	RC	SP	PD	MR	WE	LC	OE	RD	MA	WL	OL	Total	VCI Score
101	100	100	101	100	100	101	100	101	100	101	101	100	101	101	101
102	101	101	101	101	101	101	101	101	101	101	101	101	101	101	102
103	101	101	102	101	101	102	101	102	101	102	102	101	102	102	103
104	102	102	102	102	102	102	101	103	101	102	102	102	102	102	104
105	102	102	103	102	102	103	102	103	101	103	103	102	103	103	105
106	103	103	103	102	102	103	102	104	102	104	103	102	103	104	106
107	103	103	104	103	103	104	102	104	102	104	104	103	104	104	107
108	104	103	104	103	103	104	103	105	102	105	104	103	104	105	108
109	104	104	105	104	104	105	103	106	102	105	105	104	105	105	109
110	105	104	105	104	104	105	103	106	103	106	105	104	105	106	110
111	105	105	106	104	105	106	104	107	103	107	106	104	106	107	111
112	106	105	106	105	105	106	104	108	103	107	106	105	107	107	112
113	106	105	107	105	105	107	104	108	104	108	107	105	107	108	113
114	107	106	107	105	106	107	105	109	104	108	107	106	108	108	114
115	107	106	108	106	106	108	105	110	104	109	108	106	108	109	115
116	108	107	108	106	107	108	106	110	104	110	108	106	109	110	116
117	108	107	109	107	107	109	106	111	105	110	109	107	109	110	117
118	109	108	109	107	107	109	106	112	105	111	109	107	110	111	118
119	109	108	110	108	108	110	107	112	105	111	110	108	110	112	119
120	109	108	110	108	108	110	107	113	105	112	111	108	111	112	120
121	110	109	111	108	109	111	107	113	106	113	111	108	111	113	121
122	110	109	112	109	109	111	108	114	106	113	112	109	112	113	122
123	111	110	112	109	110	112	108	115	106	114	112	109	113	114	123
124	111	110	113	110	110	112	108	115	107	114	113	110	113	115	124
125	112	110	113	110	110	113	109	116	107	115	113	110	114	115	125
126	112	111	114	110	111	113	109	117	107	116	114	110	114	116	126
127	113	111	114	111	111	114	109	117	107	116	114	111	115	116	127
128	113	112	115	111	112	114	110	118	108	117	115	111	115	117	128
129	114	112	115	112	112	115	110	119	108	117	115	112	116	118	129
130	114	113	116	112	112	115	110	119	108	118	116	112	116	118	130
131	115	113	116	112	113	116	111	120	108	119	116	112	117	119	131
132	115	113	117	113	113	116	111	120	109	119	117	113	117	119	132
133	116	114	117	113	114	117	111	121	109	120	117	113	118	120	133
134	116	114	118	114	114	117	112	122	109	121	118	113	119	121	134
135	117	115	118	114	115	118	112	122	109	121	118	114	119	121	135
136	117	115	119	115	115	118	112	123	110	122	119	114	120	122	136
137	118	115	119	115	115	119	113	124	110	122	119	115	120	122	137
138	118	116	120	115	116	119	113	124	110	123	120	115	121	123	138
139	118	116	120	116	116	120	113	125	111	124	120	115	121	124	139
140	119	117	121	116	117	120	114	126	111	124	121	116	122	124	140
141	119	117	121	117	117	121	114	126	111	125	122	116	122	125	141
142	120	118	122	117	117	121	114	127	111	125	122	117	123	125	142
143	120	118	122	117	118	122	115	127	112	126	123	117	123	126	143
144	121	118	123	118	118	122	115	128	112	127	123	117	124	127	144
145	121	119	124	118	119	123	116	129	112	127	124	118	125	127	145
146	122	119	124	119	119	123	116	129	112	128	124	118	125	128	146
147	122	120	125	119	120	124	116	130	113	128	125	119	126	129	147
148	123	120	125	119	120	124	117	131	113	129	125	119	126	129	148
149	123	120	126	120	120	125	117	131	113	130	126	119	127	130	149
150	124	121	126	120	121	125	117	132	114	130	126	120	127	130	150
151															151
152															152
153															153
154															154
155															155
156															156
157															157
158															158
159															159
160															160

Note. Based on the correlations between the WIAT–II standard scores and the WAIS–III VCI. Presented in the order shown in the table, the correlations for the nine WIAT–II subtests are .47, .42, .52, .40, .42, .51, .35, .64, and .27, and the correlations for the five WIAT–II composites are .60, .53, .40, .55, and .61.

WRD = Word Reading
NO = Numerical Operations
RC = Reading Comprehension
SP = Spelling

PD = Pseudoword Decoding
MR = Math Reasoning
WE = Written Expression
LC = Listening Comprehension

OE = Oral Expression
RD = Reading
MA = Mathematics
WL = Written Language

OL = Oral Language

Table B.13. WIAT–II Subtest and Composite Standard Scores Predicted From WAIS–III VCI Scores (continued)

Adults

VCI Score	WRD	NO	RC	SP	PD	MR	WE	LC	OE	RD	MA	WL	OL	Total	VCI Score
40															40
41															41
42															42
43															43
44															44
45															45
46															46
47															47
48															48
49															49
50	69	62	64	68	72	63	70	65	78	60	62	70	68	59	50
51	70	63	65	69	73	64	71	66	78	60	63	70	68	60	51
52	71	64	65	69	74	65	71	66	79	61	63	71	69	61	52
53	71	64	66	70	74	65	72	67	79	62	64	71	69	62	53
54	72	65	67	71	75	66	72	68	79	63	65	72	70	62	54
55	72	66	67	71	75	67	73	69	80	64	66	73	71	63	55
56	73	67	68	72	76	67	74	69	80	64	67	73	71	64	56
57	74	67	69	72	76	68	74	70	81	65	67	74	72	65	57
58	74	68	70	73	77	69	75	71	81	66	68	74	73	66	58
59	75	69	70	74	77	70	75	71	82	67	69	75	73	67	59
60	75	70	71	74	78	70	76	72	82	68	70	76	74	67	60
61	76	71	72	75	79	71	77	73	83	68	70	76	75	68	61
62	77	71	72	76	79	72	77	73	83	69	71	77	75	69	62
63	77	72	73	76	80	73	78	74	83	70	72	78	76	70	63
64	78	73	74	77	80	73	78	75	84	71	73	78	77	71	64
65	79	74	75	78	81	74	79	76	84	72	73	79	77	71	65
66	79	74	75	78	81	75	80	76	85	72	74	79	78	72	66
67	80	75	76	79	82	76	80	77	85	73	75	80	79	73	67
68	80	76	77	79	82	76	81	78	86	74	76	81	79	74	68
69	81	77	78	80	83	77	81	78	86	75	76	81	80	75	69
70	82	77	78	81	83	78	82	79	87	76	77	82	81	75	70
71	82	78	79	81	84	79	83	80	87	77	78	82	81	76	71
72	83	79	80	82	85	79	83	80	88	77	79	83	82	77	72
73	83	80	80	83	85	80	84	81	88	78	79	84	82	78	73
74	84	80	81	83	86	81	84	82	88	79	80	84	83	79	74
75	85	81	82	84	86	82	85	83	89	80	81	85	84	80	75
76	85	82	83	85	87	82	86	83	89	81	82	85	84	80	76
77	86	83	83	85	87	83	86	84	90	81	82	86	85	81	77
78	86	83	84	86	88	84	87	85	90	82	83	87	86	82	78
79	87	84	85	87	88	84	87	85	91	83	84	87	86	83	79
80	88	85	86	87	89	85	88	86	91	84	85	88	87	84	80
81	88	86	86	88	90	86	89	87	92	85	86	88	88	84	81
82	89	86	87	88	90	87	89	87	92	85	86	89	88	85	82
83	90	87	88	89	91	87	90	88	92	86	87	90	89	86	83
84	90	88	88	90	91	88	90	89	93	87	88	90	90	87	84
85	91	89	89	90	92	89	91	90	93	88	89	91	90	88	85
86	91	89	90	91	92	90	92	90	94	89	89	91	91	89	86
87	92	90	91	92	93	90	92	91	94	89	90	92	92	89	87
88	93	91	91	92	93	91	93	92	95	90	91	93	92	90	88
89	93	92	92	93	94	92	93	92	95	91	92	93	93	91	89
90	94	92	93	94	94	93	94	93	96	92	92	94	94	92	90
91	94	93	93	94	95	93	95	94	96	93	93	95	94	93	91
92	95	94	94	95	96	94	95	94	96	94	94	95	95	93	92
93	96	95	95	96	96	95	96	95	97	94	95	96	95	94	93
94	96	95	96	96	97	96	96	96	97	95	95	96	96	95	94
95	97	96	96	97	97	96	97	97	98	96	96	97	97	96	95
96	98	97	97	97	98	97	98	97	98	97	97	98	97	97	96
97	98	98	98	98	98	98	98	98	99	98	98	98	98	98	97
98	99	98	99	99	99	99	99	99	99	98	98	99	99	98	98
99	99	99	99	99	99	99	99	99	100	99	99	99	99	99	99
100	100	100	100	100	100	100	100	100	100	100	100	100	100	100	100

Subtest Standard Scores — Composite Standard Scores

Table B.13. WIAT–II Subtest and Composite Standard Scores Predicted From WAIS–III VCI Scores (continued)

Adults

VCI Score	Subtest Standard Scores									Composite Standard Scores					VCI Score
	WRD	NO	RC	SP	PD	MR	WE	LC	OE	RD	MA	WL	OL	Total	
101	101	101	101	101	101	101	101	101	100	101	101	101	101	101	101
102	101	102	101	101	101	101	101	101	101	102	102	101	101	102	102
103	102	102	102	102	102	102	102	102	101	102	102	102	102	102	103
104	102	103	103	103	102	103	102	103	102	103	103	102	103	103	104
105	103	104	104	103	103	104	103	103	102	104	104	103	103	104	105
106	104	105	104	104	103	104	104	104	103	105	105	104	104	105	106
107	104	105	105	104	104	105	104	105	103	106	105	104	105	106	107
108	105	106	106	105	104	106	105	106	104	106	106	105	105	107	108
109	106	107	107	106	105	107	105	106	104	107	107	105	106	107	109
110	106	108	107	106	106	107	106	107	104	108	108	106	106	108	110
111	107	108	108	107	106	108	107	108	105	109	108	107	107	109	111
112	107	109	109	108	107	109	107	108	105	110	109	107	108	110	112
113	108	110	109	108	107	110	108	109	106	111	110	108	108	111	113
114	109	111	110	109	108	110	108	110	106	111	111	109	109	111	114
115	109	111	111	110	108	111	109	110	107	112	111	109	110	112	115
116	110	112	112	110	109	112	110	111	107	113	112	110	110	113	116
117	110	113	112	111	109	113	110	112	108	114	113	110	111	114	117
118	111	114	113	112	110	113	111	113	108	115	114	111	112	115	118
119	112	114	114	112	110	114	111	113	108	115	114	112	112	116	119
120	112	115	114	113	111	115	112	114	109	116	115	112	113	116	120
121	113	116	115	113	112	116	113	115	109	117	116	113	114	117	121
122	114	117	116	114	112	116	113	115	110	118	117	113	114	118	122
123	114	117	117	115	113	117	114	116	110	119	118	114	115	119	123
124	115	118	117	115	113	118	114	117	111	119	118	115	116	120	124
125	115	119	118	116	114	118	115	117	111	120	119	115	116	120	125
126	116	120	119	117	114	119	116	118	112	121	120	116	117	121	126
127	117	120	120	117	115	120	116	119	112	122	121	116	118	122	127
128	117	121	120	118	115	121	117	120	112	123	121	117	118	123	128
129	118	122	121	119	116	121	117	120	113	123	122	118	119	124	129
130	118	123	122	119	117	122	118	121	113	124	123	118	119	125	130
131	119	123	122	120	117	123	119	122	114	125	124	119	120	125	131
132	120	124	123	121	118	124	119	122	114	126	124	119	121	126	132
133	120	125	124	121	118	124	120	123	115	127	125	120	121	127	133
134	121	126	125	122	119	125	120	124	115	128	126	121	122	128	134
135	121	126	125	122	119	126	121	124	116	128	127	121	123	129	135
136	122	127	126	123	120	127	122	125	116	129	127	122	123	129	136
137	123	128	127	124	120	127	122	126	117	130	128	122	124	130	137
138	123	129	128	124	121	128	123	127	117	131	129	123	125	131	138
139	124	129	128	125	121	129	123	127	117	132	130	124	125	132	139
140	125	130	129	126	122	130	124	128	118	132	130	124	126	133	140
141	125	131	130	126	123	130	125	129	118	133	131	125	127	133	141
142	126	132	130	127	123	131	125	129	119	134	132	126	127	134	142
143	126	133	131	128	124	132	126	130	119	135	133	126	128	135	143
144	127	133	132	128	124	133	126	131	120	136	133	127	129	136	144
145	128	134	133	129	125	133	127	131	120	136	134	127	129	137	145
146	128	135	133	129	125	134	128	132	121	137	135	128	130	138	146
147	129	136	134	130	126	135	128	133	121	138	136	129	131	138	147
148	129	136	135	131	126	135	129	134	121	139	137	129	131	139	148
149	130	137	135	131	127	136	129	134	122	140	137	130	132	140	149
150	131	138	136	132	128	137	130	135	122	141	138	130	132	141	150
151															151
152															152
153															153
154															154
155															155
156															156
157															157
158															158
159															159
160															160

Note. Based on the correlations between the WIAT–II standard scores and the WAIS–III VCI. Presented in the order shown in the table, the correlations for the nine WIAT–II subtests are .61, .76, .72, .64, .55, .74, .60, .70, and .45, and the correlations for the five WIAT–II composites are .81, .76, .61, .65, and .82.

WRD = Word Reading
NO = Numerical Operations
RC = Reading Comprehension
SP = Spelling

PD = Pseudoword Decoding
MR = Math Reasoning
WE = Written Expression
LC = Listening Comprehension

OE = Oral Expression
RD = Reading
MA = Mathematics
WL = Written Language

OL = Oral Language

Table B.14. WIAT–II Subtest and Composite Standard Scores Predicted From WAIS–III POI Scores

Ages 16:0–19:11 (High School)

POI Score	Subtest Standard Scores									Composite Standard Scores					POI Score
	WRD	NO	RC	SP	PD	MR	WE	LC	OE	RD	MA	WL	OL	Total	
40															40
41															41
42															42
43															43
44															44
45															45
46															46
47															47
48															48
49															49
50	81	65	84	77	82	60	78	75	66	78	60	74	65	62	50
51	81	66	84	77	82	61	78	76	67	78	61	75	66	62	51
52	82	66	84	78	82	62	79	76	68	79	61	75	66	63	52
53	82	67	85	78	83	63	79	77	68	79	62	76	67	64	53
54	82	68	85	79	83	64	80	77	69	79	63	76	68	65	54
55	83	69	85	79	84	64	80	78	70	80	64	77	68	65	55
56	83	69	86	79	84	65	81	78	70	80	65	77	69	66	56
57	84	70	86	80	84	66	81	79	71	81	65	78	70	67	57
58	84	71	86	80	85	67	81	79	72	81	66	78	70	68	58
59	84	71	87	81	85	68	82	80	72	82	67	79	71	68	59
60	85	72	87	81	85	68	82	80	73	82	68	79	72	69	60
61	85	73	87	82	86	69	83	81	74	83	69	80	73	70	61
62	86	73	88	82	86	70	83	81	74	83	69	80	73	71	62
63	86	74	88	83	86	71	84	82	75	83	70	81	74	72	63
64	86	75	88	83	87	72	84	82	76	84	71	81	75	72	64
65	87	76	89	84	87	72	84	83	76	84	72	82	75	73	65
66	87	76	89	84	88	73	85	83	77	85	73	82	76	74	66
67	87	77	89	85	88	74	85	84	78	85	73	83	77	75	67
68	88	78	90	85	88	75	86	84	78	86	74	84	77	75	68
69	88	78	90	86	89	75	86	85	79	86	75	84	78	76	69
70	89	79	90	86	89	76	87	85	80	87	76	85	79	77	70
71	89	80	91	86	89	77	87	86	81	87	77	85	80	78	71
72	89	80	91	87	90	78	88	86	81	88	77	86	80	78	72
73	90	81	91	87	90	79	88	87	82	88	78	86	81	79	73
74	90	82	92	88	91	79	88	87	83	88	79	87	82	80	74
75	90	83	92	88	91	80	89	88	83	89	80	87	82	81	75
76	91	83	92	89	91	81	89	88	84	89	81	88	83	82	76
77	91	84	93	89	92	82	90	89	85	90	82	88	84	82	77
78	92	85	93	90	92	83	90	89	85	90	82	89	85	83	78
79	92	85	93	90	92	83	91	90	86	91	83	89	85	84	79
80	92	86	93	91	93	84	91	90	87	91	84	90	86	85	80
81	93	87	94	91	93	85	92	91	87	92	85	90	87	85	81
82	93	87	94	92	93	86	92	91	88	92	86	91	87	86	82
83	94	88	94	92	94	87	92	92	89	92	86	91	88	87	83
84	94	89	95	93	94	87	93	92	89	93	87	92	89	88	84
85	94	90	95	93	95	88	93	93	90	93	88	92	89	88	85
86	95	90	95	93	95	89	94	93	91	94	89	93	90	89	86
87	95	91	96	94	95	90	94	94	91	94	90	93	91	90	87
88	95	92	96	94	96	91	95	94	92	95	90	94	92	91	88
89	96	92	96	95	96	91	95	95	93	95	91	94	92	92	89
90	96	93	97	95	96	92	96	95	93	96	92	95	93	92	90
91	97	94	97	96	97	93	96	96	94	96	93	95	94	93	91
92	97	94	97	96	97	94	96	96	95	96	94	96	94	94	92
93	97	95	98	97	97	94	97	97	95	97	94	96	95	95	93
94	98	96	98	97	98	95	97	97	96	97	95	97	96	95	94
95	98	97	98	98	98	96	98	98	97	98	96	97	96	96	95
96	98	97	99	98	99	97	98	98	97	98	97	98	97	97	96
97	99	98	99	99	99	98	99	99	98	99	98	98	98	98	97
98	99	99	99	99	99	98	99	99	99	99	98	99	99	98	98
99	100	99	100	100	100	99	100	100	99	100	99	99	99	99	99
100	100	100	100	100	100	100	100	100	100	100	100	100	100	100	100

Table B.14. WIAT–II Subtest and Composite Standard Scores Predicted From WAIS–III POI Scores *(continued)*

Ages 16:0–19:11 (High School)

POI Score	Subtest Standard Scores									Composite Standard Scores					POI Score
	WRD	NO	RC	SP	PD	MR	WE	LC	OE	RD	MA	WL	OL	Total	
101	100	101	100	100	100	101	100	100	101	100	101	101	101	101	101
102	101	101	101	101	101	102	101	101	101	101	102	101	101	102	102
103	101	102	101	101	101	102	101	101	102	101	102	102	102	102	103
104	102	103	101	102	101	103	102	102	103	102	103	102	103	103	104
105	102	103	102	102	102	104	102	102	103	102	104	103	104	104	105
106	102	104	102	103	102	105	103	103	104	103	105	103	104	105	106
107	103	105	102	103	103	106	103	103	105	103	106	104	105	105	107
108	103	106	103	104	103	106	104	104	105	104	106	104	106	106	108
109	103	106	103	104	103	107	104	104	106	104	107	105	106	107	109
110	104	107	103	105	104	108	104	105	107	104	108	105	107	108	110
111	104	108	104	105	104	109	105	105	107	105	109	106	108	108	111
112	105	108	104	106	104	109	105	106	108	105	110	106	108	109	112
113	105	109	104	106	105	110	106	106	109	106	110	107	109	110	113
114	105	110	105	107	105	111	106	107	109	106	111	107	110	111	114
115	106	110	105	107	105	112	107	107	110	107	112	108	111	112	115
116	106	111	105	107	106	113	107	108	111	107	113	108	111	112	116
117	106	112	106	108	106	113	108	108	111	108	114	109	112	113	117
118	107	113	106	108	107	114	108	109	112	108	114	109	113	114	118
119	107	113	106	109	107	115	108	109	113	108	115	110	113	115	119
120	108	114	107	109	107	116	109	110	113	109	116	110	114	115	120
121	108	115	107	110	108	117	109	110	114	109	117	111	115	116	121
122	108	115	107	110	108	117	110	111	115	110	118	111	115	117	122
123	109	116	107	111	108	118	110	111	115	110	118	112	116	118	123
124	109	117	108	111	109	119	111	112	116	111	119	112	117	118	124
125	110	117	108	112	109	120	111	112	117	111	120	113	118	119	125
126	110	118	108	112	109	121	112	113	117	112	121	113	118	120	126
127	110	119	109	113	110	121	112	113	118	112	122	114	119	121	127
128	111	120	109	113	110	122	112	114	119	112	123	114	120	122	128
129	111	120	109	114	111	123	113	114	119	113	123	115	120	122	129
130	111	121	110	114	111	124	113	115	120	113	124	115	121	123	130
131	112	122	110	114	111	125	114	115	121	114	125	116	122	124	131
132	112	122	110	115	112	125	114	116	122	114	126	116	123	125	132
133	113	123	111	115	112	126	115	116	122	115	127	117	123	125	133
134	113	124	111	116	112	127	115	117	123	115	127	118	124	126	134
135	113	124	111	116	113	128	116	117	124	116	128	118	125	127	135
136	114	125	112	117	113	128	116	118	124	116	129	119	125	128	136
137	114	126	112	117	114	129	116	118	125	117	130	119	126	128	137
138	114	127	112	118	114	130	117	119	126	117	131	120	127	129	138
139	115	127	113	118	114	131	117	119	126	117	131	120	127	130	139
140	115	128	113	119	115	132	118	120	127	118	132	121	128	131	140
141	116	129	113	119	115	132	118	120	128	118	133	121	129	132	141
142	116	129	114	120	115	133	119	121	128	119	134	122	130	132	142
143	116	130	114	120	116	134	119	121	129	119	135	122	130	133	143
144	117	131	114	121	116	135	119	122	130	120	135	123	131	134	144
145	117	131	115	121	116	136	120	122	130	120	136	123	132	135	145
146	118	132	115	121	117	136	120	123	131	121	137	124	132	135	146
147	118	133	115	122	117	137	121	123	132	121	138	124	133	136	147
148	118	134	116	122	118	138	121	124	132	121	139	125	134	137	148
149	119	134	116	123	118	139	122	124	133	122	139	125	134	138	149
150	119	135	116	123	118	140	122	125	134	122	140	126	135	138	150
151															151
152															152
153															153
154															154
155															155
156															156
157															157
158															158
159															159
160															160

Note. Based on the correlations between the WIAT–II standard scores and the WAIS–III POI across the four age ranges. Presented in the order shown in the table, the average correlations for the nine WIAT–II subtests are .38, .70, .33, .47, .37, .79, .44, .50, and .67, and the average correlations for the five WIAT–II composites are .45, .80, .52, .70, and .77.

WRD = Word Reading
NO = Numerical Operations
RC = Reading Comprehension
SP = Spelling

PD = Pseudoword Decoding
MR = Math Reasoning
WE = Written Expression
LC = Listening Comprehension

OE = Oral Expression
RD = Reading
MA = Mathematics
WL = Written Language

OL = Oral Language

Table B.14. WIAT–II Subtest and Composite Standard Scores Predicted From WAIS–III POI Scores (continued)

College Students

POI Score	WRD	NO	RC	SP	PD	MR	WE	LC	OE	RD	MA	WL	OL	Total	POI Score
	Subtest Standard Scores									**Composite Standard Scores**					
40															40
41															41
42															42
43															43
44															44
45															45
46															46
47															47
48															48
49															49
50	86	75	79	86	88	70	82	78	81	82	70	82	76	73	50
51	86	75	80	87	88	71	83	79	81	82	71	83	76	74	51
52	86	76	80	87	88	71	83	79	82	82	71	83	77	74	52
53	86	76	81	87	89	72	83	80	82	83	72	83	77	75	53
54	87	77	81	87	89	73	84	80	82	83	73	84	78	76	54
55	87	77	81	88	89	73	84	80	83	83	73	84	78	76	55
56	87	78	82	88	89	74	84	81	83	84	74	84	79	77	56
57	88	78	82	88	90	74	85	81	83	84	74	85	79	77	57
58	88	79	83	89	90	75	85	82	84	85	75	85	80	78	58
59	88	79	83	89	90	76	85	82	84	85	76	85	80	78	59
60	88	80	83	89	90	76	86	83	85	85	76	86	81	79	60
61	89	80	84	89	91	77	86	83	85	86	77	86	81	79	61
62	89	81	84	90	91	77	87	83	85	86	77	87	82	80	62
63	89	81	85	90	91	78	87	84	86	86	78	87	82	80	63
64	90	82	85	90	91	79	87	84	86	87	79	87	83	81	64
65	90	82	86	90	92	79	88	85	87	87	79	88	83	81	65
66	90	83	86	91	92	80	88	85	87	87	80	88	83	82	66
67	90	83	86	91	92	80	88	86	87	88	80	88	84	82	67
68	91	84	87	91	92	81	89	86	88	88	81	89	84	83	68
69	91	84	87	92	93	82	89	86	88	89	82	89	85	84	69
70	91	85	88	92	93	82	89	87	88	89	82	89	85	84	70
71	92	85	88	92	93	83	90	87	89	89	83	90	86	85	71
72	92	86	88	92	93	83	90	88	89	90	83	90	86	85	72
73	92	86	89	93	93	84	90	88	90	90	84	90	87	86	73
74	92	87	89	93	94	85	91	89	90	90	85	91	87	86	74
75	93	87	90	93	94	85	91	89	90	91	85	91	88	87	75
76	93	88	90	93	94	86	91	90	91	91	86	92	88	87	76
77	93	88	91	94	94	86	92	90	91	92	86	92	89	88	77
78	94	89	91	94	95	87	92	90	92	92	87	92	89	88	78
79	94	89	91	94	95	88	93	91	92	92	88	93	90	89	79
80	94	90	92	95	95	88	93	91	92	93	88	93	90	89	80
81	94	90	92	95	95	89	93	92	93	93	89	93	91	90	81
82	95	91	93	95	96	89	94	92	93	93	89	94	91	90	82
83	95	91	93	95	96	90	94	93	93	94	90	94	92	91	83
84	95	92	93	96	96	90	94	93	94	94	90	94	92	91	84
85	96	92	94	96	96	91	95	93	94	94	91	95	93	92	85
86	96	93	94	96	97	92	95	94	95	95	92	95	93	93	86
87	96	93	95	96	97	92	95	94	95	95	92	95	94	93	87
88	97	94	95	97	97	93	96	95	95	96	93	96	94	94	88
89	97	94	95	97	97	93	96	95	96	96	93	96	95	94	89
90	97	95	96	97	98	94	96	96	96	96	94	96	95	95	90
91	97	95	96	98	98	95	97	96	97	97	95	97	96	95	91
92	98	96	97	98	98	95	97	97	97	97	95	97	96	96	92
93	98	96	97	98	98	96	98	97	97	97	96	98	97	96	93
94	98	97	98	98	99	96	98	97	98	98	96	98	97	97	94
95	99	97	98	99	99	97	98	98	98	98	97	98	98	97	95
96	99	98	98	99	99	98	99	98	98	99	98	99	98	98	96
97	99	98	99	99	99	98	99	99	99	99	98	99	99	98	97
98	99	99	99	99	100	99	99	99	99	99	99	99	99	99	98
99	100	99	100	100	100	99	100	100	100	100	99	100	100	99	99
100	100	100	100	100	100	100	100	100	100	100	100	100	100	100	100

Table B.14. WIAT–II Subtest and Composite Standard Scores Predicted From WAIS–III POI Scores (continued)

College Students

POI Score	Subtest Standard Scores									Composite Standard Scores					POI Score
	WRD	NO	RC	SP	PD	MR	WE	LC	OE	RD	MA	WL	OL	Total	
101	100	101	100	100	100	101	100	100	100	100	101	100	100	101	101
102	101	101	101	101	100	101	101	101	101	101	101	101	101	101	102
103	101	102	101	101	101	102	101	101	101	101	102	101	101	102	103
104	101	102	102	101	101	102	101	102	102	101	102	101	102	102	104
105	101	103	102	101	101	103	102	102	102	102	103	102	102	103	105
106	102	103	102	102	101	104	102	103	102	102	104	102	103	103	106
107	102	104	103	102	102	104	102	103	103	103	104	102	103	104	107
108	102	104	103	102	102	105	103	103	103	103	105	103	104	104	108
109	103	105	104	102	102	105	103	104	103	103	105	103	104	105	109
110	103	105	104	103	102	106	104	104	104	104	106	104	105	105	110
111	103	106	105	103	103	107	104	105	104	104	107	104	105	106	111
112	103	106	105	103	103	107	104	105	105	104	107	104	106	106	112
113	104	107	105	104	103	108	105	106	105	105	108	105	106	107	113
114	104	107	106	104	103	108	105	106	105	105	108	105	107	107	114
115	104	108	106	104	104	109	105	107	106	106	109	105	107	108	115
116	105	108	107	104	104	110	106	107	106	106	110	106	108	109	116
117	105	109	107	105	104	110	106	107	107	106	110	106	108	109	117
118	105	109	107	105	104	111	106	108	107	107	111	106	109	110	118
119	106	110	108	105	105	111	107	108	107	107	111	107	109	110	119
120	106	110	108	105	105	112	107	109	108	107	112	107	110	111	120
121	106	111	109	106	105	112	107	109	108	108	112	107	110	111	121
122	106	111	109	106	105	113	108	110	108	108	113	108	111	112	122
123	107	112	109	106	106	114	108	110	109	108	114	108	111	112	123
124	107	112	110	107	106	114	109	110	109	109	114	108	112	113	124
125	107	113	110	107	106	115	109	111	110	109	115	109	112	113	125
126	108	113	111	107	106	115	109	111	110	110	115	109	113	114	126
127	108	114	111	107	107	116	110	112	110	110	116	110	113	114	127
128	108	114	112	108	107	117	110	112	111	110	117	110	114	115	128
129	108	115	112	108	107	117	110	113	111	111	117	110	114	115	129
130	109	115	112	108	107	118	111	113	112	111	118	111	115	116	130
131	109	116	113	108	107	118	111	114	112	111	118	111	115	116	131
132	109	116	113	109	108	119	111	114	112	112	119	111	116	117	132
133	110	117	114	109	108	120	112	114	113	112	120	112	116	118	133
134	110	117	114	109	108	120	112	115	113	113	120	112	117	118	134
135	110	118	114	110	108	121	112	115	113	113	121	112	117	119	135
136	110	118	115	110	109	121	113	116	114	113	121	113	117	119	136
137	111	119	115	110	109	122	113	116	114	114	122	113	118	120	137
138	111	119	116	110	109	123	113	117	115	114	123	113	118	120	138
139	111	120	116	111	109	123	114	117	115	114	123	114	119	121	139
140	112	120	117	111	110	124	114	117	115	115	124	114	119	121	140
141	112	121	117	111	110	124	115	118	116	115	124	115	120	122	141
142	112	121	117	111	110	125	115	118	116	115	125	115	120	122	142
143	112	122	118	112	110	126	115	119	117	116	126	115	121	123	143
144	113	122	118	112	111	126	116	119	117	116	126	116	121	123	144
145	113	123	119	112	111	127	116	120	117	117	127	116	122	124	145
146	113	123	119	113	111	127	116	120	118	117	127	116	122	124	146
147	114	124	119	113	111	128	117	120	118	117	128	117	123	125	147
148	114	124	120	113	112	129	117	121	118	118	129	117	123	126	148
149	114	125	120	113	112	129	117	121	119	118	129	117	124	126	149
150	115	125	121	114	112	130	118	122	119	118	130	118	124	127	150
151															151
152															152
153															153
154															154
155															155
156															156
157															157
158															158
159															159
160															160

Note. Based on the correlations between the WIAT–II standard scores and the WAIS–III POI. Presented in the order shown in the table, the correlations for the nine WIAT–II subtests are .29, .50, .41, .27, .24, .59, .36, .44, and .38, and the correlations for the five WIAT–II composites are .37, .60, .35, .49, and .53.

WRD = Word Reading
NO = Numerical Operations
RC = Reading Comprehension
SP = Spelling

PD = Pseudoword Decoding
MR = Math Reasoning
WE = Written Expression
LC = Listening Comprehension

OE = Oral Expression
RD = Reading
MA = Mathematics
WL = Written Language

OL = Oral Language

Table B.14. WIAT–II Subtest and Composite Standard Scores Predicted From WAIS–III POI Scores *(continued)*

Adults

POI Score	WRD	NO	RC	SP	PD	MR	WE	LC	OE	RD	MA	WL	OL	Total	POI Score
	Subtest Standard Scores									Composite Standard Scores					
40															40
41															41
42															42
43															43
44															44
45															45
46															46
47															47
48															48
49															49
50	75	70	72	81	70	71	77	72	79	66	70	78	75	68	50
51	76	71	73	81	70	72	77	72	80	67	71	79	75	69	51
52	76	71	73	81	71	72	77	73	80	68	71	79	76	69	52
53	77	72	74	82	71	73	78	73	81	68	72	80	76	70	53
54	77	72	74	82	72	73	78	74	81	69	73	80	77	71	54
55	78	73	75	82	73	74	79	75	81	70	73	81	77	71	55
56	78	74	75	83	73	74	79	75	82	70	74	81	78	72	56
57	79	74	76	83	74	75	80	76	82	71	74	81	78	73	57
58	79	75	77	84	74	76	80	76	83	72	75	82	79	73	58
59	80	75	77	84	75	76	81	77	83	72	76	82	79	74	59
60	80	76	78	84	76	77	81	77	83	73	76	83	80	75	60
61	81	77	78	85	76	77	82	78	84	74	77	83	80	75	61
62	81	77	79	85	77	78	82	79	84	74	77	84	81	76	62
63	82	78	79	86	77	79	83	79	85	75	78	84	81	76	63
64	82	78	80	86	78	79	83	80	85	76	79	84	82	77	64
65	83	79	81	86	79	80	84	80	86	76	79	85	82	78	65
66	83	80	81	87	79	80	84	81	86	77	80	85	83	78	66
67	84	80	82	87	80	81	84	81	86	78	80	86	83	79	67
68	84	81	82	88	81	81	85	82	87	78	81	86	84	80	68
69	85	81	83	88	81	82	85	82	87	79	82	87	84	80	69
70	85	82	83	88	82	83	86	83	88	80	82	87	85	81	70
71	86	83	84	89	82	83	86	84	88	80	83	88	85	82	71
72	86	83	84	89	83	84	87	84	88	81	83	88	86	82	72
73	87	84	85	89	84	84	87	85	89	82	84	88	86	83	73
74	87	84	86	90	84	85	88	85	89	82	85	89	87	83	74
75	88	85	86	90	85	86	88	86	90	83	85	89	87	84	75
76	88	86	87	91	85	86	89	86	90	84	86	90	88	85	76
77	89	86	87	91	86	87	89	87	91	84	86	90	88	85	77
78	89	87	88	91	87	87	90	88	91	85	87	91	89	86	78
79	90	87	88	92	87	88	90	88	91	86	87	91	89	87	79
80	90	88	89	92	88	88	91	89	92	86	88	91	90	87	80
81	91	89	89	93	88	89	91	89	92	87	89	92	90	88	81
82	91	89	90	93	89	90	92	90	93	88	89	92	91	89	82
83	92	90	91	93	90	90	92	90	93	88	90	93	91	89	83
84	92	90	91	94	90	91	92	91	93	89	90	93	92	90	84
85	93	91	92	94	91	91	93	92	94	90	91	94	92	90	85
86	93	92	92	95	91	92	93	92	94	91	92	94	93	91	86
87	94	92	93	95	92	92	94	93	95	91	92	94	93	92	87
88	94	93	93	95	93	93	94	93	95	92	93	95	94	92	88
89	95	93	94	96	93	94	95	94	95	93	93	95	94	93	89
90	95	94	94	96	94	94	95	94	96	93	94	96	95	94	90
91	96	95	95	96	95	95	96	95	96	94	95	96	95	94	91
92	96	95	96	97	95	95	96	95	97	95	95	97	96	95	92
93	97	96	96	97	96	96	97	96	97	95	96	97	96	96	93
94	97	96	97	98	96	97	97	97	98	96	96	97	97	96	94
95	98	97	97	98	97	97	98	97	98	97	97	98	97	97	95
96	98	98	98	98	98	98	98	98	98	97	98	98	98	97	96
97	99	98	98	99	98	98	99	98	99	98	98	99	98	98	97
98	99	99	99	99	99	99	99	99	99	99	99	99	99	99	98
99	100	99	99	100	99	99	100	99	100	99	99	100	99	99	99
100	100	100	100	100	100	100	100	100	100	100	100	100	100	100	100

Table B.14. WIAT–II Subtest and Composite Standard Scores Predicted From WAIS–III POI Scores *(continued)*

Adults

	Subtest Standard Scores										Composite Standard Scores					
POI Score	WRD	NO	RC	SP	PD	MR	WE	LC	OE		RD	MA	WL	OL	Total	POI Score
101	100	101	101	100	101	101	100	101	100		101	101	100	101	101	101
102	101	101	101	101	101	101	101	102	101		101	101	101	101	101	102
103	101	102	102	101	102	102	101	102	101		102	102	101	102	102	103
104	102	102	102	102	102	102	102	102	102		103	102	102	102	103	104
105	102	103	103	102	103	103	102	103	102		103	103	102	103	103	105
106	103	104	103	102	104	103	103	103	102		104	104	103	103	104	106
107	103	104	104	103	104	104	103	104	103		105	104	103	104	104	107
108	104	105	104	103	105	105	104	105	103		105	105	103	104	105	108
109	104	105	105	104	105	105	104	105	104		106	105	104	105	106	109
110	105	106	106	104	106	106	105	106	104		107	106	104	105	106	110
111	105	107	106	104	107	106	105	106	105		107	107	105	106	107	111
112	106	107	107	105	107	107	106	107	105		108	107	105	106	108	112
113	106	108	107	105	108	108	106	107	105		109	108	106	107	108	113
114	107	108	108	105	109	108	107	108	106		109	108	106	107	109	114
115	107	109	108	106	109	109	107	108	106		110	109	106	108	110	115
116	108	110	109	106	110	109	108	109	107		111	110	107	108	110	116
117	108	110	109	107	110	110	108	110	107		112	110	107	109	111	117
118	109	111	110	107	111	110	108	110	107		112	111	108	109	111	118
119	109	111	111	107	112	111	109	111	108		113	111	108	110	112	119
120	110	112	111	108	112	112	109	111	108		114	112	109	110	113	120
121	110	113	112	108	113	112	110	112	109		114	113	109	111	113	121
122	111	113	112	109	113	113	110	112	109		115	113	109	111	114	122
123	111	114	113	109	114	113	111	113	109		116	114	110	112	115	123
124	112	114	113	109	115	114	111	114	110		116	114	110	112	115	124
125	112	115	114	110	115	115	112	114	110		117	115	111	113	116	125
126	113	116	114	110	116	115	112	115	111		118	115	111	114	117	126
127	113	116	115	111	116	116	113	115	111		118	116	112	114	117	127
128	114	117	116	111	117	116	113	116	112		119	117	112	114	118	128
129	114	117	116	111	118	117	114	116	112		120	117	112	115	118	129
130	115	118	117	112	118	117	114	117	112		120	118	113	115	119	130
131	115	119	117	112	119	118	115	118	113		121	118	113	116	120	131
132	116	119	118	112	119	119	115	118	113		122	119	114	116	120	132
133	116	120	118	113	120	119	116	119	114		122	120	114	117	121	133
134	117	120	119	113	121	120	116	119	114		123	120	115	117	122	134
135	117	121	119	114	121	120	116	120	114		124	121	115	118	122	135
136	118	122	120	114	122	121	117	120	115		124	121	116	118	123	136
137	118	122	121	114	123	121	117	121	115		125	122	116	119	124	137
138	119	123	121	115	123	122	118	121	116		126	123	116	119	124	138
139	119	123	122	115	124	123	118	122	116		126	123	117	120	125	139
140	120	124	122	116	124	123	119	123	117		127	124	117	120	125	140
141	120	125	123	116	125	124	119	123	117		128	124	118	121	126	141
142	121	125	123	116	126	124	120	124	117		128	125	118	121	127	142
143	121	126	124	117	126	125	120	124	118		129	126	119	122	127	143
144	122	126	125	117	127	126	121	125	118		130	126	119	122	128	144
145	122	127	125	118	127	126	121	125	119		130	127	119	123	129	145
146	123	128	126	118	128	127	122	126	119		131	127	120	123	129	146
147	123	128	126	118	129	127	122	127	119		132	128	120	124	130	147
148	124	129	127	119	129	128	123	127	120		132	129	121	124	131	148
149	124	129	127	119	130	128	123	128	120		133	129	121	125	131	149
150	125	130	128	120	130	129	124	128	121		134	130	122	125	132	150
151																151
152																152
153																153
154																154
155																155
156																156
157																157
158																158
159																159
160																160

Note. Based on the correlations between the WIAT–II standard scores and the WAIS–III POI. Presented in the order shown in the table, the correlations for the nine WIAT–II subtests are .50, .60, .56, .39, .61, .58, .47, .57, and .41, and the correlations for the five WIAT–II composites are .68, .60, .43, .51, and .64.

WRD = Word Reading
NO = Numerical Operations
RC = Reading Comprehension
SP = Spelling

PD = Pseudoword Decoding
MR = Math Reasoning
WE = Written Expression
LC = Listening Comprehension

OE = Oral Expression
RD = Reading
MA = Mathematics
WL = Written Language

OL = Oral Language

Table B.15. Differences Between Predicted and Actual WIAT–II Subtest and Composite Standard Scores Required for Statistical Significance With Prediction Based on WAIS–III Scores

Ages 16:0–19:11 (High School)

Subtests	p	FSIQ	VIQ	PIQ	VCI	POI
Word	.05	7.46	7.81	7.55	8.29	7.21
Reading	.01	9.82	10.28	9.93	10.92	9.49
Numerical	.05	8.14	8.30	8.70	8.51	9.02
Operations	.01	10.71	10.93	11.45	11.20	11.87
Reading	.05	8.50	8.87	8.41	9.26	8.18
Comprehension	.01	11.19	11.67	11.07	12.19	10.77
Spelling	.05	9.46	9.60	9.71	9.77	9.54
	.01	12.45	12.64	12.79	12.87	12.55
Pseudoword	.05	6.59	6.87	6.76	7.05	6.53
Decoding	.01	8.68	9.04	8.90	9.28	8.60
Math	.05	8.79	8.88	9.56	8.98	9.92
Reasoning	.01	11.57	11.69	12.59	11.82	13.06
Written	.05	11.02	11.12	11.25	11.25	11.15
Expression	.01	14.50	14.64	14.81	14.80	14.67
Listening	.05	13.72	13.98	13.72	14.34	13.70
Comprehension	.01	18.05	18.40	18.05	18.88	18.04
Oral	.05	11.66	11.68	11.97	11.78	12.53
Expression	.01	15.34	15.38	15.75	15.51	16.49

Composites

	p	FSIQ	VIQ	PIQ	VCI	POI
Reading	.05	5.61	6.18	5.65	6.73	5.42
	.01	7.38	8.13	7.43	8.86	7.13
Mathematics	.05	7.19	7.34	8.09	7.53	8.58
	.01	9.47	9.66	10.65	9.92	11.30
Written	.05	8.50	8.68	8.88	8.89	8.75
Language	.01	11.19	11.42	11.69	11.71	11.52
Oral	.05	11.31	11.52	11.69	11.86	11.93
Language	.01	14.89	15.17	15.39	15.61	15.71
Total	.05	6.02	6.39	6.99	6.83	7.28
	.01	7.92	8.42	9.20	8.99	9.59

Note. For all age groups, data were derived from the WIAT–II age-based reliability tables.

Table B.15. Differences Between Predicted and Actual WIAT–II
Subtest and Composite Standard Scores Required
for Statistical Significance With Prediction Based on
WAIS–III Scores *(continued)*

College Students

Subtests	p	FSIQ	VIQ	PIQ	VCI	POI
Word	.05	6.21	6.46	6.30	6.51	6.30
Reading	.01	8.17	8.50	8.30	8.57	8.29
Numerical	.05	6.99	7.05	7.68	7.02	7.65
Operations	.01	9.20	9.28	10.11	9.24	10.06
Reading	.05	6.32	6.52	6.71	6.64	6.70
Comprehension	.01	8.32	8.58	8.84	8.73	8.82
Spelling	.05	7.42	7.56	7.53	7.58	7.51
	.01	9.76	9.95	9.91	9.98	9.88
Pseudoword	.05	6.17	6.36	6.24	6.37	6.17
Decoding	.01	8.12	8.37	8.21	8.38	8.12
Math	.05	8.77	8.90	9.35	8.83	9.51
Reasoning	.01	11.55	11.71	12.31	11.63	12.52
Written	.05	14.20	14.23	14.36	14.24	14.37
Expression	.01	18.70	18.73	18.90	18.75	18.91
Listening	.05	10.93	11.13	11.15	11.25	11.13
Comprehension	.01	14.39	14.65	14.68	14.80	14.65
Oral	.05	14.79	14.80	14.97	14.79	15.00
Expression	.01	19.47	19.48	19.70	19.46	19.75

Composites

	p	FSIQ	VIQ	PIQ	VCI	POI
Reading	.05	4.92	5.36	5.15	5.46	5.05
	.01	6.47	7.05	6.78	7.19	6.65
Mathematics	.05	6.56	6.71	7.42	6.64	7.48
	.01	8.63	8.84	9.77	8.74	9.85
Written	.05	8.54	8.62	8.77	8.64	8.76
Language	.01	11.24	11.34	11.55	11.37	11.53
Oral	.05	10.51	10.65	10.81	10.68	10.86
Language	.01	13.83	14.02	14.24	14.06	14.30
Total	.05	5.09	5.42	5.76	5.48	5.87
	.01	6.70	7.14	7.58	7.21	7.72

Note. For all age groups, data were derived from the WIAT–II age-based reliability tables.

321

Table B.15. Differences Between Predicted and Actual WIAT–II
Subtest and Composite Standard Scores Required
for Statistical Significance With Prediction Based on
WAIS–III Scores *(continued)*

Adults

Subtests	p	FSIQ	VIQ	PIQ	VCI	POI
Word	.05	6.49	6.67	7.19	6.90	7.03
Reading	.01	8.54	8.78	9.46	9.08	9.26
Numerical	.05	7.40	7.72	8.17	7.94	8.06
Operations	.01	9.75	10.16	10.75	10.45	10.61
Reading	.05	6.67	6.97	7.44	7.26	7.30
Comprehension	.01	8.78	9.17	9.79	9.56	9.61
Spelling	.05	7.71	7.96	8.09	8.13	7.81
	.01	10.15	10.48	10.65	10.70	10.29
Pseudoword	.05	6.54	6.68	7.59	6.71	7.55
Decoding	.01	8.61	8.79	9.99	8.84	9.94
Math	.05	8.93	9.17	9.55	9.38	9.46
Reasoning	.01	11.76	12.07	12.57	12.35	12.45
Written	.05	14.33	14.42	14.62	14.53	14.57
Expression	.01	18.86	18.98	19.24	19.13	19.17
Listening	.05	11.03	11.16	11.56	11.37	11.48
Comprehension	.01	14.51	14.69	15.22	14.97	15.11
Oral	.05	14.84	14.88	15.03	14.93	15.05
Expression	.01	19.53	19.59	19.79	19.66	19.81

Composites

	p	FSIQ	VIQ	PIQ	VCI	POI
Reading	.05	5.49	5.97	6.93	6.32	6.71
	.01	7.23	7.86	9.12	8.32	8.83
Mathematics	.05	6.79	7.14	7.63	7.39	7.49
	.01	8.94	9.40	10.04	9.73	9.86
Written	.05	8.71	8.89	9.10	9.05	8.97
Language	.01	11.47	11.70	11.98	11.91	11.80
Oral	.05	10.56	10.70	10.97	10.88	10.92
Language	.01	13.90	14.09	14.44	14.32	14.38
Total	.05	5.47	6.01	6.62	6.35	6.46
	.01	7.20	7.91	8.71	8.36	8.51

Note. For all age groups, data were derived from the WIAT–II age-based reliability tables.

Table B.16. Differences Between Predicted and Actual WIAT–II Subtest and Composite Standard Scores Obtained by Various Percentages of the WIAT–II/WAIS–III Linking Sample With Prediction Based on WAIS–III FSIQ Scores

High School

Subtests	Percentage								
	25	20	15	10	5	4	3	2	1
Word Reading	7	9	11	14	18	19	20	22	25
Numerical Operations	7	8	10	13	17	18	19	21	23
Reading Comprehension	7	9	11	14	18	19	21	23	26
Spelling	8	9	12	14	18	19	21	23	26
Pseudoword Decoding	8	10	13	15	20	21	23	25	28
Math Reasoning	6	8	9	11	15	16	17	18	21
Written Expression	8	10	13	15	20	21	23	25	28
Listening Comprehension	7	8	10	12	16	17	18	20	22
Oral Expression	9	11	13	17	21	23	24	27	30

Composites

	25	20	15	10	5	4	3	2	1
Reading	7	8	11	13	17	18	19	21	24
Mathematics	6	7	9	11	14	15	16	18	20
Written Language	7	9	11	14	18	19	21	23	26
Oral Language	6	8	10	12	16	17	18	19	22
Total	5	7	8	10	13	14	15	16	18

Note. Percentage of individuals whose obtained achievement standard score was below their predicted-achievement score by the specified amount or more.

Table B.16. Differences Between Predicted and Actual WIAT–II Subtest and Composite Standard Scores Obtained by Various Percentages of the WIAT–II/WAIS–III Linking Sample With Prediction Based on WAIS–III FSIQ Scores *(continued)*

College Students				Percentage					
Subtests	25	20	15	10	5	4	3	2	1
Word Reading	9	11	14	17	22	23	25	27	31
Numerical Operations	8	10	13	16	20	21	23	25	29
Reading Comprehension	8	10	13	16	20	22	23	25	29
Spelling	9	11	14	17	22	24	25	28	31
Pseudoword Decoding	9	11	14	17	22	23	25	27	31
Math Reasoning	8	9	12	14	18	19	21	23	26
Written Expression	9	11	14	17	22	24	25	28	32
Listening Comprehension	8	10	12	15	19	20	21	23	27
Oral Expression	9	11	14	17	22	24	26	28	32
Composites									
Reading	8	10	12	15	19	20	22	24	27
Mathematics	7	9	11	14	18	19	20	22	25
Written Language	9	11	14	17	22	23	25	27	31
Oral Language	8	10	12	15	19	20	22	24	27
Total	7	9	11	14	17	19	20	22	25

Note. Percentage of examinees whose obtained achievement standard score was below their predicted-achievement score by the specified amount or more.

Table B.16. Differences Between Predicted and Actual WIAT–II Subtest and Composite Standard Scores Obtained by Various Percentages of the WIAT–II/WAIS–III Linking Sample With Prediction Based on WAIS–III FSIQ Scores *(continued)*

Adults	Percentage								
Subtests	**25**	**20**	**15**	**10**	**5**	**4**	**3**	**2**	**1**
Word Reading	8	9	12	14	19	20	21	23	26
Numerical Operations	6	7	9	11	14	15	16	18	20
Reading Comprehension	7	8	10	13	16	17	18	20	23
Spelling	8	9	12	14	18	20	21	23	26
Pseudoword Decoding	7	9	11	14	18	19	20	22	25
Math Reasoning	6	8	10	12	15	16	17	19	22
Written Expression	8	10	12	15	19	21	22	24	27
Listening Comprehension	7	9	11	13	17	18	19	21	24
Oral Expression	9	11	13	17	21	23	24	27	30
Composites									
Reading	5	6	8	10	12	13	14	15	18
Mathematics	6	7	9	11	14	15	16	18	20
Written Language	8	10	12	15	19	20	22	24	27
Oral Language	8	9	12	14	18	19	21	23	26
Total	5	7	8	10	13	14	15	16	18

Note. Percentage of examinees whose obtained achievement standard score was below their predicted-achievement score by the specified amount or more.

Table B.17. Differences Between Predicted and Actual WIAT–II Subtest and Composite Standard Scores Obtained by Various Percentages of the WIAT–II/WAIS–III Linking Sample With Prediction Based on WAIS-III VIQ Scores

High School — Percentage

Subtests	25	20	15	10	5	4	3	2	1
Word Reading	7	9	11	13	17	18	20	21	24
Numerical Operations	7	9	11	14	18	19	20	22	25
Reading Comprehension	7	9	11	13	17	18	19	21	24
Spelling	8	10	12	15	19	20	21	23	27
Pseudoword Decoding	8	10	12	15	20	21	22	24	28
Math Reasoning	7	9	11	13	17	18	19	21	24
Written Expression	8	10	13	16	20	21	23	25	29
Listening Comprehension	6	7	9	11	14	15	17	18	21
Oral Expression	9	11	14	17	22	23	25	27	31

Composites

	25	20	15	10	5	4	3	2	1
Reading	6	8	10	12	16	17	18	19	22
Mathematics	7	8	10	13	16	17	19	20	23
Written Language	8	9	12	14	19	20	21	23	26
Oral Language	6	8	10	12	16	17	18	20	22
Total	6	7	9	11	14	15	16	17	20

Note. Percentage of individuals whose obtained achievement standard score was below their predicted-achievement score by the specified amount or more.

Table B.17. Differences Between Predicted and Actual WIAT–II Subtest and Composite Standard Scores Obtained by Various Percentages of the WIAT–II/WAIS–III Linking Sample With Prediction Based on WAIS-III VIQ Scores *(continued)*

College Students   Percentage

Subtests	25	20	15	10	5	4	3	2	1
Word Reading	9	11	13	16	21	22	24	26	30
Numerical Operations	9	11	13	16	21	23	24	26	30
Reading Comprehension	8	10	13	16	20	22	23	25	29
Spelling	9	11	14	17	22	23	25	27	31
Pseudoword Decoding	9	11	14	17	22	23	25	27	31
Math Reasoning	8	10	12	15	19	20	22	24	27
Written Expression	9	11	14	18	23	24	26	28	32
Listening Comprehension	8	9	12	14	18	20	21	23	26
Oral Expression	9	12	14	18	23	24	26	29	33

Composites

	25	20	15	10	5	4	3	2	1
Reading	8	9	12	14	18	20	21	23	26
Mathematics	8	10	12	15	19	20	22	24	27
Written Language	9	11	14	17	22	23	25	27	31
Oral Language	8	10	12	15	20	21	22	24	28
Total	7	9	11	14	18	19	21	22	25

Note. Percentage of examinees whose obtained achievement standard score was below their predicted-achievement score by the specified amount or more.

Table B.17. Differences Between Predicted and Actual WIAT–II Subtest and Composite Standard Scores Obtained by Various Percentages of the WIAT–II/WAIS–III Linking Sample With Prediction Based on WAIS-III VIQ Scores *(continued)*

Adults				Percentage					
Subtests	25	20	15	10	5	4	3	2	1
Word Reading	8	10	12	15	19	21	22	24	27
Numerical Operations	6	8	10	12	15	16	17	19	21
Reading Comprehension	7	9	11	13	17	18	19	21	24
Spelling	8	9	12	14	18	20	21	23	26
Pseudoword Decoding	8	10	12	15	19	20	22	24	27
Math Reasoning	7	8	10	12	16	17	18	20	23
Written Expression	8	10	12	15	20	21	23	25	28
Listening Comprehension	7	9	11	14	18	19	21	22	25
Oral Expression	9	11	14	17	22	23	25	27	31
Composites									
Reading	5	7	8	10	13	14	15	17	19
Mathematics	6	8	10	12	15	16	17	19	21
Written Language	8	10	12	15	19	21	22	24	27
Oral Language	8	10	12	15	19	20	21	23	27
Total	5	7	8	10	13	14	15	16	18

Note. Percentage of examinees whose obtained achievement standard score was below their predicted-achievement score by the specified amount or more.

Table B.18. Differences Between Predicted and Actual WIAT–II Subtest and Composite Standard Scores Obtained by Various Percentages of the WIAT–II/WAIS–III Linking Sample With Prediction Based on WAIS-III PIQ Scores

High School	Percentage								
Subtests	**25**	**20**	**15**	**10**	**5**	**4**	**3**	**2**	**1**
Word Reading	9	11	14	17	22	23	25	27	31
Numerical Operations	8	10	12	15	19	20	22	24	27
Reading Comprehension	9	11	14	17	22	24	26	28	32
Spelling	9	11	13	16	21	22	24	26	30
Pseudoword Decoding	9	11	14	17	22	24	25	28	31
Math Reasoning	7	9	11	13	17	18	20	21	24
Written Expression	9	11	13	17	21	23	24	27	30
Listening Comprehension	9	11	13	16	21	23	24	26	30
Oral Expression	9	11	14	17	22	23	25	27	31
Composites									
Reading	9	11	13	17	21	23	24	27	30
Mathematics	7	9	11	13	17	18	20	21	24
Written Language	8	10	13	16	21	22	23	26	29
Oral Language	8	10	12	15	19	20	22	24	27
Total	7	9	11	13	17	18	19	21	24

Note. Percentage of individuals whose obtained achievement standard score was below their predicted-achievement score by the specified amount or more.

Table B.18. Differences Between Predicted and Actual WIAT–II Subtest and Composite Standard Scores Obtained by Various Percentages of the WIAT–II/WAIS–III Linking Sample With Prediction Based on WAIS-III PIQ Scores *(continued)*

College Students	Percentage								
Subtests	**25**	**20**	**15**	**10**	**5**	**4**	**3**	**2**	**1**
Word Reading	9	12	15	18	23	25	27	29	33
Numerical Operations	8	10	13	16	21	22	23	26	29
Reading Comprehension	9	11	14	17	22	23	25	27	31
Spelling	10	12	15	18	23	25	27	29	33
Pseudoword Decoding	10	12	15	18	23	25	27	29	33
Math Reasoning	8	10	12	15	20	21	23	25	28
Written Expression	9	11	14	18	23	24	26	28	32
Listening Comprehension	9	11	14	17	22	23	25	27	30
Oral Expression	9	11	14	17	23	24	26	28	32

Composites									
Reading	9	11	14	17	22	24	25	28	31
Mathematics	8	10	12	15	19	20	22	24	27
Written Language	9	11	14	17	23	24	26	28	32
Oral Language	9	11	13	16	21	23	24	26	30
Total	8	10	13	16	20	22	23	25	29

Note. Percentage of examinees whose obtained achievement standard score was below their predicted-achievement score by the specified amount or more.

Table B.18. Differences Between Predicted and Actual WIAT–II Subtest and Composite Standard Scores Obtained by Various Percentages of the WIAT–II/WAIS–III Linking Sample With Prediction Based on WAIS-III PIQ Scores *(continued)*

Adults				Percentage					
Subtests	25	20	15	10	5	4	3	2	1
Word Reading	8	10	13	16	20	21	23	25	29
Numerical Operations	7	9	11	14	18	19	21	23	26
Reading Comprehension	8	10	12	15	19	20	22	24	27
Spelling	9	11	13	16	21	22	24	26	30
Pseudoword Decoding	8	9	12	14	18	20	21	23	26
Math Reasoning	8	9	12	14	19	20	21	23	26
Written Expression	8	11	13	16	21	22	24	26	29
Listening Comprehension	8	10	12	15	19	20	22	24	27
Oral Expression	9	11	14	17	22	23	25	27	31
Composites									
Reading	6	8	10	12	16	17	18	20	22
Mathematics	7	9	11	14	18	19	21	23	26
Written Language	9	11	13	16	21	22	24	26	30
Oral Language	8	10	13	16	20	22	23	25	29
Total	7	9	11	13	17	18	20	21	24

Note. Percentage of examinees whose obtained achievement standard score was below their predicted-achievement score by the specified amount or more.

Table B.19. Differences Between Predicted and Actual WIAT–II Subtest and Composite Standard Scores Obtained by Various Percentages of the WIAT–II/WAIS–III Linking Sample With Prediction Based on WAIS-III VCI Scores

High School	Percentage								
Subtests	**25**	**20**	**15**	**10**	**5**	**4**	**3**	**2**	**1**
Word Reading	7	9	11	14	18	19	20	22	25
Numerical Operations	8	10	12	15	19	20	22	24	27
Reading Comprehension	7	9	11	14	18	19	20	22	25
Spelling	8	10	13	15	20	21	23	25	28
Pseudoword Decoding	8	10	13	16	21	22	24	26	29
Math Reasoning	8	10	12	15	19	20	22	24	27
Written Expression	9	11	13	16	21	22	24	26	30
Listening Comprehension	6	8	9	12	15	16	17	19	21
Oral Expression	9	11	14	17	22	24	25	28	32

Composites									
Reading	7	9	11	13	17	18	19	21	24
Mathematics	8	9	12	14	19	20	21	23	26
Written Language	8	10	12	15	20	21	22	25	28
Oral Language	7	8	11	13	17	18	19	21	24
Total	7	8	10	13	16	17	19	20	23

Note. Percentage of individuals whose obtained achievement standard score was below their predicted-achievement score by the specified amount or more.

Table B.19. Differences Between Predicted and Actual WIAT–II Subtest and Composite Standard Scores Obtained by Various Percentages of the WIAT–II/WAIS–III Linking Sample With Prediction Based on WAIS-III VCI Scores *(continued)*

College Students

Subtests	Percentage								
	25	20	15	10	5	4	3	2	1
Word Reading	9	11	14	17	22	23	25	27	31
Numerical Operations	9	11	14	17	22	24	25	28	32
Reading Comprehension	9	11	13	16	21	22	24	26	30
Spelling	9	11	14	17	22	24	26	28	32
Pseudoword Decoding	9	11	14	17	22	24	25	28	32
Math Reasoning	9	11	13	16	21	22	24	26	30
Written Expression	9	12	14	18	23	24	26	29	33
Listening Comprehension	8	10	12	15	19	20	22	24	27
Oral Expression	10	12	15	18	24	25	27	29	33

Composites

Reading	8	10	12	15	20	21	22	24	28
Mathematics	9	11	13	16	21	22	24	26	30
Written Language	9	11	14	17	23	24	26	28	32
Oral Language	8	10	13	16	21	22	23	26	29
Total	8	10	12	15	20	21	22	24	28

Note. Percentage of examinees whose obtained achievement standard score was below their predicted-achievement score by the specified amount or more.

Table B.19. Differences Between Predicted and Actual WIAT–II Subtest and Composite Standard Scores Obtained by Various Percentages of the WIAT–II/WAIS–III Linking Sample With Prediction Based on WAIS-III VCI Scores *(continued)*

Adults	Percentage								
Subtests	**25**	**20**	**15**	**10**	**5**	**4**	**3**	**2**	**1**
Word Reading	8	10	12	15	19	21	22	24	27
Numerical Operations	7	8	10	13	16	17	18	20	23
Reading Comprehension	7	9	11	13	17	18	19	21	24
Spelling	8	10	12	15	19	20	22	24	27
Pseudoword Decoding	8	10	13	16	21	22	23	26	29
Math Reasoning	7	8	11	13	17	18	19	21	24
Written Expression	8	10	12	15	20	21	22	25	28
Listening Comprehension	7	9	11	14	18	19	20	22	25
Oral Expression	9	11	14	17	22	23	25	27	31
Composites									
Reading	6	7	9	11	14	15	16	18	21
Mathematics	7	8	10	12	16	17	18	20	23
Written Language	8	10	12	15	20	21	22	24	28
Oral Language	8	10	12	15	19	20	21	23	27
Total	6	7	9	11	14	15	16	18	20

Note. Percentage of examinees whose obtained achievement standard score was below their predicted-achievement score by the specified amount or more.

Table B.20. Differences Between Predicted and Actual WIAT–II Subtest and Composite Standard Scores Obtained by Various Percentages of the WIAT–II/WAIS–III Linking Sample With Prediction Based on WAIS-III POI Scores

High School	Percentage								
Subtests	**25**	**20**	**15**	**10**	**5**	**4**	**3**	**2**	**1**
Word Reading	9	11	14	18	23	24	26	28	32
Numerical Operations	7	9	11	14	18	19	20	22	25
Reading Comprehension	9	12	15	18	23	25	26	29	33
Spelling	9	11	14	17	22	23	25	27	31
Pseudoword Decoding	9	12	14	18	23	24	26	28	32
Math Reasoning	6	8	10	12	15	16	17	19	21
Written Expression	9	11	14	17	22	23	25	27	31
Listening Comprehension	9	11	13	17	21	23	24	27	30
Oral Expression	7	9	11	14	18	19	21	23	26
Composites									
Reading	9	11	14	17	22	23	25	27	31
Mathematics	6	8	9	11	15	16	17	18	21
Written Language	9	11	13	16	21	22	24	26	30
Oral Language	7	9	11	14	18	19	20	22	25
Total	7	8	10	12	16	17	18	20	22

Note. Percentage of individuals whose obtained achievement standard score was below their predicted-achievement score by the specified amount or more.

Table B.20. Differences Between Predicted and Actual WIAT–II Subtest and Composite Standard Scores Obtained by Various Percentages of the WIAT–II/WAIS–III Linking Sample With Prediction Based on WAIS-III POI Scores *(continued)*

College Students

Subtests	Percentage								
	25	20	15	10	5	4	3	2	1
Word Reading	10	12	15	18	23	25	27	29	33
Numerical Operations	9	11	13	16	21	23	24	26	30
Reading Comprehension	9	11	14	17	22	24	25	28	32
Spelling	10	12	15	18	24	25	27	29	33
Pseudoword Decoding	10	12	15	18	24	25	27	30	34
Math Reasoning	8	10	12	15	20	21	23	25	28
Written Expression	9	12	14	18	23	24	26	29	32
Listening Comprehension	9	11	14	17	22	23	25	27	31
Oral Expression	9	11	14	18	23	24	26	28	32

Composites

	25	20	15	10	5	4	3	2	1
Reading	9	12	14	18	23	24	26	28	32
Mathematics	8	10	12	15	20	21	23	25	28
Written Language	9	12	14	18	23	24	26	29	32
Oral Language	9	11	13	17	21	23	24	27	30
Total	9	11	13	16	21	22	24	26	29

Note. Percentage of examinees whose obtained achievement standard score was below their predicted-achievement score by the specified amount or more.

Table B.20. Differences Between Predicted and Actual WIAT–II Subtest and Composite Standard Scores Obtained by Various Percentages of the WIAT–II/WAIS–III Linking Sample With Prediction Based on WAIS-III POI Scores *(continued)*

Adults					Percentage				
Subtests	25	20	15	10	5	4	3	2	1
Word Reading	9	11	13	17	21	23	24	27	30
Numerical Operations	8	10	12	15	20	21	22	24	28
Reading Comprehension	8	10	13	16	20	22	23	25	29
Spelling	9	11	14	17	23	24	26	28	32
Pseudoword Decoding	8	10	12	15	20	21	22	24	28
Math Reasoning	8	10	13	16	20	21	23	25	28
Written Expression	9	11	14	17	22	23	25	27	31
Listening Comprehension	8	10	13	16	20	22	23	25	29
Oral Expression	9	11	14	17	22	24	25	28	32
Composites									
Reading	7	9	11	14	18	19	21	23	26
Mathematics	8	10	12	15	20	21	23	25	28
Written Language	9	11	14	17	22	24	25	28	31
Oral Language	9	11	13	16	21	22	24	26	30
Total	8	10	12	15	19	20	22	24	27

Note. Percentage of examinees whose obtained achievement standard score was below their predicted-achievement score by the specified amount or more.

Discrepancy Score Tables Based on Simple-Difference Method

Table C.1. Differences Between WAIS–III FSIQ Scores and WMS–III Index Scores Required for Statistical Significance by Age (Simple-Difference Method)

WMS-III Index	Significance Level	Mean All Ages	16-17	18-19	20-24	25-29	30-34	35-44	45-54	55-64	65-69	70-74	75-79	80-84	85-89
								Age Group							
Auditory Immediate	.05	8.8	10.6	9.3	9.3	8.3	7.8	8.8	8.3	8.8	8.3	9.3	8.3	7.8	9.3
	.01	11.6	14.0	12.2	12.2	11.0	10.2	11.6	11.0	11.6	11.0	12.2	11.0	10.2	12.2
Visual Immediate	.05	13.1	13.5	14.1	12.8	12.5	12.1	12.1	11.8	13.5	14.4	14.1	14.4	12.5	12.8
	.01	17.3	17.7	18.6	16.9	16.4	16.0	16.0	15.5	17.7	19.0	18.6	19.0	16.4	16.9
Immediate Memory	.05	9.7	12.1	10.2	9.8	9.3	8.8	9.3	8.3	9.8	9.3	10.6	10.2	8.8	10.2
	.01	12.8	16.0	13.4	12.8	12.2	11.6	12.2	11.0	12.8	12.2	14.0	13.4	11.6	13.4
Auditory Delayed	.05	11.7	15.3	12.5	12.1	11.0	11.0	10.2	11.4	12.1	11.8	11.4	11.0	10.2	12.5
	.01	15.4	20.1	16.4	16.0	14.5	14.5	13.4	15.0	16.0	15.5	15.0	14.5	13.4	16.4
Visual Delayed	.05	12.9	14.4	13.5	12.1	13.2	12.8	11.4	11.4	13.5	13.5	13.8	14.1	12.1	12.1
	.01	17.0	19.0	17.7	16.0	17.3	16.9	15.0	15.0	17.7	17.7	18.2	18.6	16.0	16.0
Auditory Recognition Delayed	.05	15.7	17.1	18.4	14.4	14.1	16.6	15.6	16.6	16.6	15.8	16.4	14.7	14.1	13.5
	.01	20.7	22.6	24.2	19.0	18.6	21.9	20.5	21.9	21.9	20.8	21.6	19.4	18.6	17.7
General Memory	.05	9.9	12.8	11.8	9.3	9.3	9.8	8.8	9.3	10.2	9.8	10.2	9.8	8.8	9.3
	.01	13.1	16.9	15.5	12.2	12.2	12.8	11.6	12.2	13.4	12.8	13.4	12.8	11.6	12.2
Working Memory	.05	11.9	13.2	10.2	11.4	11.4	10.6	12.1	12.5	11.4	13.2	11.0	14.4	11.0	11.8
	.01	15.6	17.3	13.4	15.0	15.0	14.0	16.0	16.4	15.0	17.3	14.5	19.0	14.5	15.5

Table C.2. Differences Between WAIS–III VIQ Scores and WMS–III Index Scores Required for Statistical Significance By Age (Simple-Difference Method)

WMS-III Index	Significance Level	Mean All Ages	Age Group												
			16–17	18–19	20–24	25–29	30–34	35–44	45–54	55–64	65–69	70–74	75–79	80–84	85–89
Auditory Immediate	.05	9.1	11.0	9.3	9.8	8.8	8.3	9.3	8.8	8.8	8.3	9.8	8.3	8.3	9.8
	.01	12.0	14.5	12.2	12.8	11.6	11.0	12.2	11.6	11.6	11.0	12.8	11.0	11.0	12.8
Visual Immediate	.05	13.4	13.8	14.1	13.2	12.8	12.5	12.5	12.1	13.5	14.4	14.4	14.4	12.8	13.2
	.01	17.6	18.2	18.6	17.3	16.9	16.4	16.4	16.0	17.7	19.0	19.0	19.0	16.9	17.3
Immediate Memory	.05	10.0	12.5	10.2	10.2	9.8	9.3	9.8	8.8	9.8	9.3	11.0	10.2	9.3	10.6
	.01	13.2	16.4	13.4	13.4	12.8	12.2	12.8	11.6	12.8	12.2	14.5	13.4	12.2	14.0
Auditory Delayed	.05	12.0	15.6	12.5	12.5	11.4	11.4	10.6	11.8	12.1	11.8	11.8	11.0	10.6	12.8
	.01	15.8	20.5	16.4	16.4	15.0	15.0	14.0	15.5	16.0	15.5	15.5	14.5	14.0	16.9
Visual Delayed	.05	13.1	14.7	13.5	12.5	13.5	13.2	11.8	11.8	13.5	13.5	14.1	14.1	12.5	12.5
	.01	17.3	19.4	17.7	16.4	17.7	17.3	15.5	15.5	17.7	17.7	18.6	18.6	16.4	16.4
Auditory Recognition Delayed	.05	15.9	17.4	18.4	14.7	14.4	16.9	15.8	16.9	16.6	15.8	16.6	14.7	14.4	13.8
	.01	20.9	22.9	24.2	19.4	19.0	22.2	20.8	22.2	21.9	20.8	21.9	19.4	19.0	18.2
General Memory	.05	10.2	13.2	11.8	9.8	9.8	10.2	9.3	9.8	10.2	9.8	10.6	9.8	9.3	9.8
	.01	13.5	17.3	15.5	12.8	12.8	13.4	12.2	12.8	13.4	12.8	14.0	12.8	12.2	12.8
Working Memory	.05	12.1	13.5	10.2	11.8	11.8	11.0	12.5	12.8	11.4	13.2	11.4	14.4	11.4	12.1
	.01	15.9	17.7	13.4	15.5	15.5	14.5	16.4	16.9	15.0	17.3	15.0	19.0	15.0	16.0

Table C.3. Differences Between WAIS–III PIQ Scores and WMS–III Index Scores Required for Statistical Significance By Age (Simple-Difference Method)

WMS-III Index	Significance Level	Mean All Ages	Age Group 16-17	18-19	20-24	25-29	30-34	35-44	45-54	55-64	65-69	70-74	75-79	80-84	85-89
Auditory Immediate	.05	10.5	12.1	11.0	11.4	9.8	10.2	10.6	10.2	10.2	9.3	10.6	10.2	9.8	10.6
	.01	13.8	16.0	14.5	15.0	12.8	13.4	14.0	13.4	13.4	12.2	14.0	13.4	12.8	14.0
Visual Immediate	.05	14.3	14.7	15.3	14.4	13.5	13.8	13.5	13.2	14.4	15.0	15.0	15.6	13.8	13.8
	.01	18.8	19.4	20.1	19.0	17.7	18.2	17.7	17.3	19.0	19.7	19.7	20.5	18.2	18.2
Immediate Memory	.05	11.3	13.5	11.8	11.8	10.6	11.0	11.0	10.2	11.0	10.2	11.8	11.8	10.6	11.4
	.01	14.8	17.7	15.5	15.5	14.0	14.5	14.5	13.4	14.5	13.4	15.5	15.5	14.0	15.0
Auditory Delayed	.05	13.0	16.4	13.8	13.8	12.1	12.8	11.8	12.8	13.2	12.5	12.5	12.5	11.8	13.5
	.01	17.1	21.6	18.2	18.2	16.0	16.9	15.5	16.9	17.3	16.4	16.4	16.4	15.5	17.7
Visual Delayed	.05	14.1	15.6	14.7	13.8	14.1	14.4	12.8	12.8	14.4	14.1	14.7	15.3	13.5	13.2
	.01	18.6	20.5	19.4	18.2	18.6	19.0	16.9	16.9	19.0	18.6	19.4	20.1	17.7	17.3
Auditory Recognition Delayed	.05	16.7	18.1	19.3	15.8	15.0	17.9	16.6	17.6	17.4	16.4	17.1	15.8	15.3	14.4
	.01	22.0	23.9	25.4	20.8	19.7	23.5	21.9	23.2	22.9	21.6	22.6	20.8	20.1	19.0
General Memory	.05	11.4	14.1	13.2	11.4	10.6	11.8	10.6	11.0	11.4	10.6	11.4	11.4	10.6	10.6
	.01	15.0	18.6	17.3	15.0	14.0	15.5	14.0	14.5	15.0	14.0	15.0	15.0	14.0	14.0
Working Memory	.05	13.1	14.4	11.8	13.2	12.5	12.5	13.5	13.8	12.5	13.8	12.1	15.6	12.5	12.8
	.01	17.3	19.0	15.5	17.3	16.4	16.4	17.7	18.2	16.4	18.2	16.0	20.5	16.4	16.9

Table C.4. Frequencies (Cumulative Percentages) of Differences Between WAIS–III FSIQ Scores and WMS–III Index Scores: All Ages (Simple-Difference Method)

WMS–III Primary Indexes	Percentage								
	25	20	15	10	5	4	3	2	1
Auditory Immediate	10	12	14	17	23	24	26	28	30
Visual Immediate	12	14	18	22	29	30	33	36	41
Immediate Memory	10	12	15	17	23	24	26	28	32
Auditory Delayed	9	12	14	17	23	25	26	30	33
Visual Delayed	12	14	17	21	26	27	30	33	41
Auditory Recog Delayed	10	12	16	20	25	26	28	30	35
General Memory	9	11	13	16	22	24	26	28	33
Working Memory	8	11	13	15	20	21	22	23	29

Table C.5. Frequencies (Cumulative Percentages) of Differences Between WAIS–III VIQ Scores and WMS–III Index Scores: All Ages (Simple-Difference Method)

WMS–III Primary Indexes	Percentage								
	25	20	15	10	5	4	3	2	1
Auditory Immediate	9	12	15	18	23	26	27	30	35
Visual Immediate	13	15	19	23	29	31	33	39	46
Immediate Memory	10	12	15	19	25	26	28	32	37
Auditory Delayed	9	12	15	18	25	26	29	31	36
Visual Delayed	12	14	18	21	28	30	33	36	45
Auditory Recog Delayed	11	13	16	19	25	28	29	32	37
General Memory	9	12	14	17	24	25	27	31	38
Working Memory	9	11	13	17	22	23	25	28	31

Table C.6. Frequencies (Cumulative Percentages) of Differences Between WAIS–III PIQ Scores and WMS–III Index Scores: All Ages (Simple-Difference Method)

WMS–III Primary Indexes	Percentage								
	25	20	15	10	5	4	3	2	1
Auditory Immediate	10	12	15	19	24	26	27	30	34
Visual Immediate	11	14	17	21	29	31	33	34	37
Immediate Memory	10	12	15	18	23	25	27	29	33
Auditory Delayed	10	12	16	19	24	25	28	30	34
Visual Delayed	10	13	16	20	27	28	30	31	38
Auditory Recog Delayed	11	14	16	20	26	27	29	32	36
General Memory	10	12	14	17	23	25	27	29	31
Working Memory	8	11	13	15	20	22	23	25	27

Note. Percentages for Tables C.4–C.6 represent the portions of the sample who obtained WMS–III Index scores lower than their WAIS–III IQ scores by the specified amount or more.

Table C.7. Differences Between WAIS–III Scores and Actual WIAT–II Subtest and Composite Standard Scores Required for Statistical Significance (Simple-Difference Method)

Ages 16:0–19:11 (High School)

Subtests	p	FSIQ	VIQ	PIQ	VCI	POI
Word	.05	8.32	8.82	10.18	9.75	10.18
Reading	.01	10.95	11.61	13.41	12.84	13.41
Numerical	.05	8.82	9.30	10.60	10.18	10.60
Operations	.01	11.61	12.24	13.95	13.41	13.95
Reading	.05	9.30	9.75	11.00	10.60	11.00
Comprehension	.01	12.24	12.84	14.48	13.95	14.48
Spelling	.05	10.18	10.60	11.76	11.39	11.76
	.01	13.41	13.95	15.48	14.99	15.48
Pseudoword	.05	7.78	8.32	9.75	9.30	9.75
Decoding	.01	10.24	10.95	12.84	12.24	12.84
Math	.05	9.30	9.75	11.00	10.60	11.00
Reasoning	.01	12.24	12.84	14.48	13.95	14.48
Written	.05	11.76	12.12	13.15	12.82	13.15
Expression	.01	15.48	15.96	17.31	16.87	17.31
Listening	.05	14.10	14.40	15.28	14.99	15.28
Comprehension	.01	18.56	18.96	20.11	19.73	20.11
Oral	.05	12.47	12.82	13.79	13.47	13.79
Expression	.01	16.42	16.87	18.15	17.73	18.15

Composites

	p	FSIQ	VIQ	PIQ	VCI	POI
Reading	.05	6.57	7.20	8.82	8.32	8.82
	.01	8.65	9.48	11.61	10.95	11.61
Mathematics	.05	7.78	8.32	9.75	9.30	9.75
	.01	10.24	10.95	12.84	12.24	12.84
Written	.05	9.30	9.75	11.00	10.60	11.00
Language	.01	12.24	12.84	14.48	13.95	14.48
Oral	.05	11.76	12.12	13.15	12.82	13.15
Language	.01	15.48	15.96	17.31	16.87	17.31
Total	.05	6.57	7.20	8.82	8.32	8.82
	.01	8.65	9.48	11.61	10.95	11.61

Note. For all age groups, data were derived from the WIAT–II age-based reliability tables.

Table C.7. Differences Between WAIS–III Scores and Actual WIAT–II Subtest and Composite Standard Scores Required for Statistical Significance (Simple-Difference Method) (continued)

College Students

Subtests	p	FSIQ	VIQ	PIQ	VCI	POI
Word Reading	.05	7.20	7.78	9.30	8.32	9.75
	.01	9.48	10.24	12.24	10.95	12.84
Numerical Operations	.05	7.78	8.32	9.75	8.82	10.18
	.01	10.24	10.95	12.84	11.61	13.41
Reading Comprehension	.05	7.20	7.78	9.30	8.32	9.75
	.01	9.48	10.24	12.24	10.95	12.84
Spelling	.05	8.32	8.82	10.18	9.30	10.60
	.01	10.95	11.61	13.41	12.24	13.95
Pseudoword Decoding	.05	7.20	7.78	9.30	8.32	9.75
	.01	9.48	10.24	12.24	10.95	12.84
Math Reasoning	.05	9.30	9.75	11.00	10.18	11.39
	.01	12.24	12.84	14.48	13.41	14.99
Written Expression	.05	14.70	14.99	15.83	15.28	16.10
	.01	19.35	19.73	20.84	20.11	21.20
Listening Comprehension	.05	11.39	11.76	12.82	12.12	13.15
	.01	14.99	15.48	16.87	15.96	17.31
Oral Expression	.05	15.28	15.56	16.37	15.83	16.63
	.01	20.11	20.48	21.55	20.84	21.89

Composites

	p	FSIQ	VIQ	PIQ	VCI	POI
Reading	.05	5.88	6.57	8.32	7.20	8.82
	.01	7.74	8.65	10.95	9.48	11.61
Mathematics	.05	7.20	7.78	9.30	8.32	9.75
	.01	9.48	10.24	12.24	10.95	12.84
Written Language	.05	9.30	9.75	11.00	10.18	11.39
	.01	12.24	12.84	14.48	13.41	14.99
Oral Language	.05	11.00	11.39	12.47	11.76	12.82
	.01	14.48	14.99	16.42	15.48	16.87
Total	.05	5.88	6.57	8.32	7.20	8.82
	.01	7.74	8.65	10.95	9.48	11.61

Note. For all age groups, data were derived from the WIAT–II age-based reliability tables.

Table C.7. Differences Between WAIS–III Scores and Actual WIAT–II Subtest and Composite Standard Scores Required for Statistical Significance (Simple-Difference Method) *(continued)*

Adults

Subtests	p	FSIQ	VIQ	PIQ	VCI	POI
Word	.05	7.20	7.78	9.30	8.32	9.75
Reading	.01	9.48	10.24	12.24	10.95	12.84
Numerical	.05	7.78	8.32	9.75	8.82	10.18
Operations	.01	10.24	10.95	12.84	11.61	13.41
Reading	.05	7.20	7.78	9.30	8.32	9.75
Comprehension	.01	9.48	10.24	12.24	10.95	12.84
Spelling	.05	8.32	8.82	10.18	9.30	10.60
	.01	10.95	11.61	13.41	12.24	13.95
Pseudoword	.05	7.20	7.78	9.30	8.32	9.75
Decoding	.01	9.48	10.24	12.24	10.95	12.84
Math	.05	9.30	9.75	11.00	10.18	11.39
Reasoning	.01	12.24	12.84	14.48	13.41	14.99
Written	.05	14.70	14.99	15.83	15.28	16.10
Expression	.01	19.35	19.73	20.84	20.11	21.20
Listening	.05	11.39	11.76	12.82	12.12	13.15
Comprehension	.01	14.99	15.48	16.87	15.96	17.31
Oral	.05	15.28	15.56	16.37	15.83	16.63
Expression	.01	20.11	20.48	21.55	20.84	21.89

Composites

	p	FSIQ	VIQ	PIQ	VCI	POI
Reading	.05	5.88	6.57	8.32	7.20	8.82
	.01	7.74	8.65	10.95	9.48	11.61
Mathematics	.05	7.20	7.78	9.30	8.32	9.75
	.01	9.48	10.24	12.24	10.95	12.84
Written	.05	9.30	9.75	11.00	10.18	11.39
Language	.01	12.24	12.84	14.48	13.41	14.99
Oral	.05	11.00	11.39	12.47	11.76	12.82
Language	.01	14.48	14.99	16.42	15.48	16.87
Total	.05	5.88	6.57	8.32	7.20	8.82
	.01	7.74	8.65	10.95	9.48	11.61

Note. For all age groups, data were derived from the WIAT–II age-based reliability tables.

Table C.8. Differences Between WAIS–III FSIQ Scores and Actual WIAT–II Subtest and Composite Standard Scores Obtained by Various Percentages of the WIAT–II/WAIS–III Linking Sample

High School

Subtests	25	20	15	10	5	4	3	2	1
Word Reading	8	10	12	15	19	20	22	24	27
Numerical Operations	7	9	11	14	18	19	20	22	25
Reading Comprehension	8	10	12	15	20	21	23	25	28
Spelling	8	10	13	16	20	21	23	25	28
Pseudoword Decoding	9	11	14	17	22	24	26	28	32
Math Reasoning	6	8	10	12	16	17	18	19	22
Written Expression	9	11	14	17	22	24	25	28	32
Listening Comprehension	7	9	11	13	17	18	19	21	24
Oral Expression	10	12	16	19	25	26	28	31	35

Composites

	25	20	15	10	5	4	3	2	1
Reading	7	9	11	14	18	19	20	22	25
Mathematics	6	8	10	12	15	16	17	19	21
Written Language	8	10	13	15	20	21	23	25	28
Oral Language	7	8	10	13	17	18	19	21	23
Total	6	7	8	10	13	14	15	17	19

Note. Percentage of individuals whose actual achievement standard score was below their FSIQ by the specified amount or more.

Table C.8. Differences Between WAIS–III FSIQ Scores and Actual WIAT–II Subtest and Composite Standard Scores Obtained by Various Percentages of the WIAT–II/WAIS–III Linking Sample *(continued)*

College Students

Subtests	25	20	15	10	5	4	3	2	1
Word Reading	10	13	16	19	25	27	29	31	35
Numerical Operations	9	11	14	18	23	24	26	28	32
Reading Comprehension	9	12	14	18	23	24	26	29	33
Spelling	11	13	16	20	26	28	30	33	37
Pseudoword Decoding	10	13	16	20	26	27	29	32	36
Math Reasoning	8	10	13	15	20	21	23	25	28
Written Expression	11	13	17	20	27	28	30	33	38
Listening Comprehension	8	10	13	16	21	22	24	26	29
Oral Expression	11	13	17	21	27	28	31	33	38

Composites

	25	20	15	10	5	4	3	2	1
Reading	9	11	13	16	21	22	24	26	30
Mathematics	8	10	12	15	19	20	22	24	27
Written Language	10	13	16	20	25	27	29	32	36
Oral Language	9	11	13	16	21	23	24	27	30
Total	8	10	12	15	19	20	22	24	27

Note. Percentage of examinees whose actual achievement standard score was below their FSIQ by the specified amount or more.

Table C.8. Differences Between WAIS–III FSIQ Scores and Actual WIAT–II Subtest and Composite Standard Scores Obtained by Various Percentages of the WIAT–II/WAIS–III Linking Sample *(continued)*

Adults					Percentage				
Subtests	**25**	**20**	**15**	**10**	**5**	**4**	**3**	**2**	**1**
Word Reading	8	10	13	16	20	21	23	25	29
Numerical Operations	6	8	9	12	15	16	17	19	21
Reading Comprehension	7	9	11	13	17	18	20	21	24
Spelling	8	10	13	16	20	21	23	25	29
Pseudoword Decoding	8	10	12	15	19	21	22	24	27
Math Reasoning	7	8	10	13	16	17	19	20	23
Written Expression	9	11	13	17	22	23	25	27	30
Listening Comprehension	7	9	11	14	18	19	21	23	26
Oral Expression	10	13	16	19	25	26	28	31	35

Composites

	25	**20**	**15**	**10**	**5**	**4**	**3**	**2**	**1**
Reading	5	7	8	10	13	14	15	16	18
Mathematics	6	8	9	12	15	16	17	19	21
Written Language	9	11	13	16	21	23	24	26	30
Oral Language	8	10	13	15	20	21	23	25	28
Total	5	7	8	10	13	14	15	17	19

Note. Percentage of examinees whose actual achievement standard score was below their FSIQ by the specified amount or more.

Table C.9. Differences Between WAIS–III VIQ Scores and Actual WIAT–II Subtest and Composite Standard Scores Obtained by Various Percentages of the WIAT–II/WAIS–III Linking Sample

High School	Percentage								
Subtests	25	20	15	10	5	4	3	2	1
Word Reading	8	9	12	14	19	20	21	23	26
Numerical Operations	8	10	12	15	19	20	22	24	27
Reading Comprehension	8	9	12	14	18	19	21	23	26
Spelling	8	10	13	16	21	22	24	26	29
Pseudoword Decoding	9	11	14	17	22	23	25	27	31
Math Reasoning	7	9	11	14	18	19	21	23	26
Written Expression	9	11	14	18	23	24	26	28	32
Listening Comprehension	6	8	10	12	15	16	17	19	22
Oral Expression	10	13	16	20	26	27	29	32	37

Composites									
Reading	7	8	10	13	17	18	19	21	23
Mathematics	7	9	11	14	18	19	20	22	25
Written Language	8	10	13	16	20	22	23	25	29
Oral Language	7	9	11	13	17	18	19	21	24
Total	6	7	9	11	15	16	17	18	21

Note. Percentage of individuals whose actual achievement standard score was below their VIQ by the specified amount or more.

Table C.9. Differences Between WAIS–III VIQ Scores and Actual WIAT–II Subtest and Composite Standard Scores Obtained by Various Percentages of the WIAT–II/WAIS–III Linking Sample *(continued)*

College Students

Subtests	Percentage								
	25	20	15	10	5	4	3	2	1
Word Reading	10	12	15	19	24	25	27	30	34
Numerical Operations	10	12	15	19	24	26	28	30	35
Reading Comprehension	9	12	15	18	23	25	26	29	33
Spelling	10	13	16	20	26	27	29	32	36
Pseudoword Decoding	10	13	16	19	25	27	29	31	36
Math Reasoning	9	11	13	17	21	23	24	27	30
Written Expression	11	14	17	21	27	29	31	34	39
Listening Comprehension	8	10	13	16	20	21	23	25	29
Oral Expression	11	14	18	22	28	30	32	35	40

Composites

	25	20	15	10	5	4	3	2	1
Reading	8	10	13	16	20	21	23	25	29
Mathematics	9	11	13	16	21	22	24	26	30
Written Language	10	13	16	20	26	27	29	32	37
Oral Language	9	11	14	17	22	23	25	27	31
Total	8	10	12	15	20	21	22	24	28

Note. Percentage of individuals whose actual achievement standard score was below their VIQ by the specified amount or more.

Table C.9. Differences Between WAIS–III VIQ Scores and Actual WIAT–II Subtest and Composite Standard Scores Obtained by Various Percentages of the WIAT–II/WAIS–III Linking Sample *(continued)*

Adults	Percentage								
Subtests	25	20	15	10	5	4	3	2	1
Word Reading	9	11	13	17	21	23	24	27	30
Numerical Operations	7	8	10	12	16	17	18	20	22
Reading Comprehension	7	9	11	14	18	19	21	22	25
Spelling	8	10	13	16	20	21	23	25	28
Pseudoword Decoding	9	11	13	17	21	23	24	27	30
Math Reasoning	7	9	11	13	17	18	20	21	24
Written Expression	9	11	14	17	22	23	25	27	31
Listening Comprehension	8	10	12	15	20	21	22	24	28
Oral Expression	10	13	16	20	25	27	29	32	36
Composites									
Reading	6	7	9	11	14	15	16	17	20
Mathematics	7	8	10	12	16	17	18	20	22
Written Language	9	11	13	17	21	23	24	27	30
Oral Language	8	10	13	16	21	22	24	26	29
Total	6	7	9	11	13	14	15	17	19

Note. Percentage of individuals whose actual achievement standard score was below their VIQ by the specified amount or more.

Table C.10. Differences Between WAIS–III PIQ Scores and Actual WIAT–II Subtest and Composite Standard Scores Obtained by Various Percentages of the WIAT–II/WAIS–III Linking Sample

High School

Subtests	Percentage								
	25	20	15	10	5	4	3	2	1
Word Reading	10	13	16	19	25	27	29	31	36
Numerical Operations	9	11	13	16	21	23	24	26	30
Reading Comprehension	11	13	17	21	27	28	30	33	38
Spelling	10	12	15	19	24	25	27	30	34
Pseudoword Decoding	11	13	16	20	26	28	30	33	37
Math Reasoning	8	9	12	14	19	20	21	23	26
Written Expression	10	13	16	19	25	26	28	31	35
Listening Comprehension	10	12	15	19	24	26	28	30	35
Oral Expression	10	13	16	19	25	27	29	31	36

Composites

	25	20	15	10	5	4	3	2	1
Reading	10	12	15	19	25	26	28	31	35
Mathematics	8	9	12	14	19	20	21	23	26
Written Language	9	12	15	18	23	25	27	29	33
Oral Language	9	11	13	16	21	22	24	26	30
Total	8	9	12	14	18	20	21	23	26

Note. Percentage of individuals whose actual achievement standard score was below their PIQ by the specified amount or more.

Table C.10. Differences Between WAIS–III PIQ Scores and Actual WIAT–II Subtest and Composite Standard Scores Obtained by Various Percentages of the WIAT–II/WAIS–III Linking Sample *(continued)*

College Students	Percentage								
Subtests	25	20	15	10	5	4	3	2	1
Word Reading	12	14	18	22	29	30	33	36	41
Numerical Operations	9	12	15	18	23	25	26	29	33
Reading Comprehension	10	13	16	20	26	27	29	32	36
Spelling	12	14	18	22	29	31	33	36	41
Pseudoword Decoding	12	15	18	23	29	31	33	36	41
Math Reasoning	9	11	14	17	22	23	25	28	31
Written Expression	11	14	17	21	27	29	31	34	39
Listening Comprehension	10	13	16	19	25	26	28	31	35
Oral Expression	11	14	17	21	27	29	31	34	38
Composites									
Reading	11	13	16	20	26	28	30	33	37
Mathematics	9	11	13	16	21	22	24	26	30
Written Language	11	14	17	21	27	29	31	34	38
Oral Language	10	12	15	19	24	26	28	30	35
Total	9	12	15	18	23	25	26	29	33

Note. Percentage of individuals whose actual achievement standard score was below their PIQ by the specified amount or more.

Table C.10. Differences Between WAIS–III PIQ Scores and Actual WIAT–II Subtest and Composite Standard Scores Obtained by Various Percentages of the WIAT–II/WAIS–III Linking Sample *(continued)*

Adults				Percentage					
Subtests	25	20	15	10	5	4	3	2	1
Word Reading	9	11	14	18	23	24	26	28	32
Numerical Operations	8	10	13	15	20	21	23	25	28
Reading Comprehension	9	11	13	16	21	22	24	26	30
Spelling	10	12	15	19	24	26	28	30	34
Pseudoword Decoding	8	10	13	16	20	21	23	25	28
Math Reasoning	8	10	13	16	21	22	23	26	29
Written Expression	10	12	15	18	24	25	27	29	33
Listening Comprehension	9	11	13	16	21	22	24	26	30
Oral Expression	11	13	16	20	26	28	30	32	37
Composites									
Reading	7	9	11	13	17	18	19	21	24
Mathematics	8	10	12	15	20	21	23	25	28
Written Language	10	12	15	19	24	26	28	30	34
Oral Language	9	12	14	18	23	24	26	28	32
Total	8	9	12	14	19	20	21	23	26

Note. Percentage of individuals whose actual achievement standard score was below their PIQ by the specified amount or more.

Table C.11. Differences Between WAIS–III VCI Scores and Actual WIAT–II Subtest and Composite Standard Scores Obtained by Various Percentages of the WIAT–II/WAIS–III Linking Sample

High School

Subtests	25	20	15	10	5	4	3	2	1
Word Reading	8	10	12	15	19	20	22	24	27
Numerical Operations	9	11	13	16	21	22	24	26	30
Reading Comprehension	8	10	12	15	19	20	22	24	27
Spelling	9	11	14	17	22	24	26	28	32
Pseudoword Decoding	10	12	15	18	23	25	27	29	33
Math Reasoning	9	11	13	16	21	23	24	27	30
Written Expression	10	12	15	19	24	25	27	30	34
Listening Comprehension	7	8	10	12	16	17	18	20	22
Oral Expression	11	13	17	20	26	28	30	33	37

Composites

	25	20	15	10	5	4	3	2	1
Reading	7	9	11	14	18	19	20	22	25
Mathematics	8	10	13	16	20	22	23	25	29
Written Language	9	11	14	17	22	23	25	27	31
Oral Language	7	9	11	14	18	19	20	22	25
Total	7	9	11	13	17	18	20	22	25

Note. Percentage of individuals whose actual achievement standard score was below their VCI by the specified amount or more.

Table C.11. Differences Between WAIS–III VCI Scores and Actual WIAT–II Subtest and Composite Standard Scores Obtained by Various Percentages of the WIAT–II/WAIS–III Linking Sample *(continued)*

College Students

Subtests	25	20	15	10	5	4	3	2	1
Word Reading	10	13	16	19	25	27	29	31	36
Numerical Operations	11	13	17	20	26	28	30	33	37
Reading Comprehension	10	12	15	19	24	25	27	30	34
Spelling	11	13	17	21	27	28	30	33	38
Pseudoword Decoding	11	13	17	20	26	28	30	33	37
Math Reasoning	10	12	15	19	24	26	28	30	34
Written Expression	11	14	17	22	28	30	32	35	40
Listening Comprehension	9	11	13	16	21	22	24	26	30
Oral Expression	12	15	18	23	29	31	34	37	42

Composites

	25	20	15	10	5	4	3	2	1
Reading	9	11	14	17	22	23	25	27	31
Mathematics	10	12	15	18	24	25	27	30	34
Written Language	11	14	17	21	27	29	31	33	38
Oral Language	10	12	15	18	23	25	27	29	33
Total	9	11	14	17	22	23	25	27	31

Note. Percentage of individuals whose actual achievement standard score was below their VCI by the specified amount or more.

Table C.11. Differences Between WAIS–III VCI Scores and Actual WIAT–II Subtest and Composite Standard Scores Obtained by Various Percentages of the WIAT–II/WAIS–III Linking Sample *(continued)*

Adults	Percentage								
Subtests	**25**	**20**	**15**	**10**	**5**	**4**	**3**	**2**	**1**
Word Reading	9	11	14	17	22	23	25	27	31
Numerical Operations	7	9	11	13	17	18	20	21	24
Reading Comprehension	8	9	12	14	18	19	21	23	26
Spelling	9	11	13	16	21	22	24	26	29
Pseudoword Decoding	9	12	15	18	23	25	27	29	33
Math Reasoning	7	9	11	14	18	19	20	22	25
Written Expression	9	11	14	17	22	23	25	27	31
Listening Comprehension	8	10	12	15	19	20	22	24	27
Oral Expression	10	13	16	20	26	27	29	32	36

Composites									
Reading	6	8	10	12	15	16	17	19	22
Mathematics	7	9	11	13	17	18	19	21	24
Written Language	9	11	14	17	22	23	25	27	31
Oral Language	8	10	13	16	21	22	23	26	29
Total	6	8	9	12	15	16	17	19	21

Note. Percentage of individuals whose actual achievement standard score was below their VCI by the specified amount or more.

Table C.12. Differences Between WAIS–III POI Scores and Actual WIAT–II Subtest and Composite Standard Scores Obtained by Various Percentages of the WIAT–II/WAIS–III Linking Sample

High School

Subtests	25	20	15	10	5	4	3	2	1
Word Reading	11	14	17	21	27	29	31	34	39
Numerical Operations	8	10	12	15	19	20	22	24	27
Reading Comprehension	11	14	18	22	28	30	32	35	40
Spelling	10	13	16	20	25	27	29	32	36
Pseudoword Decoding	11	14	17	21	28	29	31	34	39
Math Reasoning	7	8	10	12	16	17	18	20	23
Written Expression	10	13	16	20	26	27	29	32	37
Listening Comprehension	10	12	15	19	25	26	28	31	35
Oral Expression	8	10	13	15	20	21	23	25	28

Composites

Composites	25	20	15	10	5	4	3	2	1
Reading	10	13	16	20	26	27	29	32	36
Mathematics	6	8	10	12	17	16	18	19	22
Written Language	10	12	15	19	24	26	28	30	34
Oral Language	8	10	12	15	19	20	22	24	27
Total	7	9	11	13	17	18	19	21	24

Note. Percentage of individuals whose actual achievement standard score was below their POI by the specified amount or more.

Table C.12. Differences Between WAIS–III POI Scores and Actual WIAT–II Subtest and Composite Standard Scores Obtained by Various Percentages of the WIAT–II/WAIS–III Linking Sample *(continued)*

College Students	Percentage								
Subtests	**25**	**20**	**15**	**10**	**5**	**4**	**3**	**2**	**1**
Word Reading	12	15	18	22	29	31	33	36	41
Numerical Operations	10	12	15	19	24	26	28	30	35
Reading Comprehension	11	13	17	20	27	28	30	33	38
Spelling	12	15	18	23	29	31	34	37	42
Pseudoword Decoding	12	15	19	23	30	32	34	37	43
Math Reasoning	9	11	14	17	22	23	25	28	31
Written Expression	11	14	17	21	28	29	32	35	39
Listening Comprehension	11	13	16	20	26	28	30	32	37
Oral Expression	11	14	17	21	27	29	31	34	38
Composites									
Reading	11	14	17	21	27	29	31	34	39
Mathematics	9	11	14	17	22	23	25	27	31
Written Language	11	14	17	21	28	29	32	35	39
Oral Language	10	13	16	19	25	26	28	31	35
Total	10	12	15	18	24	25	27	30	34

Note. Percentage of individuals whose actual achievement standard score was below their POI by the specified amount or more.

Table C.12. Differences Between WAIS–III POI Scores and Actual WIAT–II Subtest and Composite Standard Scores Obtained by Various Percentages of the WIAT–II/WAIS–III Linking Sample *(continued)*

Adults				Percentage					
Subtests	**25**	**20**	**15**	**10**	**5**	**4**	**3**	**2**	**1**
Word Reading	10	12	15	19	25	26	28	31	35
Numerical Operations	9	11	14	17	22	23	25	27	31
Reading Comprehension	9	12	14	18	23	25	26	29	33
Spelling	11	14	17	21	27	29	31	34	38
Pseudoword Decoding	9	11	14	17	22	23	25	27	31
Math Reasoning	9	11	14	17	22	24	26	28	32
Written Expression	10	13	16	19	25	27	29	31	36
Listening Comprehension	9	12	14	18	23	24	26	28	32
Oral Expression	11	13	17	20	27	28	30	33	38

Composites									
Reading	8	10	12	15	20	21	23	25	28
Mathematics	9	11	14	17	22	23	25	27	31
Written Language	11	13	16	20	26	28	30	33	37
Oral Language	10	12	15	19	24	26	28	30	34
Total	9	11	13	16	21	22	24	26	30

Note. Percentage of individuals whose actual achievement standard score was below their POI by the specified amount or more.

Frequencies of WAIS–III IQ Score Discrepancies Based on Ability Level

Table D.1. Frequencies (Cumulative Percentages) of Differences Between WAIS–III IQ and Index Scores by Ability Level: FSIQ ≤ 79

Amount of Discrepancy	VIQ–PIQ	Scales/Indexes					
		Verbal Comprehension–Perceptual Organization	Verbal Comprehension–Working Memory	Perceptual Organization–Processing Speed	Verbal Comprehension–Processing Speed	Perceptual Organization–Working Memory	Working Memory–Processing Speed
≥40	0.0	0.0	0.0	0.0	0.0	0.0	0.0
39	0.0	0.0	0.0	0.0	0.0	0.0	0.0
38	0.0	0.0	0.0	0.0	0.0	0.0	0.0
37	0.0	0.0	0.0	0.0	0.0	0.0	0.0
36	0.0	0.0	0.0	0.0	0.0	0.0	0.0
35	0.0	0.0	0.0	0.0	0.0	0.0	0.0
34	0.0	0.0	0.0	0.0	0.0	0.0	0.0
33	0.0	0.0	0.0	0.0	0.0	0.0	1.0
32	0.0	0.0	0.0	0.0	0.0	1.0	1.0
31	0.0	0.0	0.0	0.0	0.0	1.0	1.0
30	0.0	0.0	0.0	0.0	0.0	1.0	1.0
29	0.0	0.5	0.0	0.0	0.5	1.0	1.0
28	0.0	1.0	1.0	0.0	0.5	1.0	2.0
27	0.0	1.4	1.0	0.0	0.5	2.0	2.0
26	0.0	1.4	1.0	0.5	1.0	2.0	2.0
25	0.0	1.4	3.0	1.0	1.9	3.0	4.0
24	0.0	1.9	3.0	1.4	1.9	3.0	5.1
23	0.0	3.3	3.0	2.9	3.8	3.0	7.1
22	0.5	4.3	3.0	3.8	4.3	4.0	10.1
21	1.0	5.3	5.1	4.8	5.3	5.1	10.1
20	1.4	5.3	5.1	5.7	8.1	7.1	12.1

Table D.1. Frequencies (Cumulative Percentages) of Differences Between WAIS–III IQ and Index Scores by Ability Level: FSIQ ≤ 79 (continued)

Scales/Indexes

Amount of Discrepancy	VIQ–PIQ	Verbal Comprehension–Perceptual Organization	Verbal Comprehension–Working Memory	Perceptual Organization–Processing Speed	Verbal Comprehension–Processing Speed	Perceptual Organization–Working Memory	Working Memory–Processing Speed
19	2.4	8.1	6.1	6.7	9.6	10.1	15.2
18	3.3	8.1	7.1	8.1	11.0	11.1	15.2
17	3.3	9.6	8.1	11.5	13.9	11.1	16.2
16	6.2	11.0	10.1	12.0	15.3	13.1	19.2
15	7.2	11.0	13.1	14.4	16.7	15.2	21.2
14	9.1	13.4	13.1	15.8	19.1	18.2	23.2
13	12.0	16.3	18.2	17.7	21.5	20.2	31.3
12	14.8	20.6	18.2	22.5	25.8	25.3	36.4
11	17.7	23.4	22.2	24.9	33.0	33.3	39.4
10	20.6	31.1	26.3	31.1	37.8	34.3	45.5
9	27.8	33.0	30.3	37.3	43.1	38.4	56.6
8	32.1	43.5	45.5	41.1	47.4	42.4	64.6
7	37.8	46.4	46.5	48.8	51.7	47.5	70.7
6	46.4	56.5	54.5	53.1	56.9	53.5	76.8
5	52.6	59.8	56.6	60.3	63.2	55.6	78.8
4	61.2	70.3	64.6	66.0	68.4	70.7	80.8
3	71.3	73.2	74.7	77.0	78.0	79.8	89.9
2	84.2	89.0	86.9	85.2	84.7	92.9	92.9
1	94.7	91.9	94.9	95.7	97.6	97.0	98.0
0	100.0	100.0	100.0	100.0	100.0	100.0	100.0
Mean	6.1	7.4	7.2	7.5	8.2	8.0	10.3
SD	4.9	6.1	6.1	6.1	6.5	6.6	6.8
Median	5.0	6.0	6.0	6.0	7.0	6.0	9.0

The differences between IQ and Index Scores are non-directional; for example a difference of 26 points refers to PIQ minus VIQ and to VIQ minus PIQ and it was obtained by 2% of the sample. If the values are divided by two, they will approximate the differences between IQ and Index scores had they been directional.

Table D.2. Frequencies (Cumulative Percentages) of Differences Between WAIS–III IQ and Index Scores by Ability Level: FSIQ 80–89

Scales/Indexes

Amount of Discrepancy	VIQ–PIQ	Verbal Comprehension–Perceptual Organization	Verbal Comprehension–Working Memory	Perceptual Organization–Processing Speed	Verbal Comprehension–Processing Speed	Perceptual Organization–Working Memory	Working Memory–Processing Speed
≥40	0.0	0.0	0.0	0.3	0.3	0.0	1.0
39	0.0	0.0	0.0	0.3	0.6	0.0	1.0
38	0.0	0.0	0.0	0.6	0.8	0.0	1.0
37	0.0	0.0	0.0	0.6	0.8	1.5	1.0
36	0.0	0.0	0.0	0.8	0.8	1.5	1.0
35	0.0	0.3	0.0	0.8	0.8	1.5	1.0
34	0.0	0.3	0.0	0.8	0.8	1.5	1.0
33	0.0	0.6	1.0	1.4	0.8	2.0	1.5
32	0.0	0.6	1.5	1.9	1.4	3.0	2.5
31	0.0	1.7	2.0	1.9	1.7	3.5	2.5
30	0.0	1.7	2.0	2.5	2.5	4.0	4.0
29	0.3	1.7	2.0	3.0	2.5	4.0	4.0
28	0.3	1.9	2.5	3.9	3.0	6.0	4.5
27	0.6	2.8	3.0	4.1	4.1	6.5	4.5
26	1.1	3.6	4.0	4.7	4.7	7.0	5.0
25	1.4	4.4	4.5	4.7	6.6	7.5	5.0
24	1.7	5.0	5.5	6.4	8.6	9.0	7.0
23	2.2	6.4	6.5	7.5	9.9	10.4	8.0
22	2.2	7.7	8.5	7.7	11.6	10.4	9.0
21	3.3	8.6	9.5	8.8	13.0	12.4	10.9
20	4.7	9.1	12.4	10.2	15.2	12.9	12.4

Table D.2. Frequencies (Cumulative Percentages) of Differences Between WAIS–III IQ and Index Scores by Ability Level: FSIQ 80–89 (continued)

Scales/Indexes

Amount of Discrepancy	VIQ–PIQ	Verbal Comprehension–Perceptual Organization	Verbal Comprehension–Working Memory	Perceptual Organization–Processing Speed	Verbal Comprehension–Processing Speed	Perceptual Organization–Working Memory	Working Memory–Processing Speed
19	5.8	11.6	14.9	11.9	17.4	14.4	13.4
18	6.6	12.4	14.9	14.1	18.2	14.4	14.9
17	8.8	14.6	16.4	17.4	20.4	15.4	16.4
16	11.0	16.6	18.9	19.6	21.5	19.4	18.4
15	13.3	18.2	20.4	23.2	25.4	24.9	25.9
14	16.6	20.7	23.4	25.4	27.3	25.9	28.4
13	21.5	27.6	26.9	29.3	32.0	27.4	36.8
12	24.0	29.6	26.9	32.3	35.1	29.9	38.8
11	28.2	35.4	29.4	34.5	38.7	33.3	43.3
10	32.3	39.5	36.3	38.1	43.9	36.8	44.8
9	36.7	46.1	41.8	42.3	47.8	43.3	49.3
8	43.6	50.0	49.3	44.8	52.8	50.7	54.7
7	48.6	56.6	51.2	54.1	61.6	54.2	58.2
6	54.4	61.9	60.2	59.4	65.5	60.7	65.2
5	60.2	67.7	62.7	68.5	71.3	66.2	67.7
4	69.9	76.5	72.6	76.0	77.3	82.1	76.6
3	78.5	80.7	79.1	81.5	82.0	86.6	84.6
2	87.6	91.7	89.6	90.9	92.5	95.0	92.5
1	96.4	93.4	92.5	94.2	95.6	97.0	98.0
0	100.0	100.0	100.0	100.0	100.0	100.0	100.0
Mean	7.6	9.1	8.9	9.3	10.2	9.8	10.2
SD	5.9	7.1	7.6	7.8	8.1	8.2	8.1
Median	6.0	7.5	7.0	7.0	8.0	8.0	8.0

The differences between IQ and Index Scores are non-directional; for example a difference of 26 points refers to PIQ minus VIQ and to VIQ minus PIQ and it was obtained by 2% of the sample. If the values are divided by two, they will approximate the differences between IQ and Index scores had they been directional.

Table D.3. Frequencies (Cumulative Percentages) of Differences Between WAIS–III IQ and Index Scores by Ability Level: FSIQ 90–109

Scales/Indexes

Amount of Discrepancy	VIQ–PIQ	Verbal Comprehension–Perceptual Organization	Verbal Comprehension–Working Memory	Perceptual Organization–Processing Speed	Verbal Comprehension–Processing Speed	Perceptual Organization–Working Memory	Working Memory–Processing Speed
≥40	0.0	0.2	0.5	0.7	0.6	0.0	1.0
39	0.0	0.2	0.5	0.7	0.7	0.0	1.2
38	0.0	0.2	0.5	0.8	0.7	0.2	1.4
37	0.0	0.2	1.4	1.1	1.1	0.3	1.5
36	0.0	0.4	1.4	1.5	1.6	0.7	2.0
35	0.0	0.5	1.4	1.5	2.0	0.7	2.4
34	0.1	0.7	1.7	1.7	2.9	0.7	2.5
33	0.2	0.8	1.7	2.0	3.0	1.2	3.1
32	0.3	1.4	2.0	2.4	3.4	1.4	3.6
31	0.4	1.6	2.2	2.7	4.3	1.4	3.7
30	0.6	1.9	2.9	3.8	4.9	1.9	4.2
29	0.7	2.2	2.9	4.1	5.4	2.7	4.2
28	1.1	2.6	3.6	4.6	6.2	3.7	6.1
27	1.5	3.7	4.1	5.1	6.8	4.4	7.3
26	1.7	3.9	4.4	6.7	8.1	4.9	8.3
25	2.4	5.1	5.3	7.8	9.0	6.3	10.4
24	2.8	5.5	5.9	8.5	11.2	7.8	10.9
23	3.7	7.4	7.1	10.9	12.5	8.5	11.9
22	4.6	8.2	8.8	12.7	14.4	9.8	13.6
21	5.8	10.4	9.5	14.3	16.2	11.0	14.6
20	7.0	11.3	12.1	16.6	18.3	12.9	16.3

Table D.3. Frequencies (Cumulative Percentages) of Differences Between WAIS–III IQ and Index Scores by Ability Level: FSIQ 90–109 (continued)

Amount of Discrepancy	VIQ-PIQ	Verbal Comprehension–Perceptual Organization	Verbal Comprehension–Working Memory	Perceptual Organization–Processing Speed	Verbal Comprehension–Processing Speed	Perceptual Organization–Working Memory	Working Memory–Processing Speed
19	8.8	13.4	13.1	18.7	21.3	15.1	17.8
18	10.8	15.5	15.1	20.8	22.9	16.1	21.4
17	12.1	18.2	19.4	23.3	26.8	18.8	22.9
16	15.3	19.9	21.1	25.1	28.9	19.9	27.3
15	17.5	23.1	24.3	29.4	32.1	24.3	30.4
14	20.2	26.1	27.3	32.8	35.3	27.3	32.6
13	23.6	29.9	31.2	35.9	39.7	30.2	37.0
12	27.5	33.3	36.8	40.0	44.2	33.1	39.6
11	32.4	37.4	40.6	43.5	47.0	40.4	44.7
10	37.2	42.5	46.2	48.5	53.3	44.7	45.8
9	43.0	47.3	48.7	51.8	56.0	48.9	53.7
8	48.3	52.6	55.7	57.9	61.1	54.0	58.7
7	54.6	58.4	58.1	62.8	65.9	59.3	63.8
6	61.9	63.2	66.4	70.1	70.3	64.3	69.9
5	68.1	69.3	69.9	75.1	77.3	69.8	73.5
4	74.9	75.8	78.8	80.4	81.2	75.9	80.8
3	82.4	81.8	84.2	85.8	88.0	81.5	86.6
2	88.8	89.7	89.6	93.0	93.9	89.6	92.9
1	96.6	96.2	99.0	96.8	97.3	96.3	96.9
0	100.0	100.0	100.0	100.0	100.0	100.0	100.0
Mean	8.6	9.6	10.1	11.1	11.8	9.9	11.3
SD	6.4	7.6	7.8	8.5	8.8	7.8	8.9
Median	7.0	8.0	8.0	9.0	10.0	8.0	9.0

Scales/Indexes

The differences between IQ and Index Scores are non-directional; for example a difference of 26 points refers to PIQ minus VIQ and to VIQ minus PIQ and it was obtained by 2% of the sample. If the values are divided by two, they will approximate the differences between IQ and Index scores had they been directional.

Table D.4. Frequencies (Cumulative Percentages) of Differences Between WAIS–III IQ and Index Scores by Ability Level: FSIQ 110–119

Amount of Discrepancy	VIQ–PIQ	Verbal Comprehension–Perceptual Organization	Verbal Comprehension–Working Memory	Perceptual Organization–Processing Speed	Verbal Comprehension–Processing Speed	Perceptual Organization–Working Memory	Working Memory–Processing Speed
≥40	0.2	0.5	0.4	0.5	1.5	1.3	0.0
39	0.7	0.5	0.4	0.5	1.5	1.3	0.0
38	0.7	0.5	0.4	0.5	1.5	1.3	0.0
37	1.0	0.7	0.4	0.5	1.9	1.3	0.9
36	1.0	0.7	0.4	0.5	2.2	1.7	1.7
35	1.2	0.7	0.4	1.0	2.7	1.7	2.1
34	1.2	1.7	0.4	1.5	2.9	2.1	2.1
33	1.7	2.2	0.4	2.4	3.6	2.6	2.1
32	1.7	2.7	2.1	3.4	4.1	2.6	2.6
31	1.9	3.4	2.1	3.9	5.6	3.4	3.0
30	1.9	3.6	2.1	4.9	6.6	3.8	5.1
29	2.2	3.9	3.0	6.3	7.5	5.6	5.6
28	2.7	5.1	3.0	7.1	7.8	6.4	6.0
27	2.9	5.4	3.4	8.3	9.7	6.8	8.5
26	4.4	6.3	3.8	9.7	11.7	8.5	10.3
25	4.6	7.8	5.6	11.2	12.4	10.3	11.5
24	5.4	8.8	5.6	11.9	13.6	10.7	13.7
23	6.8	12.4	7.7	13.6	15.6	11.1	15.4
22	8.0	13.1	8.1	16.5	17.5	11.5	17.1
21	8.5	14.8	9.8	18.2	20.4	13.2	18.4
20	9.2	16.5	9.8	21.4	22.4	14.5	20.9

Scales/Indexes

Table D.4. Frequencies (Cumulative Percentages) of Differences Between WAIS–III IQ and Index Scores by Ability Level: FSIQ 110–119 (continued)

Scales/Indexes

Amount of Discrepancy	VIQ–PIQ	Verbal Comprehension–Perceptual Organization	Verbal Comprehension–Working Memory	Perceptual Organization–Processing Speed	Verbal Comprehension–Processing Speed	Perceptual Organization–Working Memory	Working Memory–Processing Speed
19	11.2	19.5	15.0	24.8	25.8	17.5	22.2
18	13.6	22.9	18.4	27.5	28.2	17.9	25.2
17	18.2	24.8	22.2	29.2	31.4	20.1	27.4
16	20.4	27.3	26.9	31.1	34.8	21.8	31.2
15	22.6	29.2	32.1	36.3	40.4	24.8	32.9
14	24.8	30.9	35.9	38.2	42.6	29.5	36.3
13	27.7	38.4	36.8	41.6	47.4	30.3	41.0
12	32.4	39.7	42.3	44.5	50.6	39.3	44.4
11	38.0	45.3	43.6	49.1	54.0	39.3	46.2
10	43.8	45.7	48.7	54.3	59.1	50.4	52.1
9	48.4	53.0	50.4	57.9	61.3	52.1	57.7
8	51.8	56.2	57.3	65.2	65.9	60.3	63.2
7	58.9	61.6	61.1	67.9	70.1	62.4	64.1
6	64.7	66.9	67.9	72.0	74.7	68.4	67.1
5	70.8	73.2	75.6	75.7	79.3	76.5	76.1
4	76.4	80.0	82.1	81.0	84.4	79.9	81.6
3	83.2	83.5	90.2	88.8	86.6	87.2	86.3
2	89.3	91.2	91.9	92.9	94.2	90.6	91.9
1	96.8	94.2	100.0	98.3	98.3	99.6	97.9
0	100.0	100.0	100.0	100.0	100.0	100.0	100.0
Mean	9.6	11.0	10.7	12.2	13.1	10.9	11.9
SD	7.6	8.7	7.8	8.9	9.4	8.6	8.9
Median	8.0	9.0	9.0	10.0	12.0	10.0	10.0

The differences between IQ and Index Scores are non-directional; for example a difference of 26 points refers to PIQ minus VIQ and to VIQ minus PIQ and it was obtained by 2% of the sample. If the values are divided by two, they will approximate the differences between IQ and Index scores had they been directional.

Table D.5. Frequencies (Cumulative Percentages) of Differences Between WAIS–III IQ and Index Scores by Ability Level: FSIQ ≥ 120

Scales/Indexes

Amount of Discrepancy	VIQ–PIQ	Verbal Comprehension–Perceptual Organization	Verbal Comprehension–Working Memory	Perceptual Organization–Processing Speed	Verbal Comprehension–Processing Speed	Perceptual Organization–Working Memory	Working Memory–Processing Speed
≥40	0.4	0.8	1.6	1.7	2.5	0.0	1.6
39	0.8	0.8	1.6	2.5	3.3	0.8	1.6
38	0.8	1.2	1.6	2.5	3.7	0.8	1.6
37	1.2	1.2	1.6	2.9	3.7	1.6	2.4
36	1.2	1.2	1.6	2.9	3.7	1.6	2.4
35	1.2	1.2	1.6	3.3	5.0	1.6	2.4
34	1.2	1.2	1.6	4.6	5.0	1.6	3.9
33	1.2	1.7	1.6	4.6	7.1	2.4	4.7
32	1.2	2.1	1.6	5.0	7.5	2.4	4.7
31	1.2	2.9	2.4	5.0	7.9	3.9	6.3
30	1.7	3.3	2.4	6.6	8.7	4.7	7.9
29	1.7	3.7	3.9	7.9	9.5	4.7	8.7
28	1.7	4.6	5.5	9.1	10.8	6.3	11.0
27	2.5	5.8	6.3	11.2	12.9	6.3	14.2
26	2.5	6.2	7.9	11.2	15.4	6.3	15.0
25	4.6	7.1	8.7	12.0	17.0	7.1	16.5
24	5.8	8.7	11.0	13.7	17.8	7.1	18.1
23	7.9	8.7	12.6	15.8	21.2	9.4	18.9
22	9.5	9.5	15.0	18.7	22.8	10.2	22.8
21	10.8	11.2	18.9	18.7	27.0	14.2	25.2
20	14.5	15.4	22.0	22.8	28.6	15.7	26.0

Table D.5. Frequencies (Cumulative Percentages) of Differences Between WAIS–III IQ and Index Scores by Ability Level: FSIQ ≥ 120 *(continued)*

Scales/Indexes

Amount of Discrepancy	VIQ–PIQ	Verbal Comprehension–Perceptual Organization	Verbal Comprehension–Working Memory	Perceptual Organization–Processing Speed	Verbal Comprehension–Processing Speed	Perceptual Organization–Working Memory	Working Memory–Processing Speed
19	16.2	17.4	25.2	26.1	29.5	18.9	29.1
18	17.8	22.4	29.9	27.0	34.0	19.7	29.9
17	19.9	26.1	32.3	30.3	37.3	27.6	32.3
16	23.7	27.8	36.2	31.5	41.5	29.1	35.4
15	24.5	29.9	37.0	33.6	44.8	30.7	38.6
14	29.0	30.7	37.0	36.9	49.0	35.4	40.2
13	32.4	33.6	40.9	41.1	51.0	37.0	44.9
12	38.6	35.7	45.7	44.0	56.4	43.3	49.6
11	41.5	42.7	51.2	47.7	62.2	44.9	52.0
10	48.1	47.7	59.1	54.4	67.2	48.8	55.9
9	53.5	52.7	60.6	56.0	71.0	50.4	63.8
8	59.8	59.8	63.0	63.5	71.8	55.1	69.3
7	62.2	64.3	66.9	68.0	74.7	61.4	74.0
6	67.2	68.9	70.1	73.0	78.4	68.5	78.7
5	71.4	71.8	81.1	74.7	81.3	73.2	84.3
4	75.5	77.6	82.7	78.0	84.2	77.2	87.4
3	83.0	83.0	87.4	83.8	87.1	85.0	89.8
2	88.8	91.3	88.2	89.2	92.1	89.0	90.6
1	97.1	98.8	96.9	96.7	97.9	96.9	97.6
0	100.0	100.0	100.0	100.0	100.0	100.0	100.0
Mean	10.3	10.9	12.3	12.4	14.6	11.0	13.7
SD	7.9	8.5	9.0	9.9	10.2	8.6	9.9
Median	9.0	9.0	11.0	10.0	13.0	9.0	11.0

The differences between IQ and Index Scores are non-directional; for example a difference of 26 points refers to PIQ minus VIQ and to VIQ minus PIQ and it was obtained by 2% of the sample. If the values are divided by two, they will approximate the differences between IQ and Index scores had they been directional.

Table D.6. Frequencies of Directional Discrepancies Between WAIS–III IQ and Index Scores

Amount of Discrepancy	VIQ–PIQ	Verbal Comprehension– Perceptual Organization	Verbal Comprehension– Working Memory	Perceptual Organization– Processing Speed	Verbal Comprehension– Processing Speed	Perceptual Organization– Working Memory	Working Memory– Processing Speed
–40 or less	0.0	0.2	0.1	0.3	0.3	0.2	0.4
–39	0.1	0.2	0.1	0.3	0.4	0.2	0.4
–38	0.1	0.2	0.1	0.4	0.5	0.2	0.4
–37	0.1	0.2	0.5	0.5	0.8	0.6	0.5
–36	0.1	0.2	0.5	0.7	1.0	0.7	0.7
–35	0.1	0.2	0.5	0.7	1.2	0.7	0.9
–34	0.1	0.4	0.5	0.9	1.6	0.7	1.0
–33	0.2	0.5	0.6	1.1	1.6	0.9	1.2
–32	0.2	0.7	1.0	1.3	1.8	1.0	1.4
–31	0.2	0.9	1.2	1.5	2.4	1.2	1.4
–30	0.2	1.1	1.3	1.8	2.7	1.4	2.1
–29	0.3	1.3	1.4	2.1	3.0	2.0	2.2
–28	0.5	1.5	1.4	2.5	3.3	2.7	3.0
–27	0.5	2.0	1.6	2.7	3.6	3.0	3.4
–26	0.7	2.2	1.9	3.4	4.2	3.1	4.1
–25	0.9	2.7	2.2	3.8	4.8	3.8	5.2
–24	1.0	2.9	2.8	4.3	5.9	4.3	5.8

Note. Values are based on data from WAIS–III standardization sample. $N = 2,450$ except for comparisons with WMI, where $N = 1,250$. Discrepancies of 0 were excluded.

Table D.6. Frequencies of Directional Discrepancies Between WAIS–III IQ and Index Scores *(continued)*

Scales/Indexes

Amount of Discrepancy	VIQ–PIQ	Verbal Comprehension–Perceptual Organization	Verbal Comprehension–Working Memory	Perceptual Organization–Processing Speed	Verbal Comprehension–Processing Speed	Perceptual Organization–Working Memory	Working Memory–Processing Speed
−23	1.5	3.8	3.1	5.3	6.5	4.7	6.3
−22	1.8	4.3	4.0	6.0	7.5	5.2	7.1
−21	2.5	5.1	4.6	6.7	8.2	5.8	8.0
−20	3.2	6.0	6.0	8.1	9.5	7.0	8.8
−19	4.1	6.9	7.0	9.2	10.5	7.7	9.9
−18	5.1	8.4	8.0	10.1	11.5	8.4	10.9
−17	6.2	9.5	9.5	11.6	13.2	9.6	11.8
−16	7.8	10.7	10.8	12.4	14.2	10.9	13.4
−15	8.9	11.8	11.8	14.5	16.2	12.0	15.4
−14	10.5	13.0	13.5	16.2	17.5	14.2	16.8
−13	12.0	15.4	15.0	18.0	19.8	15.4	19.5
−12	14.2	16.4	16.6	19.9	21.9	17.9	21.0
−11	16.4	19.2	17.8	21.8	23.8	19.5	22.8
−10	19.1	20.7	21.4	23.9	26.7	22.7	23.8
−9	22.3	23.6	22.6	26.0	28.1	24.1	28.2
−8	24.9	26.2	26.6	28.2	30.6	27.3	31.2
−7	27.5	28.7	27.3	30.9	32.8	28.5	33.0
−6	30.9	31.4	32.2	34.2	35.0	32.4	35.6

Note. Values are based on data from WAIS–III standardization sample. $N = 2,450$ except for comparisons with WMI, where $N = 1,250$. Discrepancies of 0 were excluded.

Table D.6. Frequencies of Directional Discrepancies Between WAIS–III IQ and Index Scores *(continued)*

Scales/Indexes

Amount of Discrepancy	VIQ–PIQ	Verbal Comprehension–Perceptual Organization	Verbal Comprehension–Working Memory	Perceptual Organization–Processing Speed	Verbal Comprehension–Processing Speed	Perceptual Organization–Working Memory	Working Memory–Processing Speed
–5	33.8	33.7	34.1	36.7	38.0	35.0	37.6
–4	37.4	37.8	37.4	39.6	39.5	39.5	41.2
–3	41.2	39.8	39.2	42.9	42.5	41.8	43.6
–2	44.9	43.9	41.4	46.7	46.2	45.9	47.3
–1	49.0	45.8	45.4	48.9	48.1	48.6	49.2
0	—	—	—	—	—	—	—
1	47.5	49.5	52.2	47.7	49.2	48.5	48.2
2	43.4	46.5	48.2	44.9	46.6	45.0	45.1
3	39.9	41.5	44.9	41.8	43.5	41.8	43.2
4	35.9	38.5	40.3	38.8	40.9	37.8	39.8
5	32.6	35.4	35.8	36.2	38.0	34.7	37.0
6	29.5	32.2	32.9	33.5	35.0	31.7	34.5
7	26.2	29.5	30.2	30.8	32.8	29.8	31.5
8	23.1	26.5	28.3	28.0	30.0	26.6	29.3
9	20.5	23.8	25.1	24.7	27.9	23.8	26.8
10	18.2	21.4	23.4	23.1	26.2	21.4	24.0
11	16.0	18.6	21.1	20.2	23.5	19.4	22.2
12	13.6	16.6	19.0	18.7	21.6	16.2	20.2

Note. Values are based on data from WAIS–III standardization sample. $N = 2,450$ except for comparisons with WMI, where $N = 1,250$. Discrepancies of 0 were excluded.

Table D.6. Frequencies of Directional Discrepancies Between WAIS–III IQ and Index Scores *(continued)*

Scales/Indexes

Amount of Discrepancy	VIQ–PIQ	Verbal Comprehension– Perceptual Organization	Verbal Comprehension– Working Memory	Perceptual Organization– Processing Speed	Verbal Comprehension– Processing Speed	Perceptual Organization– Working Memory	Working Memory– Processing Speed
13	11.8	14.8	16.6	16.8	19.6	14.2	18.6
14	9.9	12.5	14.6	15.4	17.8	13.4	15.8
15	8.7	11.2	13.7	14.2	16.2	12.4	14.9
16	7.8	10.0	11.7	12.4	14.7	9.7	13.4
17	6.5	9.3	10.3	11.5	13.4	9.2	11.3
18	5.6	8.0	8.6	10.3	11.7	7.8	10.6
19	4.8	7.3	7.4	9.2	10.8	7.8	9.0
20	4.1	5.8	6.2	8.1	9.2	6.0	8.4
21	3.4	5.4	5.6	7.1	8.4	5.7	7.4
22	3.1	4.5	4.8	6.5	7.0	4.6	7.0
23	2.6	4.1	4.2	5.3	6.2	4.2	5.9
24	2.1	3.1	3.3	4.4	5.2	3.8	5.3
25	1.7	2.7	3.1	4.0	4.6	3.2	4.6
26	1.3	2.0	2.4	3.4	4.2	2.7	4.2
27	1.1	1.8	2.2	3.0	3.4	2.2	3.9
28	0.7	1.5	1.8	2.4	2.7	1.9	3.0
29	0.6	1.1	1.2	2.2	2.3	1.5	2.5
30	0.5	1.0	1.0	1.9	2.1	1.4	2.4
31	0.5	1.0	0.8	1.3	1.8	1.1	2.1
32	0.4	0.7	0.7	1.3	1.5	0.9	1.8

Note. Values are based on data from WAIS–III standardization sample. $N = 2,450$ except for comparisons with WMI, where $N = 1,250$. Discrepancies of 0 were excluded.

Table D.6. Frequencies of Directional Discrepancies Between WAIS–III IQ and Index Scores *(continued)*

Scales/Indexes

Amount of Discrepancy	VIQ–PIQ	Verbal Comprehension– Perceptual Organization	Verbal Comprehension– Working Memory	Perceptual Organization– Processing Speed	Verbal Comprehension– Processing Speed	Perceptual Organization– Working Memory	Working Memory– Processing Speed
33	0.4	0.5	0.6	0.9	1.3	0.7	1.4
34	0.2	0.4	0.6	0.8	1.0	0.4	1.2
35	0.2	0.3	0.4	0.7	0.9	0.3	1.0
36	0.2	0.2	0.4	0.5	0.7	0.3	1.0
37	0.2	0.2	0.4	0.5	0.6	0.2	0.8
38	0.1	0.2	0.4	0.5	0.6	0.2	0.6
39	0.1	0.1	0.4	0.4	0.6	0.2	0.5
40 or more	0.0	0.1	0.4	0.3	0.5	0.1	0.4

Note. Values are based on data from WAIS–III standardization sample. $N = 2,450$ except for comparisons with WMI, where $N = 1,250$. Discrepancies of 0 were excluded.

Table D.7. Directional Cumulative Frequencies for WMS–III Index Score Differences

Difference	Aud Imm–Vis Imm	Aud Imm–Aud Del	Vis Imm–Vis Del	Aud Del–Del Rec	Aud Del–Vis Del	Imm Mem–Gen Mem	Imm Mem–Work Mem	Gen Mem–Work Mem	Rec Del–Vis Del
-40	1.0	0.0	0.0	0.0	0.6	0.0	0.3	0.4	0.6
-39	1.4	0.0	0.0	0.0	0.8	0.0	0.5	0.6	0.7
-38	1.4	0.0	0.0	0.0	1.0	0.0	0.6	0.7	1.4
-37	1.4	0.0	0.0	0.0	1.0	0.0	0.9	1.1	1.4
-36	1.6	0.0	0.0	0.0	1.3	0.0	1.0	1.2	1.4
-35	2.0	0.0	0.0	0.1	1.4	0.1	1.2	1.4	1.7
-34	2.2	0.2	0.0	0.2	1.6	0.1	1.4	1.6	2.2
-33	2.6	0.2	0.0	0.4	2.5	0.1	1.8	1.8	2.5
-32	2.7	0.2	0.0	0.5	2.5	0.1	2.0	1.8	3.3
-31	2.7	0.2	0.2	0.6	2.5	0.1	2.4	2.3	3.6
-30	3.2	0.2	0.2	0.7	3.4	0.1	2.6	2.5	3.8
-29	3.6	0.2	0.2	1.0	3.7	0.1	3.4	3.0	4.6
-28	3.6	0.2	0.2	1.3	3.7	0.1	4.0	3.8	5.0
-27	5.0	0.2	0.2	1.5	4.2	0.1	4.4	4.2	5.8
-26	5.9	0.2	0.2	2.0	5.2	0.1	5.0	4.5	7.7
-25	6.3	0.2	0.2	2.2	5.5	0.1	6.2	5.8	8.3
-24	7.7	0.2	0.4	2.7	7.4	0.1	7.4	6.7	8.8
-23	9.3	0.2	0.5	2.9	8.8	0.1	8.2	7.5	9.4
-22	9.8	0.6	1.0	3.6	9.0	0.2	8.9	8.2	10.6
-21	11.1	0.9	1.6	4.2	9.6	0.4	9.8	9.1	11.3
-20	12.8	1.0	1.6	4.9	11.7	0.5	11.4	10.7	12.6
-19	13.4	1.0	1.8	6.4	11.9	0.8	12.7	12.6	14.2
-18	14.6	1.3	2.6	7.5	12.6	1.2	13.8	13.5	15.3
-17	19.1	1.5	2.6	9.6	14.8	1.4	15.0	14.7	16.3
-16	19.3	2.3	3.2	10.6	15.1	1.7	15.8	16.0	18.3
-15	19.8	3.4	4.6	11.0	15.6	2.0	19.3	18.4	19.0
-14	23.0	4.2	4.6	13.0	19.8	2.7	20.5	19.3	20.2
-13	23.7	5.4	5.1	14.4	20.7	3.3	22.1	21.4	22.6
-12	24.2	6.6	8.5	17.7	21.3	4.5	24.7	23.8	24.7
-11	27.0	7.5	8.5	19.7	26.5	5.2	26.2	25.2	26.3
-10	27.5	9.0	10.4	21.3	26.6	7.8	28.5	27.6	29.1
-9	28.2	12.8	15.5	23.8	27.4	10.0	30.2	30.1	31.4
-8	33.1	15.1	16.2	24.5	32.2	12.1	32.2	32.5	32.7
-7	33.2	15.7	17.2	31.2	32.2	16.5	34.0	35.3	35.9
-6	34.8	22.6	26.2	33.1	34.2	19.8	36.7	37.4	37.0
-5	41.5	25.2	26.5	35.7	40.6	24.9	39.2	39.0	38.7
-4	41.8	25.4	27.0	41.4	40.9	29.2	41.5	42.2	41.3
-3	43.1	35.9	39.2	43.2	41.8	34.9	44.1	45.0	43.7
-2	48.8	38.5	40.1	46.4	46.9	40.2	46.1	47.0	46.7
-1	49.6	38.9	40.2	49.5	48.0	44.6	48.4	48.3	49.9
0	—	—	—	—	—	—	—	—	—

Table D.7. Directional Cumulative Frequencies for WMS–III Index Score Differences (*continued*)

Difference	Aud Imm–Vis Imm	Aud Imm–Aud Del	Vis Imm–Vis Del	Aud Del–Del Rec	Aud Del–Vis Del	Imm Mem–Gen Mem	Imm Mem–Work Mem	Gen Mem–Work Mem	Rec Del–Vis Del
1	48.8	38.5	40.1	46.4	46.9	40.2	46.1	47.0	46.7
2	43.1	35.9	39.2	43.2	41.8	34.9	44.1	45.0	43.7
3	41.8	25.4	27.0	41.4	40.9	29.2	41.5	42.2	41.3
4	41.5	25.2	26.5	35.7	40.6	24.9	39.2	39.0	38.7
5	34.8	22.6	26.2	33.1	34.2	19.8	36.7	37.4	37.0
6	33.2	15.7	17.2	31.2	32.2	16.5	34.0	35.3	35.9
7	33	15.1	16.2	24.5	32.2	12.1	32.2	32.5	32.7
8	28	12.8	15.5	23.8	27.4	10.0	30.2	30.1	31
9	28	9.0	10.4	21.3	26.6	7.8	28.5	27.6	29
10	27	7.5	8.5	19.7	26.5	5.2	26	25.2	26
11	24	6.6	8.5	17.7	21	4.5	25	24	25
12	24	5.4	5.1	14.4	21	3.3	22	21	23
13	23	4.2	4.6	13.0	20	2.7	20	19	20
14	20	3.4	4.6	11.0	16	2.0	19	18	19
15	19	2.3	3.2	10.6	15	1.7	16	16	18
16	19	1.5	2.6	10	15	1.4	15	15	16
17	15	1.3	2.6	8	13	1.2	14	14	15
18	13	1.0	1.8	6	12	0.8	13	13	14
19	13	1.0	1.6	5	12	0.5	11	11	13
20	11	0.9	1.6	4	10	0.4	10	9	11
21	10	0.6	1.0	4	9	0.2	9	8	11
22	9	0.2	0.5	3	9	0.1	8	8	9
23	8	0.2	0.4	3	7	0.0	7	7	9
24	6	0.2	0	2	6	0.0	6	6	8
25	6	0.0	0	2	5	0.0	5	4	8
26	5	0	0	2	4	0.0	4	4	6
27	4	0	0	1	4	0	4	4	5
28	4	0	0	1	3	0	3	3	5
29	3	0	0	1	3	0	3	2	4
30	3	0	0	0	2	0	2	2	4
31	3	0	0	0	2	0	2	2	3
32	3	0	0	0	2	0	2	2	2
33	2	0	0	0	2	0	1	1	2
34	2	0	0	0	1	0	1	1	2
35	2	0	0	0	1	0	1	1	1
36	1	0	0	0	1	0	1	1	1
37	1	0	0	0	1	0	1	0	1
38	1	0	0	0		0	0	0	1
39	1	0	0	0	0	0	0	0	1
40	1	0	0	0	0	0	0	0	0

APPENDIX E

WAIS–III Digit Span Backward Scaled-Score Equivalents of Raw Scores

Table E.1. WAIS–III Digit Span Backward Scaled-Score Equivalents of Raw Scores

Scaled Score	16–17	18–19	20–24	25–29	30–34	35–44	45–54	55–64	65–69	70–74	75–79	80–84	85–89
								Age Group					
1	—	—	—	—	—	—	—	—	—	—	—	—	—
2	—	0	0	0	0	0	0	0	0	0	0	0	0
3	0–1	1	1	1	1	1	1	1	1	1	1	1	1
4	2	2	2	2	2	2	2	2	2	2	2	2	2
5	3	3	3	3	3	3	—	3	3	3	3	3	3
6	4	4	4	4	4	4	3	4	4	4	4	4	—
7	5	5	5	—	—	—	4	—	—	—	—	—	4
8	—	—	—	5	5	5	5	5	5	5	5	5	5
9	6	6	6	6	6	6	6	6	6	6	6	6	6
10	7	7	7	7	7	7	7	7	7	7	7	7	—
11	8	8	8	8	—	—	—	8	8	8	8	8	7
12	—	—	9	9	8	8	8	9	9	9	—	9	8
13	9	9	10	10	9	9	9	10	—	10	8	10	—
14	10	10	—	—	10	10	10	—	10	10	9	—	9
15	11	11	11	11	11	11	—	10	—	9	9	9	10
16	12	12	12	12	12	12	11	11	10	10	10	10	—
17	13	13	13	13	13	13	12	12	11	11	11	11	11–12
18	14	14	14	14	14	14	13	13	12	12	12	12	13–14
19	—	—	—	—	—	—	14	14	13–14	13–14	13–14	13–14	13–14

Inclusion and Exclusion Criteria for Participation in Special Group Studies

General Exclusion Criteria

Potential participants were excluded from the studies if they met any of the following criteria:

- a vision or hearing impairment that precluded valid assessment,
- previous completion of the WMS–R or the WAIS–R within 8 weeks of testing,
- knowledge of English insufficient to ensure valid test results,
- evidence of receptive or expressive aphasia of a severity that would interfere with testing,
- concurrent substance or alcohol abuse (except for Alcohol-Related Disorders groups),
- disruptive behavior or insufficient compliance to ensure valid testing,
- upper extremity disability that would significantly affect motor performance during testing, or
- a history of psychotic disorder(s) (except for the Neuropsychiatric Disorders Group).

Neurological Disorders

Alzheimer's Disease

Participants with mild symptoms were included in the study if they met the following criteria:

- NINCDS–ADRDA diagnostic criteria for probable Alzheimer's disease,
- outpatient residential status,
- age of 60–80 years,
- a score of 18 or less on the *Beck Depression Inventory* (BDI; Beck & Steer, 1987) or a score less than 15 on the *Geriatric Depression Scale* (Sheikh & Yesavage, 1986; Yesavage et al., 1983), and

- a score of >95 on the *Dementia Rating Scale* (Mattis, 1988) or a score of 18–23 on the *Mini-Mental State Test* (Folstein, Folstein, & McHugh, 1975).

Potential participants were excluded from the study if they met any of the General Exclusion Criteria.

Huntington's Disease

Participation criteria included

- a family history of Huntington's disease;
- evidence of decline from a previous level of social or occupational functioning;
- presence of an upper-extremity motor disorder, typically manifested by eye–movement abnormalities, involuntary choreiform movements, or impaired initiation of voluntary movement;
- presence of a cognitive abnormality, typically manifested by impairments of initiation, executive control, attention, and learning;
- confirmation of caudate atrophy via magnetic resonance imaging (when available);
- age of 18 years or more; and
- diagnosis confirmed by presence of an expanded trinucleotide CAG repeat in chromosome 4 (namely, repeat number greater than 40) and Stage I, II, or III of Huntington's disease (total functioning capacity between 3 and 13, inclusive of the *Unified Huntington's Disease Rating Scale* (Kieburtz, Penney, Como, Ranch, & Shoulson, 1996).

Participants who otherwise would have met the criteria for the study were excluded if they met any of the General Exclusion Criteria or any of the following criteria:

- a history of serious head injury as determined by (a) loss of consciousness (LOC) for more than 20 minutes or (b) neurological or behavioral sequel of trauma to the brain, or
- current major depressive episode.

Parkinson's Disease

All participants were clinically diagnosed by neurologists and were included in the study on the basis of the following criteria:

- diagnosis by two independent neurologists based on two or more cardinal signs of Parkinson's disease (i.e., rigidity, bradykinesia, resting tremors, clinical responsiveness to levodopa as judged by attending neurologist);

- cognitive impairment demonstrated by a score of 90–125 on the DRS (Mattis, 1988); and

- a score of less than 18 on the BDI (Beck & Steer, 1987) or a score less than 21 on the *Geriatric Depression Scale* (Sheikh & Yesavage, 1986; Yesavage et al., 1983), that is, scores that are below the cutoff value for mild depression or dysthymia.

Participants were excluded from the sample if they met any of the General Exclusion Criteria.

Traumatic Brain Injury

Participants in this study met the following inclusion criteria:

- an initial score lower than 13 on the *Glasgow Coma Scale* (Jennett & Bond, 1975; Teasdale & Jennett, 1974),

- age of 16–65 years,

- occurrence of injury 6–18 months prior to testing,

- loss of consciousness for at least 60 minutes, and

- primary language of English.

Participants were excluded from the sample if they met any of the General Exclusion Criteria or if any of the following conditions existed:

- continuing posttraumatic amnesia;

- past or present medical history significant for symptoms of deficits that could significantly affect test scores (e.g., previous traumatic brain injury, cervical quadriparesis, history of learning disability, current substance abuse); or

- severe ataxia, tremors, or motor impairment precluding construction of 3 x 3 configurations of blocks (as in the Block Design subtest of the WAIS–III).

Multiple Sclerosis

Participants in this study met the following inclusion criteria:

- probable or definite MS (C. Poser, Poser, & Paty, 1984; S. Poser at al., 1986),
- age of 21–55 years, and
- a score <8 on the Kurtzke disability scale (Kurtzke, 1951, 1983).

Participants were excluded from the sample if they met any of the General Exclusion Criteria.

Temporal Lobe Epilepsy

Participation criteria for this study included

- evidence of lobectomy postoperative clinical improvement in seizure disorder,
- age of 16–60 years,
- an FSIQ score greater than 70,
- surgery 1–24 months prior to testing, and
- right or left speech dominance.

Participants were excluded from the sample if they met any of the General Exclusion Criteria.

Alcohol-Related Disorders

Chronic Alcohol Abuse

Participants in this study met the following inclusion criteria:

- *DSM–IV* criteria for alcohol abuse,
- 3 weeks of sobriety prior to testing,
- a VIQ score of at least 80,
- intact attention and language,
- inpatient residential status,
- a score less than 18 on the BDI (Beck & Steer, 1987),
- age of 35–55 years,
- from 9 to 16 years of education,
- absence of seizures and no intake of seizure medications, and
- a history of at least 2 years of alcohol abuse.

Participants were excluded from the sample if they met any of the General Exclusion Criteria.

Korsakoff's Syndrome

Participation criteria for this study included

- age of 53–74 years;
- previous diagnosis of Korsakoff's syndrome by neurological and neuro-psychological testing and, in some cases, by radiological confirmation;
- attention span within normal limits; and
- no history of visual–perceptual or language disorders.

Participants were excluded from the sample if they met any of the General Exclusion Criteria.

Neuropsychiatric Disorders: Schizophrenia

Participants with schizophrenia met the following inclusion criteria:

- full *DSM–IV* diagnostic criteria for schizophrenia of any subtype,
- outpatient status,
- age of 18–65 years, and
- clinical stability.

Participants were excluded from the sample if they met any of the General Exclusion Criteria.

Psychoeducational and Developmental Disorders

Mental Retardation

All participants for this WAIS–III study were recruited from private or public facilities according to the following inclusion criteria:

- for the group with mild mental retardation, an FSIQ score of 55–70 and VIQ and PIQ scores ≤70 on a standardized intelligence test other than the WAIS–III; for the group with moderate mental retardation, an FSIQ score of 35–55 and VIQ and PIQ scores <54 on a standardized intelligence test other than the WAIS–III;

- scores on the *Vineland Adaptive Behavior Scales* (Sparrow, Balla, & Cicchetti, 1984) consistent with the disorder, that is, a score of 55–65 for the group with mild mental retardation and a score <55 for the group with moderate mental retardation;

- age of onset earlier than 18 years; and

- no known acquired brain damage.

Participants were excluded from the sample if they met any of the General Exclusion Criteria.

Attention-Deficit/Hyperactivity Disorder

The participants in these studies met the following inclusion criteria:

- diagnosis of ADHD according to the *DSM–IV* criteria,

- an FSIQ score >90,

- a discrepancy of <15 points between ability and achievement scores,

- age of 16–24 years, and

- normal vision and hearing.

Participants were excluded from this study if they met any of the General Exclusion Criteria or any of the following criteria:

- concurrent psychopathology such as depressive disorders, anxiety disorders, or conduct disorder; or

- a previous diagnosis of a neurological disorder, such as epilepsy, brain tumor, or head injury.

Learning Disabilities

For both the WAIS–III and WMS–III studies, participants met the following criteria:

- a previous *DSM–IV* diagnosis of a learning disability, with documented supporting data, including specific test scores;

- an FSIQ score ≥90 on tests other than WAIS–III;

- a discrepancy ≥15 between measures of ability and achievement; and

- age of 16–24 years.

Participants were excluded from this study if they met any of the General Exclusion Criteria or any of the following criteria:

- concurrent psychopathology such as depressive disorders, anxiety disorders, or conduct disorders; or

- a previous diagnosis of a neurological disorder, such as epilepsy, brain tumor, or head injury.

Deaf and Hearing Impaired

Participants for this study were recruited according to the following criteria:

- no disabilities or impairments other than deafness or hearing impairment,

- American Sign Language (ASL) considered by participant as primary language, and

- age of 18–65 years.

Participants were excluded if they met any of the General Exclusion Criteria.

Examiners, Reviewers, and Participating Clinics and Organizations

Examiners

Elizabeth Abraham, MS
Catherine Acuff, PhD
Michelle Adams, MA
Shirley A. Albertson Owens, PhD
Sandra Alexander, MA
Lucy Allen, MA
Ronald O. Allen, EdD
Linda A. Allen-Clay, MS
Diana Allensworth, MA
Amy Amarello Sanford, PsyD
Cynthia Andrews, MEd
Kimberly Anthony, MS
Patricia Antonelli, MEd
Trinidad Arguelles, MS
Kara Arman, BS
Jeffrey Armstrong, EdS
Lois Armstrong, PhD
Brenda Arrington, EdS
Michelle Austin, MEd
Leslie Baker, MEd
Elvyn Barrable, MA
Mary Barrows, EdS
Michael Basso, PhD
Patricia Bates, MS
Robert Bauste, MS
Bonnie Nash Bawel, EdS
Trish Beach
Letitia Bean, MA
Elaine Beckwith, MS
Roberta G. Beeler, MEd

Katherine Bell, MA
Betsy Benson, PhD
Gary D. Berger, MEd
Karen I. Berland, PsyD
Pelagie Besson, PhD
Ruth Bewley, PhD
Julian Biller, EdS
Thomas W. Bishop, MA
Karen Blackwell, MA
Jonathon W. Blaine, BA
Deborah G. Blair, PsyD
Eadye Bollinger, MA
Mark A. Bolton, MA
Tamara Y. Boney, MS
Ray Booth, PhD
Mary Borders, MA
Barbara Bordner, BA
Robin Boren, PhD
Monica K. Borinstein, MS
Tom Bottenfield, MA
H. Marie Boultinghouse, EdD
Sara Bourque, EdD
Jan Boyle, EdS
Kathryn Bradford, MS
Mary Brant, PhD
Karen Brewer, PhD
Thomas Brewer, BS
Renee Briggs, PhD
Barbara Brinson, MA
Sekai Broaden, MEd

Charles Broadfield, PhD
Yvonne Brooks, EdD
Jane Brown, MS
Mary Brown
Thomas Brown, PhD
Joanne Browne, PhD
Kenneth M. Browner, BA
Jerome Bruns, PhD
Corby Bubp, BA
Robert Buckner, EdD
Don Cabell, PhD
Glenn E. Cahn, PhD
Thomas C. Caldwell, MA
Doris Callands, MEd
Maximo J. Callao, PhD
Carol Ann Calney, MEd
Lucille A. Cardella, MEd
Kenneth Carpinelli, MS
Marta Carrasco, MS
Della Carter, MS
Gloria G. Casanave, PsyD
Audrey L. Cercelle, EdS
Barbara D. Chaplik, PhD
Cheryl Charis Graves, MS
Madhu Chaturvedi, MA
Kathy Chauncey, MA
Lisa Childs, MS
Paul G. Chrustowski, MA
Toni Cicerello, MA
Richard A. Clark, MA
Paul G. Clements, PhD
Richard B. Cluff, PhD
Michelle Coffman, EdS
Anat Cohen Rosman, PhD
Marija Colic-Turcinov, MA
James Collier
John Consalvi, Jr., MA
Mary Lynn Cooper, MA
Amy Cosby, BS
Barbara Couvadelli, MA
Leon D. Cox, MA
Anita Craft, PhD
Jason Craggs, BA

Tim Crimmins, M.A.
Leslie L. Crossman, PhD
Anne S. Culp, EdS
Marcia B. Cunningham, MEd
Virginia L. Curulla, PhD
Patricia Kaiser Cutulle, BA
Wendy E. Cwinar, MEd
Diane L. D'Agostino, MA
Gail Dahl, BS
Gary M. Daily, MA
Christina Darby, BA
Helen Darks, EdD
June Fox Davis, EdS
Melonee Davis, EdS
Stephanie Day, MS
Debbie C. De Berry, EdS
Jody H. De La Pena, BS
Maria D. De La Sierra, MA
Judith R. Defeo, BS
Milton J. Dehn, EdD
Christa Dell, MA
D. Denard
Doina Denes, MA
Lynn Dennis, MA
Jeffrey Dersh, MA
Michelle D. DiGiovanni, MA
Joseph G. DiRaddio, MA
Nancy Dodge, PhD
Paul Donecker, MS
Becca Dotson, MA
Alan Dryden
Sharon Durkin, MA
Pamela Eckard, EdD
Steve Eckert, MA
Jan Eckman, MA
Debra Eddy, EdS
Oliver W. Edwards, EdD
Marjy Ehmer, PhD
Martha Eichenlaub, MEd
Cynthia L. Eland, MA
Judy E. Elkins, MS
Bonnie Ellefsen
Lisa Elliott, MS

Marge E. Everhart, MA
Laura M. Fairfax, PhD
Donna Fantozzi, MEd
Deborah Farrell Coleman, BS
Elias Fernandez, MA
Randy Fingerhut, MS
Mark W. Finkelstein, MA
Sandra Firth, BS
Debbie Fishman, BA
Ruth Fletes-Fonseca, BA
Ruth Fodness, MA
Ann L. Foreman, MA, MEd
Laura Guthermuth Foster, PhD
Mary Lou Francis, MA
Nicholas Fratto, EdD
Theresa Frazer, MS
Lesa A. Frazier, MA
Michael J. Furhman, PhD
Stacey L. Gabriel, EdS
Eugenio J. Galindro, MA
Kathryn Garrett, PhD
Haley Gaskell, MA
Karen Gavin, MS
Paula Gebauer, MA
Ellen A. Gertz, EdD
Kathleen Gilbert, MA
Alberta Gilinsky, PhD
Melisha Gilreath, EdS
Nancy Gimbert Fritze, MA
Christine Girard
Margaret Jo L. Glaser, PhD
Deanne R. Goben, MS
Robert Godsall
Jim Gold, PhD
Greg Golden, MS
Heather Goldman, EdS
Jacob Goldstein, MS
Claudia Goleburn, MS
Ana Gomez, PsyD
George Gonzalez, MA
Mercedes Graf, EdD
Janice J. Graham, MEd
Dee Ann Grant, BS

Gail Greenberg, MA
Karen Greep, MEd
Deborah Grisham-Blair, PsyD
Deborah Gussak, MA
William A. Haas, MEd
Christine E. Hack, MEd
Catherine J. Hadden, EdS
Kristin Hagy, MA
James Hale, MA
Nancy G. Hale, BA
Jill Hall, MA
David W. Hamilton, MA
Joanne Hamilton, BS
Debra K. Hamm, MA
Cheryl T. Hammond, MA
Holly Hancock, MA
Lucita Hanlin, MS
Michael Hans, PhD
Kathleen Hanson, MA
Sherry L. Harden, MA
David Hardy, PhD
Cynthia M. Harpenau, BA
Bea Harris, PhD
Josette Harris, PhD
Janice N. Harrison, PhD
Teresa M. Hart, PhD
Teresa Hatfield, MS
Edwina J. Hawes, PhD
Tamara L. Hazelton, MA
Amy Heefner, MS
E. Lynn Heeren, PhD
Bertha Henderson, MS
Brenda A. Henderson, PhD
Kara M. Hendry, MA
Dianne P. Hengst, MA
William Henry MC
Ann Hershberg, MS
Wilson Hess, PhD
Carol Hickam
John Robert S. Higgins, EdD
Karen Hike, MA
Fiona Hill, MA
Thomas F. Hill, MA

Beverly Hime, MA
Cindy Hogue, MEd
Lynn Hohrmann, MS
Jill Hoilien, MS
Frederick Holley, BA
Patricia D. Hollinger, MS
Margaret A. Hooks, MA
Carole Hooven, MEd
Loretta Houck, MA
Linder G. Howze, MS
David G. Hull, MA
Lori Nikkel Hurtik, MA
Margaret A. Hutmacher, MEd
Chris Huzinec
Robert Huzinec, MA
Virginia Iannone, PhD
Nancy A. M. Ingwell, PhD
Maureen Innes, EdS
S. Mohammed Iqbal, PhD
Patricia A. Isopo, MEd
Ryan D. Jaarsma, MA
Calvin C. Jackson, MA
Clare Jacobs
Estelle Jasnoff, EdD
Jean Jellema, MA
Norma O. Jenkins, EdS
Tom Jenkins, EdS
Wendy Jerred, MA
Carrie H. Johnson, MA
Renee Johnson-Shelley, EdS
Shirley Machocky Jones, MA
Devonna K. Jonsson, BS
Timothy J. Jovick, PhD
Giselle Juneau, BA
Lloyd J. Kallial, PhD
Sharon S. Kaufman, MA
Sandra Kazor, MS
Laurence Merrill Kelly, EdD
Mary Ann Kelly, MEd
Julie Kibler-Karl, MA
Brenda K. Kilpatrick, MA
Edward Kittinger,Jr., MA
Jeffery S. Kixmiller, PhD

Robin Knoblach, PhD
Richard D. Koehn, MA
Ronald Komers, MA
Brenda D. Kosaka, PhD
Christine E. Kostrubala, MA
Marlene Krupa
John A. Kupoinski, EdS
Robert A. Kutner, PsyD
Laura Lacritz, PhD
Karen Ladd, PhD
Matthew V. LaGrange, PhD
Robert J. Lamparello, BA
Rick J. LaMura, EdS
Dee Langley, MEd
Rayna P. Larson, MEd
Sue Larson, PhD
Atlas Laster, Jr., PhD
Janice F. Lawrence, EdD
Harry H. Lawson, PhD
Carla Lee
Michael Leland, PsyD
Susan Leonard, MA
Carol J. Lepera, BS
Michael H. Levine, EdS
Brian Levitt
David Libon
Maria Deinzer Lifrak, PhD
Joe A. Lipetzky, PsyD
Myra Little, MS
Gregory Littlejohn, MEd
Jerry Livesay, PhD
Catherine B. Lochner
Constance Locraft, PhD
Damond J. Logsdon, MA
Shane Lopez, MS
Andrea V. Lorkowski, MS
Stephen L. Loughhead, PhD
Jodi L. Lowther, MA
Dolores R. Ludwig, MA
Karen Luque, PsyD
John P. Lutchko, EdS
Marlene Lyman, EdS
Robert Lynch, MA

Phyllis MacCortney, PhD
Richard Mace, PhD
Linda Mack
Michael Maclean, MA
Mary J. Macys, PhD
Juliette M. Madigan, MEd
Sandra D. Mahoney, PhD
Lori Manade, MA
Gail H. Reichman Mancini, MA
Bill Maniago, MS
Mariano Maqueda, MS
Edward Marshall, MA
Beth Anne B. Martin, PhD
James M. Martin, EdD
Julie Martin, MA
Patricia Martin-Carr, MEd
Janet Martin-Day, EdS
Sherri Matkovich, EdS
Elaine S. Max, EdS
C. Jill McClanahan, EdS
Shelly McCoy, MEd
Robert B. McCue II, PsyD
Lyn McDonald, MA
Patricia McGarrey, PhD
Karen McGee, MA
Patricia McGinty, PhD
Anne P. McGloin, MA
Michael McGrath, PhD
Paige Davis McGuire, MA
Kathleen McKean, MS
Sandra McKinnis, MA
Thomas Meidinger, MS
Brad F. Meier, MS
Lewis H. Meltzer, MEd
Carol A. Micalizzi, MEd
Nancy L. Michael, EdS
Dimaris E. Michalek, EdD
Gail A. Mills Bigham, MA
Susan Mitchell, MEd
Carol Mongar, MA
Cristal T. Moore, MA
Kathryn L. Moore, MS
Luz-Martha Moore, EdS

Roy F. Morgan, MA
Linda Morris, MA
A. K. Morrison, MEd
Toby Motycka, PsyD
Dan Mungas, PhD
Sandra P. Munoz, MS
Alycia L. Muto, EdS
Donna Nallett
Howard Nathan, PhD
Myra Nathan, PhD
Nancy L. Naveaux, MS
Deborah Nemit, MEd
Charles Nguyen, MA
Deanne Nolte, MA
Michael Nomikos, MA
Cindy Nordlund, MA
Mark D. Nordlund, MA
Michael Norris, PhD
Sally O'Connor, MEd
Margaret O'Grady, PhD
Stephen L. O'Keefe, PhD
Deborah O'Meara, MA
Cynthia A. Olson, MS
Bruce J. Oppenheimer, MA
Peter Orlando, MEd
Emily G. Osgood, MS
Terry P. Overton, EdD
Linda Page, MA
Kimberly Palko
Gunda Jacobson Palmer, MEd
Anthony Paolitto
Sylvia V. Parga, MEd
Maxine Parvin, MA
Denise Peloquin, MS
Yolanda Perez, MA
Deborah M. Perry, MS
Rosario C. Pesce, PhD
Robert Peterson, MEd
Rosemary Peterson, MS
Christina Petofi-Casal, MA
Marie R. Petrie, MS
Warren Phillips, PhD
Paulette G. Pilsner, MEd

Lorine E. Pitter, MEd
Tina D. Ploof, MA
Norman Pomerantz, EdD
E. Jeanne Pound, EdS
Kathleen Powers, MA
Phillip C. Pratt, EdS
Paula Precht, MEd
Anne L. Price, MS
Mitch Prinstein, MS
Tanya Quille, PhD
Nancy D. Ramirez, MA
Julia M. Ramos-Grenier, PhD
Darcie Randleman, EdS
Dorothy M. Rasener, MA
Lisa M. Raufeisen, MS
Judith A. Reaven, PhD
Karen Reese, MA
Joanne Regina, PhD
Maryellen H. Reid, EdS
Laura Rencher, MS
Adriana Restrepo, EdS
Jean Reynolds, EdS
Dorothy Rhodes, MEd
Diana M. Richardson, MA
Robert Riedel, PhD
Jonathan F. Rightmyer, PhD
Cheryl Robbins, EdS
Larry Roberts, MS
Marva Roberts, MA
Laurie K. Robinson, BA
Nancy Robinson, MA
Carolyn Rodriguez, PhD
Jose Rodriguez
Ann Romer, EdS
Lane Roosa, EdD
Audrey A. Rosenberg, PhD
Vera Rosenhand, PhD
Maryann R. Roth, MEd
Emily Rummel, MA
Tamara L. Russell, EdS
Mark Rutledge-Gorman, PsyD
G. Nohl Sandall, PhD
Dave Sanford, PhD

Robin Satchell, EdS
Fausta M. Satterlee, MA
William H. Savage, MA
Jeanne Schillaci, MA
Linda Schmechel, PhD
Reva Schwartz, MEd
Elizabeth Ann Scott, EdS
John M. Sebben, BA
Bryan Senn, BA
Scott Senn, BS
Emanuel Shapiro, MA
Michael F. Shaughnessy, PhD
Judy Shaw, BA
Patricia T. Shea, MS
Glenn P. Shell, MEd
Julie Shifley, MA
Cleatta Jackson Shumate, MA
John M. Siebel, PhD
Ruby Simmons, MA
James Simonds, PhD
Shirley Simpson, MS
Preston Sims, PhD
Darshan Singh, EdD
Michael E. Siyufy, MS
Heidi Smaltz, MA
Barbara Smith, MA
Billie Smithson, MA
Tara Sommers, MA
Linda A. Soucek, PsyD
Susan Sperry, MA
Kenneth Stanton, MA
Pamela A. Stein, PhD
Naomi Steinberg, PhD
Roy D. Steinberg, PhD
Barbara R. Sterin, EdS
Diane Sterling, MA
Sara Stevenson, MA
Randall J. Stiles, PhD
Eloise C. Stoehr, MS
Robert J. Stoever, EdS
Michael L. Stranathon, MA
Gary K. Sturgill, PhD
Mary B. Summerville, PhD

Christine Svetina, MA
Margaret R. Swailes, MS
Charles W. Szasz, EdS
Joseph Szyszko
Scott Talbert, BS
James M. Talone, PhD
Florence Tam, PsyD
Elizabeth Tamborella, EdD
Claire Tarte, PhD
Teresa Taylor, MA
Nan Taylor-Balser, PhD
David C. Terjanian, MEd
Terry L. Thatcher, MS
Elizabeth Thomas, MS
Judy Thompson, MA
Kathi Y. Thompson, MS
Gary D. Tolman, MS
Konnie Torbahn, MA
Carolyn Truesdale, MA
Connie Tucker, MS
Gretchen Tucker, MA
Alan G. Tuft, PhD
Helen M. Tulsky, MA
Jennifer Turner, MEd
Julieanne Turnley, EdS
M. Eron Tworetzky, MA
Jan M. Ueckert, MEd
Hiromi Unno, MA
Karen J. VanHandel, MS
Dale J. Veith, MS
Sister Sue Verbiscus SC
David Vesel, MA
Nicole Vincent, MS
Elizabeth A. Vosper, MEd
Brian Wagner, MS
Sharon Wakefield-Brown, MEd
Marie Walbridge, PhD
Robin Walker, BA
Robert Walkow, MEd
Louise Walsh, MA
Amy Sanford Walters, PhD
Robert Walters, PsyD
Victoria Ware, EdS

Shirley M. Warford, MEd
Valarie Warmflash, PhD
Barry A. Wartenberg, MA
Fiona F. Weekes, MA
Fredric J. Weiner, EdD
Sally A. Weisman, MS
Patricia Weiss, EdD
Cecily Weistein, MA
Sylvia Weisz, MEd
Patricia J. Wellman, MEd
Kim R. Welsh, EdS
Marc U. Wenzel, MA
Jim G. White, EdS
Kristin Wiens, MA
Martin J. Wiese, PhD
Barbara Wilkerson
Beatrice B. Wilkins, MEd
Greg Williams
Judy Wolfram, MA
Dennis Wood, PhD
Walter M. Wood, EdD
John L. Woodard, PhD
John Woodland, MA
William H. Worrall, MA
Gloria B. Wuhl, PhD
Tim Wynkoop, PhD
Terri B. Yerman, MA
Jennifer L. Yount, MA
Margaret Zabel, EdS

Validity Studies Cooperators

Bradley N. Axelrod, PhD
William B. Barr, PhD
James T. Becker, PhD
Robert Bornstein, PhD
Rosemary Bowler, PhD
Jeffrey Braden, PhD
Thomas Brown , PhD
Robert Buchanan MD
Meryl Butters, PhD
Gordon Chelune, PhD
C. Munro Cullum, PhD
Michael J. Furhman, PhD
Jim Gold, PhD
Robert Heaton, PhD
David O. Herman, PhD
Elizabeth Heron, PhD

Jeffery S. Kixmiller, PhD
Kathleen Knee, PhD
Christine E. Kostrubala, MA
Maria Deinzer Lifrak, PhD
Thomas Lozinski, PhD
Donald Marion MD
Dan Mungas, PhD
Anthony Paolo, PhD
Marie R. Petrie MS
Joseph Ryan, PhD
Donald H. Saklofske, PhD
David Salmon, PhD
Vicki Schwean, PhD
Esther Strauss, PhD
Michael Whetstone, PhD
John L. Woodard, PhD

Reviewers and Consultants

Jennifer Abe–Kim, PhD
Kenneth Adams, PhD
Andres Barona, PhD
Russell M. Bauer, PhD
Linas A. Bieliauskas, PhD
Lawrence M. Binder, PhD
Robert Bornstein, PhD
Jeffrey Braden, PhD
Patricia Brazil, PhD
Nelson Butters, PhD
Meryl Butters, PhD
John B. Carroll, PhD
Gordon J. Chelune, PhD
Cindy Cimino, PhD
Raymond M. Costello, PhD
Munro Cullum, PhD
Malcolm Cummings, PhD
Dean Dellis, PhD
Barry Dewlan, PhD
Maureen Drews, PhD
Ruben J. Echemendia, PhD
Eugene Emory, PhD
Ian Evans, PhD

Candace M. Fleming, PhD
Michael D. Franzen, PhD
Craig Frisby, PhD
Lucy Frontera, PhD
Ollie Gibbs EdD
David Goh, PhD
Jim Gold, PhD
Richard Gorsuch, PhD
Patti L. Harrison, PhD
Robert Heaton, PhD
Janet Helms, PhD
David Herman, PhD
Elizabeth Heron, PhD
George W. Hynd EdD
Robert Ivnik, PhD
Sharon Johnson, PhD
Edith Kaplan, PhD
Alan Kaufman, PhD
Jeff King, PhD
Essie Knuckle, PhD
Glenn Larrabee, PhD
Asenath LaRue, PhD
Muriel D. Lezak, PhD

David W. Loring, PhD
Hector Machabanski, PhD
Charlie Magruder, PhD
David Martino, PhD
Neil Massoth, PhD
Joseph D. Matarazzo, PhD
Kevin Miller, PhD
Charles Morton, PhD
Hector F. Myers, PhD
Tom Oakland, PhD
Sumie Okazaki, PhD
Esteban Olmeda, PhD
Elijio Padilla, PhD
Anthony Paolo, PhD
Marcel Ponton, PhD
Anthony Puente , PhD
Chris Randolph, PhD
Gale H. Roid, PhD

Joseph J. Ryan, PhD
Jonathon Sandoval, PhD
Jerome Sattler, PhD
Abigail Sivan, PhD
John Slate, PhD
Jean Spruill, PhD
Herbert H. Stenson, PhD
Martha Storandt, PhD
Lisa Ann Suzuki, PhD
Pat Tanner-Halverson, PhD
John F. Taylor, PhD
Pat Thompson, PhD
Alexander I. Tröster, PhD
Joseph Trimble, PhD
Susana Urbina, PhD
Rodney Vanderploeg, PhD
Irla Lee Zimmerman, PhD

Participating Schools and Organizations

B'Nai Tikvah, Deerfield, IL
Cleveland Clinic Florida,
    Ft. Lauderdale, FL
Cleveland Clinic Foundation,
    Cleveland, OH
Commander's House Senior Citizen
    Center, San Antonio, TX
Comprehensive Neuropsychological
    Services, Albany, NY
Emory University, Atlanta, GA
Evanston Township High School,
    Evanston, IL
Goodwill Industries of San Antonio, TX
Jersey Shore Medical Center Behavioral
    Health Services, Neptune, NJ
Long Island Jewish Medical Center,
    Research Department, Glen Oaks, NY
Lutheran High School, San Antonio, TX
MacArthur High School Band, San
    Antonio, TX
Maryland Psychiatric Research Center,
    Baltimore, MD

Metro Health Care Campaign, San
    Antonio, TX
St. John's Regional Hospital,
    Rehabilitation Administration,
    Springfield, MO
The Research General Post Fund,
    Pittsburgh, PA
University of California San Diego,
    Department of Neurosciences, La
    Jolla, CA
University of Kansas Medical Center,
    Kansas City, KS
University of Saskatchewan, Saskatoon,
    SK, Canada
University of Texas Southwestern
    Medical Center at Dallas, Dallas, TX
University of Wisconsin Madison,
    Department of Educational
    Psychology, Madison, WI
Wilford Hall Medical Center, San
    Antonio, TX

REFERENCES

Ackerman, P. T., Dykman, R. A., & Peters, J. E. (1976). Hierarchical factor patterns on the WISC as related to areas of learning deficit. *Perceptual and Motor Skills, 42*, 583–615.

Adams, J. H., Graham, D. I., Murray, L. S., & Scott, G. (1982). Diffuse anoxal injury due to nonmissle head injury in humans: An analysis of 45 cases. *Annals of Neurology, 12*, 557–563.

Akaike, H. (1987). Factor analysis and AIC. *Psychkometrika, 52*(3), 317–332.

Alexander, G. E., Prohovnik, I., Stern, Y., & Mayeux, R. (1994). WAIS–R subtest profile and cortical perfusion in Alzheimer's disease. *Brain and Cognition, 24*, 24–43.

Allen, M. J., & Yen, W. M. (1979). *Introduction to measurement theory.* Monterey, CA: Brooks/Cole.

Almkvist, O., Bäckman, L., Basun, H., & Wahlund, L. O. (1993). Patterns of neuropsychological performance in Alzheimer's disease and vascular dementia. *Cortex, 29*, 661–673.

American Association on Mental Retardation. (1992). *Mental retardation: Definitions, classification, and systems of supports* (9th ed.). Washington, DC: Author.

American Psychiatric Association. (1994). *Diagnostic and statistical manual of mental disorders* (4th ed.). Washington, DC: Author.

Anastasi, A., & Urbina, S. (1997). *Psychological testing* (7th ed.). Upper Saddle River, NJ: Prentice Hall.

Andreasen, N. C., & Carpenter, W. T., Jr. (1993). Diagnosis and classification of schizophrenia. *Schizophrenia Bulletin, 19*(2), 199–214.

Angoff, W. H. (1984). *Scales, norms, and equivalent scores.* Princeton, NJ: Educational Testing Service.

Annegers, J. F., Grabow, J. D., Kurland, L. T., & Laws, E. R. (1980). The incidence, causes, and secular trends of head trauma in Olmstead County, Minnesota, 1935–1974. *Neurology, 30*, 912–919.

Arcia, E., & Gualtieri, C. T. (1994). Neurobehavioural performance of adults with closed-head injury, adults with attention deficit, and controls. *Brain Injury, 8*(5), 395–404.

Arnau, R. C., & Thompson, B. (2000). Second-order confirmatory factor analysis of the WAIS–III. *Psychological Assessment, 7*(3), 237–246.

Arnold, S. E., Hyman, B. T., Van Hoesen, G. W., & Damasio, A. R. (1991). Some cytoarchitectural abnormalities of the entorhinal cortex in schizophrenia. *Archives of General Psychiatry, 48*, 625–632.

Arria, A. M., Tarter, R. E., Kabene, M. A., Laird, S. B., Moss, H., & Van Thiel, D. H. (1991). The role of cirrhosis in memory functioning of alcoholics. *Alcoholism: Clinical and Experimental Research, 15*(6), 932–937.

Atkinson, L. (1992) Mental retardation and WAIS–R scatter analysis. *Journal of Intellectual Disability Research, 36*, 443–448.

Atkinson, R. C., & Shiffrin, R. M. (1968). A proposed system and its control processes. In K. W. Spence & J. T. Spence (Eds.), *The psychology of learning and motivation: Advances in research and theory* (Vol. 2, pp. 82–90). New York: Academic Press.

Axelrod, B. N. (2002). Validity of the *Wechsler Abbreviated Scale of Intelligence* and other very short forms of estimating intellectual functioning. *Assessment, 9*(1), 17–23.

Baddeley, A. D. (1986). *Working memory*. Oxford, England: Oxford University Press.

Baddeley, A. D. (1992). Is working memory working? The fifteenth Bartlett lecture. *The Quarterly Journal of Experimental Psychology, 441*(1), 3–29.

Baddeley, A. D., & Hitch, G. (1974). Working memory. In G. H. Bower (Ed.), *The psychology of learning and motivation: Advances in research and theory* (Vol. 8, pp. 47–90). San Diego, CA: Academic Press.

Bannatyne, A. (1968). Diagnosing learning disabilities and writing remedial prescriptions. *Journal of Learning Disabilities, 1*(4), 242–249.

Bannatyne, A. (1974). Diagnosis: A note on recategorization of the WISC scaled scores. *Journal of Learning Disabilities, 7*(5), 272–273.

Barkley, R. A., Anastopoulos, A. D., Guevremont, D. C., & Fletcher, K. E. (1991). Adolescents with ADHD: Patterns of behavioral adjustment, academic functioning, and treatment utilization. *Journal of the American Academy of Child and Adolescent Psychiatry, 30*(5), 752–761.

Barona, A., Reynolds, C. R., & Chastain, R. (1984). A demographically based index of pre-morbid intelligence for the WAIS–R. *Journal of Consulting and Clinical Psychology, 52*(5), 885–887.

Basso, M. R., Harrington, K., Matson, M., & Lowery, N. (2000). Sex differences on the WMS–III: Findings concerning Verbal Paired Associates and Faces. *Clinical Neuropsychologist, 14*(2), 231–235.

Baving, L., Laucht, M., & Schmidt, M. H. (1999). Atypical frontal brain activation in ADHD: Preschool and elementary school boys and girls. *Journal of the American Academy of Child and Adolescent Psychiatry, 38*(11), 1363–1371.

Bawden, H. N., Knights, R. M., & Winogron, H. W. (1985). Speeded performance following head injury in children. *Journal of Clinical and Experimental Neuropsychology, 7*(1), 39–54.

Beardsworth, E. D., & Zaidel, D. W. (1994). Memory for faces in epileptic children before and after brain surgery. *Journal of Clinical and Experimental Neuropsychology, 16*(4), 589–596.

Beck, A. T., & Steer, R. A. (1987). *Beck Depression Inventory*. San Antonio, TX: The Psychological Corporation.

Bentler, P. M. (1980). Multivariate analysis with latent variables: Causal modeling. *Annual Review of Psychology, 31*, 419–456.

Bentler, P. M., & Wu, E. J. C. (1993). *EQS/Windows user's guide (Version 4)*. Los Angeles: BMDP Statistical Software.

Benton, A. L., Eslinger, P. J., & Damasio, A. R. (1981). Normative observations on neuropsychological test performances in old age. *Journal of Clinical Neuropsychology, 3*(1), 33–42.

Benton, A. L., & Hamsher, K. deS. (1994). *Multilingual Aphasia Examination* (3rd ed.). Iowa City: AJA Associates.

Benton, A. L., Hamsher, K. deS., Varney, N. R., & Spreen, O. (1983). *Judgment of Line Orientation, Form H*. New York: Oxford University Press.

Berardi, A., Haxby, J. V., Grady, C. L., & Rapoport, S. I. (1991). Asymmetries of brain glucose metabolism and memory in the healthy elderly. *Developmental Neuropsychology, 7*(1), 87–97.

Berg, E. A. (1948). A simple objective technique for measuring flexibility in thinking. *Journal of General Psychology, 39*, 15–22.

Berk, R. A. (1984). *Screening and diagnosis of children with learning disabilities.* Springfield, IL: Charles C. Thomas.

Biederman, J., Faraone, S. V., Spencer, T., Wilens, T., Norman, D., Lapey, K. A., et al. (1993). Patterns of psychiatric comorbidity, cognition, and psychosocial functioning in adults with attention deficit hyperactivity disorder. *American Journal of Psychiatry, 150*(12), 1792–1798.

Bigler, E. D., Johnson, S. C., Anderson, C. V., Blatter, D. D., Gale, S. D., Russo, A. A., et al. (1996). Traumatic brain injury and memory: The role of hippocampal atrophy. *Neuropsychology, 10*(3), 333–342.

Blair, J. R., & Spreen, O. (1989). Predicting premorbid IQ: A revision of the National Adult Reading Test. *Clinical Neuropsychologist, 3*(2), 129–136.

Blyler, C. R., Gold, J. M., Iannone, V. N., Buchanan, R. W. (2000). Short form of the WAIS–III for use with patients with schizophrenia. *Schizophrenia Research, 46*, 209–215.

Bohman, M., Cloninger, R., Sigvardsson, S., & von Knorring, A. L. (1987). The genetics of alcoholisms and related disorders. *Journal of Psychiatric Research, 21*(4), 447–452.

Bollen, K. A. (1989). *Structural equations with latent variables.* New York: Wiley.

Bollen, K. A., & Long, J. S. (1993). Introduction. In K. A. Bollen & J. S. Long (Eds.), *Testing structural equation models* (pp. 1–9). Newbury Park, CA: Sage.

Bondi, M. W., Monsch, A. U., Galasko, D., Butters, N., Salmon, D. P., & Delis, D. C. (1994). Preclinical cognitive markers of dementia of the Alzheimer type. *Neuropsychology, 8*(3), 374–384.

Bornstein, R. A., & Chelune, G. J. (1988). Factor structure of the Wechsler Memory Scale—Revised. *The Clinical Neuropsychologist, 2*(2), 107–115.

Bornstein, R. A., Chelune, G. J., & Prifitera, A. (1989). IQ–memory discrepancies in normal and clinical samples. *Journal of Consulting and Clinical Psychology, 1*(3), 203–206.

Bowden, S. C., Whelan, G., Long, C. M., & Clifford, C. C. (1995). Temporal stability of the WAIS–R and WMS–R in a heterogeneous sample of alcohol dependent clients. *The Clinical Neuropsychologist, 9*(2), 194–197.

Braden, J. P. (1990). Do deaf persons have a characteristic psychometric profile on the Wechsler Performance scales? *Journal of Psychoeducational Assessment, 8*, 518–526.

Braden, J. P. (1992). Intellectual assessment of deaf and hard–of–hearing people: A quantitative and qualitative research synthesis. *School Psychology Review, 21*(1), 82–94.

Braden, J. P., & Weiss, L. (1988). Effects of simple difference versus regression discrepancy methods: An empirical study. *Journal of School Psychology, 26*, 133–142.

Brandt, J. (1992). Detecting amnesia's impostors. In L. R. Squire & N. Butters (Eds.), *Neuropsychology of memory* (2nd ed., pp. 156–165). New York: Guilford Press.

Brandt, J. A., & Bylsma, F. W. (1993). The dementia of Huntington's disease. In R. W. Parks, R. F. Zec, & R. S. Wilson (Eds.), *Neuropsychology of Alzheimer's disease and other dementias* (pp. 265–282). New York: Oxford University Press.

Brandt, J., & Butters, N. (1986). The neuropsychology of Huntington's disease. *Trends in Neuroscience, 9*, 118–120.

Brennen, R. L. (1983). *Elements of generalizability theory.* Iowa City, IA: American College Testing Program.

Brinkman, S. D., & Braun, P. (1984). Classification of dementia patients by a WAIS profile related to central cholinergic deficiencies. *Journal of Clinical Neuropsychology, 6*(4), 393–400.

Brody, N. (1992). *Intelligence* (2nd ed.). San Diego, CA: Academic Press.

Brooks, D. N. (1976). Wechsler Memory Scale performance and its relationship to brain damage after severe closed head injury. *Journal of Neurology, Neurosurgery, and Psychiatry, 39*(6), 593–601.

Brown, R. G., & Marsden, C. D. (1986). Visuospatial function in Parkinson's disease. *Brain, 109,* 987–1002.

Brown, T. E. (1996). *Brown Attention–Deficit Disorder Scales.* San Antonio, TX: The Psychological Corporation.

Burke, H. R. (1985). Raven's Progressive Matrices (1938): More on norms, reliability, and validity. *Journal of Clinical Psychology, 41*(2), 231–235.

Burke, H. R., & Bingham, W. C. (1969). Raven's Progressive Matrices: More on construct validity. *Journal of Psychology, 72,* 247–251.

Burton, D. B., Mittenberg, W., & Burton, C. A. (1993). Confirmatory factor analysis of the Wechsler Memory Scale—Revised standardization sample. *Archives of Clinical Neuropsychology, 8*(6), 467–475.

Butters, N. (1986). The clinical aspects of memory disorders. In T. Incagnoli, G. Goldstein, & C. J. Golden (Eds.), *Clinical application of neuropsychological test batteries* (pp. 361–382). New York: Plenum Press.

Butters, N., & Cermak, L. S. (1980). *Alcoholic Korsakoff's syndrome.* New York: Academic Press.

Butters, N., Salmon, D. P., Cullum, C. M., Cairns, P., Tröster, A. I., Jacobs, D., et al. (1988). Differentiation of amnesic and demented patients with the Wechsler Memory Scale—Revised. *The Clinical Neuropsychologist, 2*(2), 133–148.

Butters, N., Sax, D., Montgomery, K., & Tarlow, S. (1978). Comparison of the neuropsychological deficits associated with early and advanced Huntington's disease. *Archives of Neurology, 35*(9), 585–589.

Butters, N., Wolfe, J., Martone, M., Granholm, E., & Cermak, L. S. (1985). Memory disorders associated with Huntington's disease: Verbal recall, verbal recognition and procedural memory. *Neuropsychologia, 23*(6), 729–743.

Campbell, D. T., & Fiske, D. W. (1959). Convergent and discriminant validation by the multitrait–multimethod matrix. *Psychological Bulletin, 56,* 81–105.

Capruso, D. X., & Levin, H. S. (1992). Cognitive impairment following closed head injury. *Neurologic Clinics, 10*(4), 879–893.

Carlesimo, G. A., & Caltagirone, C. (1995). Components in the visual processing of known and unknown faces. *Journal of Clinical and Experimental Neuropsychology, 17*(5), 691–705.

Carlson, R. A., Khoo, B. H., Yaure, R. G., & Schneider, W. (1990). Acquisition of a problem–solving skill: Levels of organization and use of working memory. *Journal of Experimental Psychology: General, 119*(2), 193–214.

Carroll, J. B. (1993). *Human cognitive abilities: A survey of factor-analytic studies.* New York: Cambridge University Press.

Carroll, J. B. (1997). The three-stratum theory of cognitive abilities. In D. P. Flanagan, J. L. Genshaft, & P. L. Harrison (Eds.), *Contemporary intellectual assessment: Theories, tests, and issues* (pp. 122–130). New York: Guilford Press.

Castellanos, F. X., Giedd, J. N., Marsh, W. L., Hamburger, S. D., Vaituzis, A. C., Dickstein, D. P., et al. (1996). Quantitative brain magnetic resonance imaging in attention-deficit hyperactivity disorder. *Archives of General Psychiatry, 53*(7), 607–616.

Castellanos, F. X., Giedd, J. N., Eckburg, P., Marsh, W. L., Vaituzis, A. C., Kaysen, D. et al. (1994). Quantitative morphology of the caudate nucleus in attention deficit hyperactivity disorder. *American Journal of Psychiatry, 151*(12), 1791–1796.

Cattell, R. B. (1943). The measurement of adult intelligence. *Psychological Bulletin, 40*(3), 153–193.

Cattell, R. B. (1963). Theory of fluid and crystallized intelligence: A critical experiment. *Journal of Educational Psychology, 54*(1), 1–22.

Cattell, R. B., & Horn, J. L. (1978). A check on the theory of fluid and crystallized intelligence with description of new subtest designs. *Journal of Educational Measurement, 15*(3), 139–164.

Chelune, G. J., & Bornstein, R. A. (1988). WMS–R patterns among patients with unilateral brain lesions. *The Clinical Neuropsychologist, 2*(2), 121–132.

Chelune, G. J., Bornstein, R. A., & Prifitera, A. (1990). The Wechsler Memory Scale—Revised: Current status and applications. In J. Rosen, P. McReynolds, & G. J. Chelune (Eds.), *Advances in psychological assessment* (Vol. 7, pp. 66–95). New York: Plenum Press.

Chelune, G. J., Naugle, R. I., Lüders, H., Sedlak, J., & Awad, I. A. (1993). Individual change after epilepsy surgery: Practice effects and base-rate information. *Neuropsychology, 7*(1), 41–52.

Cohen, J. (1952a). A factor-analytically based rationale for the Wechsler–Bellevue. *Journal of Consulting Psychology, 16*, 272–277.

Cohen, J. (1952b). Factors underlying Wechsler–Bellevue performance of three neuropsychiatric groups. *Journal of Abnormal and School Psychology, 47*, 359–364.

Cohen, J. (1957a). A factor-analytically based rationale for the Wechsler Adult Intelligence Scale. *Journal of Consulting Psychology, 21*(6), 451–457.

Cohen, J. (1957b). The factorial structure of the WAIS between early adulthood and old age. *Journal of Consulting Psychology, 21*(4), 283–290.

Cohen, M. (1997). *Children's Memory Scale.* San Antonio, TX: The Psychological Corporation.

Conrad, A. J., Abebe, T., Austin, R., Forsythe, S., & Scheibel, A. B. (1991). Hippocampal pyramidal cell disarray in schizophrenia as a bilateral phenomenon. *Archives of General Psychiatry, 48*, 413–417.

Cooper, E. H., & Pantle, A. J. (1967). The total-time hypothesis in verbal learning. *Psychological Bulletin, 68*(4), 221–234.

Cooper, J. A., Sagar, H. J., Jordan, N., Harvey, N. S., & Sullivan, E. V. (1991). Cognitive impairment in early, untreated Parkinson's disease and its relationship to motor disability. *Brain, 114*, 2095–2122.

Cordoni, B. K., O'Donnell, J. P., Ramaniah, N. V., Kurtz, J., & Rosenshein, K. (1981). Wechsler adult intelligence score patterns for learning disabled young adults. *Journal of Learning Disabilities, 14*(7), 404–407.

Corina, D. P., Richards, T. L., Serafini, S., Richards, A. L., Steury, K., Abbott, R. D., et al (2001). MRI auditory language differences between dyslexic and able reading children. *Neuroreport, 12*(6), 1195–1201.

Corsi, P. M. (1972). *Human memory and the medial temporal region of the brain.* Unpublished doctoral dissertation, McGill University, Montreal, Canada.

Costa, L. D. (1975). The relation of visuospatial dysfunction to digit span performance in patients with cerebral lesions. *Cortex, 11,* 31–36.

Craft, N. P., & Kronenberger, E. J. (1979). Comparability of WISC–R and WAIS IQ scores in educable mentally handicapped adolescents. *Psychology in the Schools, 16*(4), 502–504.

Crawford, J. R. (1992). Current and premorbid intelligence measures in neuropsychological assessment. In J. R. Crawford, D. M. Parker, & W. W. McKinlay (Eds.), *A handbook of neuropsychological assessment* (pp. 21–49). Hillsdale, NJ: Erlbaum.

Crocker, L., & Algina, J. (1986). *Introduction to classical and modern test theory.* Fort Worth, TX: Harcourt Brace Jovanovich College.

Cronbach, L. J., Gleser, G. C., Nanda, H., & Rajaratnam, N. (1972). *The dependability of behavioral measurements: Theory of generalizability for scores and profiles.* New York: Wiley.

Cronbach, L. J., Rajaratnam, N., & Gleser, G. C. (1963). Theory of generalizability: A liberalization of reliability theory. *British Journal of Statistical Psychology, 16*(2), 137–163.

Cutting, J. (1978). Patterns of performance in amnesic subjects. *Journal of Neurology, Neurosurgery, and Psychiatry, 41*(3), 278–282.

Daneman, M., & Carpenter, P. A. (1980). Individual differences in working memory and reading. *Journal of Verbal Learning and Verbal Behavior, 19,* 450–466.

Daum, I., Schugens, M. M., Spieker, S., Poser, U., Schonle, P. W., & Birbaumer, N. (1995). Memory and skill acquisition in Parkinson's disease and frontal lobe dysfunction. *Cortex, 31,* 413–432.

Davila, M. D., Shear, P. K., Lane, B., Sullivan, E. V., & Pfefferbaum, A. (1994). Mammillary body and cerebellar shrinkage in chronic alcoholics: An MRI and neuropsychological study. *Neuropsychology, 8*(3), 433–444.

Davis, F. B. (1959). Interpretation of differences among averages and individual test scores. *Journal of Educational Psychology, 50*(4), 162–170.

de Jong, P. F., & Das–Smaal, E. A. (1995). Attention and intelligence: The validity of the Star Counting Test. *Journal of Educational Psychology, 87*(1), 80–92.

de Jonge, P., & de Jong, P. F. (1996). Working memory, intelligence and reading ability in children. *Personality and Individual Differences, 21*(6), 1007–1020.

Delis, D. C., Kramer, J. H., Kaplan, E., & Ober, B. A. (1987). *California Verbal Learning Test—Adult Version.* San Antonio, TX: The Psychological Corporation.

Delis, D. C., Massman, P. J., Butters, N., Salmon, D. P., Cermak, L. S., & Kramer, J. H. (1991). Profiles of demented and amnesic patients on the California Verbal Learning Test: Implications for the assessment of memory disorders. *Psychological Assessment: A Journal of Consulting and Clinical Psychology, 3*(1), 19–26.

Denckla, M. B. (1993). The child with developmental disabilities grown up: Adult residua of childhood disorders. *Behavioral Neurology, 11*(1), 105–125.

Denckla, M. B. (1996). A theory and model of executive function. In G. R. Lyon & N. A. Krasnegor (Eds.), *Attention, memory, and executive function* (pp. 263–278). Baltimore: Paul. H. Brookes.

Desai, M. M. (1955). The relationship of the Wechsler–Bellevue Verbal scale and the Progressive Matrices Test. *Journal of Consulting Psychology, 19*(1), 60.

Developmentally Disabled Assistance and Bill of Rights Act of 1975, 42 U.S.C. §6001.

Dichter, M. A. (1994). The epilepsies and convulsive disorders. In K. J. Isselbacher, E. Braunwald, J. D. Wilson, J. B. Martin, A. S. Fauci, & D. L. Kasper (Eds.), *Harrison's principles of internal medicine* (13th ed., Vol. 2, pp. 2223–2233). New York: McGraw–Hill.

Dickerson, F. B., Ringel, N. B., & Boronow, J. J. (1991). Neuropsychological deficits in chronic schizophrenics: Relationship with symptoms and behavior. *Journal of Nervous and Mental Disease, 179*(12), 744–749.

Dikmen, S. S., Machamer, J. E., Winn, H. R., & Temkin, N. R. (1995). Neuropsychological outcome at 1-year post head injury. *Neuropsychology, 9*(1), 80–90.

Dikmen, S., Reitan, R. M., & Temkin, N. R. (1983). Neuropsychological recovery in head injury. *Archives of Neurology, 40*, 333–338.

Donders, J., Tulsky, D. S., & Zhu, J. (2001). Criterion validity of new WAIS–III subtest scores after traumatic brain injury. *Journal of the International Neuropsychological Society, 7*(7), 892–898.

Doss, R. C., Chelune, G. J., & Naugle, R. I. (2000). Comparability of the expanded WMS–III standardization protocol to the published WMS–III among right and left temporal lobectomy patients. *Clinical Neuropsychologist, 14*(4), 468–473.

Du, A. T., Schuuf, N., Amend, D., Laasko, M. P., Hsu, Y. Y., Jagust, W. J., et al. (2001). Magnetic resonance imaging of the entorhinal cortex and hippocampus in mild cognitive impairment and Alzheimer's disease. *Journal of Neurology, Neurosurgery and Psychiatry, 71*(4), 431–432.

Dudek, F. J. (1979). The continuing misinterpretation of the standard error of measurement. *Psychological Bulletin, 86*(2), 335–337.

Eckardt, M. J., Rohrbaugh, J. W., Stapleton, J. M., Davis, E. Z., Martin, P. R., & Weingartner, H. J. (1996). Attention-related brain potential and cognition in alcoholism-associated organic brain disorders. *Biological Psychiatry, 39*, 143–146.

Education for All Handicapped Children Act of 1975, 20 U.S.C. §1400 et seq.

Ellenberg, L., Rosenbaum, G., Goldman, M. S., & Whitman, R. D. (1980). Recoverability of psychological functioning following alcohol abuse: Lateralization effects. *Journal of Consulting and Clinical Psychology 48*(4), 503–510.

Ellis, R. J., & Oscar–Berman, M. (1989). Alcoholism, aging, and functional cerebral asymmetries. *Psychological Bulletin, 106*(1), 128–147.

Elwood, R. W. (1991). Factor structure of the Wechsler Memory Scale—Revised (WMS–R) in a clinical sample: A methodological reappraisal. *The Clinical Neuropsychologist, 5*(4), 329–337.

Fisher, D. C., Ledbetter, M. F., Cohen, N. J., Marmor, D., & Tulsky, D. S. (2000). WAIS–III and WMS–III profiles of mildly to severely brain-injured patients. *Applied Neuropsychology, 7*(3), 126–132.

Fisher, J. S. (1988). Using the Wechsler Memory Scale—Revised to detect and characterize memory deficits in multiple sclerosis. *The Clinical Neuropsychologist, 2*(2), 149–172.

Flanagan, D. P., & McGrew, K. S. (1997). A cross-battery approach to assessing and interpreting cognitive abilities: Narrowing the gap between practice and cognitive science. In D. P. Flanagan, J. L. Genshaft, & P. L. Harrison (Eds.), *Contemporary intellectual assessment: Theories, tests, and issues* (pp. 314–325). New York: Guilford Press.

Flynn, J. R. (1984). The mean IQ of Americans: Massive gains 1932 to 1978. *Psychological Bulletin, 95*(1), 29–51.

Flynn, J. R. (1987). Massive IQ gains in 14 nations: What IQ tests really measure. *Psychological Bulletin, 101*(2), 171–191.

Folstein, M. F., Folstein, S. E., & McHugh, P. R. (1975). "Mini-Mental State": A practical method for grading the cognitive state of patients for the clinician. *Journal of Psychiatric Research, 12,* 189–198.

Frank, Y., & Pavlakis, S. G. (2001). Brain imaging in neurobehavioral disorders. *Pediatric Neurology, 25*(4), 278–287.

Franzen, M. D. (1989). *Reliability and validity in neuropsychological assessment.* New York: Plenum Press.

Fry, A. F., & Hale, S. (1996). Processing speed, working memory, and fluid intelligence: Evidence for a developmental cascade. *Psychological Science, 7*(4), 237–241.

Fuld, P. A., Katzman, R., Davies, P., & Terry, R. D. (1982). Intrusions as a sign of Alzheimer's dementia: Chemical and pathological verification. *Annals of Neurology, 11*(2), 155–159.

Gathercole, S. E. (1994). Neuropsychology and working memory: A review. *Neuropsychology, 8*(4), 494–505.

Georgiewa, P., Rzanny, R., Gaser, C., Gerhard, U. J., Vieweg, U., Freesmeyer, D., et al. (2002). Phonological processing in dyslexic children: A study combining functional imaging and event related potentials. *Neuroscience Letters, 18*(1), 5–8.

Gfeller, J. D., & Rankin, E. J. (1991). The WAIS–R profile as a cognitive marker of Alzheimer's disease: A misguided venture? *Journal of Clinical and Experimental Neuropsychology, 13*(4), 629–636.

Giedd, J. N., Blumenthal, J., Molloy, E., & Castellanos, F. X. (2001). Brain imaging of attention deficit/hyperactivity disorder. *Annals of the New York Academy Science, 931,* 33–49.

Glenn, S. W., & Parsons, O. A. (1990). The role of time in neuropsychological performance: Investigation and application in an alcoholic population. *The Clinical Psychologist, 4*(4), 344–354.

Glenn, S. W., Parsons, O. A., Sinha, R., & Stevens, L. (1988). The effects of repeated withdrawals from alcohol on the memory of male and female alcoholics. *Alcohol and Alcoholism, 23*(5), 337–342.

Glutting, J. J., McDermott, P. A., & Stanley, J. C. (1987). Resolving differences among methods of establishing confidence limits for test scores. *Educational and Psychological Measurement, 47*(3), 607–614.

Gold, J. M., Carpenter, C., Randolph, C., Goldberg, T. E., & Weinberger, D. R. (1997). Auditory working memory and Wisconsin Card Sorting Test performance in schizophrenia. *Archives of General Psychiatry, 54,* 159–165.

Gold, J. M., Hermann, B. P., Randolph, C., Wyler, A. R., Goldberg, J. F., & Weinberger, D. R. (1994). Schizophrenia and temporal lobe epilepsy: A neuropsychological analysis. *Archives of General Psychiatry, 54,* 265–272.

Goldberg, T. E., Weinberger, D. R., Berman, K. F., Pliskin, N. H., & Podd, M. H. (1987). Further evidence for dementia of the prefrontal type in schizophrenia? A controlled study of teaching the Wisconsin Card Sorting Test. *Archives of General Psychiatry, 44*, 1008–1014.

Goldman, R. S., Axelrod, B. N., Giordani, B. J., Foster, N., & Berent, S. (1992). Longitudinal sensitivity of the Fuld Cholinergic Profile to Alzheimer's disease. *Journal of Clinical and Experimental Neuropsychology, 14*(4), 566–574.

Goldstein, F. C., & Levin, H. S. (1990). Epidemiology of traumatic brain injury: Incidence, clinical characteristics, and risk factors. In E. D. Bigler (Ed.), *Traumatic brain injury: Mechanisms of damage, assessment, intervention, and outcome* (pp. 51–67). Austin, TX: Pro-Ed.

Goldstein, F. C., Levin, H. S., Presley, R. M., Searcy, J., Colohan, A. R. T., Eisenberg, H. M., et al. (1994). Neurobehavioral consequences of closed head injury in older adults. *Journal of Neurology, Neurosurgery, and Psychiatry, 57*(8), 961–966.

Goldstein, F. C., McKendall, R. R., & Haut, M. W. (1992). Gist recall in multiple sclerosis. *Archives of Neurology, 49*(10), 1060–1064.

Gorsuch, R. L. (1983). *Factor analysis* (2nd ed.). Hillsdale, NJ: Erlbaum.

Gorsuch, R. L. (1996). Number of exploratory factors: A clarification of the eigenvalues > 1 criterion. San Diego, CA: Fuller Theological Seminary, Graduate School of Psychology.

Grant, D. A., & Berg, E. A. (1948). A behavioral analysis of the degree of reinforcement and ease of shifting to new responses in a Weigl-type card-sorting problem. *Journal of Experimental Psychology, 38*, 404–411.

Grigsby, J., Ayarbe, S. D., Kravcisin, N., & Busenbark, D. (1994). Working memory impairment among persons with chronic progressive multiple sclerosis. *Journal of Neurology, 241*, 125–131.

Grober, E., & Sliwinski, M. (1991). Development and validation of a model estimating premorbid verbal intelligence in the elderly. *Journal of Clinical and Experimental Neuropsychology, 13*(6), 933–949.

Guilford, J. P. (1954). *Psychometric methods* (2nd ed.). New York: McGraw–Hill.

Guilford, J. P., & Fruchter, B. (1978). *Fundamental statistics in psychology and education* (6th ed.). New York: McGraw–Hill.

Gur, R. C., Jaggi, J. L., Ragland, J. D., Resnick, S. M., Shtasel, D., Muenz, L., et al. (1993). Effects of memory processing on regional brain activation: Cerebral blood flow in normal subjects. *International Journal of Neuroscience, 72*, 31–44.

Gur, R. E., Mozley, P. D., Resnick, S. M., Shtasel, D., Kohn, M., Zimmerman, R., et al. (1991). Magnetic resonance imaging in schizophrenia: I. Volumetric analysis of brain and cerebrospinal fluid. *Archives of General Psychiatry, 48*, 407–412.

Gustafsson, J. E. (1984). A unifying model for the structure of intellectual abilities. *Intelligence, 8*, 179–203.

Hall, J. C. (1957). Correlation of a modified form of Raven's Progressive Matrices (1938) with the Wechsler Adult Intelligence Scale. *Journal of Consulting Psychology, 21*(1), 23–26.

Hambleton, R. K. (1993). Principles and selected applications of item response theory. In R. L. Linn (Ed.), *Educational measurement* (3rd ed., pp. 147–200). Phoenix, AZ: Oryx Press.

Hambleton, R. K. (1994). Guidelines for adapting educational and psychological tests: A progress report. *European Journal of Psychological Assessment, 10*(3), 229–244.

Harrison, P. L. (1990). Mental retardation, adaptive behavior assessment, and giftedness. In A. S. Kaufman (Ed.), *Assessing adolescent and adult intelligence* (pp. 533–585). Boston: Allyn & Bacon.

Hart, R. P., Kwentus, J. A., Wade, J. B., & Hamer, R. M. (1987). Digit symbol performance in mild dementia and depression. *Journal of Consulting and Clinical Psychology, 55*(2), 236–238.

Haslam, C., Batchelor, J., Fearnside, M. R., Haslam, S. A., Hawkins, S., & Kenway, E. (1994). Post-coma disturbance and post-traumatic amnesia as nonlinear predictors of cognitive outcome following severe closed head injury: Findings from the Westmead Head Injury Project. *Brain Injury, 8*(6), 519–528.

Hauser, S. L. (1994). Multiple sclerosis and other demyelinating diseases. In K. J. Isselbacher, E. Braunwald, J. D. Wilson, J. B. Martin, A. S. Fauci, & D. L. Kasper (Eds.), *Harrison's principles of internal medicine* (13th ed., Vol. 2, pp. 2287–2295). New York: McGraw–Hill.

Haut, M. W., Weber, A. M., Demarest, D., Keefover, R. W., & Rankin, E. D. (1996). Controlling for constructional dysfunction with the visual reproduction subtest of the Wechsler Memory Scale—Revised in Alzheimer's disease. *The Clinical Neuropsychologist, 10*(3), 309–312.

Haut, M. W., Weber, A. M., Wilhelm, K. L., Keefover, R. W., & Rankin, E. D. (1994). The visual reproduction subtest as a measure of visual perceptual/constructional functioning in dementia of the Alzheimer's type. *The Clinical Neuropsychologist, 8*(2), 187–192.

Hawkins, K. A. (1999). Memory deficits in patients with schizophrenia: Preliminary data from the Wechsler Memory Scale–Third Edition support earlier findings. *Journal of Psychiatry and Neuroscience, 24*(4), 341–347.

Hawkins, K. A., & Tulsky, D. A. (2001). The influence of IQ stratification on WAIS–III/WMS–III FSIQ–General Memory Index discrepancy base-rates in the standardization sample. *Journal of the International Neuropsychological Society, 7*(7), 875–880.

Heaton, R. K., Baade, L. E., & Johnson, K. L. (1978). Neuropsychological test results associated with psychiatric disorders in adults. *Psychological Bulletin, 85*(1), 141–162.

Heaton, R. K., Chelune, G. J., Talley, J. L., Kay, G. G., & Curtiss, G. (1993). *Wisconsin Card Sorting Test manual—Revised and expanded*. Odessa, FL: Psychological Assessment Resources.

Heaton, R. K., & Crowley, T. J. (1981). Effects of psychiatric disorders and their somatic treatments on neuropsychological test results. In S. B. Filskov & T. J. Boll (Eds.), *Handbook of clinical neuropsychology* (pp. 481–525). New York: Wiley.

Heaton, R. K., Nelson, L. M., Thompson, D. S., Burks, J. S., & Franklin, G. M. (1985). Neuropsychological findings in relapsing-remitting and chronic-progressive multiple sclerosis. *Journal of Consulting and Clinical Psychology, 53*(1), 103–110.

Heaton, R., Paulsen, J. S., McAdams, L. A., Kuck, J., Zisook, S., Braff, D., et al. (1994). Neuropsychological deficits in schizophrenics: Relationship to age, chronicity, and dementia. *Archives of General Psychiatry, 51*, 469–476.

Heilbronner, R. L. (1992). The search for a "pure" visual memory test: Pursuit of perfection? *Clinical Neuropsychologist, 6*(1), 105–112.

Hoehn, M. M., & Yahr, M. D. (1967). Parkinsonism: Onset, progression, and mortality. *Neurology 17*(5), 427–442.

Hoff, A. L., Riordan, H., O'Donnell, D. W., Morris, L., & DeLisi, L. E. (1992). Neuropsychological functioning of first-episode schizophreniform patients. *American Journal of Psychiatry, 149*(7), 898–903.

Holdnack, J. A., Ledbetter, M. F., & Cohen, M. (1996, August). Performance of children with ADD on the Children's Memory Scale. *Presented at the 75th Annual American Psychological Association Convention,* Toronto, Ontario.

Holdnack, J. A., Moberg, P. J., Arnold, S. E., Gur, R. C., & Gur, R. E. (1995). Speed of processing and verbal learning deficits in adults diagnosed with attention deficit disorder. *Neuropsychiatry, Neuropsychology, and Behavioral Neurology, 8*(4), 282–292.

Holland, P. W., & Thayer, D. T. (1988). Differential item performance and the Mantel–Haenszel procedure. In H. Wainer & H. I. Braun (Eds.), *Test validity* (pp. 129–145). Hillsdale, NJ: Erlbaum.

Iverson, G. L. (2001). Interpreting change on the WAIS–III/WMS–III in clinical samples. *Archives of Clinical Neuropsychology, 16,* 183–191.

Ivnik, R. J., Malec, J. F., Smith, G. E., Tangalos, E. G., Petersen, R. C., Kokmen, E., et al. (1992). Mayo's older Americans normative studies: WAIS–R norms for ages 56–97. *The Clinical Neuropsychologist, 6*(Suppl.), 1–30.

Jacobs, D. M., Sano, M., Dooneief, G., Marder, K., Bell, K. L., & Stern, Y. (1995). Neuropsychological detection and characterization of preclinical Alzheimer's disease. *Neurology, 45,* 957–962.

Jacobs, D., Tröster, A. I., Butters, N., Salmon, D. P., & Cermak, L. S. (1990). Intrusion errors on the visual reproduction test of the Wechsler Memory Scale and the Wechsler Memory Scale—Revised: An analysis of demented and amnesic patients. *The Clinical Neuropsychologist, 4*(2), 177–191.

Jennett, B., & Bond, M. (1975). Assessment of outcome after severe brain damage. *Lancet, 1,* 480–484.

Jones, B., & Parsons, O. A. (1971). Impaired abstracting ability in chronic alcoholics. *Archives of General Psychiatry, 24,* 71–75.

Jöreskog, K. G. (1993). Testing structural equation models. In K. A. Bollen & J. S. Long (Eds.), *Testing structural equation models* (pp. 294–316). Newbury Park, CA: Sage.

Jöreskog, K. G., & Sörbom, D. (1993). *LISREL 8: User's reference guide.* Chicago: Scientific Software International.

Jurden, F. H. (1995). Individual differences in working memory and complex cognition. *Journal of Educational Psychology, 87,* 93–102.

Kaplan, E. (1988). A process approach to neuropsychological assessment. In T. J. Boll & B. K. Bryant (Eds.), *Clinical neuropsychology and brain function: Research, measurement, and practice* (pp. 129–167). Washington, DC: American Psychological Association.

Kaplan, E., Fein, D., Morris, R., & Delis, D. C. (1991). *WAIS–R as a Neuropsychological Instrument.* San Antonio, TX: The Psychological Corporation.

Kaplan, E., Goodglass, H., & Weintraub, S. (1983). *The Boston Naming Test* (2nd ed.). Philadelphia: Lea & Febiger.

Kataria, S., Hall, C. W., Wong, M. M., & Keys, G. F. (1992). Learning styles of LD and NLD ADHD children. *Journal of Clinical Psychology, 48*(3), 371–378.

Katz, L., Goldstein, G., Rudisin, S., & Bailey, D. (1993). A neuropsychological approach to the Bannatyne recategorization of the Wechsler intelligence scales in adults with learning disabilities. *Journal of Learning Disabilities, 26*(1), 65–72.

Kaufman, A. S. (1975). Factor analysis of WISC–R at 11 age levels between $6\frac{1}{2}$ and $16\frac{1}{2}$ years. *Journal of Consulting and Clinical Psychology, 43*(2), 135–147.

Kaufman, A. S. (1979). *Intelligent testing with the WISC–R.* New York: Wiley.

Kaufman, A. S. (1990). *Assessing adolescent and adult intelligence.* Boston: Allyn & Bacon.

Kaufman, A. S. (1994). *Intelligent testing with the WISC–III.* New York: Wiley.

Kaufman, A. S., Reynolds, C. R., & McLean, J. E. (1989). Age and WAIS–R intelligence in a national sample of adults in the 20- to 74-year age range: A cross-sectional analysis with educational level controlled. *Intelligence, 13*(3), 235–253.

Kaufman, A. S., & Van Hagen, J. (1977). Investigation of the WISC–R for use with retarded children: Correlation with the 1972 Stanford–Binet and comparison of WISC and WISC–R profiles. *Psychology in the Schools, 14*(1), 10–14.

Kender, J. P., Greenwood, S., & Conard, E. (1985). WAIS–R performance patterns of 565 incarcerated adults characterized as underachieving readers and adequate readers. *Journal of Learning Disabilities, 18*(7), 379–383.

Kieburtz, K., Penney, J. B., Como, P., Ranch, N., & Shoulson, I. (1996). Unified Huntingont's Disease Rating Scale: Reliability and consistency. *Movement Disorders, 11*(2), 136–142.

Killgore, W. D. S., & DellaPietra, L. (2000a). Item response biases on the Logical Memory Delayed Recognition subtest of the Wechsler Memory Scale–III. *Psychological Reports, 86*(3, Pt.1), 851–857.

Killgore, W. D. S., & DellaPietra, L. (2000b). Using the WMS–III to detect malingering: Empirical validation of the rarely missed index (RMI). *Journal of Clinical and Experimental Neuroopsychology, 22*(6), 761–771.

Kopelman, M. D. (1994). Working memory in the amnesic syndrome and degenerative dementia. Special section: Working memory. *Neuropsychology, 8*(4), 555–562.

Kostrubala, C., & Braden, J. P. (1997, April). Testing with the WAIS–III in individuals who are deaf. Paper presented at the annual convention of the National Association of School Psychologists, Orange County, CA.

Kraus, J. F., Black, M. A., Hessol, N., Ley, P., Rokaw, W., Sullivan, C., et al. (1984). The incidence of acute brain injury and serious impairment in a defined population. *American Journal of Epidemiology, 119*(2), 186–201.

Krupp, L. B., Sliwinski, M., Masur, D. M., Friedberg, F., & Coyle, P. K. (1994). Cognitive functioning and depression in patients with chronic fatigue syndrome and multiple sclerosis. *Archives of Neurology, 51*(7), 705–710.

Kurtzke, J. F. (1951). A new scale for evaluating disability in multiple sclerosis. *Journal of the American Academy of Neurology, 5*, 580–583.

Kurtzke, J. F. (1983). Rating neurologic impairment in multiple sclerosis: An expanded disability status scale (EDSS). *Neurology, 33*, 1444–1452.

Kyllonen, P. C. (1987). Theory-based cognitive assessment. In J. Zeidner (Ed.), *Human productivity enhancement: Organizations, personnel, and decision making.* (Vol. 2, pp. 338–381). New York: Praeger.

Kyllonen, P. C., & Christal, R. E. (1987). Cognitive modeling of learning abilities: A status report of LAMP. In R. Dillon & J. W. Pelligrino (Eds.), *Testing: Theoretical and applied issues.* New York: Freeman.

Kyllonen, P. C., & Christal, R. E. (1990). Reasoning ability is (little more than) working-memory capacity?! *Intelligence, 14,* 389–433.

Kyllonen, P. C., & Stephens, D. L. (1990). Cognitive abilities as determinants of success in acquiring logic skill. *Learning and Individual Differences, 2*(2), 129–160.

Lafayette Instrument Company. (1989). *Grooved Pegboard.* Lafayette, IN: Author.

Leckliter, I. N., Matarazzo, J. D., & Silverstein, A. B. (1986). A literature review of factor analytic studies of the WAIS–R. *Journal of Clinical Psychology, 42,* 332–342,

Ledbetter, M. F., & Prifitera, A. (1993, November). Education-adjusted percent retention scores based on the Wechsler Memory Scale—Revised standardization sample. Paper presented at the 13th annual meeting of the National Academy of Neuropsychology, Phoenix, AZ.

Levin, H. S., Goldstein, F. C., High, W. M., Jr., & Eisenberg. H. M. (1988). Disproportionately severe memory deficit in relation to normal intellectual functioning after closed head injury. *Journal of Neurology, Neurosurgery, and Psychiatry 51*(10), 1294–1301.

Levine, B., & Iscoe, I. A. (1954). A comparison of Raven's Progressive Matrices (1938) with a short form of the Wechsler–Bellevue. *Journal of Consulting Psychology, 18*(1), 10.

Levine, E. S. (1974). Psychological tests and practices with the deaf: A survey of the state of the art. *Volta Review, 76,* 298–319.

Lezak, M. D. (1995). *Neuropsychological assessment* (3rd ed.). New York: Oxford University Press.

Lineweaver, T. T., & Chelune, C. J. (2000, November). *Use of the WAIS–III and WMS–III in the context of serial assessment and meaningful change.* Paper presented at the meeting of the National Academy of Neuropsychology, Orlando, FL.

Litvan, I., Grafman, J., Vendrell, P., & Martinez, J. M. (1988). Slowed information processing in multiple sclerosis. *Archives of Neurology, 45,* 281–285.

Loge, D. V., Staton, R. D., & Beatty, W. W. (1990). Performance of children with ADHD on tests sensitive to frontal lobe dysfunction. *Journal of the American Academy of Child and Adolescent Psychiatry, 29*(4), 540–545.

Logie, R. H. (1995). *Visuo–spatial working memory.* Hove, East Sussex, UK: Erlbaum.

Logie, R. H. (1996). The seven ages of working memory. In J. T. E. Richardson, R. W. Engle, L. Hasher, R. H. Logie, E. R. Stoltzfus, & R. T. Zacks (Eds.), *Working memory and human cognition* (pp. 31–65). New York: Oxford University Press.

Loring, D. W. (1989). The Wechsler Memory Scale—Revised, or the Wechsler Memory Scale—Revisited? *The Clinical Neuropsychologist, 3*(1), 59–69.

Macartney–Filgate, M. S., & Vriezen, E. R. (1988). Intercorrelation of clinical tests of verbal memory. *Archives of Clinical Neuropsychology, 3,* 121–126.

Magnusson, D. (1967). *Test theory.* Reading, MA: Addison–Wesley.

Mahurin, R. K, Feher, E. P., Nance, M. L., Levy, J. K., & Pirozzolo, F. J. (1993). Cognition in Parkinson's disease and related disorders. In R. W. Parks, R. F. Zec, & R. S. Wilson (Eds.), *Neuropsychology of Alzheimer's disease and other dementias* (pp. 308–349). New York: Oxford University Press.

Maller, S. J., & Braden, J. P. (1992). The construct and criterion–related validity of the WISC–III with deaf adolescents. *Journal of Psychoeducational Assessment* [WISC–III Monograph], 105–113.

Malloy, P., Noel, N., Rogers, S., Longabaugh, R., & Beattie, M. (1989). Risk factors for neuropsychological impairment in alcoholics: Antisocial personality, age, years of drinking, and gender. *Journal of Studies on Alcohol, 50*(5), 422–426.

Malloy, P. F., & Richardson, E. D. (1994). Assessment of frontal lobe functions. Special issue: The frontal lobes and neuropsychiatric illness. *The Journal of Neuropsychiatry and Clinical Neurosciences, 6*(4), 399–410.

Marsh, H. W., Balla, J. R., & McDonald, R. P. (1988). Goodness-of-fit indexes in confirmatory factor analysis: The effect of sample size. *Psychological Bulletin, 103*(3), 391–410.

Martin, J. B., & Gusella, J. F. (1986). Huntington's disease: Pathogenesis and management. *New England Journal of Medicine, 315*(20), 1267–1276.

Massman, P. J., Delis, D. C., Butters, N., Dupont, R. M., & Gillin, J. C. (1992). The subcortical dysfunction hypothesis of memory deficits in depression: Neuropsychological validation in a subgroup of patients. *Journal of Clinical and Experimental Neuropsychology, 14*(5), 687–706.

Massman, P. J., Delis, D. C., Butters, N., Levin, B. E., & Salmon, D. P. (1990). Are all subcortical dementias alike? Verbal learning and memory in Parkinson's and Huntington's disease patients. *Journal of Clinical and Experimental Neuropsychology, 12*(5), 729–744.

Masur, D. M., Sliwinski, M., Lipton, R. B., Blau, A. D., & Crystal, H. A. (1994). Neuropsychological prediction of dementia and the absence of dementia in healthy elderly persons. *Neurology, 44*, 1427–1432.

Matarazzo, J. D. (1972). *Wechsler's measurement and appraisal of adult intelligence* (5th ed.). Baltimore: Williams & Wilkins.

Matarazzo, J. D. (1990). Psychological assessment versus psychological testing: Validation from Binet to the school, clinic, and courtroom. *American Psychologist, 45*(9), 999–1017.

Matarazzo, J. D., Daniel, M. H., Prifitera, A., & Herman, D. O. (1988). Inter-subtest scatter in the WAIS–R standardization sample. *Journal of Clinical Psychology, 44*, 940–950.

Matarazzo, J. D., & Herman, D. O. (1985). Clinical uses of the WAIS–R: Base rates of differences between VIQ and PIQ in the WAIS–R standardization sample. In B. B. Wolman (Ed.), *Handbook of intelligence: Theories, measurements, and applications* (pp. 899–932). New York: Wiley.

Mataro, M., Garcia-Sanchez, C., Junque, C., Estevez-Gonzalez, A., & Pujol, J. (1997). Magnetic resonance imaging measurement of the caudate nucleus in adolescents with attention-deficit hyperactivity disorder and its relationship with neuropsychological and behavioral measures. *Archives of Neurology, 54*(8), 963–968.

Mattis, S. (1988). *Dementia Rating Scale.* Odessa, FL: Psychological Assessment Resources.

Mattson, A. J., & Levin, H. S. (1990). Frontal lobe dysfunction following closed head injury: A review of the literature. *Journal of Nervous and Mental Disease, 178*(5), 282–291.

Maurelli, M., Marchioni, E., Cerratano, R., Bosone, D., Bergmaschi, R., Citterio, A., et al. (1992). Neuropsychological assessment in MS: Clinical, neurophysiological and neuroradiological relationships. *Acta Neurologica Scandinavica 86*(2), 124–128.

McCurry, S. M., Fitz, A. G., & Teri, L. (1994). Comparison of age-extended norms for the Wechsler Adult Intelligence Scale—Revised in patients with Alzheimer's disease. *Psychological Assessment, 6*(3), 231–235.

McIntosh, G. C. (1992). Neurological conceptualization of epilepsy. In T. L. Bennett (Ed.), *The neuropsychology of epilepsy: Critical issues in neuropsychology* (pp. 17–37). New York: Plenum Press.

McKhann, G., Drachman, D., Folstein, M., Katzman, R., Price, D., & Stadlan, E. M. (1984). Clinical diagnosis of Alzheimer's disease: Report of the NINCDS–ADRDA work group under the auspices of Department of Health and Human Services Task Force on Alzheimer's Disease. *Neurology, 34*, 939–944.

McLaurin, W. A., & Farrar, W. E. (1973). Validities of the Progressive Matrices Tests against IQ and grade point average. *Psychological Reports, 32*, 803–806.

McMillan, T. M., Powell, G. E., Janota, I., & Polkey, C. E. (1987). Relationships between neuropathology and cognitive functioning in temporal lobectomy patients. *Journal of Neurology, Neurosurgery, and Psychiatry, 50*(2), 167–176.

McQuaid, M. F., & Alovisetti, M. (1981). School psychological services for hearing–impaired children in the New York and New England area. *American Annals of the Deaf, 126*, 37–42.

Miller, G. A. (1956). The magical number seven, plus or minus two: Some limits on our capacity for processing information. *Psychological Review, 63*, 81–97.

Millis, S. R., Malina, A. C., Bowers, D. A., & Ricker, J. H. (1999). Confirmatory factor analysis of the Wechsler Memory Scale–III. *Journal of Clinical and Experimental Neuropsychology, 21*(1), 87–93.

Milner, B. (1968). Visual recognition and recall after right temporal-lobe excision in man. *Neuropsychologia, 6*, 191–209.

Milner, B. (1975). Psychological aspects of focal epilepsy and its neurosurgical management. *Advances in Neurology, 8*, 299–321.

Morris, J. C., Heyman, A., Mohs, R. C., Hughes, J. P., van Belle, G., Fillenbaum, G., et al. (1989). The consortium to establish a registry for Alzheimer's disease (CERAD): Part I. Clinical and neuropsychological assessment of Alzheimer's disease. *Neurology, 39*(9), 1159–1165.

Morris, J. C., Storandt, M., Miller, J. P., McKeel, D. W., Price, J. L., Rubin, E. H., et al. (2001). Mild cognitive impairment represents early-stage Alzheimer disease. *Archives of Neurology, 58*(10), 1705–1706.

Mungas, D. (1983). Differential clinical sensitivity of specific parameters of the Rey Auditory–Verbal Learning Test. *Journal of Consulting and Clinical Psychology, 51*(6), 848–855.

Naglieri, J. A. (1980). WISC–R subtest patterns for learning disabled and mentally retarded children. *Perceptual and Motor Skills, 51*, 605–606.

Naugle, R. I, Chelune, G. J., Cheek, R., Lüders, H., & Awad, I. A. (1993). Detection of changes in material-specific memory following temporal lobectomy using the Wechsler Memory Scale—Revised. *Archives of Clinical Neuropsychology, 8*(5), 381–395.

Naugle, R. I., Chelune, G. J., Schuster, J., Lüders, H. O., & Comair, Y. (1994). Recognition memory for words and faces before and after temporal lobectomy. *Assessment, 1*(4), 373–381.

Neisser, U., Boodoo, G., Bouchard, T. J., Jr., Boykin, A. W., Brody, N., Ceci, S. J., et al. (1996). Intelligence: Knowns and unknowns. *American Psychologist, 51*(2), 77–101.

Nelson, H. E. (1982). *National Adult Reading Test (NART): Test manual.* Windsor: NFER–Nelson.

Nettelbeck, T., & Rabbitt, P. M. A. (1992). Aging, cognitive performance, and mental speed. *Intelligence, 16(2)*, 189–205.

Newcombe, F., de Haan, E. H. F., Ross, J., & Young, A. W. (1989). Face processing, laterality and contrast sensitivity. *Neuropsychologia, 27*(4), 523–538.

Newell, A. (1973). Productions systems: Models of control structures. In W. G. Chase (Ed.), *Visual information processing* (pp. 463–526). New York: Academic Press.

Newell, A., & Simon, H. A. (1972). *Human problem solving.* Englewood Cliffs, NJ: Prentice–Hall.

Nicolson, R. I., Fawcett, A. J., & Dean, P. (2001). Developmental dyslexia: The cerebellar deficit hypothesis. *Trends in Neurosciences, 24*(9), 508–511.

Nunnally, J. (1978). *Psychometric theory* (2nd ed.). New York: McGraw–Hill.

O'Mahony, J. F., & Doherty, B. (1993). Patterns of intellectual performance among recently abstinent alcohol abusers on WAIS–R and WMS–R subtests. *Archives of Clinical Neuropsychology, 8*, 373–380.

O'Mahony, J. F., & Doherty, B. (1996). Intellectual impairment among recently abstinent alcohol abusers. *British Journal of Clinical Psychology, 35*, 77–83.

Ormrod, J. E., & Lewis, M. A. (1985). Comparison of memory skills in learning disabled, low-reading, and nondisabled adolescents. *Perceptual and Motor Skills, 61*(1), 191–195.

Orsini, A., Fragassi, N. A., Chiacchio, L., Falanga, A. M., Cocchiaro, C., & Grossi, D. (1987). Verbal and spatial memory span in patients with extrapyramidal diseases. *Perceptual and Motor Skills, 65*, 555–558.

Oscar–Berman, M., Clancy, J. P., & Weber, D. A. (1993). Discrepancies between IQ and memory scores in alcoholism and aging. *The Clinical Neuropsychologist, 7*(3), 281–296.

Palmer, K., Wang, H. X., Backman, L., Winblad, B., & Fratiglioni, L. (2002). Differential evolution of cognitive impairment in nondemented older persons: Results from the Kungsholmen project. *American Journal of Psychiatry, 159*(3), 436–442.

Parsons, O. A., & Farr, S. P. (1981). The neuropsychology of alcohol and drug use. In S. B. Filskov & T. J. Boll (Eds.), *Handbook of clinical neuropsychology* (pp. 320–365). New York: Wiley.

Parsons, O. A., & Prigatano, G. P. (1978). Methodological considerations in clinical neuropsychological research. *Journal of Consulting and Clinical Psychology, 46*(4), 608–619.

Paulsen, J. S., Heaton, R. K., Sadek, J. R., Perry, W., Delis, D. C., Braff, D., et al. (1995). The nature of learning and memory impairments in schizophrenia. *Journal of the International Neuropsychological Society, 1*(1), 88–99.

Payne, R. W., & Jones, H. G. (1957). Statistics for the investigation of individual cases. *Journal of Clinical Psychology, 13*, 115–121.

Pennington, B. F., Bennetto, L., McAleer, O., & Roberts, R. J. (1996). Executive functions and working memory. In G. R. Lyon & N. A. Krasnegor (Eds.), *Attention, memory, and executive function* (pp. 327–348). Baltimore: Paul H. Brookes.

Pennington, B. P., & Ozonoff, S. (1996). Executive functions and developmental psychopathology. *Journal of Child Psychology and Psychiatry, 37*(1), 51–87.

Peterson, R. C., Doody, R., Kurz, A., Mohs, R. C., Morris, J. C., Rabins, P. V., et al. (2001). Current concepts in mild cognitive impairment. *Archives of Neurology, 58*(12), 1985–1992.

Pickles, D. G. (1966). The Wechsler Performance Scale and its relationship to speech and educational response in deaf slow-learning children. *Teacher of the Deaf, 64,* 382–393.

Pilgrim, B. M., Meyers, J. E., Bayless, J., & Whetstone, M. M. (1999). Validity of the Ward seven-subtest WAIS–III short form in a neuropsychological population. *Applied Neuropsychology, 6*(4), 243–246.

Pirozzolo, F. J., Hansch, E. C., Mortimer, J. A., Webster, D. D., & Kuskowski, M. A. (1982). Dementia in Parkinson's disease: A neuropsychological analysis. *Brain and Cognition, 1,* 71–83.

Portin, R., Muuriaisniemi, M. L., Joukamaa, M., Saarijarvi, S., Helenius, H., & Salokangas, R. K. (2001). Cognitive impairment and the 10-year survival probability of a normal 62-year-old population. *Scandinavian Journal of Psychology, 42*(4), 359–366.

Poser, C. M., Poser, S., & Paty, D. W. (1984). A revised numerical scoring system for multiple sclerosis. In C. M. Poser (Ed.), *The diagnosis of multiple sclerosis* (pp. 234–241). New York: Thieme–Stratton.

Poser, S., Poser, W., Schlaf, G., Firnhaber, W., Lauer, K., Wolter, M., et al. (1986). Prognostic indicators in multiple sclerosis. *Acta Neurologica Scandinavica, 74,* 387–392.

Powell, D. H. (1994). *Profiles in cognitive aging.* Cambridge, MA: Harvard University Press.

Powell, D. H., Kaplan, E. F., Whitla, D., Weintraub, S., Catlin, R., & Funkenstein, H. H. (1993). *MicroCog: Assessment of Cognitive Functioning.* San Antonio, TX: The Psychological Corporation.

Price, L. R., Tulsky, D., Millis, S., & Weiss, L. (in press). Redefining the factor structure of the Wechsler Memory Scale–III: Confirmatory factor analysis with cross-validation. *Journal of Clinical and Experimental Neuropsychology.*

Prifitera, A., & Dersh, J. (1992). Base rates of the WISC–III diagnostic subtest patterns among normal, learning-disabled, and ADHD samples. *Journal of Psychoeducational Assessment* (WISC–III Monograph], 43–55.

Prifitera, A., & Ledbetter, M. F. (1992, November). Normative delayed recall rates based on the Wechsler Memory Scale—Revised standardization sample. Paper presented at the 12th annual meeting of the National Academy of Neuropsychology, Pittsburgh, PA.

Prigatano, G. P. (1974, May). *Memory deficit in head injured patients.* Paper presented at the meeting of the Southwestern Psychological Association, El Paso, TX.

Prigatano, G. P. (1977). The Wechsler Memory Scale is a poor screening test for brain dysfunction. *Journal of Clinical Psychology, 33*(3), 772–777.

Prigatano, G. P. (1978). Wechsler Memory Scale: A selective review of the literature [Special Monograph Supplement]. *Journal of Clinical Psychology, 34*(4), 816–832.

The Psychological Corporation. (1992). *Wechsler Individual Achievement Test.* San Antonio, TX: Author.

The Psychological Corporation. (1999). *The Wechsler Abbreviated Scale of Intelligence Manual.* San Antonio, TX: Author.

The Psychological Corporation. (2001). *Wechsler Test of Adult Reading.* San Antonio, TX: Author.

The Psychological Corporation. (2002a). *Wechsler Individual Achievement Test–2nd Edition Examiner's Manual.* San Antonio, TX: Author.

The Psychological Corporation. (2002b). *Wechsler Individual Achievement Test–2nd Edition Scoring and Normative Supplement for Grades PreK–12.* San Antonio, TX: Author.

The Psychological Corporation. (2002c). *Wechsler Individual Achievement Test–2nd Edition Supplement for College Students and Adults.* San Antonio, TX: Author.

Pugh, K. R., Mencl, W. E., Jenner, A. R., Katz, L., Frost, S. J., Lee, J. R., et al. (2001). Neurobiological studies of reading and reading disability. *Journal of Communication Disorders, 34*(6), 479–492.

Pugh, K. R., Mencl, W. E., Shaywitz, B. A., Shaywitz, S. E., Fulbright, R. K., Constable, R. T., et al. (2000). The angular gyrus in developmental dyslexia: Task-specific differences in functional connectivity within posterior cortex. *Psychological Science,11*(1), 51–56.

Putnam, S. H., Ricker, J. H., Ross, S. R., & Kurtz, J. E. (1999). Considering premorbid functioning: Beyond cognition to a conceptualization of personality in postinjury functioning. In J. J. Sweet (Ed.), *Forensic neuropsychology: Fundamentals and Practice* (pp. 39–81). Lisse, The Netherlands: Swets & Zeitlinger.

Quadfasel, A. F., & Pruyser, P. W. (1955). Cognitive deficit in patients with psycho-motor epilepsy. *Epilepsia, 4,* 80–90.

Quinlan, D. M., & Brown, T. E. (1997). Assessment of working memory impairment in adults with ADHD. Manuscript in preparation.

Randolph, C., Mohr, E., & Chase, T. N. (1993). Assessment of intellectual function in dementing disorders: Validity of WAIS–R short forms for patients with Alzheimer's, Huntington's, and Parkinson's disease. *Journal of Clinical and Experimental Neuropsychology, 15*(5), 743–753.

Rao, S. M., Hammeke, T. A., McQuillen, M. P., Khatri, B. O., & Lloyd, D. (1984). Memory disturbance in chronic progressive multiple sclerosis. *Archives of Neurology, 41,* 625–631.

Raven, J. C. (1976). *Standard Progressive Matrices.* Oxford, England: Oxford Psychologists Press.

Reed, R. J., Grant, I., & Rourke, S. B. (1992). Long-term abstinent alcoholics have normal memory. *Alcoholism: Clinical and Experimental Research, 16*(4), 677–683.

Reid, D. B., & Kelly, M. P. (1993). Wechsler Memory Scale—Revised in closed head injury. *Journal of Clinical Psychology, 49*(2), 245–254.

Reitan, R. M., & Wolfson, D. (1993). *Halstead–Reitan Neuropsychological Battery.* Tucson, AZ: Neuropsychology Press.

Rey, A. (1941). L'examen psychologique dans les cas d'encéphalopathie traumatique. *Archives de Psychologie, 28,* 286–340.

Rey, A. (1959). Sollicitation de la mémoire de fixation par des mots et des objets présentés simultanément. *Archives de Psychologie, 37,* 126–139.

Reynolds, C. R. (1985). Critical measurement issues in learning disabilities. *The Journal of Special Education, 18*(4), 451–475.

Reynolds, C. R. (1990). Conceptual and technical problems in learning disability diagnosis. In C. R. Reynolds & R. W. Kamphaus (Eds.), *Handbook of psychological and educational assessment of children: Intelligence and achievement* (pp. 571–592). New York: Guilford Press.

Rhodes, S. S., & Jasinski, D. R. (1990). Learning disabilities in alcohol-dependent adults: A preliminary study. *Journal of Learning Disabilities, 23*(9), 551–556.

Richards, T. L., Dager, S. R., Corina, D., Serafini, S., Heide, A. C., Steury, K., et al. (1999). Dyslexic children have abnormal brain lactate response to reading-related language tasks. *American Journal of Neuroradiology, 20*(8), 1393–1398.

Richardson, J. T. E. (1996). Evolving concepts of working memory. In J. T. E. Richardson, R. W. Engle, L. Hasher, R. H. Logie, E. R. Stoltzfus, & R. T. Zacks (Eds.), *Working memory and human cognition* (pp. 3–30). New York: Oxford University Press.

Richardson, S. A., & Koller, H. (1985). Epidemiology. In A. M. Clarke, A. B. D. Clarke, & J. M. Berg (Eds.), *Mental deficiency: The changing outlook* (4th ed., pp. 27–52). London: Methuen.

Ritchie, K., Artero, S., & Touchon, J. (2001). Classification criteria for mild cognitive impairment: A population-based validation study. *Neurology, 56*(1), 37–42.

Rizzo, L., Danion, J. M., Van Der Linden, M., Grange, D., & Rohmer, J. G. (1996). Impairment of memory for spatial context in schizophrenia. *Neuropsychology, 10*(3), 376–384.

Roid, G. H., Prifitera, A., & Ledbetter, M. F. (1988). Confirmatory analysis of the factor structure of the Wechsler Memory Scale—Revised. *The Clinical Neuropsychologist, 2*(2), 116–120.

Rosenberg, H. M., Ventura, S. J., Maurer, J. D., Heuser, R. L., & Freedman, M. A. (1996). Births and deaths: United States, 1995. *Monthly Vital Statistics Report, 45*(3, Suppl. 2). (Preliminary Data from the Centers for Disease Control and Prevention/ National Center for Health Statistics).

Roth, D. L., Conboy, T. J., Reeder, K. P., & Boll, T. J. (1990). Confirmatory factor analysis of the Wechsler Memory Scale—Revised in a sample of head-injured patients. *Journal of Clinical and Experimental Neuropsychology, 12*(4), 834–842.

Rourke, S. B., & Løberg, T. (1996). The neurobehavioral correlates of alcoholism. In I. Grant & K. M. Adams (Eds.). *Neuropsychological assessment of neuropsychiatric disorders* (2nd ed., pp. 423–485). New York: Oxford University Press.

Rubia, K., Overmeyer, S., Taylor, E., Brammer, M., Williams, S. C., Simmons, A., et al. (1999). Hypofrontality in attention deficit hyperactivity disorder during higher-order motor control: A study with functional MRI. *American Journal of Psychiatry, 156*(6), 891–896.

Rubin, H. H., Goldman, J. J., & Rosenfeld, J. G. (1985). A comparison of WISC–R and WAIS–R IQs in a mentally retarded residential population. *Psychology in the Schools, 22*, 392–397.

Rudel, R. G., & Denckla, M. B. (1974). Relation of forward and backward digit repetition to neurological impairment in children with learning disabilities. *Neuropsychologia, 12*, 109–118.

Rugel, R. P. (1974). WISC subtest scores of disabled readers: A review with respect to Bannatyne's recategorization. *Journal of Learning Disabilities, 7*(1), 57–64.

Russell, E. W. (1975). A multiple scoring method for the assessment of complex memory functions. *Journal of Consulting and Clinical Psychology, 43*(6), 800–809.

Ryan, C., & Butters, N. (1980). Learning and memory impairments in young and old alcoholics: Evidence for premature-aging hypothesis. *Alcoholism: Clinical and Experimental Research, 4*(3), 288–293.

Ryan, C., & Butters, N. (1983). Cognitive deficits in alcoholics. In B. Kissen & H. Begleiter, (Eds.). *The pathogenesis of alcoholism: Biological factors* (pp. 485–538). New York: Plenum Press.

Ryan, J. J. (1999). Two types of tables for use with the seven-subtest short forms of the WAIS–III. *Journal of Psychoeducational Assessment, 17*, 145–151.

Ryan, J. J., Ament, P. A., & Arb, J. D. (2000). Supplementary WMS–III tables for determining primary subtest strengths and weaknesses. *Psychological Assessment, 12*(2), 193–196.

Ryan, J. J., & Lewis, C. V. (1988). Comparison of normal controls and recently detoxified alcoholics on the Wechsler Memory Scale—Revised. *The Clinical Neuropsychologist, 2*(2), 173–180.

Ryan, J. J., Lopez, S. J., & Werth, T. R. (1998). Administration time estimates for WAIS–III subtests, scales, and short forms in a clinical sample. *Journal of Psychoeducational Assessment, 16*, 315–323.

Ryan, J. J., Paolo, A. M., & Brungardt, T. M. (1990). Standardization of the Wechsler Adult Intelligence Scale—Revised for persons 75 years and older. *Psychological Assessment, 2(4)*, 404–411.

Ryan, J. J., Paolo, A. M., Oehlert, M. E., & Coker, M. C. (1991). Relationship of sex, race, age, education, and level of intelligence to the frequency of occurrence of a WAIS–R marker for dementia of the Alzheimer's type. *Developmental Neuropsychology, 7*(4), 451–458.

Ryan, J. J., Sattler, J. M., & Lopez, S. J. (2000). Age effects on Wechsler Adult Intelligence Scale–III subtests. *Archives of Clinical Neuropsychology, 15*(4), 311–317.

Ryan, J. J., & Ward, L. C. (1999). Validity, reliability, and standard errors of measurement for two seven-subtest short forms of the Wechsler Adult Intelligence Scale–III. *Psychological Assessment, 11*(2), 207–211.

Ryan, L., Clark, C. M., Klonoff, H., Li, D., & Paty, D. (1996). Patterns of cognitive impairment in relapsing-remitting multiple sclerosis and their relationship to neuropathology on magnetic resonance images. *Neuropsychology, 10(2)*, 176–193.

Saklofske, D. H., Hildebrand, D. K., & Gorsuch, R. L. (2000). Replication of the factor structure of the Wechsler Adult Intelligence Scale–Third Edition with a Canadian sample. *Psychological Assessment, 12*(4), 436–439.

Salmon, D. P., Butters, N., & Heindel, W. C. (1993). Alcoholic dementia and related disorders. In R. W. Parks, R. F. Zec, & R. S. Wilson (Eds.), *Neuropsychology of Alzheimer's disease and other dementias* (pp. 186–209). New York: Oxford University Press.

Sandoval, J., Sassenrath, J., & Penaloza, M. (1988). Similarity of WISC–R and WAIS–R scores at age 16. *Psychology in the Schools, 25*(4), 373–379.

Sattler, J. M. (1992). *Assessment of children: WISC–III and WPPSI–R supplement.* San Diego, CA: Author

Sattler, J. M., & Ryan, J. J. (1999). *Assessment of children: WAIS–III supplement.* La Mesa, CA: Jerome M. Sattler Publishing.

Saykin, A. J., Gur, R. C., Gur, R. E., Mozley, D., Mozley, L. H., Resnick, S. M., et al. (1991). Neuropsychological function in schizophrenia: Selective impairment in memory and learning. *Archives of General Psychiatry, 48,* 618–624.

Saykin, A. J., Shtasel, D. L., Gur, R. E., Kester, D. B., Mozley, L. H., Stafiniak, P., et al. (1994). Neuropsychological deficits in neuroleptic naïve patients with first-episode schizophrenia. *Archives of General Psychiatry, 51,* 124–131.

Schoenberg, B. S. (1987). Epidemiology of movement disorders. In C. D. Marsden & S. Fahn (Eds.), *Movement disorders* (pp. 17–32). Boston: Butterworth.

Schuckit, M. A., Smith, T. L., Anthenelli, R., & Irwin, M. (1993). Clinical course of alcoholism in 636 male inpatients. *American Journal of Psychiatry, 150*(5), 786–792.

Schultz, R. T., Cho, N. K., Staib, L. H., Kier, L. E., Fletcher, J. M., Shaywitz, S. E., et al. (1994). Brain morphology in normal and dyslexic children: The influence of sex and age. *Annals of Neurology, 35*(6), 732–742.

Schwean, V. L., Saklofske, D. H., Yackulic, R. A., & Quinn, D. (1992). WISC–III performance of ADHD children. *Journal of Psychoeducational Assessment* [WISC–III Monograph], 56–70.

Schweinberger, S. R., Buse, C., Freeman, R. B., Jr., Schonle, P. W., & Sommer, W. (1992). Memory search for faces and digits in patients with unilateral brain lesions. *Journal of Clinical and Experimental Neuropsychology, 14*(5), 839–856.

Seidman, L. J., Yurgelun–Todd, D., Kremen, W. S., Woods, B. T., Goldstein, J. M., Faraone, S. V., et al. (1994). Relationship of prefrontal and temporal lobe MRI measures to neuropsychological performance in chronic schizophrenia. *Biological Psychiatry, 35,* 235–246.

Semrud-Clikeman, M., Steingard, R. J., Filipek, P., Biederman, J., Bekken, K., & Renshaw, P. F. (2000). Using MRI to examine brain-behavior relationships in males with attention deficit disorder with hyperactivity. *Journal of the American Academy of Child and Adolescent Psychiatry, 39*(4), 477–484.

Shakow, D. (1963). Psychological deficit in schizophrenia. *Behavioral Science, 8*(4), 275–305.

Shapiro, R. M. (1993). Regional neuropathology in schizophrenia: Where are we? Where are we going? *Schizophrenia Research, 10*(3), 187–239.

Sheikh, J. I., & Yesavage, J. A. (1986). Geriatric Depression Scale (GDS): Recent evidence and development of a shorter version. *Clinical Gerontology, 5,* 165–173.

Shepard, L. A. (1980). An evaluation of the regression discrepancy method for identifying children with learning disabilities. *Journal of Special Education, 14*(1), 79–91.

Shimamura, A. P., & Squire, L. R. (1984). Paired-associate learning and priming effects in amnesia: A neuropsychological study. *Journal of Experimental Psychology: General, 113*(4), 556–570.

Shrout, P. E., & Fleiss, J. L. (1979). Intraclass correlations: Uses in assessing rater reliability. *Psychological Bulletin, 86*(2), 420–428.

Shum, D. H. K., McFarland, K., & Bain, J. D. (1994). Effects of closed-head injury on attentional processes: Generality of Sternberg's additive factor method. *Journal of Clinical and Experimental Neuropsychology, 16*(4), 547–555.

Silverstein, A. B. (1968). Validity of a new approach to the design of WAIS, WISC, and WPPSI short forms. *Journal of Consulting and Clinical Psychology, 32*(4), 478–479.

Silverstein, A. B. (1981). Reliability and abnormality of test score differences. *Journal of Clinical Psychology, 37*(2), 392–394.

Silverstein, A. B. (1982). Two- and four-subtest short forms of the Wechsler Adult Intelligence Scale—Revised. *Journal of Consulting and Clinical Psychology, 50*(3), 415–418.

Simon, C. L., & Clopton, J. R. (1984). Comparison of WAIS and WAIS–R scores of mildly and moderately mentally retarded adults. *American Journal of Mental Deficiency, 89*(3), 301–303.

Smith, G. E., Ivnik, R. J., Malec, J. F., Kokmen, E., Tangalos, E. G., & Kurland, L. T. (1992). Mayo's older Americans normative studies (MOANS): Factor structure of a core battery. *Psychological Assessment, 4*(3), 382–390.

Smith, G. E., Ivnik, R. J., Malec, J. F., Petersen, R. C., Kokmen, E., & Tangalos, E. G. (1994). Mayo cognitive factors scales: Derivation of a short battery and norms for factor scores. *Neuropsychology, 8*(2), 194–202.

Smith, M. L., & Milner, B. (1989). Right hippocampal impairment in the recall of spatial location: Encoding deficit or rapid forgetting? *Neuropsychologia, 27*(1), 71–81.

Spalletta, G., Pasini, A., Pau, F., Guido, G., Menghini, L., & Caltagirone, C. (2001). Prefrontal blood flow dysregulation in drug naive ADHD children without structural abnormalities. *Journal of Neural Transmission, 108*(10), 1203–1216.

Sparrow, S. S., Balla, D. A., & Cicchetti, D. V. (1984). *Vineland Adaptive Behavior Scales.* Circle Pines, MN: American Guidance Service.

Spearman, C. (1904). "General intelligence," objectively determined and measured. *American Journal of Psychology, 15,* 201–293.

Spearman, C. (1970). *The abilities of man: Their nature and measurement.* New York: AMS Press. (Original work published 1932)

Spencer, T., Biederman, J., Wilens, T., & Faraone, S. V. (1994). Is attention-deficit hyperactivity disorder in adults a valid disorder? *Harvard Review of Psychiatry, 1,* 326–335.

Spitz, H. H. (1972). Note on immediate memory for digits: Invariance over the years. *Psychological Bulletin, 78*(3), 183–185.

Spreen, O., & Strauss, E. (1998). *A compendium of neuropsychological tests: Administration, norms, and commentary* (2nd ed.). New York: Oxford University Press.

Spruill, J. (1991). A comparison of the Wechsler Adult Intelligence Scale—Revised with the Stanford–Binet Intelligence Scale (4th edition) for mentally retarded adults. *Psychological Assessment: A Journal of Consulting and Clinical Psychology, 3*(1), 1–3.

Squire, L. R. (1987). *Memory and brain.* New York: Oxford University Press.

Squire, L. R. (1992). Memory and the hippocampus: A synthesis from findings with rats, monkeys and humans. *Psychological Review, 99,* 195–231.

Squire, L., & Butters, N. (Eds.). (1992). *Neuropsychology of memory* (2nd ed.). New York: Guilford Press.

Stanley, J. C. (1971). Reliability. In R. L. Thorndike (Ed.), *Educational measurement* (2nd ed., pp. 356–442). Washington, DC: American Council on Education.

Sternberg, R. J. (1980). Factor theories of intelligence are all right almost. *Educational Researcher, 9,* 6–13, 18.

Sternberg, R. J. (1995). *In search of the human mind.* Fort Worth, TX: Harcourt Brace College.

Storandt, M. (1994). General principles of assessment of older adults. In M. Storandt & G. R. VandenBos (Eds.), *Neuropsychological assessment of dementia and depression in older adults: A clinician's guide* (pp. 7–32). Washington, DC: American Psychological Association.

Storandt, M., & Hill, R. D. (1989). Very mild senile dementia of the Alzheimer type: II. Psychometric test performance. *Archives of Neurology, 46,* 383–386.

Stuss, D. T., Alexander, M. P., Palumbo, C. L., Buckle, L., Sayer, L., & Pogue, J. (1994). Organizational strategies of patients with unilateral or bilateral frontal lobe injury in word list learning tasks. *Neuropsychology, 8*(3), 355–373.

Stuss, D. T., & Benson, D. F. (1984). Neuropsychological studies of the frontal lobes. *Psychological Bulletin, 95*(1), 3–28.

Stuss, D. T., & Benson, D. F. (1986). *The frontal lobes.* New York: Raven Press.

Stuss, D. T., Eskes, G. A., & Foster, J. K. (1994). Experimental neuropsychological studies of the frontal lobe functions. In F. Boller & J. Grafman (Eds.), *Handbook of neuropsychology* (Vol. 9, pp. 149–185). Amsterdam: Elsevier.

Sullivan, P. M., & Schulte, L. E. (1992). Factor analysis of WISC–R with deaf and hard-of-hearing children. *Psychological Assessment, 4*(4), 537–540.

Swanson, H. L. (1993). Working memory in learning disability subgroups. *Journal of Experimental Child Psychology, 56*(1), 87–114.

Swanson, H. L., Cochran, K. F., & Ewers, C. A. (1990). Can learning disabilities be determined from working memory performance? *Journal of Learning Disabilities, 23*(1), 59–67.

Swirsky–Sacchetti, T., Mitchell, D. R., Seward, J., Gonzales, C., Lublin, F., Knobler, R., et al. (1992). Neuropsychological and structural brain lesions in multiple sclerosis: A regional analysis. *Neurology, 42,* 1291–1295.

Tamkin, A. S., & Dolenz, J. J. (1990). Cognitive impairment in alcoholics. *Perceptual and Motor Skills, 70,* 816–818.

Tanaka, J. S. (1993). Multifaceted conceptions of fit in structural equation models. In K. A. Bollen & J. S. Long (Eds.), *Testing structural equation models* (pp. 10–39). Newbury Park, CA: Sage.

Tarter, R. E. (1973). An analysis of cognitive deficits in chronic alcoholics. *Journal of Nervous and Mental Disease, 157*(2), 138–147.

Tarter, R. E., Hegedus, A. M., Goldstein, G., Shelly, C., & Alterman, A. (1984). Adolescent sons of alcoholics: Neuropsychological and personality characteristics. *Alcoholism: Clinical and Experimental Research, 8*(2), 216–222.

Taylor, A. E., Saint–Cyr, J. A., & Lang, A. E. (1990). Memory and learning in early Parkinson's disease: Evidence for a "frontal-lobe syndrome." *Brain and Cognition, 13,* 211–232.

Taylor, M. J., & Heaton, R. K. (2001). Sensitivity and specificity of the WAIS–III/ WMS–III demographically corrected factor scores in neuropsychological assessment. *Journal of the International Neuropsychological Society, 7*(7), 867–874.

Teasdale, G., & Jennett, B. (1974). Assessment of coma and impaired consciousness. *Lancet, 2,* 81–83.

Thorndike, E. L., Lay, W., & Dean, P. R. (1909). The relation of accuracy in sensory discrimination to general intelligence. *American Journal of Psychology, 20,* 364–369.

Thorndike, R. L., Hagen, E. P., & Sattler, J. M. (1986). *Stanford–Binet Intelligence Scale: Fourth Edition: Technical manual.* Chicago: Riverside.

Trahan, D. E., Larrabee, G. J., Quintana, J. W., Goethe, K. E., & Willingham, A. C. (1989). Development and clinical validation of an expanded paired associate test with delayed recall. *The Clinical Neuropsychologist, 3*(2), 169–183.

Trenerry, M. R., Jack, C. R., Jr., Cascino, G. D., Sharbrough, F. W., & Ivnik, R. J. (1996). Sex differences in the relationship between visual memory and MRI hippocampal volumes. *Neuropsychology, 10*(3), 343–351.

Tröster, A. I., Butters, N., Salmon, D. P., Cullum, C. M., Jacobs, D., Brandt, J., et al. (1993). The diagnostic utility of savings scores: Differentiating Alzheimer's and Huntington's diseases with logical memory and visual reproduction tests. *Journal of Clinical and Experimental Neuropsychology, 15*(5), 773–788.

Trott, L. A. (1984). Providing school psychological services to hearing-impaired students in New Jersey. *American Annals of the Deaf, 129,* 319–323.

Tucker, L. R., & Lewis, C. (1973). A reliability coefficient for maximum likelihood factor analysis. *Psychometrika, 38*(1), 1–10.

Tulsky, D. S., Ivnik, R. J., Price, L. R., & Wilkins, C. (in press). Assessment of cognitive functioning with WAIS–III and WMS–III: Development of a 6-factor model. In D. S. Tulsky, et al. (Eds.), *Clinical Interpretation of the WAIS–III and WMS–III.* San Diego: Academic Press.

Tulsky, D., & Price, L. R. (in press). The joint WAIS–III and WMS–III factor structure: Part I. Development of a 6-factor model of cognitive functioning. *Journal of Psychological Assessment.*

Tulsky, D. S., Rolfhus, E. L., & Zhu, J. (2000). Two-tailed versus one-tailed base rates of discrepancy scores in the WAIS–III. *Clinical Neuropsychologist, 14*(4), 451–460.

Tulsky, D. S., Saklofske, D. H., Wilkins, C., & Weiss, L. (2001). Development of a general ability index for the Wechsler Adult Intelligence Scale–Third Edition. *Psychological Assessment, 13*(4), 566–571.

Tulsky, D. S., & Zhu, J. (2000). Could test length or order affect scores on Letter–Number Sequencing of the WAIS–III and WMS–III? Ruling out effects of fatigue. *Clinical Neuropsychologist, 14*(4), 474–478.

Tulsky, D., Zhu, J., & Vasquez, C. (1998). The clinical utility of the WAIS–III IQ and index scores in patients with neuropsychological disorders. Annual Convention of the International Neuropsychological Society, Honolulu. *Journal of the International Neuropsychological Society, 3.*

Tuokko, H. A., Frerichs, R. J., & Kristjansson, B. (2001). Cognitive impairment, no dementia: Concepts and issues. *International Psychogeriatrics, 13*(1), 183–202.

Turner, M. L., & Engle, R. W. (1989). Is working memory capacity task dependent? *Journal of Memory and Language, 28,* 127–154.

U.S. Bureau of the Census. (1995). *Current population survey, March 1995* [Machine–readable data file]. Washington, DC: U.S. Bureau of the Census (Producer/Distributor).

U.S. Bureau of the Census. (1997). *P–251095.* Washington, DC: Author.

Ward, L. C. (1990). Prediction of verbal, performance, and full scale IQs from seven subtests of the WAIS–R. *Journal of Clinical Psychology, 46*(4), 436–440.

Ward, L. C., Ryan, J. J., & Axelrod, B. N. (2000). Confirmatory factor analyses of the WAIS–III standardization data. *Psychological Assessment, 12*(3), 341–345.

Watson, B. U., Sullivan, P. M., Moeller, M. P., & Jensen, J. K. (1982). Nonverbal intelligence and English language ability in deaf children. *Journal of Speech and Hearing Disorders, 47,* 199–204.

Watson, C. G., & Klett, W. G. (1974). Are nonverbal IQ tests adequate substitutes for the WAIS? *Journal of Clinical Psychology, 30*(1), 55–57.

Wechsler, D. (1939). *Wechsler–Bellevue Intelligence Scale.* New York: The Psychological Corporation.

Wechsler, D. (1944). *The measurement of adult intelligence* (3rd ed.). Baltimore: Williams & Wilkins.

Wechsler, D. (1945). A standardized memory scale for clinical use. *The Journal of Psychology, 19,* 87–95.

Wechsler, D. (1950). Cognitive, conative, and non–intellective intelligence. *American Psychologist, 5,* 78–83.

Wechsler, D. (1955). *Wechsler Adult Intelligence Scale.* New York: The Psychological Corporation.

Wechsler, D. (1975). Intelligence defined and undefined: A relativistic appraisal. *American Psychologist, 30,* 135–139.

Wechsler, D. (1981). *Wechsler Adult Intelligence Scale—Revised.* San Antonio, TX: The Psychological Corporation.

Wechsler, D. (1987). *Wechsler Memory Scale—Revised.* San Antonio, TX: The Psychological Corporation.

Wechsler, D. (1991). *Wechsler Intelligence Scale for Children—Third Edition.* San Antonio, TX: The Psychological Corporation.

Wechsler, D. (1997a). *Wechsler Adult Intelligence Scale—Third Edition.* San Antonio, TX: The Psychological Corporation.

Wechsler, D. (1997b). *Wechsler Memory Scale—Third Edition.* San Antonio, TX: The Psychological Corporation.

Weinberger, D. R., Berman, K. F., & Zec, R. F. (1986). Physiologic dysfunction of dorsolateral prefrontal cortex in schizophrenia: I. Regional cerebral blood flow evidence. *Archives of General Psychiatry, 43,* 114–126.

Weintraub, S., & Mesulam, M.-M. (1985). Mental state assessment of young and elderly adults in behavioral neurology. In M.-M. Mesulam (Ed.), *Principles of behavioral neurology* (pp. 71–123). Philadelphia: F. A. Davis.

Welsh, K., Butters, N., Hughes, J., Mohs, R., & Heyman, A. (1991). Detection of abnormal memory decline in mild cases of Alzheimer's disease using CERAD neuropsychological measures. *Archives of Neurology, 48,* 278–281.

Wilde, N., Strauss, E., Chelune, G. J., Loring, D. W., Martin, R. C., Hermann, B. P., et al. (2001). WMS–III performance in patients with temporal lobe epilepsy: Group differences and individual classification. *Journal of the International Neuropsychological Society, 7*, 881–891.

Woltz, D. J. (1988). An investigation of the role of working memory in procedural skill acquisition. *Journal of Experimental Psychology: General, 117*(3), 319–331.

Woodard, J. L. (1993). Confirmatory factor analysis of the Wechsler Memory Scale—Revised in a mixed clinical population. *Journal of Clinical and Experimental Neuropsychology, 15*(6), 968–973.

Woodcock, R. W. (1990). Theoretical foundations of the WJ–R measures of cognitive ability. *Journal of Psychoeducational Assessment, 8*, 231–258.

Woodcock, R. W. (1997). The Woodcock–Johnson Tests of Cognitive Ability—Revised. In D. P. Flanagan, J. L. Genshaft, & P. L. Harrison (Eds.), *Contemporary intellectual assessment: Theories, tests, and issues* (pp. 230–246). New York: Guilford Press.

Worden, P. E. (1986). Prose comprehension and recall in disabled learners. In S. J. Ceci (Ed.), *Handbook of Cognitive, Social and Neuropsychological Aspects of Learning Disabilities* (Vol. 1, pp. 241–261). New York: Erlbaum.

Yesavage, J. A., Brink, T. L., Rose, T. L., Lum, O., Huang, V., Adey, M., et al., (1983). Development and validation of a geriatric depression screening scale: A preliminary report. *Journal of Psychiatric Research, 17*(1), 37–49.

Zec, R. F. (1993). Neuropsychological functioning in Alzheimer's disease. In R. W. Parks, R. F. Zec, & R. S. Wilson (Eds.), *Neuropsychology of Alzheimer's disease and other dementias* (pp. 3–80). New York: Oxford University Press.

Zhu, J., & Tulsky, D. S. (2000). Co-norming of the WAIS–III and WMS–III: Is there a test-order effect on IQ and memory scores? *Clinical Neuropsychologist, 14*(1), 1.

Zhu, J., Tulsky, D. S., Price, L., & Chen, H. Y. (2001). WAIS–III reliability data for clinical groups. *Journal of the International Neuropsychological Society, 7*, 862–866.